The World's Air Forces

The World's
AIR FORCES

General Editor **Chris Chant**

CHARTWELL
BOOKS INC.

Published by Chartwell Books Inc.
A Division of Book Sales Inc.
110 Enterprise Avenue
Secaucus, New Jersey 07094

ISBN 089009–269–9
Library of Congress Catalog Card Number 78–65756

Typeset and printed in Great Britain

Contents

Introduction

The World's Air Forces is intended as a manageable but nonetheless comprehensive guide to the air forces of the world at the beginning of 1979, and it is hoped that periodic editions of the book will enable the information to be updated in the light of developments. Unfortunately, it is in the very nature of such works that they are inherently 'out-of-date', perhaps by only a few months, as continued procurement of new equipment, the phasing out of older equipment and attrition ('natural' in the event of disasters such as fire, which cost the Australian navy a high proportion of its aircraft strength in December 1976, and 'operational' in the event of hostilities and accidents) alter the situation. At the same time political and economic fluctuations alter the number of aircraft on order (a case in point being Iran in the aftermath of the Shah's downfall at the beginning of 1979: the interim government of Mr Bakhtiar cut foreign orders considerably, and the current Islamic government, beset by internal problems associated with left-wing guerrillas, is likely to cut the remaining orders still further). More changes in air force strengths have resulted from the clashes between Tanzania and Uganda, the overrunning of Kampuchea by Vietnam, and the 'punitive' campaign launched by China against Vietnam. Of lesser compass are the short-lived civil war in Chad and a number of other limited engagements. In general, however, the aircraft types and strengths quoted in the present work are up-to-date as far as the beginning of 1979.

For a variety of reasons it has been impossible to cover every type of aircraft currently operated by the world's air forces, and an editorial selection of the types covered has therefore been inevitable. The types covered, accordingly, are basically the following:

   (i) combat aircraft currently in service
  (ii) combat aircraft in the final stages of development
 (iii) the more important communications/liaison aircraft currently in service
 (iv) the more important training aircraft currently in service
  (v) some of the more interesting obsolescent and obsolete aircraft still in limited service
 (vi) missiles (air-to-air, air-to-surface and surface-to-surface) currently operated by the world's air forces.

Although pure logic would dictate that aircraft operated by navies and armies should be located in the appropriate companion volumes (*The World's Navies* and *The World's Armies*), it has been felt better and neater to include all aircraft in the present work. However, the aircraft types and strengths operated by navies and armies have been included in the two companion volumes so that the reader may refer across between the volumes if desired.

The volume is arranged alphabetically by country, and consists of two main 'strands':

 (a) the tabular sections detailing the numbers and types of aircraft operated by each country's air arms (air force, army and navy as appropriate), together with an organisational break-down of the more important air arms
 (b) the technical sections giving details of the aircraft.

A third, occasional, strand is provided by brief examinations of the nature and capabilities of the world's most important (not necessarily largest) air forces.

Rather than locate the aircraft types by country of origin, which would have led to a considerable internal imbalance in the book, most aircraft being produced by France, Italy, Japan, the Union of Soviet Socialist Republics, the United Kingdom and the United States of America, it has been decided to arrange the aircraft types alphabetically by name of manufacturer, but within the section covering one of the user countries: for example, though the LTV (Vought) F-8 Crusader is of American origin and initial manufacture, it is listed under France, whose *Aéronavale* uses the type. The reader may find each type covered by recourse to the index, which gives the location of all entries. A further rationale for this editorial decision is that in some instances, older aircraft are no longer used by the country of origin, but are nonetheless still in widespread service with other nations.

Each technical entry has been designed to provide an easily assimilable, but relatively complete, quantity of data, to allow the reader to assess the capabilities of the aircraft, together with brief notes designed to elucidate the aircraft's (or missile's) history, design and variants. Where there are variants of the aircraft or missile, the notes indicate to which of the variants the technical specification applies, unless the variants differ so little that the same technical specification is applicable to all.

Within each technical entry for aircraft there are 15 sub-headings (16 in the case of helicopters):

   (i) *Type* indicates the purpose for which the aircraft is used
  (ii) *Crew* indicates the normal operating crew of the aircraft, plus the number of passengers that can be carried (where appropriate)
 (iii) *Wings* indicates the structural type and medium of the fuselage (body)
  (iv) *Fuselage* indicates the structural type and medium of the fuselage (body)
   (v) *Tail unit* indicates the structural type and medium of the tail unit
  (vi) *Landing gear* indicates the nature and operation of the landing gear
 (vii) *Powerplant* indicates the type and power of the engine used in the aircraft
(viii) *Fuel capacity* indicates the internal, and where applicable the external, fuel capacity of the aircraft
  (ix) *Avionics* indicates the nature of the radar and other electronic operational equipment carried by the aircraft (in general only combat radar and electronics have been identified)
   (x) *Armament* indicates the weapons that can be carried internally and externally (the specifications for the more modern aircraft are fuller, because these aircraft can carry a more diverse and potent variety of weapons, especially on their external hardpoints)
  (xi) *Dimensions* indicates the overall (except where specified to the contrary) wingspan, length and height of the aircraft
 (xii) *Wing area* indicates the gross wing area of the aircraft
(xiii) *Weights* indicates the aircraft's empty equipped, normal take-off and maximum take-off weights
 (xiv) *Performance* indicates the aircraft's performance in terms of speed (maximum and cruising), climb, service ceiling and various ranges
  (xv) *Used* indicates the user nations
 (xvi) *Notes* gives a brief summary of the aircraft's history and variants, where applicable.

The same parameters have been applied to helicopters, *mutatis mutandis*. *Rotor* has replaced *Wings*; *Tail unit* has been omitted (generally being included with *Rotor*); *Dimensions*: span referring to the diameter of the main rotor and length generally referring to the length of the helicopter's fuselage; and *Rotor disc area* replacing *Wing area*, and referring to the area of the main rotor disc(s).

For missiles the categories of sub-heading within each entry are as follows:

   (i) *Type* indicates the function of the missile
  (ii) *Guidance* indicates the means by which the missile is guided in flight, and the principle used for this purpose
 (iii) *Dimensions* indicates the fin span, body diameter and length of the missile
  (iv) *Booster* indicates the method by which the missile is accelerated at launch from stationary towards cruising speed
   (v) *Sustainer* indicates the method by which the missile is maintained at cruising speed
  (vi) *Warhead* indicates the nature and weight of the warhead (occasionally the weight of the explosive within the warhead)
 (vii) *Weights* indicates the weight of the missile at launch and after all fuel has been burnt out
(viii) *Performance* indicates the weapon's speed, range and (where relevant) the circular error probable (CEP) or the radius of the circle within which half the missiles fired at the same target may be expected to fall
  (ix) *Used* indicates user nations
   (x) *Notes* give a brief summary of the missile's history and variants, where applicable.

All measurements are given in Imperial and metric equivalents, the following conversion factors having been used:

pound to kilogram: divide by 2.2046
gallon to litre: multiply by 4.54596 (NB:1 US gallon equals 0.8327 Imperial
    gallon, or 3.78542 litres)
inch to centimetre: multiply by 2.54
inch to millimetre: multiply by 25.4
foot to metre: divide by 3.2808
ft² to m²: divide by 10.7639
mile (and mph) to kilometre (and kph): multiply by 1.6094.

Where the compiler of the technical sections has been unable to find an exact figure, or sources conflict, he has left the sub-heading blank, so that the reader may fill in the space for himself should he be able to find a figure that satisfies him. In this context, the publishers would be most grateful for any comments on the book and for any further information readers may be able to supply.

Afghanistan

10,000 men and 144 combat aircraft, plus 12,000 reservists.

3 lt bomber sqns with 30 Il-28.
6 FGA sqns: 4 with 50 MiG-17, 2 with 24 Su-7BM.
3 interceptor sqns with 40 MiG-21.
2 transport sqns with 10 An-2, 10 Il-14, 2 Il-18.
3 helicopter sqns with 18 Mi-4, 13 Mi-8.
Trainers incl 20 MiG-15/-17UTI/-21U, 2 Il-28U.
AA-2 'Atoll' AAM.
1 AD div: 1 SAM bde (3 bns with 48 SA-2, SA-3), 1 AA bde (2 bns with 37mm, 85mm, 100mm guns), 1 radar bde (3 bns).

Ilyushin Il-14 'Crate'

Type: transport aircraft
Crew: five, plus up to 36 passengers
Wings: metal cantilever low-wing monoplane
Fuselage: metal semi-monocoque
Tail unit: metal cantilever
Landing gear: hydraulically actuated retractable tricycle unit
Powerplant: two Shvetsov ASh-82T radial engines, each rated at 1,900 hp and driving a metal three-blade propeller
Fuel capacity: 1,330 gallons (6,500 litres) in eight wing, centre-section and fuselage tanks
Avionics: communication and navigation equipment
Armament: none
Dimensions: Span 104 ft (31.7 m)
　　　　　　　Length 73 ft 2¼ in (22.31 m)
　　　　　　　Height
Wing area: 1,076.4 ft² (100.0 m²)
Weights: Empty 27,998 lb (12,700 kg)
　　　　　　Loaded
　　　　　　Maximum 38,581 lb (17,500 kg)
Performance: speed 268 mph (431 kph) at 7,875 ft (2,400 m); cruising speed 217 mph (350 kph) at 9,840 ft (3,000 m); range

1,087 miles (1,750 km) at maximum take-off weight with a payload of 3,527 lb (1,600 kg) at 9,840 ft (3,000 m); service ceiling 24,280 ft (7,400 m)
Used also by: Albania, Algeria, Bulgaria, China, Congo, Cuba, Czechoslovakia, East Germany, Egypt, Ethiopia, Guinea-Bissau, Hungary, Indonesia, Iraq, Mongolia, North Korea, North Yemen, Poland, Romania, South Yemen, Syria, USSR, Vietnam, Yugoslavia
Notes: The Il-14 is basically a modification of the Il-12 civil and military transport, and first flew in 1950. The type entered both civil and military service in 1954. There were several variants:
1. Il-14P passenger model, for up to 26 passengers
2. Il-14M passenger model, with a lengthened fuselage for up to 36 passengers
3. Il-14G freight model, with large doors and a payload of 6,614 lb (3,000 kg)
4. Czech-built Avia 14T freight version with a payload of 7,716 lb (3,494 kg) and a range of 2,237 miles (5,150 km).

Mil Mi-1 'Hare'

Type: utility helicopter
Crew: one, plus up to three passengers
Rotor: metal cantilever three-blade main rotor; metal cantilever three-blade tail rotor
Fuselage: metal covered steel tube main fuselage; metal semi-monocoque tail boom
Landing gear: fixed tricycle unit

Powerplant: one Ivchenko AI-26V (PZL-Kalisz AI-26V in most modern examples) radial, rated at 575 hp
Fuel capacity: 53 gallons (240 litres) in a tank in the rear of the engine compartment, plus 35 gallons (160 litres) in an optional external tank
Avionics: communications and navigation equipment
Armament: none

Dimensions: Span 46 ft 11 in (14.35 m)
Length (fuselage) 39 ft 4¾ in (12.1 m)
Height (rotors turning) 10 ft 10 in (3.31 m)
Rotor disc area: 1,741 ft² (161.7 m²)
Weights: Empty 4,145 lb (1,880 kg)
Loaded 5,291 lb (2,400 kg)
Maximum 5,622 lb (2,550 kg)
Performance: speed 105 mph (170 kph); cruising speed 90 mph (145 kph); climb 1,378 ft (420 m) per minute at sea level; service ceiling 13,120 ft (4,000 m) at a weight of 5,622 lb (2,550 kg); hovering ceiling in ground effect 6,560 ft (2,000 m); range 367 miles (590 km) with auxiliary tank
Used also by: Cuba, Czechoslovakia, East Germany, Hungary, Mongolia, Poland, USSR, Yugoslavia
Notes: The Mi-1 first flew in 1950, and entered service with the Russian air forces in 1951. Production ended in 1962 with the delivery of the last Polish-made WSK-Swidnik SM-2 derivative. The maximum slung payload is 1,102 lb (500 kg).

Yakovlev Yak-11 'Moose'

Type: basic trainer
Crew: two, seated in tandem
Wings: metal cantilever low-wing monoplane
Fuselage: steel-tube construction
Tail unit: metal cantilever
Landing gear: pneumatically actuated retractable tailwheel unit
Powerplant: one Shvetsov ASh-21 radial engine, rated at 800 hp

Fuel capacity: 79 gallons (359.5 litres) in two centre-section main tanks and one collector tank
Avionics: communication and navigation equipment
Armament: one 7.62-mm ShKAS machine-gun and practice bombs
Dimensions: Span 30 ft 10 in (9.4 m)
Length 27 ft 10¾ in (8.5 m)
Height 9 ft 2½ in (2.8 m)
Wing area: 165.4 ft² (15.4 m²)
Weights: Empty 4,630 lb (2,100 kg)
Loaded
Maximum 5,379 lb (2,440 kg)
Performance: speed 286 mph (460 kph) at 7,380 ft (2,250 m); service ceiling 23,290 ft (7,100 m); range 800 miles (1,290 km)
Used also by: Algeria, Bulgaria, Hungary, Iraq, Mongolia, North Yemen, Somali Republic, Syria, Vietnam
Notes: The Yak-11 first flew in 1946, and has a clear resemblance to the Yak fighter types of World War II. It probably entered service with the Russian air forces in 1948, and has since that time served with numerous air arms in a number of training and utility roles.

Yakovlev Yak-18 'Max'

Type: primary trainer and utility aircraft
Crew: two, seated in tandem
Wings: metal cantilever low-wing monoplane
Fuselage: steel tube construction
Tail unit: braced metal unit
Landing gear: pneumatically actuated retractable tricycle unit

Powerplant: one Ivchenko AI-14RF radial engine, rated at 300 hp
Fuel capacity: 28½ gallons (130 litres) in two wing-root tanks
Avionics: communications equipment
Armament: none
Dimensions: Span 34 ft 9¼ in (10.6 m)
Length 27 ft 4¾ in (8.35 m)
Height 7 ft (2.13 m)
Wing area: 182.9 ft² (17.0 m²)
Weights: Empty about 2,259 lb (1,025 kg)
Loaded
Maximum 2,447 lb (1,110 kg)
Performance: speed 199 mph (320 kph) at sea level; climb 1 minute 42 seconds to 3,280 ft (1,000 m); service ceiling 22,960 ft (7,000 m); range 249 miles (400 km)
Used also by: Bulgaria, Guinea-Bissau, Hungary, Mongolia, North Korea, Syria, Vietnam
Notes: The Yak-18 first flew in 1946, and is the most widely used primary trainer in the Warsaw Pact nations. There are several versions:
1. Yak-18 with the 160-hp Shvetsov M-11 radial and a tailwheel landing gear
2. Yak-18U with a tricycle undercarriage
3. Yak-18A with the 300-hp Ivchenko AI-14RF radial, a variable-pitch propeller and cleaner lines
4. Yak-18P and Yak-18PM aerobatic aircraft (the technical specification above applies to the PM)
5. Yak-18T with a wider fuselage and accommodation for four, powered by the 360-hp Vedeneev M-14P radial.

Albania

8,000 men (1,500 conscripts) and 101 combat aircraft, plus 5,000 reservists.

2 AWX sqns with 10 MiG-17/F-4, 13 MiG-19/F-6.
6 interceptor sqns with 24 MiG-15/F-2, 10 MiG-17/F-4, 32 MiG-19/F-6, 12 MiG-21/F-8.
1 transport sqn with 4 Il-14, 10 An-2.
2 helicopter sqns with 30 Mi-4.
Trainers incl 10 MiG-15UTI.

Mikoyan-Gurevich MiG-15 'Fagot'

Type: fighter
Crew: one
Wings: metal cantilever mid-wing monoplane
Fuselage: metal semi-monocoque
Tail unit: metal cantilever
Landing gear: hydraulically actuated retractable tricycle unit
Powerplant: one Klimov VK-1A turbojet, rated at 6,990-lb (3,171-kg) static thrust, plus provision for RATO units
Fuel capacity:
Avionics: communication and navigation equipment
Armament: one N-37 37-mm cannon with 40 rounds, two NS-23 23-mm cannon with 80 rounds each, and up to 1,102 lb (500 kg) of external stores or tanks on each of two underwing hardpoints

Dimensions: Span 33 ft 0¾ in (10.08 m)
Length 36 ft 3¼ in (11.05 m)
Height 11 ft 1¾ in (3.4 m)
Wing area: 221.7 ft² (20.6 m²)
Weights: Empty 7,495 lb (3,400 kg)
Loaded 10,934 lb (4,960 kg)
Maximum 12,756 lb (5,786 kg)
Performance: speed 684 mph (1,100 kph) at 39,370 ft (12,000 m); climb 11,480 ft (3,500 m) per minute at sea level; service ceiling 51,000 ft (15,545 m); range with maximum fuel 1,242 miles (2,000 km)
Used also by: many nations
Notes: Russia's first high-performance jet fighter, the MiG-15 first flew in 1947, entered service in 1948, but was little known in the west until the type's combat debut in Korea in 1950. The MiG-15 was also built in China as the Shenyang F-2, and it is this version which is used by China, Pakistan and Vietnam. For its time, the MiG-15 had first-class rate of climb, acceleration and ceiling, though it was not a

good gun platform and had stability problems at high speed. There are several versions:
1. MiG-15 initial production model with the 5,005-lb (2,270-kg) RD-45F engine, the Russian version of the Rolls-Royce Nene centrifugal flow turbojet and an armament of one 37- and one 23-mm cannon
2. MiG-15SD (or -15bis) with the 5,952-lb (2,700-kg) VK-1 or 6,990-lb (3,170-kg) VK-1A engines, with three-gun armament, external stores and higher performance, to which the technical specification above relates
3. MiG-15UTI 'Mongol' two-seat trainer
4. MiG-15T and -15SDT target-tugs
5. MiG-15SP-5 two-seat all-weather fighter derived from the MiG-15UTI and fitted with Izumrud radar in a bullet fairing over the nose.

Algeria

5,000 men and 204 combat aircraft.

1 lt bomber sqn with 24 Il-28.
3 interceptor sqns with 90 MiG-21.
4 FGA sqns: 2 with 20 Su-7BM, 2 with 30 MiG-17.
1 COIN sqn with 20 Magister.
OCU with 20 MiG-15.
2 transport sqns with 8 An-12, 10 F27, 4 Il-14, 4 Il-18.
4 helicopter sqns with 4 Mi-6, 42 Mi-4, 12 Mi-8, 5 Puma, 6 Hughes 269A.
Other ac incl 1 King Air, 3 Super King Air, 3 Queen Air, 2 CL-215.
Trainers incl MiG-15/-17/-21U, Su-7U, 19 Yak-11.
AA-2 'Atoll' AAM.
SA-2 SAM.
Naval Air Arm
(3 F28 transport ac on order.)

Mil Mi-4 'Hound'

Type: utility helicopter
Crew: two or three, plus up to 14 passengers
Rotor: duralumin cantilever four-blade main rotor; bakelite ply cantilever three-blade tail rotor
Fuselage: metal semi-monocoque
Landing gear: fixed four-wheel unit
Powerplant: one Shvetsov ASh-82V piston engine, rated at 1,700 hp for take-off and 1,370 hp for continuous running
Fuel capacity: 220 gallons (1,000 litres) in the fuselage, plus provision for one 110-gallon (500-litre) auxiliary tank in the hold
Avionics: communication and navigation equipment
Armament: none
Dimensions: Span 68 ft 11 in (21.0 m)
Length (fuselage) 55 ft 1 in (16.79 m)
Height 14 ft 5¼ in (4.4 m)

Rotor disc area: 3,728 ft² (46.4 m²)
Weights: Empty 11,614 lb (5,268 kg)
Loaded 16,204 lb (7,350 kg)
Maximum 17,196 lb (7,800 kg)
Performance: speed 130 mph (210 kph) at 4,920 ft (1,500 m); cruising speed 99 mph (160 kph); service ceiling 19,685 ft (6,000 m); range 370 miles (595 km)
Used also by: Afghanistan, Albania, Bulgaria, China, Cuba, Czechoslovakia, East Germany, Egypt, Finland, India, Indonesia, Iraq, Mali, Mongolia, North Korea, North Yemen, Poland, Romania, Somali Republic, South Yemen, Syria, USSR, Vietnam, Yugoslavia
Notes: The first Mi-4 flew in 1952, and appears to owe much in concept to the Sikorsky S-55. The military freight version has clamshell rear doors, and can lift loads of up to 4,409 lb (2,000 kg) in the cargo hold, or 3,306 lb (1,500 kg) slung under the fuselage.

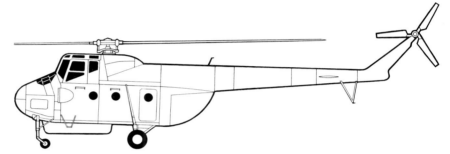

Potez-Air Fouga CM–170R Magister

Type: trainer and light attack aircraft
Crew: two, seated in tandem
Wings: metal cantilever low mid-wing monoplane
Fuselage: metal semi-monocoque
Tail unit: metal cantilever
Landing gear: hydraulically actuated retractable tricycle unit
Powerplant: two Turboméca Marboré II turbojets, each rated at 880-lb (440-kg) static thrust

Fuel capacity:
Avionics: communication and navigation equipment
Armament: two 7.5-mm MAC 52 machine-guns with 200 rounds per gun, plus two 90- or 120-mm rockets, or two 110-lb (50-kg) bombs under the wings
Dimensions: Span 39 ft 10½ in (12.15 m)
    Length 32 ft 9¾ in (10.0 m)
    Height 9 ft 2¼ in (2.8 m)
Wing area: 186.215 ft² (17.3 m²)
Weights: Empty 4,740 lb (2,150 kg)
    Loaded 6,614 lb (3,000 kg)
    Maximum 7,055 lb (3,200 kg)

Performance: speed 407 mph (655 kph) at 22,950 ft (7,000 m); climb 3,345 ft (1,020 m) per minute at sea level; service ceiling 39,370 ft (12,000 m); range 737 miles (1,185 km)
Used also by: Bangladesh, Belgium, Cameroon, Eire, El Salvador, Finland, France, Israel, Lebanon, Libya, Senegal, Togo
Notes: The Magister was the world's first turbojet-powered trainer to get into production, the prototype flying in 1952 and production aircraft following in 1953.

Angola

1,500 men and 31 combat aircraft.

15 MiG-17, 12 MiG-21, 4 G-91 fighters.
Transports incl 6 Noratlas, 2 C-45, 3 C-47, 10 Do 27, 5 An-26, 2 Turbo-Porter, Islander.
Some 7 Mi-8, 24 *Alouette* III, 2 Bell 47 helicopters.
3 MiG-15UTI trainers.
AA-2 'Atoll' AAM.

Douglas Aircraft C-47

Type: transport aircraft
Crew: two, plus up to 27 passengers
Wings: metal cantilever low-wing monoplane
Fuselage: metal semi-monocoque
Tail unit: metal cantilever
Landing gear: hydraulically actuated retractable tailwheel unit
Powerplant: two Pratt & Whitney R-1830-92 radial engines, each rated at 1,200 hp and driving a three-blade metal Hamilton Standard propeller
Fuel capacity: 670 gallons (3,046 litres)
Avionics: communication and navigation equipment
Armament: none
Dimensions: Span 95 ft 6 in (29.1 m)
    Length 63 ft 9 in (19.43 m)
    Height 17 ft (5.18 m)

Wing area: 987 ft² (91.7 m²)
Weights: Empty 18,200 lb (8,255 kg)
    Loaded 26,000 lb (11,794 kg)
    Maximum 31,000 lb (14,062 kg)
Performance: speed 230 mph (370 kph) at 8,500 ft (2,590 m); cruising speed 185 mph (298 kph); climb 1,130 ft (344 m) per minute at sea level; climb 9 minutes 36 seconds to 10,000 ft (3,050 m); service ceiling 23,200 ft (7,070 m); range 1,600 miles (2,575 km) with payload; ferry range 2,135 miles (3,435 km)
Used also by: many nations
Notes: The C-47 is the military version of the DC-3 airliner, and was a vital aircraft during World War II for transport, freighting, airborne use (including glider towing), and a variety of other roles. Since the end of World War II, the type has continued in service with a number of civil and military operators.

Argentina

20,000 men and 184 combat aircraft.

1 bomber sqn with 9 Canberra B.62, 2 T.64.
4 FB sqns with 70 A-4P Skyhawk.
1 FB sqn with 20 F-86F.
3 FGA sqns with 48 MS760A Paris I.
1 interceptor sqn with 16 Mirage IIIEA, 2 IIIDA.
1 COIN sqn with 17 IA 58 *Pucará*.
1 assault helicopter sqn with 14 Hughes 500M, 6 UH-1H.
1 SAR sqn with 3 HU-16B ac, 12 *Lama*, 2 S-58T, 2 S-61N/R helicopters.
5 transport sqns with 1 Boeing 707-320B, 7 C-130E/H, 1 Sabreliner, 2 Learjet 35A, 3 G 222, 13 C-47, 10 F27, 6 F28, 6 DHC-6, 22 IA50 *Guarani* II, 2 Merlin IVA, Electra.
1 Antarctic sqn with 2 DHC-2, 3 DHC-3, 1 LC-47 ac, 1 S-61R helicopter.
1 comms sqn with 4 Commander, 14 Shrike Commander, Paris, T-34, IA 35 *Huanquero*.
Helicopters incl 4 UH-1D, 3 UH-19, 3 Bell 47G.
Trainers incl 35 T-34, 12 Paris, 37 Cessna 182.
R.530 AAM, AS.11/12 ASM.
(7 Mirage IIIEA, 33 IA 58 *Pucará*, 16 Turbo Commander ac; 3 CH-47, 8 Bell 212 helicopters on order.)

Naval Air Force
4,000; 34 combat aircraft.
1 FB sqn with 15 A-4Q.
1 MR sqn with 6 S-2A/E, 10 SP-2H, 3 HU-16B, PBY-5A.
Transports incl 3 Electra, 2 C-54, 2 DC-4, 8 C-47, 1 HS 125, 1 *Guarani* II, 1 Sabreliner.
Other ac incl 2 DHC-2, 1 DHC-6, 2 Super King Air, 4 Queen Air, 4 Piper Navajo, 4 Turbo-Porter.
Helicopters incl 4 S-61D, 6 *Alouette* III, 3 UH-19, 5 S-55, 3 Bell 47G.
Trainers incl 12 M.B.326GB, 12 T-6/-28, 2AT-11, 3 T-34C.
(12 T-34C trg ac, 3 Lynx helicopters on order.)

Army Air Arm
1 aviation bn.
5 Turbo Commander 690A, 2 DHC-6, 3 G222, 4 Swearingen Metro IIIA, 4 Queen Air, 1 Sabreliner, 5 Cessna 207, 15 Cessna 182, 20 U-17A/B, 5 T-41 ac; 7 Bell 206, 4 FH-1100, 20 UH-1H, 4 Bell 47G, 2 Bell 212 helicopters.
(5 Turbo Commander ac; 3 CH-47C helicopters on order.)

Avions Marcel Dassault Mirage III

Type: fighter-bomber
Crew: one
Wings: metal cantilever low-wing monoplane
Fuselage: metal semi-monocoque
Tail unit: metal cantilever
Landing gear: hydraulically actuated retractable tricycle unit
Powerplant: one SNECMA Atar 9C turbojet, rated at 13,680-lb (6,205-kg) static thrust with afterburner; one optional SEPR 844 rocket delivering 3,300-lb (1,497-kg) static thrust
Fuel capacity: 733 gallons (3,330 litres) carried internally when rocket motor not fitted, plus optional two 132-, 285- or 374-gallon (600-, 1,300- or 1,700-litre) drop tanks
Avionics: comprehensive navigation and communication equipment, plus Cyrano II fire-control radar, navigation computer, bombing computer and automatic gunsight
Armament: two 30-mm DEFA cannon with 125 rounds per gun and two 1,000-lb (454-kg) bombs, or one AS.30 air-to-surface missile and two 1,000-lb (454-kg) bombs, or JL-100 18-rocket pods under the wings for ground-attack missions; one Matra R.530 air-to-air missile, two Sidewinder air-to-air missiles and two 30-mm DEFA cannon for interception missions
Dimensions: Span 26 ft 11½ in (8.22 m)
Length (III-E) 49 ft 3½ in (15.03 m); (III-R) 50 ft 10¼ in (15.5 m); Height 13 ft 11¼ in (4.25 m)
Wing area: 375 ft² (34.85 m²)
Weights: Empty (III-E) 15,540 lb (7,050 kg)
Empty (III-R) 14,550 lb (6,600 kg)
Maximum 29,760 lb (13,500 kg)
Performance: (Mirage III-E 'clean') speed 1,460 mph (2,350 kph) or Mach 2.2 at 39,375 ft (12,000 m); cruising speed Mach 0.9 at 36,000 ft (11,000 m); climb 3 minutes to 36,000 ft (11,000 m) at Mach 0.9; service ceiling 55,775 ft (17,000 m); service ceiling with rocket motor 75,450 ft (23,000 m); combat radius (ground attack mission) 745 miles (1,200 km)
Used also by: Australia, Brazil, Egypt, France, Israel, Lebanon, Libya, Pakistan, South Africa, Spain, Switzerland, Venezuela
Notes: One of the most successful postwar fighter aircraft, the Mirage III was introduced in 1956. Current models include:
Mirage III-D two-seat version for training and strike missions
Mirage III-D2Z for South Africa
Mirage III-E long range fighter-bomber and intruder aircraft
Mirage III-R reconnaissance variant of the Mirage III-E with five OMERA Type 31 cameras
Mirage III-R2Z version of the III-R for South Africa
Mirage III-RD variant of the III-R with improved naviation radar.

Cessna Aircraft Turbo-Skywagon T207

Type: utility aircraft
Crew: one, plus up to seven passengers
Wings: metal braced high-wing monoplane
Fuselage: metal semi-monocoque
Tail unit: metal cantilever
Landing gear: fixed tricycle unit
Powerplant: one turbo-charged Continental TSI0-520-M piston engine, rated at 310 hp and driving a McCauley metal three-blade propeller
Fuel capacity: 54 gallons (246 litres) in two bladder tanks in the wings, plus optional tankage to increase capacity to 70 gallons (318 litres)
Avionics: communication and navigation equipment
Armament: none
Dimensions: Span 35 ft 10 in (10.92 m)
Length 31 ft 9 in (9.68 m)
Height 9 ft 6½ in (2.91 m)
Wing area: 174 ft² (16.17 m²)
Weights: Empty 2,071 lb (939 kg)
Loaded
Maximum 3,800 lb (1,724 kg)
Performance: (at maximum take-off weight) speed 196 mph (315 kph) at 17,000 ft (5,180 m); cruising speed 185 mph (298 kph) at 20,000 ft (6,100 m); climb 885 ft (270 m) per minute at sea level; service ceiling 26,000 ft (7,925 m); range 691 miles (1,112 km) with maximum fuel at 10,000 ft (3,050 m)
Used also by: Indonesia, Liberia
Notes: The turbo-charged engine improves the performance of the T207 significantly compared with that of the Model 207.

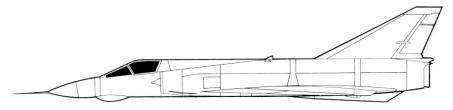

Fábrica Militar de Aviones IA 35
Huanquero

Type: multi-purpose aircraft
Crew: three, plus up to six passengers
Wings: metal cantilever low-wing monoplane
Fuselage: metal semi-monocoque
Tail unit: metal cantilever
Landing gear: hydraulically actuated retractable tricycle unit
Powerplant: two Instituto Aerotecnico IA 19R *El Indio* radial engines, each rated at 750 hp and driving a three-blade metal propeller
Fuel capacity:
Avionics: communication and navigation equipment
Armament: two 0.5-in (12.7-mm) Browning machine-guns, two 220-lb (100-kg) or four 110-lb (50-kg) bombs, and two 5-in (127-mm) or eight 2.25-in (57-mm) rockets under the wings
Dimensions: Span 64 ft 3 in (19.6 m)
Length 45 ft 10 in (13.95 m)
Height
Wing area: 452 ft² (42.0 m²)
Weights: Empty 7,700 lb (3,495 kg)
Loaded 12,540 lb (5,670 kg)
Maximum
Performance: 236 mph (380 kph) at 9,840 ft (3,000 m); cruising speed 205 mph (330 kph) at 980 ft (300 m); climb 1,300 ft (395 m) per minute at sea level; service ceiling 21,320 ft (6,500 m); range 900 miles (1,450 km)
Used only by: Argentina
Notes: The IA 35 first flew in 1953, and entered service in 1957. There are four variants:
1. Type IA trainer for pilot, navigator and radio operator training
2. Type IB light bomber and close support aircraft, to which the specification above applies
3. Type III ambulance aircraft, with a crew of three and up to four litters and an attendant
4. Type IV photographic aircraft.

Fábrica Militar de Aviones IA 50
Guarani II

Type: light transport
Crew: two, plus up to 15 passengers
Wings: metal cantilever low-wing monoplane
Fuselage: metal semi-monocoque
Tail unit: metal cantilever
Landing gear: hydraulically actuated retractable tricycle unit
Powerplant: two Turboméca Bastan VIA turboprops, each rated at 930 shp and driving a Ratier-Figeac three-blade metal propeller
Fuel capacity: 420 gallons (1,910 litres) internally, plus 77 gallons (350 litres) in each of two optional wingtip tanks
Avionics: comprehensive communication and navigation equipment
Armament: none
Dimensions: Span 64 ft 3¼ in (19.59 m)
Length 50 ft 2½ in (15.3 m)
Height 18 ft 5 in (5.61 m)
Wing area: 450 ft² (41.81 m²)
Weights: Empty 8,650 lb (3,924 kg)
Loaded
Maximum 17,085 lb (7,750 kg)
Performance: speed 310 mph (500 kph); cruising speed 305 mph (491 kph); climb 2,640 ft (805 m) per minute at sea level; service ceiling 41,000 ft (12,500 m); range

1,240 miles (1,995 km) with maximum payload; range 1,600 miles (2,575 km) with maximum fuel
Used only by: Argentina
Notes: The original *Guarani* I turboprop-powered transport flew in the early 1960s, and from it was derived the *Guarani* II, which made its first flight in 1963. The *Guarani* II differs from its predecessor in having more powerful engines, single vertical tail surfaces, a shorter fuselage and other detail improvements such as pressurisation. Maximum payload is 3,307 lb (1,500 kg).

Fábrica Militar de Aviones IA 58
Pucará

Type: counter-insurgency aircraft
Crew: two, seated in tandem
Wings: cantilever duralumin semi-monocoque monoplane
Fuselage: duralumin semi-monocoque
Tail unit: cantilever duralumin semi-monocoque
Landing gear: hydraulically actuated retractable tricycle unit
Powerplant: two 1,022-ehp Turboméca Astazou turboprops driving three-blade Hamilton Standard 23LF/1015-0 metal propellers
Fuel capacity: 313 gallons (1,422 litres) in two fuselage and two wing tanks, plus an

optional 66-gallon (300-litre) drop tank under each wing
Avionics: Bendix DFA-73A-1 ADF, Bendix RTA-42A VHF communications, Bendix RNA-2bc VHF navigation, Northern NF-420 HF 55B communications, plus optional weather radar, IFF and VHF/FM tactical communications system
Armament: two 20-mm Hispano cannon and four 7.62-mm FN machine-guns in the fuselage; one attachment point under fuselage and under each wing for up to 3,307 lb (1,500 kg) of external stores (including drop tanks)
Dimensions: Span 47 ft 6¾ in (14.5 m)
Length 46 ft 9 in (14.25 m)
Height 17 ft 7 in (5.36 m)
Wing area: 326.1 ft² (30.3 m²)
Weights: Empty 8,900 lb (4,037 kg)
Loaded
Maximum 14,991 lb (6,800 kg)
Performance: speed 310 mph (500 kph) at 9,840 ft (3,000 m); cruising speed 267 mph (430 kph); climb 3,543 ft (1,080 m) per minute at sea level; service ceiling 27,165 ft (8,280 m) at 13,668-lb (6,200-kg) all-up weight; range 1,890 miles (3,042 km) at 16,404 ft (5,000 m) with maximum fuel (all performance figures at maximum take-off weight unless otherwise specified)
Used also by: Bolivia (?)
Notes: The IA 58 first flew in 1967, and is a COIN derivative of the IA 50.

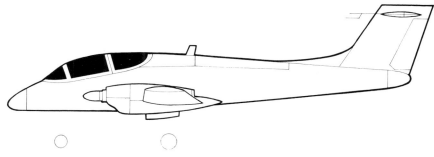

Lockheed Aircraft L.188 Electra

Type: transport aircraft
Crew: five, plus up to 99 passengers
Wings: metal cantilever low-wing monoplane
Fuselage: metal semi-monocoque
Tail unit: metal cantilever
Landing gear: hydraulically actuated retractable tricycle unit
Powerplant: four Allison 501-D13 turboprops, each rated at 3,750 ehp and driving a four-blade metal propeller
Fuel capacity:
Avionics: comprehensive communication and navigation equipment
Armament: none
Dimensions: Span 99 ft (30.17 m)
Length 104 ft 6½ in (31.86 m)
Height 31 ft 11¼ in (9.73 m)
Wing area: 1,300 ft² (120.77 m²)
Weights: Empty 57,000 lb (25,855 kg)
Loaded 85,500 lb (38,783 kg)
Maximum 116,000 lb (52,617 kg)
Performance: speed 448 mph (721 kph) at 12,000 ft (3,658 m); cruising speed 405 mph (652 kph) at 22,000 ft (6,706 m); range 3,450 miles (5,552 km) with maximum payload
Used also by: Bolivia
Notes: The Electra was the first US turboprop

transport, but was not a particularly successful aircraft, except in its P-3 Orion maritime reconnaissance form.

Morane-Saulnier MS.760 Paris

Type: liaison aircraft and trainer
Crew: two or four
Wings: metal cantilever low mid-wing monoplane
Fuselage: metal semi-monocoque
Tail unit: metal cantilever
Landing gear: hydraulically actuated retractable tricycle unit
Powerplant: two Turboméca Marboré II turbojets, each rated at 880-lb (400-kg) static thrust
Fuel capacity:
Avionics: communication and navigation equipment
Armament: a wide variety of armament installations is possible, including weapons such as the 30-mm DEFA cannon, 7.62-mm machine-guns, rockets, 110-lb (50-kg) bombs, and 250-lb (113-kg) bombs
Dimensions: Span 33 ft 3 in (10.13 m)
Length 32 ft 10¾ in (10.0 m)
Height 8 ft 6 in (2.6 m)

17

Wing area: 193.68 ft² (18.0 m²)
Weights: Empty 4,280 lb (1,940 kg)
Loaded
Maximum 7,435 lb (3,372.5 kg)
Performance: speed 405 mph (650 kph) at
sea level; climb 2,264 ft (690 m) per
minute at sea level; service ceiling 32,810
ft (10,000 m); range 930 miles (1,500 km)
Used also by: France, Paraguay
Notes: The prototype Paris first flew in 1954,
and production aircraft in 1958.

Australia

The Royal Australian Air Force

The pace of modern technology, with its concomitant exorbitant costs, has nowhere made itself more felt than in military aircraft. It has made it all but impossible for small countries to produce their own sophisticated military aircraft, and very costly even to equip their air forces with the best aircraft imported from the larger countries which can afford, or have persuaded themselves that they can afford, the enormous research and development programmes associated with high-performance combat aircraft. Australia is very much a case in point: her air force is small, but of high quality, and most of the aircraft have had to be imported. The Royal Australian Air Force numbers 21,631 personnel, some 30.9 per cent of the armed forces, whose budget is some 2.64 per cent of the gross national product.

Australia's air defence problem is a considerable one, for she is a very large country, with targets widespread, and the forces to defend them small. In these circumstances, her best defence is perhaps the distance she lies from any possible aggressor. Any attack on Australia would therefore have to rely on seaborne air power, offering the Royal Australian Air Force and Fleet Air Arm the concentrated targets they are well equipped to attack, or on a small number of extemporised bases on conquered territory, also offering the Australian air forces good targets. The centre of Australian air defence must be long-range strike, therefore, and here the two F-111C squadrons would come into their own, possible aggressors lacking any effective means of neutralising such advanced aircraft. For local defence Australia has three interceptor/FGA squadrons of Mirage IIIO fighters, two of the squadrons being based in Malaysia. Reconnaissance is well catered for by the two F-111 squadrons, one Canberra B.20 squadron, and two P-3 Orion maritime reconnaissance squadrons. Transport presents little difficulty, the Australians having five aircraft transport squadrons and one helicopter transport squadron, with more C-130 transports on order. This will allow fairly substantial ground forces and their equipment to be moved to crisis spots with speed, and once in the threatened area the troops will have fair tactical mobility thanks to the existence of three utility helicopter squadrons with Bell UH-1Hs.

By the standards prevailing in southeast Asia and Australasia, the Royal Australian Air Force is possibly the best, but doubts arise as to her ability to fight a war because of her almost total lack of reserves. There are some operational types in the operational conversion unit and training squadrons, but the commitment of these to front-line service would keep the air force operational for only a short time should losses prove severe, or Australia become embroiled in a war of more than a few days' duration.

21,630 men and 117 combat aircraft, plus 475 reservists in 5 Citizen's Air Force squadrons.

2 strike/recce sqns with 22 F-111C.
3 interceptor/FGA sqns with 48 Mirage IIIO.
1 recce sqn with 13 Canberra B.20.
2 MR sqns: 1 with 10 P-3B Orion; 1 with 10 P-3C (being delivered).
5 transport sqns: 2 with 24 C-130A/E; 2 with 22 DHC-4; 1 with 2 BAC 111, 2 HS-748, 3 Mystère 20.
Transport flts with 17 C-47.
1 Forward Air Controller flight with 6 CA-25.
1 OCU with 14 Mirage IIIO/D.
1 helicopter transport sqn with 6 CH-47 Chinook (6 more in reserve).
3 utility helicopter sqns with 47 UH-1H Iroquois.
Trainers incl 80 M.B.326, 8 HS 748 T.2, 37 CT-4 Airtrainer.
Sidewinder, R.530 AAM.
(12 C-130H transports on order.)

Fleet Air Arm
22 combat aircraft.
1 FB sqn with 8 A-4G Skyhawk.
2 ASW sqns with 3 S-2E, 11 S-2G Tracker (5 in reserve).
1 ASW/SAR helicopter sqn with 7 Sea King, 2 Wessex 31B.
1 helicopter sqn with 5 Bell UH-1H, 2 Bell 206B, 4 Wessex 31B.
1 trg sqn with 8 M.B.326H, 3 TA-4G, 5 A-4G, 2 HS 748 ECM trg ac.
Reserves: 925 (with trg obligations).

Army Air Arm
1 aviation regt.
17 Pilatus Porter, 9 Nomad ac; 50 Bell 206B-1 helicopters.

Avions Marcel Dassault *Mystère* 20/Falcon 20

Type: light transport aircraft
Crew: two, plus up to 14 passengers
Wings: metal cantilever low-wing monoplane
Fuselage: metal semi-monocoque
Tail unit: metal cantilever
Landing gear: hydraulically actuated retractable tricycle unit
Powerplant: two General Electric CF700-2D-2 turbofans, each rated at 4,315-lb (1,960-kg) static thrust
Fuel capacity: 1,150 gallons (5,240 litres) in two integral wing and two fuselage tanks
Avionics: comprehensive communication and navigation equipment
Armament: none
Dimensions: Span 53 ft 6 in (16.3 m)
Length 56 ft 3 in (17.15 m)
Height 17 ft 5 in (5.32 m)
Wing area: 440 ft² (41.0 m²)
Weights: Empty 15,970 lb (7,240 kg)
Loaded
Maximum 28,660 lb (13,000 kg)
Performance: cruising speed 536 mph (862 kph) at 25,000 ft (7,620 m); ceiling 42,000 ft (12,800 m); range 2,220 miles (3,570 km) with a payload of 1,600 lb (725 kg) and maximum fuel
Used also by: Belgium, Canada, Central African Republic, Egypt, France, Gabon, Iran, Jordan, Libya, Norway, Pakistan, Saudi Arabia
Notes: The prototype of the *Mystère* 20/ Falcon 20 series of executive transports flew in 1963, and the type has found a ready military and civil market. The maximum payload of the F series, to which the technical specification above applies, is 3,320 lb (1,500 kg).

Commonwealth Aircraft CA-25
Winjeel

Type: trainer and forward air controller aircraft
Crew: three
Wings: metal cantilever low-wing monoplane
Fuselage: metal semi-monocoque
Tail unit: metal cantilever
Landing gear: fixed tailwheel unit
Powerplant: one Pratt & Whitney R-985-AN-2 radial engine, rated at 445 hp and driving a two-blade metal propeller
Fuel capacity:
Avionics: communication and navigation equipment
Armament: none
Dimensions: Span 38 ft 7½ in (11.77 m)
Length 28 ft 0½ in (8.55 m)
Height 9 ft 1 in (2.77 m)
Wing area: 249 ft² (23.13 m²)
Weights: Empty 3,289 lb (1,492 kg)
Loaded 4,265 lb (1,935 kg)
Maximum

Performance: speed 186 mph (299 kph); cruising speed 165 mph (266 kph) at 8,500 ft (2,590 m); climb 1,500 ft (457 m) per minute at sea level; service ceiling 18,000 ft (5,486 m); range 870 miles (1,400 km)
Used only by: Australia
Notes: The CA-25 first flew in 1952 under the designation CA-22, and the initial production aircraft entered service in 1955.

De Havilland Aircraft of Canada DHC-4 Caribou

Type: STOL tactical transport
Crew: three, plus up to 32 troops
Wings: metal cantilever high-wing inverted gull monoplane
Fuselage: metal semi-monocoque
Tail unit: metal cantilever
Landing gear: hydraulically actuated retractable tricycle unit
Powerplant: two Pratt & Whitney R-2000-D5 radial engines, each rated at 1,450 hp and driving a metal three-blade propeller
Fuel capacity: 690 gallons (3,137 litres)
Avionics: comprehensive communication and navigation equipment
Armament: none
Dimensions: Span 95 ft 7½ in (29.15 m)
Length 72 ft 7 in (22.13 m)
Height 31 ft 9 in (9.7 m)
Wing area: 912 ft² (84.73 m²)
Weights: Empty 18,260 lb (8,283 kg)
Loaded 28,500 lb (12,928 kg)
Maximum 31,300 lb (14,197 kg)
Performance: speed 216 mph (347 kph) at 5,000 ft (1,525 m); cruising speed 182 mph (293 kph) at 7,500 ft (2,285 m); climb 1,355 ft (413 m) per minute at sea level; service ceiling 24,800 ft (7,560 m); range 242 miles (390 km) with maximum payload; range 1,307 miles (2,103 km) with maximum fuel
Used also by: Cameroon, India, Kenya, Malaysia, Spain, Tanzania, Zaire, Zambia
Notes: The DHC-4 STOL transport made its first flight in 1958, and entered service in 1961. Its maximum payload is 8,740 lb (3,965 kg).

General Dynamics F-111

Type: multi-role combat aircraft
Crew: two, seated side by side
Wings: metal cantilever variable-geometry shoulder-mounted monoplane
Fuselage: aluminium alloy, steel and titanium semi-monocoque
Tail unit: metal cantilever
Landing gear: hydraulically actuated retractable tricycle unit
Powerplant: two Pratt & Whitney TF 30-P-100 turbofans, each rated at 25,100 lb (11,385 kg) with afterburning
Fuel capacity: about 4,000 gallons (18,184 litres) in fuselage and wing tanks, plus up to 2,997 gallons (13,626 litres) in six underwing drop tanks
Avionics: very comprehensive communication and navigation/attack equipment, varying from model to model. The FB-111A strategic bombing model has the most advanced equipment, including AN/APN-185 doppler navigation radar, AN/APQ-114 attack radar, AN/APQ-128 terrain-following radar and AN/APN-176 radar altimeter

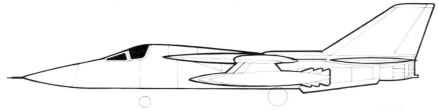

Armament: one 20-mm M61 multi-barrel cannon and two B43 nuclear bombs in a bay, and external stores on six underwing pylons (F-111F). Up to eight pylons can be used, and maximum armament load that can be carried is fifty 750-lb (340-kg) bombs, for a maximum payload of 37,500 lb (17,010 kg), on the FB-111A strategic bombing variant, which can carry an alternative load of six Boeing AGM-69A SRAMs (short-range attack missiles) on six underwing pylons. Maximum external load of the F-111A is about 30,000 lb (13,608 kg) of bombs, fuel tanks, missiles and rocket pods

Dimensions: Span (spread) 63 ft (19.2 m)
Span (swept) 31 ft 11½ in (9.74 m)
Length 73 ft 6 in (22.4 m)
Height 17 ft 1½ in (5.22 m)

Wing area: 525 ft² (48.77 m²)

Weights: Empty 47,481 lb (21,537 kg)
Loaded
Maximum 100,000 lb (45,359 kg)

Performance: (at maximum take-off weight) speed 1,650 mph (2,656 kph) or Mach 2.5 at 40,000 ft (12,200 m); speed 800 mph (1,287 kph) or Mach 1.2 at low altitude; service ceiling more than 59,000 ft (18,000 m); range on internal fuel 2,925 miles (4,707 km)

Used also by: USA

Notes: The F-111 family stems from a 1960 requirement for a multi-role combat aircraft able to comply with a number of USAF and USN requirements. At first known as the TFX, the design emerged as the F-111, although the type has always been used as a bomber not as a fighter. There are various versions:

1. F-111A tactical fighter-bomber, with 18,500-lb (8,390-kg) TF30-P-3s, Triple Plow 1 intakes and Mark I avionics
2. F-111B for the US Navy was cancelled
3. F-111C strike aircraft for the Royal Australian Air Force, similar to the FB-111 but with TF30-P-3 engines, Triple Plow 1 intakes and Mark I avionics
4. F-111D, similar to the F-111E, but with TF 30-P-9 engines, Triple Plow 2 air intakes and Mark II avionics, improving air-to-air capability
5. F-111E, which appeared before the F-111D, but also had TF 30-P-9 engines and Triple Plow 2 intakes, and was used as a tactical fighter-bomber, with Mark I avionics
6. F-111F tactical fighter-bomber, with TF 30-P-100 engines, but cost-reduced Mark IIB avionics, a mixture of those fitted to the FB-111A and F-111E, and Triple Plow 2 intakes
7. FB-111A strategic bomber variant with larger wings and complex electronics (Mark IIB) and Triple Plow 2 intakes
8. EF-111A, an ECM type under development by Grumman with EA-6 Prowler electronics.

Largely as a result of a poor press, the F-111 family has never received the accolades due to it as a great combat aircraft.

Austria

4,000 men (2,000 conscripts) and 30 combat aircraft, plus 700 reservists (the air force is part of the Austrian Army).

3 FB sqns with 30 Saab 105Ö.
1 transport sqn with 2 Skyvan, 12 Turbo-Porter.
6 helicopter sqns with 23 AB-204B, 13 AB-206A, 24 *Alouette* III, 12 OH-58B, 2 S-65Oe (HH-53).
2 trg sqns with 18 Saab 91D, 7 Saab 105Ö.
Other ac incl 23 Cessna L-19, 3 DHC-2.
4 indep AD bns.
300 20mm Oerlikon, 70 35mm Z/65, Z/75, 60 40mm Bofors AA guns; Super-Bat and Skyguard AD system. (12 AB-212 helicopters on order.)

Bell Helicopter Textron OH-58 Kiowa

Type: light observation helicopter
Crew: two, plus up to two passengers
Rotor: aluminium and light alloy cantilever two-blade main rotor; aluminium cantilever two-blade tail rotor
Fuselage: aluminium alloy box, semi-monocoque and monocoque
Landing gear: twin light alloy skids
Powerplant: one Allison T63-A-700 turbo-shaft, rated at 317 shp
Fuel capacity: 60.7 gallons (276 litres)
Avionics: communication and navigation equipment
Armament: one XM-27 armament kit, using the 7.62-mm Minigun
Dimensions: Span 35 ft 4 in (10.77 m)
Length (fuselage) 32 ft 7 in (9.93 m)
Height 9 ft 6½ in (2.91 m)
Rotor disc area: 978.8 ft² (90.93 m²)
Weights: Empty (58A) 1,464 lb (664 kg); (58C) 1,585 lb (719 kg)
Loaded (58A) 2,313 lb (1,049 kg); (58C) 2,434 lb (1,104 kg)
Maximum (58A) 3,000 lb (1,360 kg); (58C) 3,200 lb (1,451 kg)
Performance: (OH-58A at a take-off weight of 2,768 lb/1,255 kg) speed 138 mph (222 kph) at sea level; cruising speed 117 mph (188 kph); climb 1,780 ft (543 m) per minute at sea level; service ceiling 18,900 ft (5,760 m); hovering ceiling in ground effect 13,600 ft (4,145 m); endurance 3 hours 50 minutes; range 305 miles (490 km) on scouting mission with armament
Used also by: Australia, Brazil, Canada, Finland, Greece, Iran, Italy, Jamaica, Saudi Arabia, Spain, Turkey, USA
Notes: Basically similar to the Model 206A JetRanger, the OH-58A was accepted for US service in 1968. The main variants are:
1. OH-58A for US and Canadian service, to which the above details apply
2. OH-58B for Australian and Austrian service, machines being produced in the USA and Australia
3. OH-58C for US service, with improved cockpit, 420-shp T63-A-270 engine and IR reduction package, adding to 'hot and high' operation performance and reducing chances of detection.

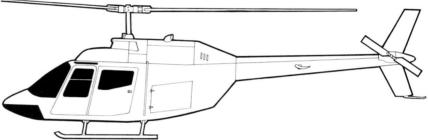

De Havilland Aircraft of Canada DHC-2 Beaver

Type: utility transport
Crew: one, plus up to six passengers
Wings: metal high-wing braced monoplane
Fuselage: metal semi-monocoque
Tail unit: metal cantilever
Landing gear: fixed tailwheel unit
Powerplant: one Pratt & Whitney R-985-AN-1 radial engine, rated at 450 hp and driving a two-blade metal propeller
Fuel capacity:
Avionics: communication and navigation equipment
Armament: none
Dimensions: Span 48 ft (14.63 m)
Length 30 ft 3 in (9.22 m)
Height 9 ft (2.74 m)
Wing area: 250 ft² (23.23 m²)
Weights: Empty 2,850 lb (1,293 kg)
Loaded 5,100 lb (2,313 kg)
Maximum
Performance: speed 163 mph (262 kph) at 5,000 ft (1,524 m); cruising speed 143 mph (230 kph); climb 1,020 ft (311 m) per minute at sea level; service ceiling 18,000 ft (5,486 m); range 733 miles (1,180 km)
Used also by: Argentina, Colombia, Dominican Republic, Kenya, Laos, Philippines, Turkey, Zambia
Notes: The prototype of the Beaver first flew in 1947, and has since served with distinction in many air forces requiring a light transport capable of operating in difficult conditions.

Saab-Scania 105

Type: multi-role military aircraft
Crew: one or two, seated side-by-side, or one and up to three passengers
Wings: metal cantilever shoulder-mounted monoplane
Fuselage: metal semi-monocoque
Tail unit: metal cantilever
Landing gear: retractable tricycle unit
Powerplant: two General Electric J85-GE-17B turbojets, each rated at 2,850-lb (1,293-kg) static thrust
Fuel capacity: 440 gallons (2,000 litres) in two fuselage and two wing tanks, plus provision for external drop tanks under the wings
Avionics: comprehensive communication and navigation/attack equipment, including Saab RGS-2 sighting system for air-to-air and air-to-surface weapons, with the option of laser rangefinding
Armament: all carried externally, on six underwing hardpoints, the inner four being capable of lifting 992 lb (450 kg) each and the outer two 606 lb (275 kg) each, up to a maximum of 5,180 lb (2,350 kg) with reduced fuel load, or 3,748 lb (1,700 kg) with maximum internal fuel load. Typical loads comprise six 500-lb (227-kg) bombs; four 750-lb (340-kg) bombs and two RB324 Sidewinder air-to-air missiles; four 1,000-lb (454-kg) bombs and two Sidewinders; four 500-lb (227-kg) bombs and two 30-mm cannon pods; twelve 135-mm rockets; eight 135-mm rockets and two

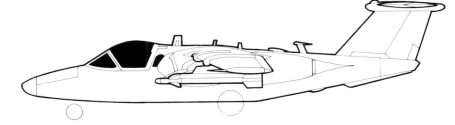

30-mm cannon pods; and a variety of drop tanks, ECM pods and reconnaissance pods
Dimensions: Span 31 ft 2 in (9.5 m)
Length 35 ft 5¼ in (10.8 m)
Height 8 ft 10 in (2.7 m)
Wing area: 175 ft² (16.3 m²)
Weights: Empty 6,757 lb (3,065 kg)
Loaded 10,714 lb (4,860 lb)
Maximum 14,330 lb (6,500 kg)
Performance: speed at 9,546 lb (4,330 kg) 613 mph (970 kph) at sea level; speed at 12,731 lb (5,775 kg) 510 mph (820 kph) at 32,800 ft (10,000 m); climb at 10,582 lb (4,800 kg) 11,155 ft (3,400 m) per minute at sea level; climb at 13,893 lb (6,302 kg) to 32,800 ft (10,000 m) in 11 minutes 50 seconds; service ceiling 42,650 ft (13,000 m); combat radius with six 500-lb (227-kg) bombs and 5 minutes of combat on a hi-lo-hi mission 431 miles (695 km); ferry range 1,572 miles (2,530 km)
Used also by: Sweden

Notes: Designed originally for training and light ground attack missions, the Saab 105 can also undertake reconnaissance, target flying, and liaison duties. The technical description above refers to the Saab 105G, a company demonstration model derived from the Austrian Saab 105Ö, and having a greater ground-attack capability with more weapons and improved electronics.

Bahrain

Police force only.

2 Scout helicopters.

Bangladesh

5,000 men and 9 combat aircraft.

1 FB sqn with 9 MiG-21MF.
1 transport sqn with 1 An-24, 2 An-26.
1 helicopter sqn with 4 *Alouette* III, 2 Wessex HC.2, 6 Bell 212, 8 Mi-8.
Trainers incl 2 MiG-21U, 6 Magister.
AA-2 'Atoll' AAM.

Antonov An-24 'Coke'

Type: transport aircraft
Crew: four or five, plus up to 38 passengers
Wings: metal cantilever high-wing monoplane
Fuselage: metal semi-monocoque
Tail unit: metal cantilever
Landing gear: hydraulically actuated retractable tricycle unit
Powerplant: two Ivchenko AI-24A turboprops, each rated at 2,550 ehp and driving a four-blade metal propeller
Fuel capacity: 1,220 gallons (5,550 litres) in four bag tanks in the centre section and in outer wing integral tanks, plus provision for four more tanks in the centre section and for RATO units
Avionics: comprehensive communication and navigation equipment
Armament: none
Dimensions: Span 95 ft 9½ in (29.2 m)
Length 77 ft 2½ in (23.53 m)
Height 27 ft 3½ in (8.32 m)
Wing area: 807.1 ft² (74.98 m²)
Weights: Empty 30,997 lb (14,060 kg)
Loaded 44,052 lb (20,000 kg)
Maximum 46,300 lb (21,000 kg)
Performance: (at maximum take-off weight) cruising speed 280 mph (450 kph) at 19,700 ft (6,000 m); service ceiling 27,560 ft (8,400 m); range with maximum payload 397 miles (640 km); range with maximum fuel and a payload of 3,554 lb (1,612 kg) 1,864 miles (3,000 km)
Used also by: Bulgaria, China, Congo, Cuba, Czechoslovakia, Hungary, Iraq, Laos, Mali, Mongolia, Mozambique, North Korea, Poland, Romania, Somali Republic, South Yemen, Sudan, Syria, USSR, Vietnam
Notes: The prototype An-24 made its first flight in 1959, and entered service with civil and military operators in 1963 and 1964. There are several versions:
1. An-24V Series I initial production model for 44 passengers
2. An-24V Series II for 50 passengers
3. An-24P firefighting model
4. An-24RV, similar to the Series II but with a 1,985-lb (900-kg) RU 19-300 auxiliary turbojet in the starboard nacelle to improve performance and take-off
5. An-24T freighting aircraft, to which the technical specification above relates
6. An-24RT, similar to the An-24T but with the RU 19-300 auxiliary turbojet.

The maximum payload of the An-24T is 10,168 lb (4,612 kg).

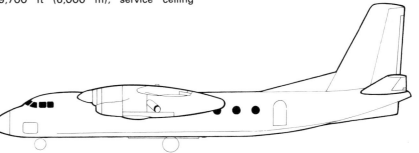

Belgium

19,400 men (3,200 conscripts) and 148 combat aircraft.

5 FB sqns: 2 with 36 F/TF-104G,
3 with 54 Mirage VBA/D.
2 AWX sqns with 36 F-104G, 4 TF-104G.
1 recce sqn with 18 Mirage VBR.
2 transport sqns with 12 C-130H, 3 HS 748, 6 Merlin IIIA, 2 Falcon 20, 2 Boeing 727QC.
1 SAR sqn with 4 HSS-1, 5 Sea King Mk 48 helicopters.
37 Magister, 33 SF. 260, 12 T-33 trainers.
Sidewinder AAM.
8 SAM sqns with Nike Hercules.
(116 F-16A/B fighters, 33 AlphaJet trg ac, Super Sidewinder, AIM-7E Sparrow AAM, 40 BDX APC on order.)
Naval Air Arm
3 *Alouette* III helicopters.
Army Air Arm
6 Piper Super Cub, 12 BN Islander ac, 74 *Alouette* II helicopters; 31 *Epervier* RPV.

British Aerospace (Hawker Siddeley Aviation) 748 Andover

Type: passenger and freight transport
Crew: three, plus up to 58 passengers
Wings: metal cantilever low-wing monoplane
Fuselage: metal semi-monocoque
Tail unit: metal cantilever
Landing gear: hydraulically actuated retractable tricycle unit
Powerplant: two Rolls-Royce Dart R.Da 7 Mk 535-2 turboprops, each rated at 2,280 ehp and driving a Dowty Rotol four-blade metal propeller
Fuel capacity: 1,440 gallons (6,550 litres) in two integral wing tanks
Avionics: comprehensive communication and navigation equipment
Armament: none
Dimensions: Span 98 ft 6 in (30.02 m)
Length 67 ft (20.42 m)
Height 24 ft 10 in (7.57 m)
Wing area: 810.75 ft² (75.35 m²)
Weights: Empty 25,453 lb (11,545 kg)
Loaded
Maximum 51,000 lb (23,133 kg)
Performance: cruising speed 281 mph (452 kph) for civil version at a weight of 38,000

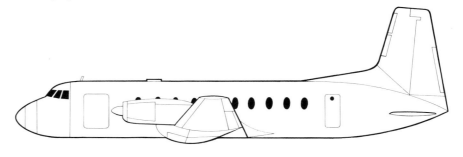

lb (17,236 kg); climb 1,420 ft (433 m) per minute at sea level for civil version at a weight of 38,000 lb (17,236 kg); service ceiling 25,000 ft (7,620 m); combat radius with a load of 9,000 lb (4,082 kg) on a supply dropping mission 720 miles (1,158 km); range with a payload of 14,027 lb (6,363 kg) 1,474 miles (2,372 km)

Used also by: Australia, Brazil, Brunei, Came-roon, Colombia, Ecuador, India, New Zealand, South Korea, Tanzania, Thailand, UK, Upper Volta, Venezuela, Zambia

Notes: The HS 748 Military Transport is the military version of the Series 2A civil transport, with a large freight door and capable of a military overload. Maximum payload is 17,547 lb (7,959 kg).

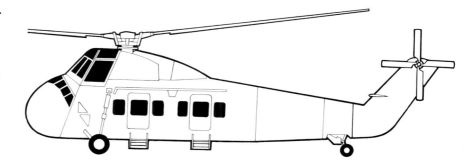

Sikorsky Aircraft Division H-34 Choctaw

Type: assault helicopter
Crew: two, plus up to 18 passengers
Rotor: metal cantilever four-blade main rotor; metal cantilever four-blade tail rotor
Fuselage: metal semi-monocoque
Landing gear: fixed tailwheel unit
Powerplant: one Wright R-1820-84 radial engine, rated at 1,525 hp
Fuel capacity: 255 gallons (1,159 litres)
Avionics: comprehensive communication and navigation equipment
Armament: none
Dimensions: Span 56 ft (17.06 m)
Length 46 ft 9 in (14.25 m)
Height 15 ft 11 in (4.85 m)
Rotor disc area: 2,460 ft² (228.54 m²)
Weights: Empty 7,630 lb (3,461 kg)
Loaded 13,000 lb (5,900 kg)
Maximum 14,000 lb (6,350 kg)
Performance: speed 123 mph (198 kph) at sea level; cruising speed 98 mph (158 kph); climb 1,100 ft (335 m) per minute at sea level; service ceiling 9,500 ft (2,895 m); range 182 miles (293 km)
Used also by: Argentina, Central African Empire, Haiti, Indonesia, Laos, Nicaragua, Philippines, Thailand
Notes: Built under the company designation S-58, the type first flew in 1954, and was built for the USAF and USN, the latter having been responsible for the initial specification, for a utility helicopter with A/S capability greater than that of the earlier Sikorsky S-55. Operated by the USAF as the H-34 and the USN as the HO4S or HRS. The S-58's naval designation is HSS Seabat in the utility role, and HUS Seahorse in the utility role. The maximum slung load is 5,000 lb (2,268 kg).

Benin

150 men.

3 medium transports.
5 light transports.
1 Bell 47 helicopter.
1 *Alouette* II helicopter.

Max Holste MH.1521M
Broussard

Type: utility transport
Crew: two, plus up to four passengers
Wings: metal braced high-wing monoplane
Fuselage: metal tube structure
Tail unit: metal cantilever
Landing gear: fixed tailwheel unit
Powerplant: one Pratt & Whitney R-985-AN radial engine, rated at 450 hp and driving a two-blade metal propeller
Fuel capacity:
Avionics: communication and navigation equipment
Armament: none
Dimensions: Span 45 ft 1 in (13.75 m)

Length 28 ft 2½ in (8.6 m)
Height 9 ft 2 in (2.8 m)
Wing area: 273.4 ft² (25.4 m²)
Weights: Empty 3,637 lb (1,650 kg)
Loaded
Maximum 5,953 lb (2,700 kg)
Performance: speed 161 mph (260 kph) at 3,280 ft (1,000 m); climb 785 ft (240 m) per minute at sea level; range 745 miles (1,200 km)
Used also by: Central African Republic, Congo, France, Morocco, Senegal
Notes: The prototype of the *Broussard* flew in 1952, and the type entered service shortly afterwards. The keynote of the design is simplicity and ruggedness, to ensure serviceability in remote areas.

Bolivia

4,000 men and 42 combat aircraft.

1 fighter/training sqn with 10 T-33A/N.
2 COIN sqns with 18 EMB-326GB, 10 T-6D, 4 T-28A/D.
Transports incl 3 C-130H, 1 Electra, 2 C-54, 1 Sabreliner, 1 Learjet, 5 *Arava*, 4 CV-440, 10 C-47, 1 C-46, 2 Cessna 402, 1 Turbo-Porter, 2 Turbo-Centurion, 11 Cessna 185, 1 Super King Air, 1 Cessna 421.
1 helicopter sqn with 9 Hughes 500M, 3 Hiller OH-23C/D.
Trainers incl Cessna 310, 6 T-41D, 12 T-23 *Uirapuru*, 5 Fokker S-11, 6 SF.260M.
(1 *Arava*, 16 Turbo-Porter on order.)

Douglas Aircraft C-54
Skymaster

Type: transport aircraft
Crew: four, plus up to 50 passengers
Wings: metal cantilever low-wing monoplane
Fuselage: metal semi-monocoque
Tail unit: metal cantilever
Landing gear: hydraulically actuated retractable tricycle unit
Powerplant: four Pratt & Whitney R-2000-7 radial engines, each rated at 1,350 hp and driving a metal three-blade propeller
Fuel capacity:
Avionics: comprehensive communication and navigation equipment
Armament: none
Dimensions: Span 117 ft 6 in (35.8 m)
Length 93 ft 10 in (28.6 m)
Height 27 ft 6 in (8.38 m)

Wing area: 1,460 ft² (135.64 m²)
Weights: Empty 37,000 lb (16,783 kg)
Loaded 62,000 lb (28,123 kg)
Maximum 73,000 lb (33,113 kg)
Performance: speed 265 mph (426 kph) at 19,600 ft (5,974 m); cruising speed 230 mph (370 kph) at 15,200 ft (4,633 m); climb 14 minutes 48 seconds to 10,000 ft (3,050 m); service ceiling 22,000 ft (6,705 m); range 3,900 miles (6,277 km)
Used also by: Argentina, Chad, Colombia, Egypt, Ethiopia, Mauritania, Mexico, Niger, Paraguay, Peru, South Korea, Turkey, Zaire
Notes: The C-54 is the military version of the Douglas DC-4 civil airliner, and in fact preceded it into service, the first 24 C-54s being civil DC-4As taken over on the production line in December 1941. The last production model was the C-54G, which had 1,450hp R-2000-9 radials.

Hughes Helicopter Model 500M

Type: light observation helicopter
Crew: two, seated side-by-side
Rotor: aluminium cantilever four-blade main rotor; steel and glassfibre cantilever two-blade tail rotor
Fuselage: aluminium semi-monocoque
Landing gear: twin metal skids
Powerplant: one Allison Model 250-C18A turboshaft, rated at 317 shp but derated to 278 shp for take-off and 243 shp for continuous running
Fuel capacity: 50 gallons (227 litres) in bladder tanks in the rear fuselage
Avionics: communication and navigation equipment, and Spanish examples have a AN/ASQ-81 magnetic anomaly detector for A/S purposes
Armament: various armament options are available, including machine-guns and grenade launchers; Spanish machines have provision for two Mark 44 homing torpedoes
Dimensions: Span 26 ft 4 in (8.03 m)
Length (fuselage) 23 ft (7.01 m)
Height 8 ft 1½ in (2.48 m)
Rotor disc area: 544.63 ft² (50.6 m²)
Weights: Empty 1,130 lb (512 kg)
Loaded 2,550 lb (1,157 kg)
Maximum 3,000 lb (1,360 kg)

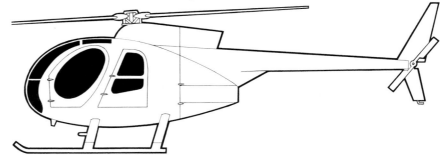

Performance: (at maximum take-off weight) speed 152 mph (244 kph) at 1,000 ft (305 m); cruising speed 135 mph (217 kph) at sea level; climb 1,700 ft (518 m) per minute at sea level; service ceiling 14,400 ft (4,390 m); hovering ceiling in ground effect 8,200 ft (2,500 m); range 366 miles (606 km) at 4,000 ft (1,220 m)
Used also by: Argentina, Denmark, Haiti, Sierre Leone, Spain
Notes: This is basically an uprated version of the OH-6A.

North American Aviation T-28 Trojan

Type: trainer and light ground-attack aircraft
Crew: two, seated in tandem
Wings: metal cantilever low-wing monoplane
Fuselage: metal semi-monocoque
Tail unit: metal cantilever
Landing gear: hydraulically actuated retractable tricycle unit
Powerplant: one Wright R-1830-56S radial engine, rated at 1,350 hp and driving a metal three-blade propeller
Fuel capacity:
Avionics: communication and navigation equipment
Armament: six underwing hardpoints for a variety of external loads, including the General Electric 7.62-mm Minigun pod, napalm tanks, 500-lb (227-kg) bombs, and rocket pods

Dimensions: Span 40 ft 7 in (12.37 m)
Length 32 ft 9 in (9.98 m)
Height 12 ft 7 in (3.84 m)
Wing area: 268 ft² (24.89 m²)
Weights: Empty 5,250 lb (2,381 kg)
Loaded 6,500 lb (2,948 kg)
Maximum 8,250 lb (3,742 kg)
Performance: 352 mph (567 kph) at 18,000 ft (5,486 m); service ceiling 37,000 ft (11,278 m); range 1,200 miles (1,931 km)
Used also by: Argentina, Dominican Republic, Egypt, Ethiopia, Honduras, Kampuchea, Laos, Mexico, Nicaragua, Philippines, South Korea, Thailand, USA
Notes: The T-28 trainer first flew in 1949, and entered service with the USAF as a basic and primary trainer (T-28A) in 1950.

There are several models:
1. T-28A trainer for the USAF with an 800-hp Wright R-1300-1 radial, two 0.5-in (12.7-mm) machine-guns, and light bombs or rocket pods under the wings
2. T-28B trainer for the USN with a 1,425-hp Wright R-1820-86 radial
3. T-28C trainer for the USN, identical with the T-28B but for the addition of an arrester hook
4. T-28D counter-insurgency aircraft with a 1,425-hp Wright R-1820-56S radial, with underwing attachment points for armament. The technical specification above applies to this model
5. AT-28 ground-attack aircraft, with a 3,750-ehp Avco Lycoming T55 turboprop.

Brazil

42,800 men and 135 combat aircraft.

1 interceptor sqn with 11 Mirage IIIEBR, 4 DBR.
2 FGA sqns with 34 F-5E, 5 F-5B.
8 COIN/recce sqns with 39 AT-26 *Xavante*, 20 T-25 Universal ac, 6 UH-1D, 4 Bell 206, 4 OH-6A helicopters.
1 ASW sqn with 8 S-2E, 8 S-2A (7 in carrier).
1 MR sqn with 6 EMB-111.
4 SAR sqns with 11 SA-16 Albatross, 3 RC-130E, 6 PBY-5A ac, 5 SH-1D, UH-1H, Bell 47G helicopters.
12 transport sqns with 2 Boeing 737, 10 C-130E/H, 2 KC-130H, 9 HS-125, 1 Viscount, 12 HS 748, 21 DHC-5, 74 EMB-110 *Bandeirante* (56 C-95, 6 R-95, 4 EC-95, 8 C-95A), 5 EMB-121 *Xingu* ac, 6 AB-206 helicopters.
3 liaison sqns with L-42, T-25, O-1E, 10 EMB-810C (Seneca II) ac, UH-1H helicopters.
Trainers incl 100 T-23 *Uirapuru*, 130 T-25, 10 T-33, 50 AT-26.
R.530 AAM.
(4 Mirage IIIEBR interceptors, 50 AT-26 trg, 12 EMB-110 (C-95A) transports, 6 EMB-111M MR ac on order.)

Naval Air Force
1 ASW sqn with 5 SH-3D Sea King helicopters.
1 utility sqn with 5 Whirlwind, 6 Wasp, 1 FH-1100, 2 Bell 47G, 18 AB-206B, 2 Lynx helicopters.
1 trg sqn with 10 Hughes 269/300 helicopters. (7 Lynx helicopters on order.)

Army Air Arm
40 L-42 *Regente*, O-1E lt ac; 10 AB-206A helicopters.

Empresa Brasileira de Aeronáutica AT-26 *Xavante*

Type: trainer and ground attack aircraft
Crew: two, in tandem
Wings: metal stressed-skin monoplane
Fuselage: metal semi-monocoque
Tail unit: metal cantilever semi-monocoque
Landing gear: hydraulically actuated retractable tricycle unit
Powerplant: one Rolls-Royce Bristol Viper 20 Mark 540 turbojet, rated at 3,410-lb (1,547-kg) static thrust
Fuel capacity: 306 gallons (1,392 litres) in main fuselage tank and two fixed wingtip tanks, plus two optional 73-gallon (332-litre) underwing tanks
Avionics: comprehensive communications and navigation equipment, mostly of Bendix and Collins manufacture
Armament: various loads (bombs, rocket pods, gun pods, reconnaissance pods and fuel tanks) can be carried on six underwing points. The largest bombs carried are 500-lb (227-kg) ones, the standard guns are 7.62-mm machine-guns, and the rockets are of either 37- or 70-mm calibre
Dimensions: Span 35 ft 7¼ in (10.85 m)
Length 35 ft 0¼ in (10.67 m)
Height 12 ft 2 in (3.72 m)

Wing area: 208.3 ft² (19.35 m²)
Weights: Empty 5,920 lb (2,685 kg) T; 5,640 lb (2,558 kg) A
Loaded
Maximum 10,090 lb (4,577 kg) T; 11,500 lb (5,216 kg) A (T = trainer; A = attack model without rear ejector-seat and wingtip fuel)
Performance: (trainer at 8,680-lb/3,937-kg take-off weight without underwing tanks) speed 539 mph (867 kph); cruising speed 495 mph (797 kph); climb 6,050 ft (1,844 m) per minute at sea level; time to 20,000 ft (6,100 m) 4 mins 10 secs; service ceiling 47,000 ft (14,325 m); range 1,150 miles (1,850 km)
Performance: (attack model at combat weight of 10,500 lb/4,763 kg) never-exceed speed 483 mph (778 kph); climb 3,550 ft (1,082 m) per minute at sea level; time to 20,000 ft (6,100 m) 8 mins; service ceiling 39,000 ft (11,900 m); combat radius at maximum take-off weight 403 miles (648 km)
Used also by: Bolivia, Paraguay, Togo
Notes: Licence-built version of the Italian Aermacchi M.B. 326GB with Brazilian armament and American electronics. For other models, see Italian entry.

Empresa Brasileira de Aeronáutica EMB-111

Type: land-based maritime reconnaissance aircraft
Crew: five
Wings: cantilever aluminium alloy monoplane
Fuselage: aluminium alloy semi-monocoque
Tail unit: cantilever metal semi-monocoque
Landing gear: hydraulically actuated retractable tricycle unit
Powerplant: two Pratt & Whitney Aircraft of Canada PT 6A-34 turboprops, each rated at 750 shp and driving a three-blade metal propeller
Fuel capacity: 569 gallons (2,586 litres) in fuel wing and two wingtip tanks
Avionics: AIL AN/APS-128 (SPAR-1) sea patrol airborne search radar in nose radome, plus comprehensive navigation and communications equipment, mostly of Bendix and Collins manufacture
Armament: none
Dimensions: Span 52 ft 4½ in (15.96 m)
Length 48 ft 7¾ in (14.83 m)
Height 15 ft 6½ in (4.74 m)

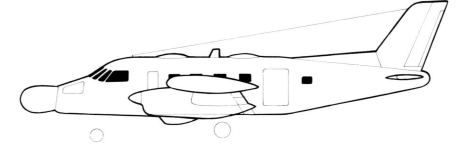

Wing area: 322 ft² (22.6 m²)
Weights: Empty 8,521 lb (3,865 kg)
  Loaded
  Maximum 15,432 lb (7,000 kg)
Performance (estimated): cruising speed 251 mph (404 kph) at 9,845 ft (3,000 m); climb 1,300 ft (396 m) per minute at sea level; service ceiling 22,500 ft (6,860 m); range 1,785 miles (2,872 km) at 10,000 ft (3,050 m) at 14,043 lb (6,370 kg) weight

(all performance figures at maximum take-off weight unless otherwise specified)
Used also by: Chile, Sudan
Notes: A derivative of the EMB-110 civil and military transport with uprated engines and special search equipment. A 50-million-candlepower searchlight is fitted in the starboard wing leading edge; and smoke grenades and flares (the latter up to

200,000 candlepower) are carried.
  Users of the EMB-110 Bandeirante in its military forms include:
Brazilian AF (EMB-110 12-seat transport as C-95, EMB-110B aerial photogrammetric aircraft as R-95, EMB-110K1 cargo model as C-95A); Chilean NAF (EMB-110C 15-seat transport as EMB-110C(N)); and Uruguayan AF (EMB-110C).

Grumman Aircraft S-2 Tracker

Type: anti-submarine search and strike aircraft
Crew: four
Wings: metal cantilever shoulder-wing monoplane
Fuselage: metal semi-monocoque
Tail unit: metal cantilever
Landing gear: hydraulically actuated retractable tricycle unit
Powerplant: two Wright R-1820-82WA radial engines, each rated at 1,525 hp and driving a three-blade metal propeller
Fuel capacity: 4,368 lb (1,981 kg)
Avionics: comprehensive communication and navigation/attack equipment, including APN-122 doppler radar and ASQ-10 magnetic anomaly detector
Armament: the weapons bay can accommodate two homing torpedoes, two Mark 101 depth bombs, or four 385-lb (175-kg) depth charges, and the six underwing pylons can accommodate 5-in (127-mm) rockets, Zuni rockets, 7.62-mm Minigun pods, ASMs, or other loads
Dimensions: Span 72 ft 7 in (22.13 m)
  Length 43 ft 6 in (13.26 m)
  Height 16 ft 7 in (5.06 m)
Wing area: 499 ft² (46.36 m²)
Weights: Empty 18,750 lb (8,505 kg)
  Loaded
  Maximum 29,150 lb (13,222 kg)
Performance: speed 267 mph (430 kph); cruising speed 149 mph (240 kph) at

1,500 ft (457 m); climb 1,390 ft (425 m) per minute at sea level; service ceiling 21,000 ft (6,400 m); range 1,300 miles (2,095 km)
Used also by: Argentina, Australia, Canada, Italy, Japan, Peru, South Korea, Taiwan, Thailand, Turkey, Venezuela
Notes: The S-2 was initially known as the S2F, the prototype of which first flew in

1952, and entered service in 1953. Apart from the Tracker A/S aircraft, the same basic airframe is used for the C-1 Trader carrier on-board delivery aircraft for nine passengers, and the E-1 Tracer airborne early warning aircraft, with long-range surveillance radar in a large radome above the fuselage, and triple fins and rudders in place of the original single surfaces.

Sociedade Aerotec T-23
Uirapuru

Type: primary trainer
Crew: two, seated side-by-side
Wings: metal cantilever low-wing monoplane
Fuselage: aluminium and steel semi-monocoque
Tail unit: metal and glassfibre cantilever
Landing gear: fixed tricycle unit
Powerplant: one Lycoming O-320-B2B piston engine, rated at 160 hp and driving a Sensenich metal two-blade propeller
Fuel capacity: 31 gallons (140 litres) in two integral wing leading-edge tanks, plus optional 8.8-gallon (40-litre) wingtip tanks

Avionics: communication and navigation equipment
Armament: none
Dimensions: Span 27 ft 10¾ in (8.5 m)
  Length 21 ft 8 in (6.6 m)
  Height 8 ft 10 in (2.7 m)
Wing area: 145.3 ft² (13.5 m²)
Weights: Empty 1,191 lb (540 kg)
  Loaded
  Maximum 1,825 lb (840 kg)

Performance: (at maximum take-off weight) speed 141 mph (227 kph); cruising speed 115 mph (185 kph); climb 836 ft (255 m) per minute at sea level; service ceiling 14,760 ft (4,500 m); range 495 miles (800 km); endurance 4 hours 30 minutes
Used also by: Bolivia, Guatemala, Paraguay
Notes: The *Uirapuru* was designed as a private venture, and is now the Brazilian Air Force's standard primary trainer.

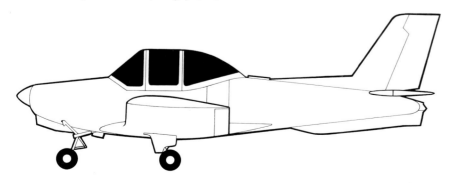

Sociedade Construtora Aeronáutica Neiva T-25 Universal

Type: basic trainer
Crew: two or three
Wings: metal cantilever low-wing monoplane
Fuselage: steel tube centre fuselage and aluminium semi-monocoque rear fuselage
Tail unit: metal cantilever
Landing gear: hydraulically actuated retractable tricycle unit
Powerplant: one Lycoming IO-540-K1D5 piston engine, rated at 300 hp and driving a Hartzell metal two-blade propeller
Fuel capacity: 73 gallons (332 litres) in six wing tanks
Avionics: communication and navigation equipment
Armament: two underwing attachment points for 7.62-mm machine-gun pods
Dimensions: Span 36 ft 1 in (11.0 m)
Length 28 ft 2½ in (8.6 m)
Height 9 ft 9¾ in (3.0 m)
Wing area: 185.14 ft² (17.2 m²)
Weights: Empty 2,535 lb (1,150 kg)
Loaded
Maximum 3,747 lb (1,700 kg)
Performance: (at maximum take-off weight) speed 184 mph (296 kph) at sea level; cruising speed 174 mph (280 kph) at sea level; climb 1,050 ft (320 m) per minute at sea level; service ceiling 16,400 ft (5,000 m); range 932 miles (1,500 km)
Used also by: Chile
Notes: The T-25 is a basic trainer and utility aircraft. There is also under consideration the Universal II, with a more powerful engine, currently under consideration for the air force.

Westland Aircraft Scout and Wasp

Type: multi-role helicopter
Crew: two, plus up to four passengers
Rotors: metal cantilever four-blade main rotor; metal cantilever two-blade tail rotor
Fuselage: metal tube structure and metal semi-monocoque tailboom
Landing gear: twin metal skids (Scout) or fixed quadricycle unit (Wasp)
Powerplant: one Rolls-Royce (Blackburn) Nimbus 102 turboshaft, rated at 685 shp (Scout), or one Rolls-Royce (Blackburn) Nimbus 503 turboshaft, rated at 710 shp (Wasp)
Fuel capacity: 155 gallons (705 litres)
Avionics: comprehensive communication and navigation equipment
Armament: flexible guns of up to 20-mm calibre, fixed machine-gun installations, rocket pods, or guided weapons such as the SS.11 ATGW (Scout); two Mark 44 A/S torpedoes (Wasp)
Dimensions: Span 32 ft 3 in (9.83 m)
Length (fuselage) 30 ft 4 in (9.24 m)
Height (rotors turning) 11 ft 8 in (3.56 m)
Rotor disc area: 816.9 ft² (75.89 m²)
Weights: Empty (S) 3,232 lb (1,465 kg); (W) 3,452 lb (1,566 kg)
Loaded
Maximum (S) 5,300 lb (2,405 kg); (W) 5,500 lb (2,495 kg)
Performance: (Scout) speed 131 mph (211 kph) at sea level; climb 1,670 ft (510 m) per minute at sea level; effective ceiling 13,400 ft (4,085 m); range with four passengers 315 miles (410 km)
Performance: (Wasp) speed 120 mph (193 kph) at sea level; climb 1,440 ft (439 m) per minute at sea level; effective ceiling 12,200 ft (3,720 m); range with four passengers 270 miles (435 km)
Used also by: Bahrain, Netherlands, New Zealand, South Africa, UK
Notes: The Scout and Wasp both stem from the Saunders-Roe P.531 light helicopter, which first flew in 1958. The first AH.1 Scout for the British Army flew in 1961, and the first HAS.1 Wasp for the Royal Navy in 1962. The last machine to be delivered was a Wasp, in 1974.

Brunei

1 HS 748 transport.
2 Piper Cherokee trainers.
3 Bell 205, 3 Bell 206, 4 Bell 212 helicopters.

Bulgaria

25,000 men (13,000 conscripts) and 263 combat aircraft, plus 20,000 reservists.

6 FGA sqns with 72 MiG-17, some MiG-23/-27.
10 interceptor sqns: 4 with 53 MiG-21, 1 with 20 MiG-19, 5 with 64 MiG-17.
3 recce sqns with 10 MiG-21, 24 MiG-15.
1 transport regt with 6 Il-14, 4 Il-18, 4 An-24, 2 Tu-134.
1 helicopter regt with 30 Mi-4, 30 Mi-2 and Mi-8.
Operational trainers incl 20 MiG-21U; other trg ac incl 80 L-29, Yak-11/-18, 50 MiG-15/-17/-21UTI.
AA-1 'Alkali', AA-2 'Atoll' AAM.
26 SA-2, 8 SA-3 SAM bns.
1 para regt.
Naval Air Arm
6 Mi-4 ASW helicopters.

Mikoyan-Gurevich MiG-17 'Fresco'

Type: fighter
Crew: one
Wings: metal cantilever mid-wing monoplane
Fuselage: metal semi-monocoque
Tail unit: metal cantilever
Landing gear: hydraulically actuated retractable tricycle unit
Powerplant: one Klimov VK-1F turbojet, rated at 7,495-lb (3,400-kg) static thrust with afterburning
Fuel capacity: 310 gallons (1,410 litres) in two fuselage tanks, plus provision for two 53- or 88-gallon (240- or 400-litre) underwing drop tanks
Avionics: comprehensive communication and navigation equipment, plus Izumrud 'Scan Odd' airborne interception and ranging radar in some models
Armament: one N-37 37-mm cannon with 40 rounds and two NS-23 23-mm cannon with 80 rounds per gun in early models; three Nudelmann-Rikter NR-23 23-mm cannon in MiG-17P and -17PF; four AA-1 'Alkali' beam-riding air-to-air missiles under the wings of the MiG-17PFU; and two hardpoints under each wing for the carriage of pods with eight 55-mm rockets, 210-mm rockets, 4,960-lb (2,250-kg) bombs, smaller bombs and drop tanks
Dimensions: Span 31 ft (9.45 m)
Length 36 ft 3 in (11.05 m)
Height 11 ft (3.35 m)
Wing area: 243.3 ft² (22.6 m²)
Weights: Empty 9,040 lb (4,100 kg)
Loaded 11,773 lb (5,340 kg)
Maximum 14,770 lb (6,700 kg)
Performance: speed 711 mph (1,145 kph) at 9,840 ft (3,000 m); climb 12,795 ft (3,900 m) per minute at sea level; service ceiling 54,460 ft (16,600 m); range at high altitude with two drop tanks 913 miles (1,470 km)
Used also by: Afghanistan, Albania, Algeria, Angola, China, Congo, Cuba, East Germany, Egypt, Guinea-Bissau, Indonesia, Mali, Nigeria, North Korea, North Yemen, Poland, Romania, Somali Republic, South Yemen, Sri Lanka, Sudan, Syria, Uganda, USSR, Vietnam
Notes: The MiG-17, though superficially similar to the MiG-15 in design, is in fact a totally new aircraft intended to overcome the MiG-15's poor characteristics at high speed. This was achieved by increasing the wings' angle of sweep and reducing the thickness:chord ratio by some 2 per cent. The rear fuselage is longer, and the tail surfaces have greater sweep. The prototype took to the air in 1950, and service introduction followed in 1952. The type has also been built in China as the Shenyang F-4. There are several variants of the basic MiG-17:
1. MiG-17 'Fresco-A' initial production model with narrow airbrakes for day interception
2. MiG-17S (later P) 'Fresco-B' all-weather interceptor with Izumrud radar
3. MiG-17F 'Fresco-C' with the afterburning VK-1F, wider airbrakes, and an exposed tailpipe, to which the technical specification applies
4. MiG-17PF 'Fresco-D' all-weather version of the MiG-17F with an afterburning engine and search radar
5. MiG-19PFU 'Fresco-E' version of the MiG-17PF with four beam-riding AA-1 'Alkali' air-to-air missiles.

The MiG-17 was also built in Czechoslovakia as the S-104, and in Poland as the LIM-5.

Tupolev Tu-134 'Crusty'

Type: medium-range transport
Crew: three, plus up to 80 passengers
Wings: metal cantilever low-wing monoplane
Fuselage: metal semi-monocoque
Tail unit: metal cantilever
Landing gear: hydraulically actuated retractable tricycle unit
Powerplant: two Soloviev D-30 turbofans, each rated at 14,990-lb (6,800-kg) static thrust
Fuel capacity: 3,630 gallons (16,500 litres) in six wing tanks
Avionics: comprehensive communication and navigation equipment
Armament: none
Dimensions: Span 95 ft 2 in (29.01 m)
Length 121 ft 6½ in (37.05 m)
Height 30 ft (9.14 m)
Wing area: 1,370.3 ft² (127.3 m²)
Weights: Empty 63,950 lb (29,000 kg)
Loaded
Maximum 103,600 lb (47,000 kg)
Performance: cruising speed at a weight of 92,600 lb (42,000 kg) at 32,800 ft (10,000 m) 550 mph (885 kph); service ceiling at maximum take-off weight 39,000 ft (11,900 m); range with maximum payload 1,243 miles (2,000 km); range with a payload of 8,800 lb (4,000 kg) 2,175 miles (3,500 km)
Used also by: Czechoslovakia, East Germany, Poland, USSR
Notes: Although designed as a civil airliner, the Tu-134 is readily converted to military use. There are two versions:
1. Tu-134, with a length of 114 ft 8 in (34.95 m), a passenger capacity of 72, a maximum payload of 16,975 lb (7,700 kg) and a range of 2,175 miles (3,500 km) with a payload of 6,600 lb (3,000 kg)
2. Tu-134A 'stretched' version, to which the technical specification above applies. The maximum payload of this version is 18,075 lb (8,200 kg).

Burma

7,500 men and 16 combat aircraft.

2 COIN sqns with 6 AT-33, 10 SF.260M.
Transports incl 4 C-47, 4 F27, 7 Pilatus PC-6/-6A, 6 Cessna 180.
Helicopters incl 10 KB-47G, 2 KV-107/II, 7 HH-43B, 10 *Alouette III*, 14 UH-1.
Trainers incl 10 T-37C (18 PC-7 Turbo-Trainers on order).

De Havilland Aircraft of Canada Chipmunk

Type: elementary trainer
Crew: one
Wings: metal cantilever low-wing monoplane
Fuselage: metal semi-monocoque
Tail unit: metal cantilever
Landing gear: fixed tailwheel unit
Powerplant: one de Havilland Gipsy Major 8 inline engine, rated at 145 hp and driving a two-blade metal propeller
Fuel capacity:
Avionics: communication and navigation equipment
Armament: none
Dimensions: Span 34 ft 4 in (10.46 m)
Length 25 ft 8 in (7.82 m)
Height 7 ft 1 in (2.16 m)
Wing area: 172 ft² (15.98 m²)
Weights: Empty 1,417 lb (643 kg)
Loaded 2,000 lb (907 kg)
Maximum
Performance: speed 138 mph (222 kph) at sea level; cruising speed 119 mph (192 kph); climb 800 ft (244 m) per minute at sea level; climb 7 minutes 18 seconds to 5,000 ft (1,524 m); service ceiling 16,000 ft (4,877 m); range 300 miles (483 km); endurance 2 hours 18 minutes
Used also by: Lebanon, Portugal, Sri Lanka, Thailand
Notes: The Chipmunk was designed by the de Havilland company to succeed the legendary Tiger Moth as an elementary trainer, and first flew in 1946 near Toronto in Canada, where it had been designed. The first Chipmunks, designated T.10 by the RAF, entered service in 1950.

De Havilland Aircraft of Canada DHC-3 Otter

Type: utility transport
Crew:
Wings: metal high-wing braced monoplane
Fuselage: metal semi-monocoque
Tail unit: metal cantilever
Landing gear: fixed tailwheel unit
Powerplant: one Pratt & Whitney R-1340-S1H1-G radial engine, rated at 600 hp and driving a three-blade metal propeller
Fuel capacity:
Avionics: communication and navigation equipment
Armament: none
Dimensions: Span 58 ft (17.68 m)
Length 41 ft 10 in (12.75 m)
Height 12 ft 7 in (3.84 m)
Wing area: 375 ft² (34.84 m²)
Weights: Empty 4,168 lb (1,890 kg)
Loaded
Maximum 8,000 lb (3,629 kg)
Performance: speed 160 mph (258 kph) at 5,000 ft (1,524 m); cruising speed 138 mph (222 kph); climb 735 ft (224 m) per minute at sea level; service ceiling 18,800 ft (5,730 m); range 960 miles (1,545 km)
Used also by: Argentina, Canada, Colombia, Egypt, Ethiopia, India, Indonesia, Nicaragua, Paraguay
Notes: The prototype of the Otter flew in 1951, and the type has since made a great name for itself as a light transport in difficult areas.

Lockheed Aircraft T-33

Type: advanced trainer and light attack aircraft
Crew: two, seated in tandem
Wings: metal cantilever low-wing monoplane
Fuselage: metal semi-monocoque
Tail unit: metal cantilever
Landing gear: hydraulically actuated retractable tricycle unit
Powerplant: one Allison J33-A-35 turbojet, rated at 5,400-lb (2,449-kg) static thrust with water injection
Fuel capacity:
Avionics: comprehensive communication and navigation equipment
Armament: two 0.5-in (12.7-mm) Browning M-3 machine-guns
Dimensions: Span 38 ft 10½ in (11.85 m)
Length 37 ft 9 in (11.5 m)
Height 11 ft 4 in (3.45 m)
Wing area: 238 ft² (22.1 m²)
Weights: Empty 8,084 lb (3,667 kg)
Loaded 11,965 lb (5,427 kg)
Maximum 14,442 lb (6,550 kg)
Performance: speed 543 mph (874 kph) at 25,000 ft (7,620 m); 600 mph (966 mph) or Mach 0.787 at sea level; climb 5,525 ft (1,684 m) per minute at sea level; climb 6 minutes 30 seconds to 25,000 ft (7,620 m); service ceiling 47,500 ft (14,478 m); range 1,345 miles (2,165 km)

Used also by: Belgium, Bolivia, Brazil, Canada, Chile, Egypt, Ethiopia, France, Greece, Guatemala, Indonesia, Iran, Japan, Malaysia, Nicaragua, Pakistan, Peru, Philippines, Portugal, South Korea, Spain, Taiwan, Thailand, Turkey, USA, Yugoslavia

Notes: The T-33 was developed from the F-80C Shooting Star fighter by the simple expedient of inserting a new section, 38½ in (97.8 cm) long, in the fuselage for the additional cockpit necessary in a trainer. The prototype, the TF-80C, first flew in 1948, and was taken into service as the T-33A in 1949. The type was also built for the USN as the TV-2, later T-33B, SeaStar. Some 5,819 of the type were built between 1949 and 1959, making the T-33 the most numerous trainer built since 1945. There are five principal variants:

1. RT-33A reconnaissance aircraft, with a crew of one and photographic equipment in the nose
2. DT-33A drone director conversion of the basic type
3. AT-33A interdiction and close air support aircraft, with additional armament
4. WT-33A meteorological aircraft
5. QT-33A drone aircraft.

Burundi

3 DC-3 transports.
Some helicopters.

Cameroon

300 men.

4 Magister COIN aircraft/trainers.
2 C-130 transports.
4 C-47 transports.
2 DHC-4 transports.
2 HS 748 transports.
9 light aircraft.
3 *Alouette* II/III helicopters.
1 Puma helicopter.

Canada

The Canadian Armed Forces (Air)

Since 1968 the Canadian services have been part of the unified Canadian Armed Forces, most of the country's air units falling under the administrative control of the Air Command. Personnel strength is about 36,500, some 45.6 per cent of the total armed forces, whose budget amounts to 1.84 per cent of the gross national product. Unusually, the air force is the largest of Canada's armed forces. Inevitably, the defence of Canada is inextricably bound up with that of the United States, as part of NATO and as part of continental North America.

The Air Defence Group of the Canadian Armed Forces is part of NORAD (North American Air Defense Command), which has its HQ at Colorado Springs. The ADG has four main and 17 auxiliary sites of the 31 which form the Distant Early Warning (DEW) Line system, running approximately along the line of the 70th parallel. The ADG also runs the 24 long-range radar stations of the Pine Tree Line. The air component of the ADG consists of three all-weather interceptor squadrons with CF-101 aircraft, and one ECM squadron with a variety of aircraft.

The Air Transport Group has four transport squadrons with medium lift aircraft, and four squadrons with light and medium lift aircraft, and some helicopters, with further transport machines on order.

The Maritime Air Group (of three maritime patrol squadrons with CP-107 Argus aircraft, one training and one testing squadron, each equipped with Argus aircraft, one maritime reconnaissance squadron with CP-121 Tracker aircraft, two ASW squadrons with CH-124 (SH-3A) helicopters, and two training and utility squadrons with a variety of types) is administratively controlled by the Air Command, but comes under the operational control of the Maritime Command, with some justification. Already a formidable force, the Maritime Air Group's efficiency will be further improved when the 18 CP-140 Aurora (P-3 Orion) aircraft on order are delivered.

The main tactical element under exclusive Canadian command is 10 Tactical Air Group, which has two fighter squadrons with CF-5 aircraft, five helicopter squadrons with Iroqois and Kiowa helicopters, and one transport squadron with Chinook helicopters.

Deployed in Europe, under the operational command of the 4th Allied Tactical Air Force, is 1 Canadian Air Group, which has three fighter squadrons of CF-104 aircraft. Also in Europe are some Kiowa helicopters. The balance of the Air Command is made up of attached elements of Communications Command and the Canadian Forces Training System.

Given the tasks facing it, and the limited resources of the country, Canada has a well balanced air force, with particularly strong maritime and helicopter forces. However, in the near future, considerable thought will have to be given to the upgrading of the aircraft allocated to the NORAD organisation. Moreover, the Air Command has only 700 reservists of the Air Reserve Group, with four wings of transport aircraft. This is hardly sufficient to sustain the regular air force in sustained combat operations, but it is hard to see what Canada can do when her forces are entirely volunteer in origin.

36,500 men and about 214 combat aircraft.

2 trg sqns: 1 with 16 CF-5A, 19 CF-5D; 1 with 10 CF-104, 10 CF-104D.

Air Defence Group:
4 main, 17 auxiliary sites of Distant Early Warning (DEW) Line.
24 long-range radar sites (Pine Tree Line).
3 AWX sqns with 36 CF-101 Voodoo.
1 ECM sqn with 8 CF-100, 3 CC-117 (Falcon 20), 15 T-33.

Air Transport Group:
4 transport sqns: 2 with 24 C-130E/H, 1 with 5 CC-137 (Boeing 707), 1 with 7 Cosmopolitan, 4 CC-117.
4 transport/SAR sqns with 14 CC-115 Buffalo, 8 CC-138 Twin Otter ac, 3 CH-113 Labrador, 3 CH-113A *Voyageur*, 3 CH-135 (UH-1N) helicopters.
1 SAR unit with 3 CH-113 helicopters.
(2 DHC-7 transports on order.)

Maritime Air Group:
3 maritime patrol sqns, 1 trg and 1 testing sqn with 26 CP-107 Argus.
1 MR sqn with 13 CP-121 (Tracker).
2 ASW helicopter sqns with 26 CH-124 (SH-3A).
2 sqns with 9 T-33, 3 CP-121 ac, 6 CH-124 helicopters.
(18 CP-140 Aurora (Orion) on order.)

10 Tactical Air Group (10 TAG):
2 fighter sqns with 20 CF-5, 4 CF-5D.
5 helicopter sqns with 30 CH-135, 37 CH-136 (Kiowa).
1 transport sqn with 8 CH-147 (Chinook) helicopters.

1 Canadian Air Group (1 CAG):
3 fighter sqns with 54 CF-104 and 6 CF-104D.
Sidewinder, AIM-4D Falcon AAM.

Deployment:
Europe: 1 Canadian Air Group (1 CAG), 11 CH-136 (Kiowa) helicopters.

Reserves: 700. Air Reserve Group: 4 wings with DHC-3, DHC-6 and C-47.

Avro Canada CF-100

Type: all-weather interceptor
Crew: two, seated in tandem
Wings: metal cantilever low-wing monoplane
Fuselage: metal semi-monocoque
Tail unit: metal cantilever
Landing gear: hydraulically actuated retractable tricycle unit
Powerplant: two Rolls-Royce Bristol Orenda 11 turbojets, each rated at 7,275-lb (3,300-kg) static thrust
Fuel capacity:
Avionics: comprehensive communication and navigation/attack equipment
Armament: 58 or 106 2.75-in (70-mm) Mighty Mouse air-to-air rockets
Dimensions: Span 58 ft (17.7 m)
Length 54 ft 1 in (16.5 m)
Height 15 ft 7 in (4.72 m)
Wing area:
Weights: Empty about 18,000 lb (8,200 kg)
Loaded
Maximum 37,000 lb (16,780 kg)
Performance: speed 650 mph (1,045 kph) at 10,000 ft (3,050 m); speed 587 mph (945 kph) or Mach 0.89 at 40,000 ft (12,192 m); climb 8,500 ft (2,591 m) per minute at sea level; climb 5 minutes to 30,000 ft (9,144 m); service ceiling 54,000 ft (16,460 m); range 2,000 miles (3,220 km)

Used only by: Canada
Notes: The CF-100 was the first combat aircraft to be designed and built in Canada, the prototype first flying in 1950. From the start, the design was intended for night-fighting and all-weather operations in Canadian conditions. There were several models built before production ended in 1958:

1. CF-100 Mark 2 unarmed preproduction model, with Orenda 2 turbojets
2. CF-100 Mark 3, with Orenda 8 engines, Hughes APG-33 radar, and a belly pack of eight 0.5-in (12.7-mm) machine-guns
3. CF-100 Mark 4, with Orenda 11 engines, APG-40 radar and a main armament of 58 Mighty Mouse rockets in two wingtip pods, plus an additional 48 rockets, or eight 0.5-in (12.7-mm) machine-guns, or four 30-mm cannon
4. CF-100 Mark 5, similar to the Mark 4, but with a 6 ft (1.83 m) increase in span.

The Mark 6 was to have had afterburning engines and Sparrow 2 air-to-air missiles, but was cancelled. Most survivors have now been converted into training aircraft or electronic warfare machines.

Canadair CP-107 (CL-28) Argus

Type: maritime patrol and anti-submarine aircraft
Crew: 15
Wings: metal cantilever low-wing monoplane
Fuselage: metal semi-monocoque
Tail unit: metal cantilever
Landing gear: hydraulically actuated retractable tricycle unit

Powerplant: four Wright R-3350-32W (TC18-EA1) Turbo-Compound radial engines, each rated at 3,700 hp and driving a four-blade metal propeller
Fuel capacity:
Avionics: comprehensive communication and navigation/attack equipment, including APS-20 search radar, magnetic anomaly detector (MAD) and ECM equipment

Armament: up to 8,000 lb (3,629 kg) of bombs, depth charges, mines, acoustic torpedoes and homing torpedoes can be carried in two internal weapons bays, and another 7,600 lb (3,450 kg) of weapons can be carried on two underwing racks
Dimensions: Span 142 ft 3½ in (43.37 m)
　　　　　　Length 128 ft 3 in (39.1 m)
　　　　　　Height 36 ft 9 in (11.2 m)
Wing area: 2,075 ft² (192.77 m²)

Weights: Empty 81,500 lb (36,967 kg)
　　　　　Loaded
　　　　　Maximum 148,000 lb (67,130 kg)
Performance: speed 288 mph (463 kph) at sea level; speed 315 mph (507 kph) at 20,000 ft (6,096 m); climb 1,700 ft (518 m) per minute at sea level; service ceiling 29,000 ft (8,840 m); range 5,900 miles (9,495 km); endurance 30 hours
Used only by: Canada

Notes: The Argus maritime patrol aircraft is derived from the Bristol Britannia turbo-prop-powered airliner. The same wings, empennage and undercarriage are used, married to a highly modified fuselage and turbo-compound piston engines. The first Argus flew in 1957, and was followed by 12 Argus Mark 1 aircraft, before the Argus Mark 2, with improved electronics, appeared. There is also a transport version, the CL-44D (CC-106), in most respects similar to the Britannia parent type.

McDonnell Aircraft F-101 Voodoo

Type: fighter-bomber, interceptor and reconnaissance aircraft
Crew: one or two, seated in tandem
Wings: metal cantilever low mid-wing monoplane
Fuselage: metal cantilever
Tail unit: metal cantilever
Landing gear: hydraulically actuated retractable tricycle unit
Powerplant: two Pratt & Whitney J57-P-13 turbojets, each rated at 14,880-lb (6,750-kg) static thrust with afterburning
Fuel capacity:
Avionics: comprehensive communication and navigation/attack equipment
Armament: none
Dimensions: Span 39 ft 8 in (12.09 m)
　　　　　　Length 69 ft 3 in (21.1 m)
　　　　　　Height 18 ft (5.49 m)
Wing area: 368 ft² (34.19 m²)
Weights: Empty 28,000 lb (12,700 kg)
　　　　　Loaded
　　　　　Maximum 51,000 lb (23,133 kg)
Performance: speed 1,100 mph (1,770 kph) or Mach 1.66 at 36,000 ft (10,975 m); service ceiling 52,000 ft (15,850 m); range 1,700 miles (2,736 km)
Used only by: Canada
Notes: The F-101 Voodoo owes its birth to McDonnell's abortive F-88 Voodoo escort

fighter of 1948, which failed because it lacked the range to escort the mighty Convair B-36 strategic bomber. The new version first flew in 1954, and the type entered service in 1957, the last aircraft being delivered to the USAF in 1961. There were several variants:

1. F-101A single-seat fighter-bomber, with an armament of one megaton-class nuclear store under the fuselage, two 2,000-lb (907-kg) bombs under the wings, four 20-mm cannon, and three AIM-4 Falcon air-to-air missiles
2. F-101B two-seat interceptor, with 14,990-lb (6,800-kg) J57-P-53 or 55 engines, a speed of 1,220 mph (1,963 kph) or Mach 1.85, a range of 1,550 miles (2,500 km), and an armament of three AIM-4D Falcon air-to-air missiles and two AIR-2 Genie nuclear air-to-air missiles (known as F-101F in Canadian service)
3. F-101C single-seat fighter-bomber, with one megaton-class bomb under the fuselage, two 2,000-lb (907-kg) bombs under the wings, and three 20-mm M-39 cannon
4. RF-101A to RF-101G unarmed reconnaissance aircraft (the specification above applies to the RF-101)
5. TF-101 two-seat armed trainer.

It has been built by Canada and is known there as the CF-101.

Central African Republic

100 men.

1 DC-3 transport.
1 DC-4 transport.
1 C-47 transport.
1 Caravelle transport.
1 Falcon transport.
10 AL.60.
6 *Broussard*.
2 Rallye.
1 *Alouette* II helicopter.
5 H-34 helicopters.

Sud-Aviation Caravelle

Type: medium transport aircraft
Crew: four, and up to 80 passengers
Wings: metal cantilever low-wing monoplane
Fuselage: metal semi-monocoque
Tail unit: metal cantilever
Landing gear: hydraulically actuated retractable tricycle unit
Powerplant: two Rolls-Royce Avon RA.29 Mark 533R turbojets, each rated at 12,600-lb (5,715-kg) static thrust
Fuel capacity: 4,180 gallons (19,000 litres)
Avionics: comprehensive communication and navigation equipment
Armament: none
Dimensions: Span 112 ft 6½ in (34.3 m)
　　　　　　Length 105 ft 0¼ in (32.01 m)
　　　　　　Height 28 ft 7¼ in (8.72 m)
Wing area: 1,579.06 ft² (146.7 m²)
Weights: Empty 63,173 lb (28,655 kg)
　　　　　Loaded
　　　　　Maximum 110,231 lb (50,000 kg)
Performance: cruising speed 488 mph (785 kph) at 35,000 ft (10,670 m); service ceiling 39,370 ft (12,000 m); range 1,451 miles (2,335 km) with maximum payload
Used also by: Chad, Mauritania, Sweden, Yugoslavia
Notes: The first Caravelle civil airliner flew in 1955, and a number of examples have found their way into air force inventories as medium transports. Maximum payload (Series 10R) is 20,720 lb (9,400 kg).

Chad

200 men.

4 A-1D FGA.
3 C-54 transports.
9 C-47 transports.
1 Caravelle transport.
2 Turbo-Porter transports.
6 light trainers/liaison aircraft.
11 *Alouette* II/III helicopters.
4 Puma helicopters.

Douglas Aircraft A-1 Skyraider

Type: attack bomber and multi-role aircraft
Crew: one
Wings: metal cantilever low-wing monoplane
Fuselage: metal semi-monocoque
Tail unit: metal cantilever
Landing gear: hydraulically actuated retractable tailwheel type
Powerplant: one Wright R-3350-26W radial engine, rated at 3,020 hp and driving a four-blade propeller
Fuel capacity: 316 gallons (1,437 litres)
Avionics: comprehensive communication and navigation/attack equipment
Armament: very varied, but generally four 20-mm cannon and up to 8,000 lb (3,630 kg) of external stores carried on 15 pylons (seven under each wing, and one under the fuselage)
Dimensions: Span 50 ft (15.24 m)
Length 38 ft 2 in (11.63 m)
Height 15 ft 5 in (4.7 m)
Wing area: 400 ft² (37.16 m²)
Weights: Empty 10,546 lb (4,784 kg)
Loaded 18,263 lb (8,284 kg)
Maximum about 25,000 lb (11,340 kg)

Performance: speed 321 mph (517 kph) at 18,300 ft (5,578 m); cruising speed 198 mph (319 kph); climb 2,800 ft (853 m) per minute at sea level; service ceiling 32,700 ft (9,967 m); range 915 miles (1,473 km)
Used also by: Gabon
Notes: The A-1 Skyraider is one of the world's classic military aircraft, conceived during World War II (the prototype made its first flight in March 1945), and still performing creditably in combat more than twenty years later, in an age of sophisticated jet aircraft and advanced electronics. The Skyraider, like Ed Heinemann's later A-4 Skyhawk attack bomber, has the great advantage of basic simplicity and strength, first-class detail design, the ability to carry heavy external loads, and great versatility. There were several main variants:
1. AD-1 single-seat torpedo- and dive-bomber, with R-3350-24W engine
2. AD-2 single-seat attack aircraft, with greater structural strength, more fuel capacity, and the R-3350-26W engine (the technical specification applies to this model)
3. AD-3 anti-submarine detection and attack, and in the AD-3W with airborne early warning (AEW) radar in a radome under the fuselage
4. AD-4 anti-submarine detection and attack aircraft, with APS-19A radar in place of APS-4
5. AD-5 (later A-1E) modernised multi-role aircraft, with a wider fuselage and the capability of carrying 12 passengers.
6. AD-6 (A-1H) low-level bomber and multi-role aircraft
7. AD-7 (A-1J) low-level tactical attack aircraft with strengthened wings.

Chile

11,000 men and 97 combat aircraft.

3 FB sqns with 20 Hunter F.71, 18 F-5E/F.
1 fighter/trg sqn with 9 F-80C, 8 T-33A.
2 COIN sqns with 34 A-37B.
1 SAR/ASW sqn with 8 HU-16B Albatross.
Transports incl 2 C-130H, 5 C-118, 6 DC-6B, 12 C-47.
2 utility sqns with 11 DHC-6, 10 C-45, 1 King Air, 5 Twin Bonanza, 10 Cessna 180.
Helicopters incl 6 S-55T, 6 SL-4, 2 UH-1H, 6 UH-12E, 6 *Lama*.
Trainers incl 30 T-34, 30 T-37B, 8 T-41, 11 Vampire T.22/55, 4 Hunter T.77, 5 T-6, 9 Beech 99, 5 T-25, 1 F-27.
Sidewinder AAM.
1 AA arty regt.
(*Shafrir* AAM on order.)
Naval Air Force
500 men.
1 ASW/SAR sqn with 6 EMB-111, 2 PBY-5A, 3 PBY-6A, 4 SP-2E, 5 Beech D18S, 1 Piper Navajo, 1 F27 ac, 4 UH-19, 2 UH-1D helicopters.

Transports incl 4 C-47, 6 EMB-110C *Bandeirante*.
Helicopters incl 4 AB-206, 3 UH-19, 2 UH-1D, 12 Bell 47G, 6 *Alouette* III.
5 T-34 trainers.
(5 EMB-111N on order.)
Army Air Arm
4 O-1, 5 T-25 trg ac, 9 Puma, 3 UH-1H, 2 AB-206 helicopters.

Douglas Aircraft C-118

Type: transport aircraft
Crew: five, plus up to 74 passengers
Wings: metal cantilever low-wing monoplane
Fuselage: metal semi-monocoque
Tail unit: metal cantilever
Landing gear: hydraulically actuated retractable tricycle unit

Powerplant: four Pratt & Whitney R-2800-52W radial engines, each rated at 2,500 hp and driving a three-blade metal Hamilton Standard propeller
Fuel capacity:
Avionics: comprehensive communication and navigation equipment
Armament: none

Dimensions: Span 117 ft 6 in (35.8 m)
Length 106 ft 10 in (32.56 m)
Height 28 ft 5 in (8.66 m)
Wing area: 1,463 ft² (135.9 m²)
Weights: Empty 49,760 lb (22,571 kg)
Loaded
Maximum 107,000 lb (48,535 kg)
Performance: speed 360 mph (579 kph) at 18,000 ft (5,486 m); cruising speed 307 mph (494 kph) at 22,400 ft (6,828 m); ferry range 4,910 miles (7,902 km)

Used also by: Mexico
Notes: The C-118 was developed from the civil DC-6, using the same flying surfaces and landing gear, but a new, longer, fuselage. The US Navy version was designated R6D-1. The type was built between 1951 and 1956. Maximum payload is 27,000 lb (12,247 kg).

Grumman HU-16 Albatross

Type: general-purpose amphibian
Crew: four to six, plus up to 15 passengers
Wings: metal cantilever high-wing monoplane
Fuselage: metal semi-monocoque, with a boat hull
Tail unit: metal cantilever
Landing gear: hydraulically actuated retractable tricycle unit for land operations

Powerplant: two Wright R-1820-76 radial engines, each rated at 1,425 hp and driving a metal three-blade propeller
Fuel capacity:
Avionics: communication and navigation equipment
Armament: none
Dimensions: Span 96 ft 8 in (29.46 m)
Length 61 ft 3 in (18.67 m)
Height 25 ft 10 in (7.87 m)
Wing area: 1,035 ft² (96.15 m²)
Weights: Empty 22,883 lb (10,380 kg)
Loaded 32,100 lb (14,560 kg)
Maximum 35,700 lb (16,193 kg)

Performance: speed 236 mph (380 kph); cruising speed 150 mph (241 kph); climb 1,450 ft (442 m) per minute at sea level; service ceiling 21,500 ft (6,553 m); range 2,850 miles (4,587 km)
Used also by: Argentina, Greece, Indonesia, Italy, Mexico, Pakistan, Peru, Philippines, Spain, Taiwan, Thailand, Venezuela
Notes: Design work on the Albatross began in 1944, and the prototype first flew in 1947. It entered service with the USAF as the SA-16, and with the USN as the UF-1. In 1962 the designation HU-16 was adopted.

Lockheed Aircraft F-80 Shooting Star

Type: fighter-bomber
Crew: one
Wings: metal cantilever low-wing monoplane
Fuselage: metal semi-monocoque
Tail unit: metal cantilever
Landing gear: hydraulically actuated retractable tricycle unit
Powerplant: one Allison J33-A-23 turbojet, rated at 5,400-lb (2,450-kg) static thrust
Fuel capacity:
Avionics: comprehensive communication and navigation/attack equipment

Armament: six 0.5-in (12.7-mm) machine-guns, plus two 1,000-lb (454-kg) bombs or ten 5-in (127-mm) rockets
Dimensions: Span 38 ft 10½ in (11.85 m)
Length 34 ft 6 in (10.51 m)
Height 11 ft 8 in (3.55 m)
Wing area: 238 ft² (22.1 m²)
Weights: Empty 8,240 lb (3,741 kg)
Loaded
Maximum 15,336 lb (6,963 kg)
Performance: speed 580 mph (933 kph) at 7,000 ft (2,134 m); cruising speed 439 mph (707 kph); climb 6,870 ft (2,094 m) per minute at sea level; service ceiling 48,000 ft (14,630 m); range 1,380 miles (2,220 km)

Used also by: Burma, Colombia, Honduras, Italy, Mexico, Pakistan, Thailand, Uruguay, Yugoslavia
Notes: The Shooting Star was developed as the P-80, which made its first flight in 1944, and entered service in 1945. The F-80C version, to which the specification above relates, was heavily involved in the Korean War, and notable relatives of the Shooting Star are the F-94 Starfire, which had a primary armament of 48 Mighty Mouse unguided rockets, and the T-33/T2V trainers.

China

The Chinese Air Force

Like the other armed services of the Chinese nation, the air force is only just beginning to emerge from the period in which the 'people's war' concept prevailed. In this, the most economical, and also optimal politico-military, solution to China's military needs was to rely on large numbers of personnel equipped with *matériel* of the least technical sophistication. Thus the will of the people would inevitably prevail, despite heavy losses. The late 1960s, coinciding with the practical appreciation of Chairman Mao Tse-tung's necessary mortality, saw a gradual swing away from this political tenet. The People's Liberation Army is still equipped only for defensive war, or offensive operations very close to China, as the logistic forces are small and woefully ill-equipped. The air force is designed to provide large scale tactical support for this force, with longer range operations geared to the cutting of the enemy's lines of communication. Some progress has been made with the development of nuclear weapons and the missiles to carry them, but these are still far behind Russian, American and even European weapons in range, payload and accuracy. It must be borne in mind, however, that the 1980s will probably see a burgeoning of China's nuclear capabilities as the programme continues to expand.

China's air force has about 400,000 personnel, including 120,000 air defence, this figure being about 9.25 per cent of the total armed forces, which enjoy the benefits of about 10 per cent of the gross national product according to informed western sources. The strategic forces comprise about 30 to 40 CSS-2 intermediate-range ballistic missiles, 30 to 40 CSS-1 medium-range ballistic missiles, and some 80 Tu-16 medium bombers, all of them directed towards Russia, whose very considerable armed presence along the Chinese frontier is thought to present a real threat to the security of Sinkiang province in particular.

The rest of the air force consists of about 5,000 combat aircraft, many of them distinctly elderly. The main striking force is made up of about 80 Tu-16 medium bombers, supported by a few Tu-4 heavy and about 300 Il-28 and 100 Tu-2 light bombers. Only the Il-28 and Tu-16 bombers are of any real operational significance.

Considering the size of the ground forces they have to support, the Chinese have remarkably few tactical support aircraft, a mere 500 MiG-15 and F-9 'Fantan' fighter-bombers, with cannon, light bombs and unguided rockets as their primary weapons. Chinese technology has yet to produce sophisticated air-to-surface missiles.

Just as surprisingly, the Chinese air force has very large numbers of fighters, some 4,000 or so, for the defence of metropolitan China. These are mostly MiG-17/F-4, MiG-19/F-6 and MiG-21/F-8 aircraft, with a smattering of F-9s, organised into large fighter regiments, in turn grouped together as divisions.

Tactical transport is performed by some 450 fixed- and 350 rotary-winged aircraft, though the transport arm can call on an additional 500 civil transports if necessary. In recent years the Chinese have acquired a number of foreign types, as is apparent by an examination of the types of transport used.

The naval air arm is partially integrated with the air force, especially in the provision of fighters for the air defence network for China's major cities, industries, military installations and weapon production centres. Of the 4,500 fighter aircraft available overall, some 4,000 are allocated to the air defence system, leaving only about 500 fighters for the tactical defence of the People's Liberation Army in the field. The air defence organisation also has about 100 CSA-1 (Chinese-built SA-2) SAMs, and more than 100,000 AA guns. The utility of these last is problematical, especially against strategic attack by modern bombers.

The Chinese air force is therefore large. However, it is almost totally obsolescent in its aircraft and its tactical doctrines. But there are signs that China has realised the need for reform, and it seems likely that during the 1980s great improvements will be made.

400,000 men, including 120,000 air defence personnel, and about 5,000 combat aircraft.

Strategic Forces
IRBM: 30–40 CSS-2.
MRBM: 30–40 CSS-1.
Aircraft: about 80 Tu-16 med bombers.
Air Force
100,000, incl strategic forces and 120,000 AD personnel; about 5,000 combat aircraft.
About 80 Tu-16 'Badger' and a few Tu-4 'Bull' med bombers.
About 300 Il-28 'Beagle' and 100 Tu-2 'Bat' lt bombers.
About 500 MiG-15 and F-9 'Fantan' FB.
About 4,000 F-4/6, 80 F-8 and some F-9 fighters organised into air divs and regts.
About 450 fixed-wing transport ac, incl some 300 An-2, about 100 Li-2, 50 Il-14 and Il-18, some An-12/-24/-26 and Trident. 350 helicopters, incl Mi-4, Mi-8 and 16 Super *Frelon*. These could be supplemented by about 500 ac from the Civil Aviation Administration, of which about 150 are major transports.
There is an AD system, capable of providing a limited defence of key urban and industrial areas, military installations and weapon complexes. Up to 4,000 naval and air force fighters are assigned to this role, also about 100 CSA-1 (SA-2) SAMs and over 10,000 AA guns.
Naval Air Force
30,000; about 700 shore-based combat aircraft, organised into 4 bomber and 5 fighter divs, incl about 130 Il-28 torpedo- carrying, Tu-16 med and Tu-2 lt bombers and some 500 fighters, incl MiG-17, MiG-19/F-6 and some F-9; a few Be-6 'Madge' MR ac; 50 Mi-4 'Hound' helicopters and some lt transport ac. Naval fighters are integrated into the AD system.

Beriev Be-6 'Madge'

Type: maritime reconnaissance flying-boat
Crew: seven, plus a relief crew of seven
Wings: metal cantilever high gull-wing monoplane
Fuselage: metal semi-monocoque, with a boat-hull bottom
Tail unit: metal cantilever
Landing gear: none
Powerplant: two Shvetsov ASh-73TK radial engines, each rated at 2,300 hp and driving a metal four-blade propeller

Fuel capacity:
Avionics: comprehensive communication and navigation/attack equipment
Armament: five 23-mm NS-23 cannon, plus up to 13,120 lb (4,000 kg) of bombs, depth charges, mines or torpedoes carried on underwing pylons
Dimensions: Span 108 ft 2½ in (33.0 m)
Length 77 ft 3½ in (23.56 m)
Height 24 ft 7 in (7.5 m)
Wing area: 1,292 ft² (120.0 m)
Weights: Empty 41,506 lb (18,827 kg)
Loaded 51,588 lb (23,400 kg)
Maximum 61,976 lb (28,112 kg)

Performance: speed 249 mph (400 kph) at 8,200 ft (2,500 m); cruising speed 225 mph (362 kph); service ceiling 20,015 ft (6,100 m); range 3,045 miles (4,900 km)
Used only by: China
Notes: The Be-6 was Russia's first large flying-boat after World War II, and entered service in 1949. The single 23-mm cannon in the nose was often omitted, and the twin tail guns were sometimes replaced by a magnetic anomaly detector (MAD) string. The removal of the bow cannon may indicate the introduction of an airborne search radar in its place.

British Aerospace (Hawker Siddeley Aviation) Trident

Type: medium-range airliner
Crew: three, plus up to 152 passengers
Wings: metal cantilever low-wing monoplane
Fuselage: aluminium alloy semi-monocoque
Tail unit: metal cantilever
Landing gear: hydraulically actuated retractable tricycle unit

Powerplant: three Rolls-Royce Spey RB.163-25 Mark 512-5W turbofans, each rated at 11,960-lb (5,425-kg) static thrust
Fuel capacity: 6,400 gallons (29,094 litres) in five integral tanks
Avionics: comprehensive communication and navigation equipment
Armament: none
Dimensions: Span 98 ft (29.87 m)
Length 114 ft 9 in (34.97 m)
Height 27 ft (8.23 m)
Wing area: 1,462 ft² (135.82 m²)

Weights: Empty 73,200 lb (33,203 kg)
Loaded
Maximum 144,000 lb (65,315 kg)
Performance: (at maximum take-off weight) maximum cruising speed 605 mph (972 kph) or Mach 0.88 at 27,000 ft (8,230 m); range with maximum fuel and a payload of 16,520 lb (7,493 kg) 2,500 miles (4,025 km)
Used only by: China
Notes: Maximum payload is 26,800 lb (12,156 kg)

Lisunov Li-2 'Cab'

Type: transport aircraft
Crew: two, plus up to 24 passengers
Wings: metal cantilever low-wing monoplane
Fuselage: metal semi-monocoque
Tail unit: metal cantilever
Landing gear: hydraulically actuated retractable tailwheel unit

Powerplant: two Shvetsov ASh-62 radials, each rated at 1,000 hp
Fuel capacity: 670 gallons (3,046 litres)
Avionics: communication and navigation equipment
Armament: none
Dimensions: Span 95 ft 6 in (29.1 m)
Length 63 ft 9 in (19.43 m)
Height 17 ft (5.18 m)
Wing area: 987 ft² (91.7 m²)

Weights: Empty 18,200 lb (8,255 kg)
Loaded
Maximum 26,000 lb (11,795 kg)
Performance: speed 210 mph (340 kph); service ceiling 20,670 ft (6,300 m); range 1,490 miles (2,400 km)
Used also by: Hungary, Rumania, USSR, Vietnam, Yugoslavia
Notes: The Li-2 is the Douglas DC-3 built under licence, with minimal modification, in Russia.

Shenyang F-6

Type: day interceptor and air-superiority fighter
Crew: one
Wings: metal cantilever mid-wing monoplane
Fuselage: metal semi-monocoque
Tail unit: metal cantilever

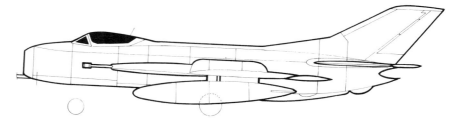

Landing gear: hydraulically actuated retractable tricycle unit
Powerplant: two Chinese-built Klimov R-9B turbojets, each rated at 5,730-lb (2,600-kg) static thrust and 7,165-lb (3,250-kg) thrust with afterburning
Fuel capacity: 477 gallons (2,170 litres) in two main and two auxiliary internal tanks, plus an optional 352 gallons (1,600 litres) in two underwing drop-tanks
Avionics: radio and blind-flying equipment, plus airborne interception radar
Armament: two or three 30-mm NR-30 cannon, plus two 551-lb (250-kg) bombs on underwing pylons, or two 212-mm (8.35-in) rockets, or two packs each containing eight air-to-air rockets (Pakistani models have the capability of carrying two Sidewinder air-to-air missiles under the wings)
Dimensions: Span 29 ft 6½ in (9.0 m)
Length 41 ft 4 in (12.6 m) for MiG-19SF version without nose probe
Height 13 ft 2¼ in (4.02 m)

Wing area: 269 ft² (25 m²)
Weights: Empty 12,700 lb (5,760 kg)
Loaded 16,755 lb (7,600 kg)
Maximum 19,180 lb (8,700 kg)
Performance: speed 902 mph (1,452 kph) at 32,800 ft (10,000 m); cruising speed 590 mph (950 kph); climb 22,635 ft (6,900 m) per minute at sea level; time to service ceiling 8 min 20 sec; service ceiling 58,725 ft (17,900 m); range with external tanks 1,366 miles (2,200 km); combat radius with drop tanks 426 miles (685 km)
Used also by: Albania, Pakistan, Tanzania, Vietnam
Notes: Chinese-built copy of the MiG-19 fighter, which has proved very successful when operating on its own terms.

Shenyang F-9

Type: fighter-bomber
Crew:
Wings:
Fuselage:
Tail unit:
Landing gear:
Powerplant:
Fuel capacity:
Avionics:
Armament:
Dimensions: Span about 33 ft 5 in (10.2 m)
Length about 50 ft (15.25 m)
Height
Wing area:
Weights: Empty
Loaded
Maximum about 22,050 lb (10,000 kg)
Performance: speed about Mach 2; combat radius about 500 miles (800 km)
Used only by: China
Notes: This fighter-bomber, based on the F-6, first flew in the early 1970s. It is larger than the F-6, and has lateral air intakes instead of the F-6's nose intake to allow the use of nose-mounted radar. Once the Rolls-Royce Spey engine has entered production in China, it seems likely that the F-9 or a development of it will be produced to use the engine.

Tupolev Tu-2 'Bat'

Type: medium bomber
Crew: three
Wings: metal cantilever mid-wing monoplane
Fuselage: metal semi-monocoque
Tail unit: metal cantilever
Landing gear: hydraulically actuated retractable tailwheel unit
Powerplant: two Shvetsov ASh-82FN radial engines, each rated at 1,850 hp and driving a metal four-blade propeller
Fuel capacity: 616 gallons (2,800 litres) in wing tanks
Avionics: communication and navigation equipment
Armament: two 20-mm ShVAK cannon and three 12.7-mm UBT machine-guns, plus up to 5,004 lb (2,270 kg) of bombs
Dimensions: Span 61 ft 10½ in (18.8 m)
Length 45 ft 3¼ in (13.8 m)
Height 13 ft 9½ in (4.2 m)
Wing area: 525.3 ft² (48.8 m²)
Weights: Empty 18,210 lb (8,260 kg)
Loaded 25,044 lb (11,360 kg)
Maximum 28,219 lb (12,800 kg)
Performance: speed 342 mph (550 kph) at 17,716 ft (5,400 m); climb 9 minutes 30 seconds to 16,400 ft (5,000 m); service ceiling 31,170 ft (9,500 m); range 1,553 miles (2,500 km) with a bomb load of 3,307 lb (1,500 kg)
Used only by: China
Notes: The Tu-2 was developed during World War II, but most postwar examples were of the Tu-2D variant, with extended span wings (72 ft 10¼ in/22.2 m), greater fuel tankage, and a bomb load of up to 8,819 lb (4,000 kg), which could be carried for 870 miles (1,400 km).

Tupolev Tu-4 'Bull'

Type: long-range heavy bomber
Crew: 10
Wings: metal cantilever mid-wing monoplane
Fuselage: metal semi-monocoque
Tail unit: metal cantilever
Landing gear: hydraulically actuated retractable tricycle unit
Powerplant: four Shvetsov ASh-73TK radial engines, each rated at 2,300 hp and driving a metal four-blade propeller
Fuel capacity:
Avionics: comprehensive communication and navigation equipment
Armament: 10 23-mm NR-23 cannon, and up to 20,000 lb (9,070 kg) of bombs
Dimensions: Span 141 ft 4 in (43.08 m)
Length 99 ft 0¾ in (30.19 m)
Height 29 ft 7 in (9.01 m)
Wing area: 1,679.2 ft² (156.0 m²)
Weights: Empty 74,957 lb (34,000 kg)
Loaded
Maximum 104,940 lb (47,600 kg)
Performance: speed 359 mph (578 kph) at 32,810 ft (10,000 m); service ceiling 36,745 ft (11,200 m); range 3,045 miles (4,900 km) with a bomb load of 11,023 lb (5,000 kg); maximum range 3,479 miles (5,600 km)
Used only by: China
Notes: The Tu-4 is a direct copy of the American B-29 Superfortress, several examples of which landed in Russian territory towards the end of World War II. About 400 were transferred to the Chinese air force.

CSS-1

Type: medium-range ballistic missile
Guidance: probably inertial, but possibly radio command
Dimensions: Span
Body diameter
Length
Booster: storable liquid-propellant rocket
Sustainer: none
Warhead: probably nuclear, in the order of 20 kilotons, though later models may have a more powerful warhead
Weights: Launch
Burnt out
Performance: range about 1,118 miles (1,800 km), although some estimates put the figure as low as 683 miles (1,100 km)
Used only by: China
Notes: Deployed in north-east and north-west China against Russian targets, the CSS-1 is similar in many respects to the Russian SS-4. The missile was introduced to service in 1970, and is deployed in limited numbers as a deterrent against the Russians until large numbers of IRBMs and ICBMs can be made operational.

CSS-2

Type: intermediate-range ballistic missile
Guidance: probably inertial
Dimensions: Span
Body diameter
Length
Booster: storable liquid-propellant rocket
Sustainer: none
Warhead: nuclear
Weights: Launch
Burnt out
Performance: range between 1,553 and 2,485 miles (2,500 and 4,000 km)
Used only by: China
Notes: Introduced into service in 1971, this first Chinese intermediate-range strategic missile is deployed only in very limited numbers. Targeting is apparently on objectives in central and eastern Asia.

Colombia

6,500 men and 18 combat aircraft.

1 fighter/recce sqn with 14 Mirage VCOA, 4 VCOR/D.
Transports incl 2 C-130B, 8 C-54, C-45, 29 C-47, 3 HS 748, 1 F28, 9 DHC-2, 4 DHC-3.
Helicopters incl 13 AH-1H, 3 UH-1B, 6 UH-1H, 1 UH-1N, 20 OH-6A, 8 OH-13, Hughes 500 M-D.
Trainers incl 10 T-37, 6 T-38, 30 T-41D, 31 AT-33, 30 T-34.
SAR forces include PBY.
R.530 AAM.

Consolidated Aircraft PBY

Type: maritime patrol amphibian
Crew: seven to nine
Wings: metal cantilever pylon-mounted, strut-braced monoplane
Fuselage: metal semi-monocoque with a boat hull
Tail unit: metal cantilever
Landing gear: hydraulically actuated retractable tricycle unit
Powerplant: two Pratt & Whitney R-1830-92 radial engines, each rated at 1,200 hp and driving a metal three-blade propeller
Fuel capacity:
Avionics: communication and navigation/attack equipment
Armament: three 0.3-in (7.62-mm) machine-guns, two 0.5-in (12.7-mm) machine-guns, plus up to 4,000 lb (1,814 kg) of external stores
Dimensions: Span 104 ft (31.7 m)
Length 63 ft 10 in (19.46 m)
Height 20 ft 2 in (6.15 m)
Wing area: 1,400 ft² (130.0 m²)
Weights: Empty 20,910 lb (9,485 kg)
Loaded 35,420 lb (16,066 kg) Maximum
Performance: speed 175 mph (282 kph) at 7,500 ft (2,286 m); cruising speed 113 mph (182 kph); climb 620 ft (189 m) per minute at sea level; service ceiling 13,000 ft (3,962 m); range 2,350 miles (3,782 km)
Used also by: Argentina, Brazil, Chile, Dominican Republic, Ecuador, Mexico
Notes: The PBY series of flying-boats and amphibians is perhaps the greatest ever built, in number and in importance. The prototype first flew in 1935, with the first PBY-1 being delivered in 1936 to the US Navy. The last of these boats was delivered after World War II. The specification above is for the PBY-5A, which appeared in 1939, and was the first of the family to feature a retractable landing gear, making an amphibian of what became called the Catalina during World War II.

Kaman Aircraft H-43 Huskie

Type: rescue and utility helicopter
Crew: two, plus up to 10 passengers
Rotors: two metal cantilever two-blade intermeshing main rotors
Fuselage: metal semi-monocoque
Landing gear: fixed four-wheel unit
Powerplant: one Lycoming T53-L-1A turboshaft, rated at 860 ehp
Fuel capacity:
Avionics: communication and navigation equipment
Armament: none
Dimensions: Span (overall) 51 ft 6 in (15.7 m)
Length (fuselage) 25 ft (7.62 m)
Height 15 ft 6½ in (4.73 m)
Rotor disc area: (total) 3,470 ft² (322.36 m²)
Weights: Empty 4,469 lb (2,027 kg)
Loaded 6,800 lb (3,084 kg)
Maximum 8,800 lb (3,992 kg)
Performance: speed 120 mph (193 kph); cruising speed 97 mph (156 kph); climb 2,000 ft (610 m) per minute at sea level; service ceiling 25,700 ft (7,833 m); range 235 miles (378 km); endurance 3 hours 12 minutes
Used also by: Burma, Iran, Pakistan, Thailand
Notes: The Kaman H-43 air crash rescue helicopter started life as the HUK-1 and HOK-1 utility helicopters for the US Navy and US Marine Corps respectively. The HUK and HOK types were powered by 600-hp Pratt & Whitney R-1340 radials, and entered service in the mid-1950s, becoming the UH-43C and OH-43D in 1962. The USAF version, initially the piston-engined H-43A, entered service in 1958. The turboshaft-powered H-43B entered service in 1959. The two models became the HH-43A and HH-43B respectively in 1962. The crash rescue HH-43B carries a fire-fighting team and special equipment.

Congo

300 men and 10 combat aircraft.

10 MiG-15/-17 fighters.
3 C-47, 4 An-24, 1 F28, 1 *Frégate*, 5 Il-14, 3 *Broussard* transports.
4 *Alouette* II/III helicopters.

Fokker-VFW F28 Friendship

Type: transport aircraft
Crew: two or three, plus up to 65 passengers
Wings: metal cantilever low-wing monoplane
Fuselage: metal semi-monocoque
Tail unit: metal cantilever
Landing gear: hydraulically actuated retractable tricycle unit
Powerplant: two Rolls-Royce RB.183-2 Spey Mark 555-15 turbofans, each rated at 9,850-lb (4,468-kg) static thrust
Fuel capacity: 2,143 gallons (9,740 litres) in two integral wing tanks, plus 726 gallons (3,300 litres) in an optional centre-section tank group
Avionics: comprehensive communication and navigation equipment

Armament: none
Dimensions: Span 77 ft 4½ in (23.58 m)
Length 89 ft 10¾ in (27.4 m)
Height 27 ft 9½ in (8.47 m)
Wing area: 822 ft² (76.4 m²)
Weights: Empty 35.464 lb (16,084 kg)
Loaded
Maximum 65,000 lb (29,845 kg)
Performance: cruising speed 523 mph (843 kph) at 23,000 ft (7,000 m); cruising altitude 35,000 ft (10,675 m); range 1,300 miles (2,093 km) with full passenger load
Used also by: Algeria, Argentina, Colombia, Ghana, Iran, Ivory Coast, Malaysia, Nigeria, Peru, Togo
Notes: The first F28 flew in 1968, and entered service in 1969. The Peruvian aircraft is a standard Mark 1000, the first production version.

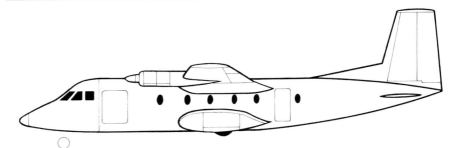

Société Nationale Industrielle Aérospatiale *Frégate*

Type: light transport
Crew: two or three, plus accommodation for 29
Wings: metal cantilever high-wing monoplane
Fuselage: alloy semi-monocoque
Tail unit: metal cantilever
Landing gear: electro-hydraulically actuated retractable tricycle unit
Powerplant: two Turboméca Bastan VII turboprops, each rated at 1,145 ehp, driving Ratier Forest metal four-blade propellers
Fuel capacity: 565 gallons (2,570 litres) in six bag-type tanks between the spars and two optional tanks in the centre section
Avionics: navigation, communications and blind-flying equipment
Armament: none

Dimensions: Span 74 ft 1¾ in (22.6 m)
Length 63 ft 3 in (19.28 m)
Height 20 ft 4½ in (6.21 m)
Wing area: 601 ft² (55.79 m²)
Weights: Empty 15,928 lb (7,225 kg)
Loaded
Maximum 23,810 lb (10,800 kg)
Performance: (at maximum take-off weight) speed 260 mph (418 kph); cruising speed 254 mph (408 kph); climb 1,380 ft (420 m) per minute at sea level; service ceiling 28,500 ft (8,690 m); 1,490 miles (2,400 km)
Used also by: France
Notes: A development of the N262 civil transport, intended for civil and military use in hot climates and high country. The main difference between the *Frégate* and the N262 is the higher power output of the former's Bastan VII engines, 1,145 ehp compared with 1,080 ehp. Maximum payload is 6,779 lb (3,075 kg).

Cuba

20,000 men, including air defence personnel, and 163 combat aircraft.

2 FB sqns with 30 MiG-17.
7 interceptor sqns: 3 with 48 MiG-21F, 2 with 30 MiG-21MF, 2 with 40 MiG-19.
1 trg sqn with 15 MiG-15.
Transports incl 50 Il-14, An-24 and An-2.
Helicopters incl 30 Mi-1, 24 Mi-4.
Trainers incl MiG-15UTI, 60 Zlin 326.
AA-2 'Atoll' AAM.
AA-1 'Alkali', AA-2 'Atoll' AAM.
24 SAM bns with 144 SA-2 'Guideline' and SA-3 'Goa'.

Ilyushin Il-18 'Coot'

Type: passenger transport
Crew: five, plus up to 122 passengers
Wings: metal cantilever low-wing monoplane
Fuselage: metal monocoque
Tail unit: metal cantilever
Landing gear: hydraulically actuated retractable tricycle unit

Powerplant: four Ivchenko AI-20M turboprops, each rated at 4,250 ehp and driving a four-blade metal propeller
Fuel capacity: 5,213 gallons (23,700 litres) in 20 bag tanks in the inner portions of the wings, and two integral tanks in the outer panels of the wings

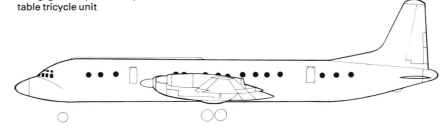

Avionics: comprehensive communication and navigation equipment
Armament: none
Dimensions: Span 122 ft 8½ in (37.4 m)
　　　　　　　Length 117 ft 9 in (35.9 m)
　　　　　　　Height 33 ft 4 in (10.17 m)
Wing area: 1,507 ft² (140.0 m²)
Weights: Empty 76,350 lb (34,630 kg)
　　　　　Loaded
　　　　　Maximum 134,925 lb (61,200 kg)
Performance: (at maximum take-off weight) cruising speed 419 mph (675 kph) at 26,250 ft (8,000 m); service ceiling at a weight of 134,482 lb (61,000 kg) 35,268 ft (10,750 m); range with maximum payload 1,990 miles (3,200 km); range with maximum fuel 3,230 miles (5,200 km)
Used also by: Afghanistan, Algeria, Bulgaria, China, North Korea, Poland, Romania, USSR, Vietnam, Yugoslavia
Notes: Designed as an airliner, the Il-18 first flew in 1957, and entered civil service in 1959. The type is also widely used by mili-

tary operators for trooping. There are several versions:

1. Il-18V initial production model with 4,000-ehp AI-20K turboprops
2. Il-18E with 4,250-ehp AI-20M engines, to which the technical specification above relates
3. Il-18D, developed from the Il-18E but with additional fuel tankage in

the wing centre section, raising capacity to 6,600 gallons (30,000 litres), maximum payload range to 2,300 miles (3,700 km), and maximum fuel range to 4,040 miles (6,500 km).

The Il-18 still holds several world records for speed and range.

Mikoyan-Gurevich MiG-19 'Farmer'

Type: fighter
Crew: one
Wings: metal cantilever mid-wing monoplane
Fuselage: metal semi-monocoque
Tail unit: metal cantilever
Landing gear: hydraulically actuated retractable tricycle unit
Powerplant: two Klimov RD-9B turbojets, each rated at 7,165-lb (3,250-kg) static thrust with afterburning
Fuel capacity: 477 gallons (2,170 litres) in centre fuselage tanks, plus provision for two 44-, 66-, 88- or 176-gallon (200-, 300-, 400- or 800-litre) underwing drop tanks
Avionics: comprehensive communication and navigation equipment, plus Izumrud 'Scan Odd' airborne interception radar on some models
Armament: one N-37 37-mm cannon with 40 rounds and two NR-23 23-mm cannon with 80 rounds each (early models) or three NR-30 30-mm cannon (later models), plus stores on four underwing hardpoints. These can consist of four AA-1 'Alkali' beam-riding air-to-air missiles on the otherwise unarmed MiG-19PM, four pods of eight 55-mm rockets, two pods of nineteen 55-mm rockets, two 220- or 325-mm rockets, two 1,102- or 551-lb (500- or 250-kg) bombs, drop tanks or K-13A 'Atoll' IR-homing air-to-air missiles (copies of the AIM-9 Sidewinder AAM)
Dimensions: Span 29 ft 6¼ in (9.0 m)
　　　　　　　Length 42 ft 11¼ in (13.08 m)
　　　　　　　Height 13 ft 2¼ in (4.02 m)

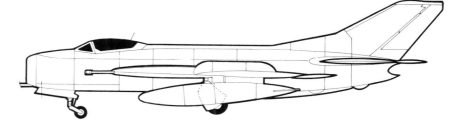

Wing area: 269 ft² (25.0 m²)
Weights: Empty 12,698 lb (5,760 kg)
　　　　　Loaded 16,755 lb (7,600 kg)
　　　　　Maximum 19,180 lb (8,700 kg)
Performance: speed 902 mph (1,452 kph) or Mach 1.35 at 32,800 ft (10,000 m); cruising speed 590 mph (950 kph) at 32,800 ft (10,000 ft); climb 22,635 ft (6,900 m) per minute at sea level; climb to 58,725 ft (17,900 m) 8 minutes 12 seconds; service ceiling 58,725 ft (17,900 m); endurance 2 hours 38 minutes; range normally 863 miles (1,390 km) at 45,930 ft (14,000 m); range with maximum fuel 1,370 miles (2,200 km)
Used also by: Bulgaria, Indonesia, North Korea, Romania, USSR
Notes: The MiG-19 bears the same relation to the MiG-15 as the North American F-100 to the North American F-86; the MiG-19 and the North American F-100 being the first Russian and American fighters to be capable of speeds in excess of Mach 1 in level flight. The MiG-19 is still a useful aircraft, its high thrust:weight ratio giving it an edge compared with aircraft such as the F-104 and MiG-21 for dogfighting, where acceleration and rate of climb are vital. The

MiG-19 was built in Czechoslovakia as the S-105 and in Poland as the LIM-7, and is still built in China as the Shenyang F-6. There are several variants:

1. MiG-19 'Farmer-A' with 6,700-lb (3,040-kg) Mikulin AM-5 engines, conventional fixed tailplane and elevators and short-barrelled cannon
2. MiG-19S with an all-moving slab tailplane
3. MiG-19P 'Farmer-B' all-weather version of the MiG-19S with airborne interception radar and a dorsal spine
4. MiG-19SF 'Farmer-C' with AM-9 afterburning engines in place of the earlier AM-5s, and long-barrelled NR-30 cannon, to which the technical specification applies
5. MiG-19PF 'Farmer-D' all-weather fighter with bullet-faired nose radar, increasing the model's length by 22 in (0.866 m)
6. MiG-19PM 'Farmer-E' with four AA-1 'Alkali' air-to-air missiles.

The MiG-19 first flew in 1953, and entered service in 1955. The MiG-19UTI is a two-seat trainer.

Zlin Moravan Národní Podnik Z-526 *Trener-Master*

Type: basic trainer
Crew: two, seated in tandem
Wings: metal cantilever low-wing monoplane
Fuselage: metal tube structure
Tail unit: metal cantilever
Landing gear: retractable tailwheel unit
Powerplant: one Walter Minor 6-III inline engine, rated at 160 hp and driving a two-blade propeller
Fuel capacity: 21⅓ gallons (97 litres)
Avionics: communication equipment

Armament: none
Dimensions: Span 34 ft 9 in (10.6 m)
　　　　　　　Length 25 ft 7 in (7.8 m)
　　　　　　　Height 6 ft 9 in (2.06 m)
Wing area: 166.3 ft² (15.45 m²)
Weights: Empty 1,499 lb (680 kg)
　　　　　Loaded 2,006 lb (910 kg)
　　　　　Maximum 2,150 lb (975 kg)
Performance: speed 152 mph (245 kph) at sea level; cruising speed 131 mph (210 kph); climb 985 ft (300 m) per minute at sea level; service ceiling 16,350 ft (5,000 m); range 404 miles (650 km)
Used only by: Cuba

Notes: The Z-326/526 was developed from the Z-226T *Trener* 6, and first flew in 1957. There is also an aerobatic version, the Z-326A *Akrobat*. The Z-526 differs from the Z-326 principally in having a constant-speed propeller.

Czechoslovakia

46,000 men (15,000 conscripts) and 613 combat aircraft, plus 50,000 reservists.

13 FGA sqns with 80 Su-7, 36 MiG-15, 42 MiG-21, 12 MiG-23.
18 interceptor sqns with 240 MiG-21, 7 MiG-15.
6 recce sqns with 24 MiG-21R, 48 L-29.
Transports incl 6 An-24, 53 Il-14, 1 Tu-134.
Helicopters incl 90 Mi-1/-2, 100 Mi-4, 20 Mi-8.
Operational trainers incl 6 Su-7B, 34 MiG-21U, 60 L-29, 24 L-39.
AA-2 'Atoll' AAM.
28 SA-2/-3 SAM bns.

Aero Vodochody Národní Podnik L-29 *Delfin* ('Maya')

Type: jet training aircraft
Crew: two, seated in tandem
Wings: metal cantilever low-wing monoplane
Fuselage: metal semi-monocoque
Tail unit: metal cantilever
Landing gear: hydraulically actuated retractable tricycle unit
Powerplant: one M 701c 500 turbojet, rated at 1,960-lb (890-kg) static thrust
Fuel capacity: $211\frac{1}{2}$ gallons (962 litres) in two fuselage tanks, plus provision for two 33-gallon (150-litre) underwing tanks
Avionics: comprehensive communication and navigation equipment
Armament: two underwing pylons can each carry one 220-lb (100-kg) bomb, one 7.62-mm machine-gun pod, or four air-to-surface rockets
Dimensions: Span 33 ft 9 in (10.29 m)
Length 35 ft $5\frac{1}{2}$ in (10.81 m)
Height 10 ft 3 in (3.13 m)
Wing area: 213.1 ft² (19.8 m²)
Weights: Empty 5,027 lb (2,280 kg)
Loaded 7,231 lb (3,280 kg)
Maximum 7,804 lb (3,540 kg)
Performance: speed 407 mph (655 kph) at 16,400 ft (5,000 m); climb 2,755 ft (840 m) per minute at sea level; service ceiling 36,000 ft (11,000 m); range 555 miles (894 km) with maximum fuel
Used also by: Bulgaria, Egypt, Guinea-Bissau, Hungary, Iraq, Nigeria, Romania, Syria, Uganda
Notes: The L-29 first flew in 1959, and was accepted as the standard trainer for the pilots of the Warsaw Pact forces with the exception of Poland. The first production aircraft flew in 1963, and the last was produced in 1974. Apart from the standard model described above, there are two other versions:
1. L-29A single-seat aerobatic model
2. L-29R counter-insurgency aircraft, with nose cameras and greater underwing armament.

Other variants were not built in quantity.

Aero Vodochody Národní Podnik L-39 Albatros

Type: basic and advanced jet trainer
Crew: two, in tandem
Wings: metal cantilever low-wing monoplane
Fuselage: metal semi-monocoque
Tail unit: metal cantilever
Landing gear: hydraulically actuated retractable tricycle unit
Powerplant: one Walter Titan (Motorlet-built Ivchenko AI-25-TL) turbofan, rated at 3,792-lb (1,720-kg) static thrust
Fuel capacity: 1,816 lb (824 kg) in rubber tanks in fuselage, and 344 lb (156 kg) in two non-jettisonable wing-tip tanks
Avionics: navigation and blind-flying equipment
Armament: a wide variety of stores can be carried on four underwing hardpoints, the inner pair capable of lifting 1,102 lb (500 kg) each, and the outer pair 551 lb (250 kg) each, up to a maximum external load of 2,425 lb (1,100 kg). Weapons that can be carried include bombs up to 1,102 lb (500 kg) in weight, pods containing up to sixteen 57-mm rockets, gun pods, air-to-air missiles, reconnaissance pods, and drop tanks (inner only)
Dimensions: Span 31 ft $0\frac{1}{2}$ in (9.46 m)
Length 40 ft 5 in (12.32 m)
Height 15 ft $5\frac{1}{2}$ in (4.72 m)
Wing area: 202.4 ft² (18.8 m²)
Weights: Empty 7,341 lb (3,330 kg)
Loaded 9,480 lb (4,300 kg)
Maximum 11,618 lb (5,270 kg)
Performance: (at normal take-off weight) speed 466 mph (750 kph) at 16,400 ft (5,000 m); cruising speed 423 mph (680 kph) at 16,400 ft (5,000 m); climb 4,330 ft (1,320 m) per minute at sea level; service ceiling 37,075 ft (11,300 m); range 565 miles (910 km) at 16,400 ft (5,000 m)
Used also by: East Germany, Hungary, Iraq
Notes: A neat and effective military trainer that has superseded the L-29 *Delfin* trainer in production. It forms part of a comprehensive trainer programme for Warsaw Pact military pilots.

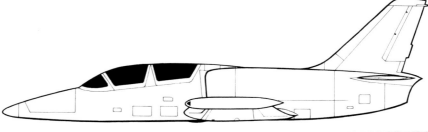

Denmark

6,900 men (1,370 conscripts) and 114 combat aircraft, plus 8,000 reservists and 12,000 Air Force Home Guard.

1 FB sqn with 20 F-35XD *Draken*.
2 FB sqns with 38 F-100D/F.
2 interceptor sqns with 40 F-104G.
1 recce sqn with 16 RF-35XD *Draken*.
1 transport sqn with 8 C-47, 3 C-130H.
1 SAR sqn with 8 S-61A helicopters.
3 TF-35XD *Draken*, 23 Saab T-17 trainers.
8 SAM sqns: 4 with 36 Nike Hercules, 4 with 24 Improved HAWK.
Sidewinder AAM; Bullpup ASM.
(58 F-16A/B fighters on order.)
Naval Air Arm
8 *Alouette* III helicopters.
(7 Lynx helicopters on order.)
Army Air Arm
9 Saab T-17 lt ac; 12 Hughes OH-6A helicopters.

North American Aviation F-100 Super Sabre

Type: interceptor and fighter-bomber
Crew: one
Wings: metal cantilever low mid-wing monoplane
Fuselage: metal semi-monocoque
Tail unit: metal cantilever
Landing gear: hydraulically actuated retractable tricycle unit
Powerplant: one Pratt & Whitney J57-P-21A turbojet, rated at 16,950-lb (7,690-kg) static thrust with afterburning
Fuel capacity: 1,739 gallons (7,905 litres) internally
Avionics: comprehensive communication and navigation/attack equipment
Armament: four 20-mm M-39E cannon with 200 rounds per gun, plus external pylons for two 375-gallon (1,705-litre) drop tanks and up to 7,500 lb (3,402 kg) of stores
Dimensions: Span 38 ft 9½ in (11.81 m)
Length 47 ft (14.325 m)
Height 16 ft 2¾ in (4.96 m)
Wing area: 385 ft² (35.77 m²)
Weights: Empty 21,000 lb (2,525 kg)
Loaded
Maximum 34,832 lb (15,800 kg)

Performance: speed 864 mph (1,390 kph) or Mach 1.31 at 35,000 ft (10,668 m); cruising speed 565 mph (909 kph) at 36,000 ft (10,973 m); climb 16,000 ft (4,900 m) per minute at sea level; service ceiling 45,000 ft (13,716 m); range 1,500 miles (2,415 km) at high altitude with drop tanks
Used also by: Taiwan, Turkey, USA
Notes: The F-100 was the world's first production supersonic aircraft, the prototype flying in 1953, and the first production aircraft entering service the same year. The last aircraft was delivered in 1959. There were several models:
1. F-100A initial production model, with the 14,500-lb (6,576-kg) J57-P-7
2. F-100C fighter-bomber with stiffened wing and four underwing hardpoints, power being provided by the 16,000-lb (7,257-kg) J57-P-29
3. F-100D, to which the technical specification above applies, with additional wing weapon capacity, an autopilot, enlarged vertical tail surfaces, and underwing flaps
4. F-100F two-seat trainer.

Saab-Scania 35 *Draken*

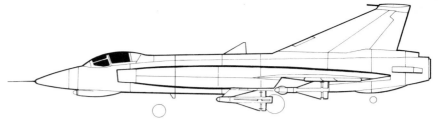

Type: multi-role all-weather combat aircraft
Crew: one or two, seated in tandem
Wings: metal cantilever mid-wing 'double delta' monoplane
Fuselage: metal semi-monocoque
Tail unit: metal cantilever
Landing gear: retractable tricycle unit
Powerplant: one Svenska Flygmotor RM6B (licence-built Rolls-Royce Avon) turbojet, rated at 15,000-lb (6,804-kg) static thrust with afterburning (in J 35A, B and C); one Svenska Flygmotor RM6C turbojet, rated at 17,110-lb (7,761-kg) static thrust with afterburning (in other models)
Fuel capacity: between 493 and 680 gallons (2,240 and 3,090 litres)
Avionics: comprehensive communication and navigation/attack equipment, including S7 collision-course fire-control system (J 35B) and L. M. Ericsson pulse-doppler radar (J 35F)
Armament: two 30-mm Aden M/55 cannon and four RB324 Sidewinder air-to-air missiles (J 35A); as J 35A plus external stores up to a weight of 2,204 lb (1,000 kg) (J 35B); none in J 35C; same as J 35B in J 35D; usually none in J 35E, but provision for same armament as J 35A; one 30-mm M/53 Aden cannon, plus two radar-homing RB27 Falcon and two infra red-homing RB28 Falcon air-to-air missiles, plus two or four RB324 Sidewinder air-to-air missiles (J 35F); two 30-mm Aden M/53 cannon, four RB324 Sidewinder air-to-air missiles, plus nine pylons capable of carrying a total of 9,000 lb (4,082 kg)
Dimensions: Span 30 ft 10 in (9.4 m)
Length 50 ft 4 in (15.4 m)
Height 12 ft 9 in (3.9 m)
Wing area: 529.6 ft² (49.2 m²)
Weights: Empty (J 35D) 16,107 lb (7,265 kg)
Empty (J 35F) 18,180 lb (8,250 kg)
Loaded
Maximum (J 35A) 18,200 lb (8,255 kg)
Maximum (J 35D) 22,663 lb (10,280 kg)
Maximum (J 35F) 27,050 lb (12,270 kg)
Maximum (F-35) 35,275 lb (16,000 kg)
Performance: (J 35D onwards, in 'clean' condition) speed 1,320 mph (2,125 kph) or Mach 2 at high altitude; speed 924 mph (1,487 kph) or Mach 1.4 with two drop tanks and two 1,000-lb (454-kg) bombs; climb 34,450 ft (10,500 m) per minute at sea level; service ceiling about 65,000 ft (20,000 m); typical range with some external weapons 800 miles (1,300 km); ferry range 2,020 miles (3,250 km)
Used also by: Finland, Sweden
Notes: The design of the J 35 was finished in 1951, and the first prototype flew in 1955, production aircraft entering service in 1958. The double delta wing planform provides excellent handling characteristics at slow speeds, making the J 35 able to operate from very short runways. The J 35D was the first Mach 2 model, other notable variants being the SK 35 twin-seat trainer and the Saab 35 produced for Denmark and Finland as the F-35 and Saab 35S respectively.

Dominican Republic

3,500 men and 43 combat aircraft.

1 bomber sqn with 7 B-26K.
1 fighter sqn with 10 Vampire F.1/ FB.50.
1 fighter/trg sqn with 20 F-51D.
1 COIN/trg sqn with 6 T-28D.
2 PBY-5A SAR ac.
1 transport sqn with 6 C-46, 6 C-47, 3 DHC-2.
Helicopters incl 3 *Alouette* II/III, 2 H-19, 2 UH-12E, 7 OH-6A.
Trainers incl 4 Cessna 172, T-6, T-11.

Curtiss-Wright Corporation Airplane Division C-46 Commando

Type: transport aircraft
Crew: four, plus up to 50 passengers
Wings: metal cantilever low-wing monoplane
Fuselage: metal semi-monocoque
Tail unit: metal cantilever
Landing gear: hydraulically actuated retractable tailwheel unit
Powerplant: two Pratt & Whitney R-2800-51 radial engines, each rated at 2,000 hp and driving a metal three-blade propeller
Fuel capacity:
Avionics: communication and navigation equipment
Armament: none
Dimensions: Span 108 ft 1 in (32.95 m)
　　　　　　　Length 76 ft 4 in (32.27 m)
　　　　　　　Height 21 ft 9 in (6.63 m)
Wing area: 1,360 ft² (126.35 m²)
Weights: Empty 32,400 lb (14,697 kg)
　　　　　Loaded 45,000 lb (20,412 kg)
　　　　　Maximum 56,000 lb (25,401 kg)
Performance: speed 269 mph (433 kph) at 15,000 ft (4,572 m); cruising speed 183 mph (295 kph); climb 1,300 ft (396 m) per minute at sea level; service ceiling 27,600 ft (8,413 m); range 1,200 miles (1,931 km)
Used also by: Bolivia, Japan, South Korea, Taiwan
Notes: Although the C-46 was larger, faster and more advanced than the C-47, it was more suitable for freighting operations than combat flying, and never acquired the same reputation as the Douglas aircraft. Designed as a civil airliner, the prototype first flew in 1940, and the first C-46 entered US service in 1942.

Hiller Aircraft UH-12 (H-23 Raven)

Type: utility helicopter
Crew: one, plus up to two passengers
Rotors: metal cantilever two-blade main rotor; metal cantilever two-blade tail rotor
Fuselage: metal tube structure, with a metal semi-monocoque tailboom
Landing gear: twin metal skids with two small manoeuvring wheels
Powerplant: one Lycoming VO-540-A1B inline engine, rated at 305 hp
Fuel capacity:
Avionics: communication equipment
Armament: none
Dimensions: Span 35 ft 5 in (10.8 m)
　　　　　　　Length (fuselage) 27 ft 11¼ in (8.52 m)
　　　　　　　Height 9 ft 9½ in (3.0 m)
Rotor disc area: 985.16 ft² (91.52 m²)
Weights: Empty 1,816 lb (824 kg)
　　　　　Loaded 2,700 lb (1,225 kg)
　　　　　Maximum
Performance: speed 95 mph (153 kph) at sea level; cruising speed 82 mph (132 kph); climb 1,050 ft (320 m) per minute at sea level; service ceiling 13,200 ft (4,025 m); hovering ceiling in ground effect 5,200 ft (1,585 m)
Used also by: Bolivia, Chile, Mexico, Paraguay
Notes: The UH-12 was developed from the Model 360 of 1946.

North American Aviation F-51 Mustang

Type: fighter and fighter-bomber
Crew: one
Wings: metal cantilever low-wing monoplane
Fuselage: metal semi-monocoque
Tail unit: metal cantilever
Landing gear: hydraulically actuated retractable tailwheel unit
Powerplant: one Packard V-1650-9 inline engine, rated at 2,218 hp and driving a metal four-blade propeller
Fuel capacity:
Avionics: communication and navigation equipment
Armament: six 0.5-in (12.7-mm) Browning MG53-2 machine-guns with 270 or 400 rounds per gun, plus one 1,000-lb (454-kg) bomb or a drop tank under each wing
Dimensions: Span 37 ft 0½ in (11.29 m)
Length 33 ft 4 in (10.16 m)
Height 13 ft 8 in (4.1 m)
Wing area: 233 ft² (21.65 m²)
Weights: Empty 6,585 lb (2,987 kg)
Loaded
Maximum 11,054 lb (5,014 kg)
Performance: speed 487 mph (784 kph) at 25,000 ft (7,620 m); cruising speed 380 mph (612 kph); climb 12 minutes 30 seconds to 30,000 ft (9,144 m); service ceiling 41,600 ft (12,680 m); range 1,530 miles (2,462 km) with drop tanks
Used only by: Dominican Republic
Notes: The first Mustang prototype flew in 1940, and the first production aircraft was delivered in 1941. The last aircraft was delivered in December 1945. Between the dates, the Mustang had emerged as World War II's best escort fighter, and probably as the war's best all-round fighter, especially once the Allison inline had been changed for the Rolls-Royce Merlin, licence-built in the USA by Packard. The F-51H, to which the technical specification above applies, was the ultimate production variant of this great fighter.

East Germany

36,000 men (15,000 conscripts) and 362 combat aircraft, plus 30,000 reservists.

3 FGA sqns with 35 MiG-17, Su-7B.
18 interceptor sqns with 270 MiG-21.
1 recce sqn with 12 MiG-21, 4 Il-14.
2 transport sqns with 20 Il-14, 3 Tu-124, 8 Tu-134.
6 helicopter sqns with 46 Mi-1, 18 Mi-4, 40 Mi-8.
41 MiG-21U, L-39 trainers.
An-14 utility transports.
Trainers incl Zlin 43.
AA-2 'Atoll' AAM.
5 AD regts with 120 57mm and 100mm AA guns.
2 SAM bns with 22 SA-2, 4 SA-3.
2 para bns.
Naval Air Arm
1 helicopter sqn with 8 Mi-4, 5 Mi-8.

Antonov An-14 *Pchelka* 'Clod'

Type: general-purpose aircraft
Crew: one, plus up to eight passengers
Wings: metal cantilever braced high-wing monoplane
Fuselage: metal semi-monocoque
Tail unit: metal cantilever
Landing gear: fixed tricycle unit
Powerplant: two Ivchenko AI-14RF piston engines, each rated at 300 hp and driving a V-530 two- or three-blade metal propeller
Fuel capacity: 84 gallons (383 litres) in four wing tanks
Avionics: communication and navigation equipment
Armament: none
Dimensions: Span 72 ft 2 in (21.99 m)
Length 37 ft 6½ in (11.44 m)
Height 15 ft 2½ in (4.63 m)
Wing area: 427.5 ft² (39.72 m²)
Weights: Empty 4,409 lb (2,000 kg)
Loaded
Maximum 7,935 lb (3,600 kg)
Performance: (at maximum take-off weight) speed 138 mph (222 kph) at 3,280 ft (1,000 m); cruising speed 112 mph (180 kph) at 6,560 ft (2,000 m); climb 1,000 ft (306 m) per minute at sea level; service ceiling 17,060 ft (5,200 m); range with maximum payload 404 miles (650 km); range with maximum fuel 497 miles (800 km)
Used only by: East Germany
Notes: The An-14 entered service in 1965, and has a maximum payload of 1,590 lb (720 kg) under normal conditions.

Sukhoi Su-7B 'Fitter'

Type: ground-attack fighter
Crew: one
Wings: metal cantilever mid-wing monoplane
Fuselage: metal semi-monocoque
Tail unit: metal cantilever
Landing gear: hydraulically actuated retractable tricycle unit
Powerplant: one Lyulka AL-7F-1 turbojet, rated at 22,046-lb (10,000-kg) static thrust with afterburning, plus provision for two JATO units under the rear fuselage
Fuel capacity: 7,000 lb (3,175 kg) internally, with provision for two 1,049-lb (476-kg) drop tanks
Avionics: comprehensive communication and navigation/attack equipment
Armament: two NR-30 30-mm cannon with 70 rounds per gun, plus external stores on four pylons, the under fuselage pair rated at 1,653 lb (750 kg) each, and the underwing pair at 1,102 lb (500 kg) each, up to a maximum of 5,512 lb (2,500 kg) except when fuel tanks are carried under the fuselage, when the maximum weapon load is reduced to 2,205 lb (1,000 kg)
Dimensions: Span 29 ft 3½ in (8.93 m)
Length with probe 57 ft (17.37 m)
Height 15 ft (4.57 m)
Wing area:
Weights: Empty 19,000 lb (8,620 kg)
Loaded 26,450 lb (12,000 kg)
Maximum 29,750 lb (13,500 kg)
Performance: speed 1,055 mph (1,700 kph) or Mach 1.6 in 'clean' condition at 36,100 ft (11,000 m); speed 788 mph (1,270 kph) or Mach 1.2 with external stores at 36,100 ft (11,000 m); climb about 29,900 ft (9,120 m) per minute at sea level; service ceiling 49,700 ft (15,150 m); combat radius 300 miles (480 km); ferry range 900 miles (1,450 km)
Used also by: Afghanistan, Algeria, Czechoslovakia, Egypt, Hungary, India, Iraq, North Korea, Poland, Syria, USSR, Vietnam
Notes: The Su-7 flew in prototype form before 1955, and entered service in 1959. A useful and sturdy aircraft, the Su-7 suffers from the voracious appetite of its Lyulka turbojet, and the limited internal fuel capacity — this means that medium-range missions can only be undertaken at the

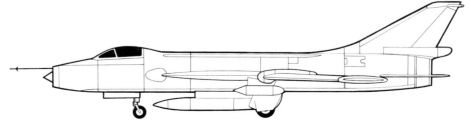

expense of weapon load, not very good at the best of times. There have been several variants:

1. Su-7B 'Fitter-A' initial production model

2. Su-7BM 'Fitter-B', similar to the Su-7B, but with a low-pressure nose-wheel tyre necessitating bulged doors, and a tail warning sensor at the top of the fin

3. Su-7U 'Moujik' two-seat trainer version, with a second cockpit in tandem and a long dorsal spine.

Tupolev Tu-124 'Cookpot'

Type: transport aircraft
Crew: three to five, plus up to 56 passengers
Wings: metal cantilever low-wing monoplane
Fuselage: metal semi-monocoque
Tail unit: metal cantilever
Landing gear: hydraulically actuated retractable tricycle unit
Powerplant: two Soloviev D-20P turbofans, each rated at 11,905-lb (5,400-kg) static thrust

Fuel capacity: 2,970 gallons (13,500 litres) in wing tanks
Avionics: comprehensive communication and navigation equipment
Armament: none
Dimensions: Span 83 ft 10 in (25.55 m)
Length 100 ft 4 in (30.58 m)
Height
Wing area: 1,284.9 ft² (119.37 m²)
Weights: Empty 50,486 lb (22,900 kg)
Loaded 80,468 lb (36,500 kg)
Maximum 82,673 lb (37,500 kg)

Performance: speed 603 mph (970 kph) at 26,245 ft (8,000 m); cruising speed 541 mph (870 kph); service ceiling 38,385 ft (11,700 m); range 1,305 miles (2,100 km) with a payload of 6,613 lb (3,000 kg)
Used also by: India, Iraq
Notes: The Tu-124 is basically a scaled-down Tu-104, with only two engines instead of four, and modifications to improve the type's short-field take-off and landing characteristics. Maximum payload is 13,227 lb (6,000 kg).

Zlin Moravan Národní Podnik 43

Type: light trainer
Crew: two, seated side by side, plus up to two passengers
Wings: metal cantilever low-wing monoplane
Fuselage: metal tube centre section and metal semi-monocoque rear fuselage
Tail unit: metal cantilever
Landing gear: fixed tricycle unit
Powerplant: one Avia M 337 A piston engine, rated at 210 hp and driving an Avia metal two-blade propeller

Fuel capacity: 28.5 gallons (130 litres) in wing leading-edge tanks, plus optional 12 gallons (55 litres) in each of two wingtip tanks
Avionics: communication and navigation equipment
Armament: none
Dimensions: Span 32 ft 0¼ in (9.76 m)
Length 25 ft 5 in (7.75 m)
Height 9 ft 6½ in (2.91 m)
Wing area: 156.1 ft² (14.5 m²)
Weights: Empty 1,609 lb (730 kg)
Loaded
Maximum 2,976 lb (1,350 kg)

Performance: (at maximum take-off weight) speed 146 mph (235 kph) at sea level; cruising speed 130 mph (210 kph); climb 689 ft (210 m) per minute at sea level; service ceiling 12,465 ft (3,800 m); range 714 miles (1,150 km) with tip tanks
Used only by: East Germany
Notes: The Zlin 43 was derived from the Zlin 42M, with a more powerful engine and an enlarged centre fuselage to accommodate two additional passengers. The type is intended for advanced navigation and instrument training, but can also be used for liaison, competitive flying, aerobatics and glider-towing.

Ecuador

4,000 men and 46 combat aircraft.

1 lt bomber sqn with 5 Canberra B.6.
1 FB sqn with 12 Jaguar A/B.
1 COIN sqn with 10 A-37B.
1 recce sqn with 6 Meteor FR.9.
1 FGA/trg sqn with 12 BAC 167 Strikemaster.
1 PBY-SA MR aircraft.
Transports incl 4 Electra, 2 C-130H, 4 DC-6B, 2 Learjet, 4 HS 748, 12 C-47, 5 C-45, 2 DHC-5, 3 DHC-6.
Helicopters incl 2 Puma, 4 *Alouette* III, 4 *Lama*, 3 Bell 47 G.
Trainers incl 20 T-34C, 20 SF.260, 24 Cessna 150A.
R.550 Magic AAM.
(18 Mirage F1C, 2 F1B, 12 Super *Mystère* B2, 2 DHC-5 on order.)

Naval Air Arm

3 Arava, 2T-37, 2T-41, 1 Cessna 320, 1 Cessna 177 ac, 2 *Alouette* III helicopters.

Army Air Arm

1 Skyvan, 6 Arava, 3 Porter transports, 7 lt ac, 2 helicopters.

British Aerospace (British Aircraft Corporation/Preston) 167 Strikemaster

Type: trainer, armament trainer and light tactical support aircraft
Crew: two, seated side-by-side
Wings: metal cantilever low-wing monoplane
Fuselage: metal semi-monocoque
Tail unit: metal cantilever
Landing gear: hydraulically actuated retractable tricycle unit
Powerplant: one Rolls-Royce Bristol Viper Mark 535 turbojet, rated at 3,140-lb (1,424-kg) static thrust
Fuel capacity: 366 gallons (1,663 litres) in two wingtip, two outer wing integral and six inner wing bag tanks
Avionics: comprehensive navigation and communication equipment
Armament: two 7.62-mm FN machine-guns with 550 rounds per gun, plus four underwing hardpoints for the carriage of external stores up to 3,000 lb (1,360 kg) in weight. Typical loads include drop tanks, pods containing 18 SNEB 68-mm rockets, LAU 68 launchers with seven rockets, 540-lb (250-kg) ballistic or retarded bombs, 540- and 1,102-lb (250- and 500-kg) bombs, banks of quadruple 80-mm SURA rockets, napalm tanks, reconnaissance pods, 143- and 275-lb (65- and 125-kg) bombs, 7.62-mm machine-guns pods, 20-mm cannon pods, and 2.75- and 3-in (70- and 76-mm) rockets
Dimensions: Span 36 ft 10 in (11.23 m)
Length 33 ft 8½ in (10.27 m)
Height 10 ft 11½ in (3.34 m)
Wing area: 213.7 ft² (19.85 m²)
Weights: Empty 6,195 lb (2,810 kg)
Loaded 10,600 lb (4,808 kg)
Maximum 11,500 lb (5,215 kg)
Performance: (at maximum take-off weight) speed in 'clean' condition 481 mph (774 kph) at 18,000 ft (5,485 m); climb 5,250 ft (1,600 m) per minute at sea level; climb to 30,000 ft (9,150 m) in 8 minutes 45 seconds; service ceiling 40,000 ft (12,200 m); combat radius with a load of 3,000 lb (1,360 kg), 5 minutes over the target, on a hi-lo-hi mission 247 miles (397 km); ferry range 1,382 miles (2,224 km)
Used also by: Kenya, Kuwait, New Zealand, Oman, Saudi Arabia, Singapore
Notes: Derived from the BAC 145 Jet Provost trainer, the BAC 167 Strikemaster maintains the same basic airframe, but has a more powerful engine and underwing hardpoints, making the type very useful for anti-insurgency operations. The first example flew in 1967. The technical details above refer specifically to the Mark 88 for the Royal New Zealand Air Force, but apply generally to other marks for different air forces.

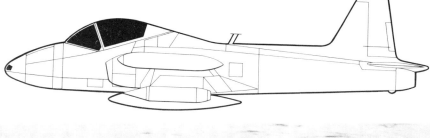

British Aerospace (English Electric) Canberra

Type: light bomber, reconnaissance, intruder and general-purpose aircraft
Crew: two
Wings: metal cantilever mid-wing monoplane
Fuselage: metal semi-monocoque
Tail unit: metal cantilever
Landing gear: hydraulically actuated retractable tricycle unit
Powerplant: two Rolls-Royce Avon 206 turbojets, each rated at 11,250-lb (5,103-kg) static thrust
Fuel capacity:
Avionics: comprehensive communication and navigation equipment
Armament: none
Dimensions: Span 67 ft 10 in (20.68 m)
　　　　　　　Length 66 ft 8 in (20.32 m)
　　　　　　　Height 15 ft 7 in (4.75 m)
Wing area:
Weights: Empty
　　　　　　Loaded 49,000 lb (22,226 kg)
　　　　　　Maximum 55,000 lb (24,948 kg)
Performance: speed 560 mph (901 kph) at 40,000 ft (12,192 m); ceiling more than 60,000 ft (18,288 m); range 4,000 miles (6,440 km) with external fuel
Used also by: Argentina, Australia, Ethiopia, India, Peru, Rhodesia, South Africa, UK, Venezuela
Notes: The English Electric Canberra has been the UK's most successful bomber since World War II. The prototype first flew in 1949, and the B.2 entered service in 1950. There have been several distinct models:

1. Canberra B.2, with 6,500-lb (2,948-kg) Avon 101 engines and a bomb load of 6,000 lb (2,722 kg)
2. Canberra PR.3, with more fuel in a longer fuselage
3. Canberra T.4 trainer with side-by-side controls
4. Canberra B.6 bomber, the updated B.2
5. Canberra PR.7 updated reconnaissance aircraft
6. Canberra B(I).8 intruder and interdiction aircraft, with 7,500-lb (3,402-kg) Avon 109 engines, four 20-mm cannon, 5,000 lb (2,268 kg) of bombs, and two AS.30 ASMs
7. Canberra PR.9 high-altitude reconnaissance aircraft, to which the specification above applies
8. Canberra T.11 and T.19 trainer versions of the B.2
9. Canberra B(I).12 interdiction aircraft.

There were many other variants for bombing, reconnaissance, electronic warfare and the like.

Gloster Aircraft Meteor

Type: fighter, reconnaissance fighter, photographic reconnaissance aircraft and trainer
Crew: one or two, seated in tandem
Wings: metal cantilever low mid-wing monoplane
Fuselage: metal semi-monocoque
Tail unit: metal cantilever
Landing gear: hydraulically actuated retractable tricycle unit
Powerplant: two Rolls-Royce Derwent 8 turbojets, each rated at 3,600-lb (1,633-kg) static thrust
Fuel capacity: 420 gallons (1,909 litres)
Avionics: communication and navigation equipment
Armament: four 20-mm Hispano cannon, plus (optionally) two 1,000-lb (454-kg) bombs or eight 80-lb (27.2-kg) rockets under the wings
Dimensions: Span 37 ft 2 in (11.3 m)
　　　　　　　Length 44 ft 7 in (13.59 m)
　　　　　　　Height 13 ft 10 in (4.22 m)
Wing area: 350 ft² (32.52 m²)
Weights: Empty 10,626 lb (4,820 kg)
　　　　　　Loaded 15,700 lb (7,121 kg)
　　　　　　Maximum 19,100 lb (8,664 kg)
Performance: speed 590 mph (950 kph) at sea level; 530 mph (853 kph) at 40,000 ft (12,192 m); climb 6,950 ft (2,118 m) per minute at sea level; service ceiling 44,000 ft (13,410 m); range 980 miles (1,577 km)
Used only by: Ecuador
Notes: The Gloster Meteor was Britain's first jet fighter, and the only Allied jet fighter to see combat in World War II. The prototype flew in 1943, and production aircraft entered service in July 1944. The main variants were:

1. Meteor F.1 with 1,700-lb (771-kg) Rolls-Royce Welland
2. Meteor F.3 with 2,000-lb (907-kg) Rolls-Royce Derwent 1
3. Meteor F.4 with 3,500-lb (1,588-kg) Derwent 5
4. Meteor PR.10 photographic reconnaissance model
5. Meteor F.8, to which the technical specification above applies
6. Meteor NF.11-14 two-seat night-fighters, with long-span wings and AI radar
7. Meteor T.7 tandem-seat trainer
8. Meteor FR.9 reconnaissance fighter
9. Meteor PR.10 photographic reconnaissance aircraft.

Egypt

The Egyptian Air Force

For some years Egypt had, with Israel, the most powerful air force in the Middle East, largely as a result of her willingness to expend a large percentage of her gross national product on military hardware, and a workable relationship with Russia, which was able to supply weapons on favourable credit terms, as well as the technical back-up and training facilities to make the air force an effective fighting force. Though the Egyptian Air Force had suffered very heavy losses in the 1956 and 1967 wars, in 1973 there were clear indications that at last it was able to operate the right aircraft with the right aircrew and the right tactical precepts. But there was still clearly much to be done before the Egyptian Air Force was a qualitative match for the Israeli Defence Forces/Air Force, its principal opponent. However, the subsequent rift with the USSR has led to the removal of the essential technical services and personnel, and the cessation of replacement deliveries, so that an unknown, but important, part of Egypt's Russian-supplied weapons are unserviceable. To get over this, Egypt has signed contracts for western technical aid and replacements, but inevitably this has taken time to come to grips with Russian equipment, and has made a real contribution to Egypt's armed forces only since 1977. At the same time, Egypt has sought new weapons from western rather than Russian origins, notably the French and British, and recently the Americans. The Egyptian Air Force has some 25,000 personnel, about 6.33 per cent of the total armed forces, which receive about 21.05 per cent of the gross national product as an annual budget.

Egyptian tactical ideas are closely modelled on Russian notions, which stress the importance of the land forces, supported by strong tactical air forces. Accordingly, the long-range strike force available to Egypt is a small one, with 23 Tu-16D/G medium bombers and five Il-28 light bombers, provided with some AS-1 'Kennel' and AS-5 'Kelt' air-to-surface missiles. These forces and missiles have not proved of any real use in previous Arab-Israeli conflicts.

Far stronger are the tactical air forces deployed by Egypt. There are three fighter-bomber regiments with 80 MiG-21F/PFM aircraft, and 90 MiG-15s and 17s; and five FGA/strike regiments with some 70 Su-7, 19 Su-20, 21 MiG-23 and 46 Mirage VDE/DD aircraft, although the MiG-23s are probably of limited serviceability only.

Local and tactical defence is in the hands of nine interceptor squadrons with 108 MiG-21MF fighters, whose serviceability is now improving rapidly as a result of British assistance.

Transport is well catered for, if only by a motley selection of types—some 55 fixed-wing aircraft of seven types, and about 210 helicopters of five types. The matter will be improved, at least insofar as homogeneity is concerned, when the 14 C-130H and 50 Lynx on order are delivered. Egypt has about 195 trainers, including 150 aircraft of communist origin, the rest being locally built *Gomhouria* aircraft.

Other aircraft on order include another 14 Mirage V FGA aircraft and 50 F-5 Tiger II aircraft, which will greatly strengthen the ground-attack arm. It is impossible to assess as yet, though, the effect that the 1977 accord between Egypt and Israel has had on the defence thinking of Egypt. It is almost certain that Egypt will take the opportunity to trim her enormously high percentile defence budget, to the inevitable anger of the other involved Arab nations.

Avions Marcel Dassault Mirage V (or 5)

Type: ground-attack aircraft
Crew: one or two
Wings: metal cantilever low-wing monoplane
Fuselage: metal semi-monocoque
Tail unit: metal cantilever
Landing gear: hydraulically actuated retractable tricycle unit
Powerplant: one SNECMA Atar 9C turbojet, rated at 13,680-lb (6,205-kg) static thrust with afterburner
Fuel capacity: 843 gallons (3,830 litres) internally, plus 220 gallons (1,000 litres) externally for ground-attack missions, or 1,034 gallons (4,700 litres) externally for interception missions
Avionics: as for Mirage III, but with optional Aïda II radar rangefinder
Armament: two 30-mm DEFA cannon with 125 rounds each, two 1,000-lb (454-kg) bombs or one AS.30 air-to-surface missile

25,000 men and about 612 combat aircraft.

23 Tu-16D/G med bombers.
5 Il-28 lt bombers.
3 FB regts with 80 MiG-21/PFM, 90 MiG-15/-17.
5 FGA/strike regts with 70 Su-7, 19 Su-20, 21 MiG-23, 46 Mirage VDE/DD.
9 interceptor sqns with 108 MiG-21MF.
Transports incl 3 C-130, 2 EC-130H, 26 Il-14, 19 An-12, 1 Falcon, 1 Boeing 707, 1 Boeing 737.
Helicopters incl 20 Mi-4, 32 Mi-6, 70 Mi-8, 30 Commando, 54 Gazelle.
Trainers incl 150 MiG-15/-21/-23U, Su-7U, L-29, 45 *Gomhouria*.
AA-2 'Atoll', R.530 AAM; AS-1 'Kennel', AS-5 'Kelt' ASM.
(42 F-5E, 8 F-5F, 14 Mirage V fighters, 14 C-130H transports, 50 Lynx helicopters on order.)
Naval Air Arm
6 Sea King ASW helicopters.

under the fuselage, and 1,000 lb (454 kg) bombs under the wings; there are seven weapon attachment points, capable of lifting a total of 8,820 lb (4,000 kg) of disposable weapons, which can include missiles, guided missiles and 68-mm JL-100 rocket pods
Dimensions: Span 26 ft 11½ in (8.22 m)
Length 50 ft 0¼ in (15.55 m)
Height 13 ft 11¼ in (4.25 m)
Wing area: 375 ft² (34.85 m²)
Weights: Empty 14,550 lb (6,600 kg)
Loaded
Maximum 29,760 lb (13,500 kg)
Performance: speed (with cannon armament but otherwise 'clean') 1,460 mph (2,350 kph) or Mach 2.2 at 39,375 ft (12,000 m); cruising speed Mach 0.9 at 36,000 ft (11,000 m); climb 6 minutes 50 seconds to 49,200 ft (15,000 m) at Mach 1.8; service ceiling 55,775 ft (17,000 m); combat radius with 2,000-lb (907-kg) load 805 miles (1,300 km) on hi-lo-hi mission, or

400 miles (650 km) on a lo-lo-lo mission; ferry range 2,485 miles (4,000 km)
Used also by: Belgium, Colombia, Egypt, France, Gabon, Libya, Pakistan, Peru, Sudan, United Arab Emirates, Venezuela, Zaire
Notes: Basically similar to the Mirage III-E, the Mirage V has the same airframe and engine, but greater fuel capacity, simplified systems and the ability to operate from unprepared strips.

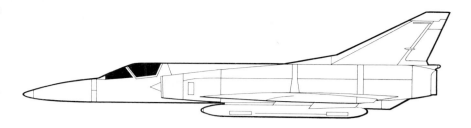

Tupolev Tu-16 'Badger'

Type: medium bomber and maritime reconnaissance/attack aircraft
Crew: seven
Wings: metal cantilever high mid-wing monoplane
Fuselage: metal semi-monocoque
Tail unit: metal cantilever
Landing gear: hydraulically actuated retractable tricycle unit
Powerplant: two Mikulin AM-3M turbojets, each rated at 20,944-lb (9,500-kg) static thrust
Fuel capacity: about 10,000 gallons (45,450 litres) in fuselage and wing tanks
Avionics: comprehensive communication and navigation/attack equipment, plus further gear depending on role
Armament: six NR-23 23-mm cannon in manned rear turret and remotely controlled forward dorsal and rear ventral turrets, and a seventh fixed cannon in the nose of aircraft not fitted with a radome, plus up to 19,800 lb (9,000 kg) of bombs in the bomb bay, and air-to-surface stand-off missiles in naval versions
Dimensions: Span 110 ft (33.5 m)
Length 120 ft (36.5 m)
Height 35 ft 6 in (10.8 m)
Wing area: about 1,820 ft² (169.0 m²)
Weights: Empty about 72,750 lb (33,000 kg)
Loaded about 150,000 lb (68,000 kg)
Maximum

Performance: (estimated, at maximum take-off weight) speed 587 mph (945 kph) at 35,000 ft (10,700 m); climb 4,100 ft per minute at sea level in 'clean' condition; service ceiling 42,650 ft (13,000 m); range with maximum bomb load 3,000 miles (4,800 km); range for reconnaissance missions 4,500 miles (7,250 km)
Used also by: China, Indonesia, USSR
Notes: Developed from the Tu-88 prototype, which flew in 1952, the Tu-16 bomber entered Russian service in 1954, and still remains in service in some numbers. The type is still under production in China. There are seven versions of the basic design:
1. Tu-16 'Badger-A' initial production version, the first Russian strategic jet bomber. The version has a glazed nose with a small radome under it. Survivors have been converted into aerial tankers. Some were supplied to Iraq

2. Tu-16 'Badger-B' maritime version with two 'Kennel' cruise missiles under the wings for the Soviet Naval Air Force
3. Tu-16 'Badger-C' with a radome replacing the nose glazing, and an AS-2 'Kipper' air-to-surface missile under the fuselage for the Soviet Naval Air Force
4. Tu-16 'Badger-D' maritime/electronic reconnaissance version, with a nose similar to that of the 'Badger-C', a larger radome under the nose, and three 'blisters' under the fuselage
5. Tu-16 'Badger-E', similar to the 'Badger-A' but with cameras in the bomb bay
6. Tu-16 'Badger-F', similar to the 'Badger-E' but with two electronic intelligence pods under the wings
7. Tu-16 'Badger-G', similar to the 'Badger-A' but with underwing pylons for two AS-5 'Kelt' air-to-surface missiles.

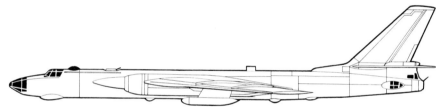

Westland Helicopters Commando

Type: tactical military helicopter
Crew: two, plus up to 28 passengers
Rotor: light alloy cantilever five-blade main rotor; light alloy cantilever six-blade tail rotor
Fuselage: light alloy stressed skin
Landing gear: fixed tailwheel unit
Powerplant: two Rolls-Royce Gnome H.1400-1 turboshafts, each rated at 1,660 shp
Fuel capacity: 800 gallons (3,636 litres) in fuselage bag tanks, plus provision for an internal auxiliary tank
Avionics: comprehensive communication and navigation equipment
Armament: missile launchers, rocket pods, turrets and flexible machine-guns to suit customer requirements
Dimensions: Span 62 ft (18.9 m)
Length (fuselage) 55 ft 10 in (17.02 m)
Height 16 ft 10 in (5.13 m)
Rotor disc area: 3,019 ft² (280.5 m²)
Weights: Empty 12,566 lb (5,700 kg)
Loaded
Maximum 21,000 lb (9,525 kg)
Performance: (at maximum take-off weight) speed 143 mph (230 kph); cruising speed 129 mph (208 kph) at sea level; climb 2,020 ft (616 m) per minute at sea level; service ceiling 10,000 ft (3,050 m); hovering ceiling in ground effect 5,000 ft (1,525 m); range with maximum load of 28 troops 276 miles (445 km); range with maximum fuel 937 miles (1,507 km)

Used also by: Qatar
Notes: Derived from the Sea King, the Commando tactical helicopter is intended for land operations only, and so the sponsons of the Sea King have been deleted, and the undercarriage made fixed. Able to deliver 28 troops, the Commando can carry an alternative load of up to 8,000 lb (3,630 kg) in weight, and can also operate in secondary search and rescue, and air-to-surface strike. There are two versions:
1. Commando Mark 1, modelled closely on the Sea King and able to carry only 21 troops
2. Commando Mark 2, to which the technical specification above relates, able to carry 28 troops.

Eire

674 men and 16 combat aircraft.

1 COIN sqn with 6 Super Magister.
1 COIN/trg sqn with 10 SF.260W.
1 liaison sqn with 8 Cessna FR-172H.
1 helicopter sqn with 8 *Alouette* III helicopters.
1 flt with 3 Dove, 1 King Air.

SIAI-Marchetti SF.260

Type: trainer and light tactical support aircraft
Crew: one, two or three
Wings: light alloy cantilever low-wing monoplane
Fuselage: light alloy semi-monocoque
Tail unit: light alloy cantilever
Landing gear: electrically actuated retractable tricycle unit
Powerplant: one Lycoming 0-540-E4A5 piston engine, rated at 260 hp and driving a Hartzell two-blade metal propeller
Fuel capacity: 53.5 gallons (243 litres) in two wing and two wingtip tanks, plus provision for two underwing auxiliary tanks, each holding 18.25 gallons (83 litres)
Avionics: communication and navigation equipment
Armament: two or four underwing hardpoints, each capable of carrying 661 lb (300 kg). Typical loads include the SIAI gun pod armed with one 7.62-mm FN machine-gun with 500 rounds, the Matra MAC AAF1 gun pod fitted with a 7.62-mm machine-gun, the Simpres AL-8-70 rocket-launcher with eight 2.75-in (70-mm) rockets, the LAU-32 launcher with seven 2.75-in (70-mm) FFAR rockets, the Simpres AL-18-50 rocket-launcher with eighteen 2-in (50-mm) rockets, the Matra F2 rocket-launcher with six 68-mm SNEB 253 rockets, the Matra 181 rocket-launcher with eighteen 37-mm rockets, the SAMP EU 32 275-lb (125-kg) fragmentation bombs, general-purpose bombs, practice bombs and reconnaissance equipment
Dimensions: Span 27 ft 4¾ in (8.35 m)
Length 23 ft 3½ in (7.1 m)
Height 7 ft 11 in (2.41 m)
Wing area: 108.7 ft² (10.1 m²)
Weights: Empty 1,794 lb (814 kg)
Loaded 2,513 lb (1,140 kg)
Maximum 2,866 lb (1,300 kg)
Performance: (at maximum take-off weight) speed 196 mph (315 kph) at sea level; cruising speed 178 mph (287 kph) at 4,925 ft (1,500 m); climb 1,099 ft (335 m) per minute at sea level; climb to 7,550 ft (2,300 m) in 10 minutes 20 seconds; service ceiling (SF. 260M) 15,300 ft (4,665 m); operational radius for a mission of 4 hours 54 minutes on a single-seat strike raid, with 5 minutes over the target 345 miles (556 km); ferry range 1,066 miles (1,716 km)
Used also by: Belgium, Bolivia, Burma, Ecuador, Italy, Libya, Morocco, Philippines, Rhodesia, Singapore, Thailand, Tunisia, United Arab Emirates, Zaire, Zambia

1. SF. 260M two and three-seat trainer
2. SF. 260W Warrior trainer and light
   tactical support model (to which the
   above specification relates)
3. SF. 260 SW Sea Warrior for maritime surveillance, search and supply
   missions. This last model has the
   four underwing hardpoints of the SF.
   260W, but enlarged tiptanks fitted
   with search radar (port) and reconnaissance gear (starboard),
   increasing overall span to 28 ft 6½ in
   (8.7 m).

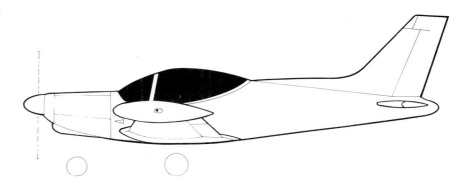

El Salvador

1,000 men.

17 *Ouragan* FGA.
4 Magister FGA.
6 C-47 and 5 Arava transports.
1 *Alouette* III, 3 *Lama* helicopters.
3 T-34, 10 T-6, 6 T-41 and 3 Magister
trainers.

Avions Marcel Dassault *Ouragan*

Type: fighter
Crew: one
Wings: metal cantilever low-wing monoplane
Fuselage: metal semi-monocoque
Tail unit: metal cantilever
Landing gear: hydraulically actuated retrac-
table tricycle unit
Powerplant: one Hispano-Suiza Nene 104B
turbojet, rated at 5,070-lb (2,300-kg)
static thrust
Fuel capacity:
Avionics: communication and navigation
equipment
Armament: four 20-mm Hispano 404
cannon, plus two 1,100-lb (500 kg) bombs
or 16 rockets under the wings

Dimensions: Span 43 ft 2 in (13.2 m)
Length 35 ft 3 in (10.75 m)
Height 13 ft 7 in (4.15 m)
Wing area: 256.18 ft² (23.8 m²)
Weights: Empty 9,150 lb (4,150 kg)
Loaded 13,646 lb (6,190 kg)
Maximum 17,416 lb (7,900 kg)
Performance: speed 584 mph (940 kph) at
sea level; climb 7,874 ft (2,400 m) per
minute at sea level; service ceiling 49,210
ft (15,000 m); range 620 miles (1,000 km)
Used only by: El Salvador
Notes: The *Ouragan* first flew in 1949, and
entered service with the French air force in
1951. The last aircraft of the type was de-
livered in 1955.

Ethiopia

2,000 men and 99 combat aircraft.

1 lt bomber sqn with 2 Canberra B.2.
6 FGA sqns: 2 with 14 F-5A/E, 1 with 7 F-86F, 2 with 50 MiG-21, 1 with 20 MiG-23.
1 COIN sqn with 6 T-28A.
1 transport sqn with 5 C-47, 2 C-54, 7 C-119G, 3 Dove, 1 Il-14, 1 DHC-3, 3 DHC-6, 8 An-12, 4 An-22.
3 trg sqns with 20 *Safir*, T-28A/D, 11 T-33A, 2 F-5B.
Helicopters incl 10 AB-204, 5 *Alouette* III, 30 Mi-8, Mi-6, 10 UH-1H, 1 Puma.

North American Aviation F-86 Sabre

Type: fighter-bomber
Crew: one
Wings: metal cantilever low-wing monoplane
Fuselage: metal semi-monocoque
Tail unit: metal cantilever
Landing gear: hydraulically actuated retractable tricycle unit
Powerplant: one General Electric J47-GE-27 turbojet, rated at 5,970-lb (2,710-kg) static thrust
Fuel capacity:
Avionics: comprehensive communication and navigation/attack equipment
Armament: six 0.5-in (12.7-mm) Colt-Browning M-3 machine-guns with 267 rounds per gun, plus hardpoints under the wings for two 1,000-lb (454-kg) bombs or two drop tanks, and eight unguided rockets or two Sidewinder air-to-air missiles
Dimensions: Span 39 ft 1 in (11.9 m)
Length 37 ft 6 in (11.43 m)
Height 14 ft 8¾ in (4.47 m)
Wing area: 288 ft² (26.76 m²)
Weights: Empty 11,125 lb (5,045 kg)
Loaded 17,000 lb (7,711 kg)
Maximum 20,611 lb (9,350 kg)
Performance: speed 678 mph (1,091 kph) or Mach 0.89 at sea level; climb 10,000 ft (3,050 m) per minute at sea level; service ceiling 50,000 ft (15,240 m); range 1,270 miles (2,044 km) with drop tanks
Used also by: Argentina, Japan, Pakistan, Peru, Philippines, South Africa, South Korea, Tunisia, Venezuela

Notes: The F-86 Sabre became famous in the Korean War as the main opponent of the Mikoyan-Gurevich MiG-15 fighter flown by the Communists, and was in many respects both an obsolete and an advanced fighter: in its primary armament, many models were obsolete, for the day of heavy machine-guns and no radar were on their way out; but its design, with clean, highly swept lines, was a portent for the future. There were several variants:

1. F-86A, with the 4,850-lb (2,200-kg) J47-GE-1, six machine-guns and 16 5-in (127-mm) rockets
2. F-86E, with the 5,200-lb (2,358-kg) J47-GE-13, slatted wings and an 'all-flying' tail (the Canadair F-86J was basically similar, though most had Avro Canada Orenda turbojets)
3. F-86F, with an improved wing and boundary layer fences (the technical specification above applies to this model)
4. F-86H, with the 9,300-lb (4,218-kg) J73-GE-3, wings of greater span, a longer fuselage, and four 20-mm M-39 cannon
5. F-86D all-weather interceptor, with the 7,650-lb (3,470-kg) J47-GE-33, and the nose recontoured to take AI radar
6. F-86L, a conversion of the F-86D with features of the F-86F, and a data link
7. F-86K all-weather fighter, with four 20-mm cannon, intended for use by NATO air forces.

There was also the naval FJ-4 Fury.

Northrop Corporation F-5 Freedom Fighter

Type: fighter and reconnaissance trainer
Crew: one or two, seated in tandem
Wings: metal cantilever low-wing monoplane
Fuselage: metal semi-monocoque
Tail unit: metal cantilever
Landing gear: hydraulically actuated retractable tricycle unit
Powerplant: two General Electric J85-GE-13 turbojets, each rated at 4,080-lb (1,850-kg) static thrust with afterburning
Fuel capacity: 485 gallons (2,207 litres) internally, plus 458 gallons (2,082 gallons) externally

Avionics: comprehensive communication and navigation/attack equipment
Armament: two 20-mm M-39A2 cannon with 280 rounds per gun, plus about 4,400 lb (1,996 kg) of stores on four underwing and one underfuselage pylon, and two AIM-9 Sidewinder air-to-air missiles on the wingtips
Dimensions: Span 25 ft 3 in (7.7 m)
Length 47 ft 2 in (14.38 m)
Height 13 ft 2 in (4.01 m)
Wing area: 170 ft² (15.79 m²)
Weights: Empty 8,085 lb (3,667 kg)
Loaded
Maximum 20,677 lb (9,379 kg)

Performance: speed 925 mph (1,489 kph) or Mach 1.4 at high altitude; climb 28,700 ft (8,760 m) per minute at sea level; service ceiling 50,500 ft (15,390 m); range 1,387 miles (2,232 km)

Used also by: Brazil, Canada, Egypt, Greece, Iran, Jordan, Kenya, Malaysia, Netherlands, Norway, Philippines, Saudi Arabia, South Korea, Spain, Sudan, Switzerland, Taiwan, Thailand, Turkey, USA, Venezuela

Notes: The F-5 was produced as a private venture, and has enjoyed remarkable sales to countries who wish to possess a supersonic fighter of relatively limited performance and low cost. The technical specification above applies to the F-5A. The models suffixed with the letters A, E and G are single-seat fighters, while those suffixed with the letters B, D and F are two-seat fighter/trainer aircraft. Reconnaissance models are prefixed RF.

Finland

3,000 men and 47 combat aircraft.

2 fighter sqns with 17 MiG-21F, 12 J 35S, 6 J 35F, 5 J 35B *Draken*.
1 OCU with 1 MiG-15UT1, 3 MiG-21U, 3 J 35C.
Transports incl 8 C-47, 2 Cessna 402.
Trainers incl 60 Magister, 25 Saab *Safir*.
Liaison ac: 5 Cherokee Arrow.
1 helicopter flt with 3 Mi-4, 6 Mi-8, 1 Hughes 500, 1 AB-206A.
AA-2 'Atoll', Falcon AAM.
(50 Hawk, 30 *Vinka* trg ac on order.)

Mikoyan-Gurevich MiG-21 'Fishbed'

Type: fighter
Crew: one
Wings: metal cantilever delta mid-wing monoplane

Fuselage: metal semi-monocoque
Tail unit: metal cantilever
Landing gear: hydraulically actuated retractable tricycle unit

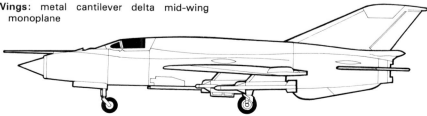

Powerplant: one Tumansky R-13-300 turbojet, rated at 14,450 lb (6,555 kg) with afterburning, plus two optional JATO units

Fuel capacity: 572 gallons (2,600 litres) in fuselage tanks, plus provision for three 108-gallon (490-litre) external auxiliary tanks

Avionics: comprehensive communication and navigation/attack equipment, including R1L 'Spin Scan' search and tracking radar, and a warning radar system

Armament: one twin-barrel GSh-23 23-mm cannon with 200 rounds in a belly pack, plus a wide variety of external stores on four underwing pylons. The external load can consist of two K-13A 'Atoll' IR-homing air-to-air missiles, and two AA-2 'Advanced Atoll' radar-homing air-to-air missiles or two UV-16-57 rocket pods, each with sixteen 57-mm rockets; or four 'Atoll' or 'Advanced Atoll' missiles; or two 'Atoll' or 'Advanced Atoll' missiles and two drop tanks; in the ground-attack role the type can carry four UV-16-57 rocket pods; or two 551-lb (250-kg) and two 1,102-lb (500-kg) bombs; or four S-24 240-mm air-to-surface missiles

Dimensions: Span 23 ft 5½ in (7.15 m)
Length 51 ft 8½ in (15.76 m)
Height 14 ft 9 in (4.6 m)

Wing area: 247 ft² (23.0 m²)

Weights: Empty 12,346 lb (5,600 lb)
Loaded (four K-13A) 18,078 lb (8,200 kg)
Maximum 21,605 lb (9,800 kg)

Performance: speed 1,385 mph (2,230 kph) or Mach 2.1 over 36,100 ft (11,000 m); speed 807 mph (1,300 kph) or Mach 1.06 at low altitude; climb 36,100 ft (11,000 m) per minute at sea level; service ceiling 59,050 ft (18,000 m); range at high altitude on internal fuel 683 miles (1,100 km); ferry range with auxiliary fuel 1,118 miles (1,800 km)

Used also by: Afghanistan, Algeria, Angola, Bangladesh, Bulgaria, China, Cuba, Czechoslovakia, East Germany, Egypt, Ethiopia, Hungary, India, Indonesia, Iraq, Laos, Mozambique, Nigeria, North Korea, Peru, Poland, Romania, Somali Republic, South Yemen, Sudan, Syria, Uganda, Vietnam, Yugoslavia

Notes: The MiG-21 is the most numerous and widely used combat aircraft of the time. The first prototype flew in 1955, and the type entered service in 1958. Quite limited in its performance and capabilities, the MiG-21 is nevertheless a useful combat aircraft as a result of its manoeuvrability, small size and relatively good dogfighting ability. There are numerous versions of the MiG-21:

1. MiG-21 'Fishbed-A' limited-production first model, with a 11,243-lb (5,100-kg) R-11 engine and two NR-30 30-mm cannon
2. MiG-21 'Fishbed-B' one-off 'pre-prototype
3. MiG-21F 'Fishbed-C' clear-weather interceptor with a 12,676-lb (5,750-kg) R-11, two K-13As and one NR-30 cannon
4. MiG-21PF 'Fishbed-D' all-weather model with R1L 'Spin Scan A' radar and slightly larger forward fuselage, with pitot boom above the nose
5. MiG-21 'Fishbed-E', similar to the 'Fishbed-D' but with vertical tail surfaces of greater chord, and a GP-9 underbelly pack for a GSh-23 23-mm twin-barrel cannon
6. MiG-21FL export version of the MiG-21PF, with 13,668-lb (6,200-kg) engine, broad-chord fin and rudder, and R2L 'Spin Scan B' radar
7. MiG-21PFS, similar to the 'Fishbed-D' but with a flap-blowing system to reduce the landing run
8. MiG-21PFM 'Fishbed-F' interim-production model of the MiG-21PFS with broader fin and rudder, and a sideways hingeing cockpit canopy
9. MiG-21 'Fishbed-G' experimental STOL model of the 'Fishbed-F' with two vertical lift engines in a lengthened fuselage
10. MiG-21PFMA 'Fishbed-J' multi-role fighter, similar to the MiG-21PFM but with fuel in a large dorsal fairing and four underwing pylons.

11. MiG-21M, similar to the MiG-21PFMA but with an internal GP-9 gun pack
12. MiG-21R 'Fishbed-H' tactical reconnaissance model based on the MiG-21PFMA with camera pod, ECM equipment and IR sensors
13. MiG-21MF 'Fishbed-J', similar to the MiG-21PFMA but with R-13-300 engines to improve performance. The technical specification relates to this model
14. MiG-21RF 'Fishbed-H' tactical reconnaissance model of the MiG-21MF with the equipment of the MiG-21R
15. MiG-21SMT 'Fishbed-K', similar to the MiG-21MF, but with the dorsal spine extended rearwards to increase fuel capacity and optional wingtip pods for ECM equipment
16. MiG-21*bis* 'Fishbed-L' multi-role fighter and ground-attack aircraft with improved electronics
17. MiG-21*bis* 'Fishbed-N' improved version of the 'Fishbed-L' with a 16,535-lb (7,500-kg) R-25 engine and updated electronics
18. MiG-21U 'Mongol' two-seat trainer based on the MiG-21F, but without cannon armament
19. MiG-21US 'Mongol-B' version of the 'Mongol-A' but with flap-blowing
20. MiG-21UM 'Mongol-B' two-seat trainer version of the MiG-21MF.

There are also versions for record-breaking.

Valmet Oy Kuoreveden Tehdas Leko-70/*Vinka*

Type: trainer
Crew: two
Wings: metal cantilever low-wing monoplane
Fuselage: aluminium alloy semi-monocoque
Tail unit: aluminium alloy cantilever
Landing gear: fixed tricycle unit
Powerplant: one Lycoming AEIO-360-A1B6 air-cooled flat-four piston engine, rated at 200 hp, driving a Hartzell two-blade metal propeller

Fuel capacity: 38.7 gallons (176 litres) in two wing-root fuel tanks
Avionics: navigation, communication and blind-flying equipment
Armament: none
Dimensions: Span 32 ft 3¾ in (9.85 m)
Length 24 ft 7¼ in (7.5 m)
Height 10 ft 10¼ in (3.31 m)
Wing area: 150.7 ft² (14.0 m²)
Weights: Empty 1,631 lb (740 kg)
Loaded
Maximum 2,645 lb (1,200 kg)

Performance: (at 2,204-lb/1,000-kg take-off weight) speed 149 mph (240 kph) at sea level; cruising speed 138 mph (222 kph) at 5,000 ft (1,555 m); climb 1,120 ft (342 m) per minute at sea level; service ceiling 16,400 ft (5,000 m); range 630 miles (1,015 km)
Used only by: Finland
Notes: Designed as *Lentokone* (aircraft, Leko for short) 70 as a Saab 91 Safir replacement for the Finnish air force. The type is also produced as a two/four seater touring aircraft.

France

The French Air Force

Although in terms of numbers the French Air Force is only the fourth strongest NATO air force, it seems clear that in terms of quality and efficiency it is second only to the United States. The reasons are twofold: firstly, a determination (of largely nationalist origins) to go it alone regardless of cost in the development of strong defence forces; and secondly, the remarkable aircraft originating from the Dassault company. The French Air Force has 100,800 personnel, about 20 per cent of the total regular strength of the armed forces, which have a budget of 4.67 per cent of the gross national product.

France is a nuclear power, and bases her strategic nuclear forces on the triad principal of submarine-launched ballistic missiles, silo-launched ballistic missiles, and air-dropped freefall atomic bombs. The air force's component of this nuclear deterrent force are two squadrons of SSBS intermediate-range ballistic missiles, each squadron having nine missiles, and six squadrons of Dassault Mirage IV bombers, 33 aircraft in all, supported by 16 similar aircraft as reserves and reconnaissance aircraft, and three squadrons of air-to-air refuelling tankers with 11 KC-135F aircraft. Both nuclear systems are limited in range, but nevertheless remain real deterrents in the European context.

The French Air Force proper remains firmly tied to tactical operations, with its forces divided into four main components: the Air Defence Command, The Tactical Air Force, Air Transport Command, and Training Command.

Air Defence Command (CAFDA) is designed for the air defence of metropolitan France, and its structure and weapons are tied into the STRIDA II (*Système de Traitement et de Représentation des Informations de Défence Aérienne*) air defence data processing and presentation system. The main burden of air defence falls on the eight interceptor squadrons, two of them with 30 Mirage IIIC and the other six with 90 Mirage F1C fighters, and the 10 SAM battalions equipped with

Crotale missiles. In support of the CAFDA operational units are four communication and liaison flights with 15 Magisters, 13 T-33As and eight *Broussards*. Manpower strength is 6,300.

The Tactical Air Force (FATAC) is designed for the tactical support of the French Army, and has two light bomber squadrons, equipped with *Vautour* IIB/Ns, though these are shortly to be phased out; 17 fighter-bomber squadrons, seven of them with 105 Mirage IIIE, two of them with 30 Mirage VF, and the other eight of them with 105 Jaguar A/E; three reconnaissance squadrons with 45 Mirage IIIR/RD; and two operational conversion units with 25 Mirage IIIB/BE/C and 25 Jaguar E. These operational and semi-operational units are supported by eight liaison and communications flights operating 25 Magister, 30 T-33A, 10 *Broussard*, five Paris, three *Frégate*, seven Noratlas and two *Mystère* 20 aircraft, and 13 *Alouette* II/III helicopters. Manpower strength is 7,400.

The French Air Force has the great advantage of knowing precisely what its role and objectives are, and in having access to sufficient funds to buy most of the aircraft it can reasonably need. The morale of the force is fairly high, and training is of the best quality.

100,800 men (38,800 conscripts) and 471 combat aircraft.

Strategic forces
IRBM: 2 sqns, each with 9 SSBS S-2 msls (to be replaced by S-3).
Bombers: 6 sqns with 33 Mirage IVA.
Tankers: 3 sqns with 11 KC-135F.
Reserve: 16 Mirage IVA (incl 12 recce).
Air Force
Air Defence Command (CAFDA): 6,300.
8 interceptor sqns: 2 with 30 Mirage IIIC, 6 with 90 Mirage F1C.
4 liaison and comms flts with 15 Magister, 13 T-33A, 8 *Broussard*.
10 SAM bns with *Crotale*.
Automatic STRIDA II air-defence system.
Tactical Air Force (FATAC): 7,400.
17 FB sqns: 7 with 105 Mirage IIIE, 2 with 30 Mirage VF, 8 with 105 Jaguar A/E.
2 lt bomber sqns with 16 *Vautour*

IIB/N (being withdrawn).
3 recce sqns with 45 Mirage IIR/RD.
2 OCU: 1 with 25 Mirage IIIB/BE/C, 1 with 25 Jaguar E.
8 liaison and comms flts with 25 Magister, 30 T-33A, 10 *Broussard*, 5 Paris, 3 *Frégate*, 7 Noratlas, 2 *Mystère* 20 ac, 13 *Alouette* II/III helicopters.
Air Transport Command (COTAM): 4,600.
7 tac transport sqns: 3 with 45 Transall C-160, 4 with 60 *Noratlas*.
4 transport sqns with 4 DC-8F, 21 *Frégate*, 8 *Mystère* 20, 5 *Caravelle*, 30 Paris, 31 *Broussard* ac, 70 *Alouette* II/III, 18 Puma hel.
Sidewinder, R.530, R.550 Magic AAM; AS.20, AS.30, Martel ASM.
Training Command (CEAA): Some 400 aircraft, incl Magister, T-33, *Mystère* IV, Falcon, *Flamant*, Noratlas, *Broussard*, Paris.
(33 Mirage F1 fighters, 200 AlphaJet trg ac, 4 Transall transports on order.)
Naval Air Force
13,000; 123 combat aircraft.
2 attack sqns with 24 *Etendard* IVM.
2 interceptor sqns with 20 F-8E (FN) Crusader.
2 ASW sqns with 24 *Alizé*.
4 MR sqns with 25 Atlantic, 10 SP-2H Neptune.
1 recce sqn with 8 *Etendard* IVP.
2 OCU with 12 *Etendard* IVM, 14 Magister, 4 Nord 262.
3 ASW helicopter sqns with 12 Super *Frelon*, 12 SH-34J, 8 *Alouette* III.
1 assault helicopter sqn with 12 *Alouette* II/III.
2 SAR sqns with 20 Alouette II/III.
1 helicopter sqn with 4 *Alouette* II, 7 Super *Frelon*, 18 Lynx.
9 comms sqns with DC-6, C-47 ac, *Alouette* II/III, 5 Super *Frelon* helicopters.
4 trg and liaison sqns with Nord 262 C-47, Falcon, Paris, *Alizé*, Rallye ac, *Alouette* II/III helicopters.
(29 Super *Etendard* fighters, 8 Lynx helicopters on order.)
Army Aviation (ALAT)
2 groups, 6 helicopter regts and 5 regional commands.
30 *Broussard*, 91 L-19 lt ac.
190 *Alouette* II, 70 *Alouette* III, 135 SA-330 Puma, 170 SA-341 Gazelle helicopters (20 Gazelle on order).

Avions Marcel Dassault
Etendard IVM

Type: carrierborne strike fighter
Crew: one
Wings: metal cantilever low mid-wing monoplane
Fuselage: metal semi-monocoque
Tail unit: metal cantilever
Landing gear: hydraulically actuated retractable tricycle unit
Powerplant: one SNECMA Atar 8B turbojet, rated at 9,700-lb (4,400-kg) static thrust
Fuel capacity:
Avionics: comprehensive communication and navigation/attack equipment, including Aïda weapon-control radar
Armament: two 30-mm DEFA cannon with 150 rounds per gun, plus four underwing pylons capable of carrying a total weight up to 3,000 lb (1,360 kg) of bombs, rocket pods and other external stores
Dimensions: Span 31 ft 5¾ in (9.6 m)
Length 47 ft 3 in (14.4 m)
Height 14 ft (4.26 m)
Wing area: 285.244 ft² (26.5 m²)
Weights: Empty 12,786 lb (5,800 kg)
Loaded
Maximum 22,486 lb (10,200 kg)
Performance: speed 683 mph (1,099 kph) at sea level; speed 673 mph (1,083 kph) or Mach 1.02 at high altitude; climb 19,685 ft (6,000 m) per minute at sea level; service ceiling 49,215 ft (15,000 m); range 1,056 miles (1,700 km) on internal fuel
Used only by: France

Notes: The *Etendard* IV, which first flew in 1956, owes its conception to the Dassault *Etendard* II (built round two 2,420-lb/1,100-kg Turboméca Gazibo engines) light interceptor project, and the *Etendard* VI project for a NATO rough-field strike fighter (built round the 4,850-lb/2,200-kg Bristol Orpheus). Dassault was certain that two fighters with so little power could be of little use, and pressed ahead with the development of the *Etendard* IV, which finally entered service with the French *Aéronavale* in two forms:
1. *Etendard* IVM strike fighter, to which the technical specification above applies
2. *Etendard* IVP reconnaissance version.

Avions Marcel Dassault Mirage IV

Type: strategic bomber
Crew: two
Wings: metal cantilever low mid-wing delta monoplane
Fuselage: metal semi-monocoque
Tail unit: metal cantilever
Landing gear: hydraulically actuated retractable tricycle unit
Powerplant: two SNECMA Atar 9K turbojets, each rated at 15,432-lb (7,000-kg) static thrust with afterburning
Fuel capacity: integral wing and fuselage tanks
Avionics: comprehensive communication and navigation/attack equipment, including CSF radar, Marconi doppler radar and Dassault computer
Armament: one 16-kiloton free-fall nuclear bomb semi-recessed under the fuselage, or 15,983 lb (7,250 kg) of bombs on hardpoints under the wings and fuselage
Dimensions: Span 38 ft 10½ in (11.85 m)
Length 77 ft 1 in (23.5 m)
Height 17 ft 8½ in (5.4 m)
Wing area: 840 ft² (78 m²)
Weights: Empty 31,967 lb (14,500 kg)
Loaded 69,665 lb (31,600 kg)
Maximum 73,800 lb (33,475 kg)
Performance: speed 1,454 mph (2,340 kph) or Mach 2.2 at 39,780 ft (12,125 m) in 'dashes'; speed 1,222 mph (1,966 kph) or Mach 1.7 at 59,875 ft (18,250 m) for sustained flying; climb 4 minutes 15 seconds to 36,090 ft (11,000 m); service ceiling 65,615 ft (20,000 m); combat radius 770 miles (1,240 km); ferry range 2,485 miles (4,000 km)
Used only by: France

Notes: Until the advent of the French surface-to-surface and submarine-to-surface ballistic missiles, France's nuclear deterrent was dependent on the Mirage IVA as a delivery system. Even today, the *Force de Frappe* relies heavily on the Mirage IVA force. The main trouble with the type, whose Mirage IV-001 prototype first flew in 1959, is acute shortage of range, only partially compensated for by the addition of KC-135F tankers to the strategic bomber force. The first production Mirage IVA flew in 1963, entering service in 1964. The family likeness to the Mirage III fighter is easily discerned, but the Mirage IVA was in fact developed from a 1956 Dassault project for a twin-engined night-fighter.

Avions Marcel Dassault Mirage F1

Type: multi-mission and attack fighter
Crew: one
Wings: metal cantilever shoulder-wing monoplane
Fuselage: metal semi-monocoque
Tail unit: metal cantilever
Landing gear: hydraulically actuated retractable tricycle unit
Powerplant: one SNECMA Atar 9K-50 turbojet, rated at 15,873-lb (7,200-kg) static thrust with afterburner
Fuel capacity: integral tanks in wings and fuselage, plus three optional drop tanks, each holding 264 gallons (1,200 litres)
Avionics: comprehensive communications and navigation equipment, plus Thomson-CSF Cyrano IV fire-control radar and CSF head-up displays for flying and fire-control
Armament: two 30-mm DEFA 553 cannon with 125 rounds per gun, plus five stores attachment points capable of lifting 8,820 lb (4,000 kg) of disposable weapons (one under the fuselage and two under each wing), plus provision for one air-to-air missile on each wingtip. The attachment points can take Matra R.530 or Super 530 air-to-air missiles for interception missions, or

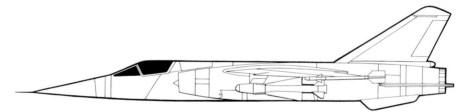

AS.37 Martel or AS.30 air-to-surface missiles for ground-attack missions; the wing-tip stations can carry Sidewinder or Matra 550 Magic air-to-air missiles; other stores include 992-lb (450-kg) bombs, napalm tanks and air-to-ground rocket pods
Dimensions: Span 27 ft 6¾ in (8.4 m)
Length 49 ft 2½ in (15.0 m)
Height 14 ft 9 in (4.5 m)
Wing area: 269.1 ft² (25.0 m²)
Weights: Empty 16,314 lb (7,400 kg)
Loaded 24,030 lb (10,900 kg)
Maximum 33,510 lb (15,200 kg)
Performance: speed Mach 2.2 at high altitude; climb 47,835 ft (14,580 m) per minute at high altitude with afterburning; service ceiling 65,600 ft (20,000 m); endurance 3 hours 45 minutes
Used also by: Ecuador, Egypt (?), Greece, Iraq, Kuwait, Libya, Morocco, Qatar, South Africa,

Spain, Sudan
Notes: Designed as a private venture to a French Air Force specification issued in 1964, the Dassault Mirage F1 is now in service as an all-weather interceptor with the French Air Force in the F1-C version. Other versions include the F1-A ground-attack/air combat version, with less sophisticated electronics and greater fuel capacity; the F1-B two-seat trainer; and the F1-E multi-mission fighter development aircraft with the SNECMA M53 afterburning turbofan in place of the turbojet.

Avions Marcel Dassault *Mystère* IV

Type: fighter-bomber
Crew: one
Wings: metal cantilever low mid-wing monoplane
Fuselage: metal semi-monocoque
Tail unit: metal cantilever
Landing gear: hydraulically actuated retractable tricycle unit
Powerplant: one Hispano-Suiza Verdon 350 turbojet, rated at 7,716-lb (3,500-kg) static thrust
Fuel capacity:
Avionics: comprehensive communication and navigation/attack equipment
Armament: two 30-mm DEFA 551 cannon with 150 rounds per gun, plus four underwing hardpoints capable of carrying 2,000 lb (907 kg) of bombs or rocket pods, or drop tanks

Dimensions: Span 36 ft 5¾ in (11.1 m)
Length 42 ft 2 in (12.9 m)
Height 14 ft 5 in (4.4 m)
Wing area: 344.5 ft² (32.0 m²)
Weights: Empty 12,950 lb (5,875 kg)
Loaded
Maximum 20,950 lb (9,500 kg)

Performance: speed 696 mph (1,120 kph) or Mach 0.913 at sea level; speed 615 mph (990 kph) or Mach 0.94 at high altitude; climb 8,860 ft (2,700 m) per minute at sea level; service ceiling 45,000 ft (13,750 m); range 820 miles (1,320 km) on internal fuel
Used also by: India

Notes: The *Mystère* IV, whose prototype first flew in 1952, was derived conceptually from the *Mystère* II, although in structure it was a completely different aircraft. The *Mystère* IV entered service in 1955, and the last of the type was delivered in 1958.

Avions Marcel Dassault Super *Etendard*

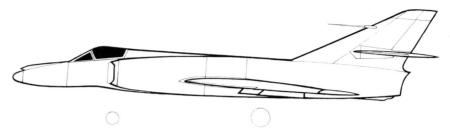

Type: strike fighter
Crew: one
Wings: metal cantilever low-wing monoplane
Fuselage: metal semi-monocoque
Tail unit: metal cantilever
Landing gear: hydraulically actuated retractable tricycle unit
Powerplant: one SNECMA Atar 8K-50 turbojet, rated at 11,265-lb (5,110-kg) static thrust
Fuel capacity: 870 gallons (3,955 litres)
Avionics: comprehensive communications and navigation equipment, plus Thomson-CSF/EMD Agave radar, and an integrated navigation/attack electronic system
Armament: two 30-mm DEFA cannon and a large variety of external stores carried on five attachment points
Dimensions: Span 31 ft 6 in (9.6 m)
Length 46 ft 11½ in (14.31 m)
Height 12 ft 8 in (3.85 m)
Wing area: 305.7 ft² (28.4 m²)
Weights: Empty 13,890 lb (6,300 kg)
Loaded 20,280 lb (9,200 kg)
Maximum 25,350 lb (11,500 kg)
Performance: speed above Mach 1 at 36,000 ft (11,000 m); speed 733 mph (1,180 kph) at low altitude; combat radius (anti-ship strike) 403 miles (650 km)
Used only by: France
Notes: Developed from the transonic *Etendard* IV-M, the Super *Etendard* is a supersonic carrierborne strike fighter, with highly sophisticated electronics, excellent high-lift devices, and a non-afterburning turbojet.

Ling-Temco-Vought Aerospace F-8 Crusader

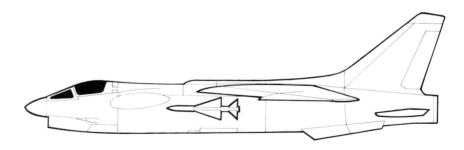

Type: fighter
Crew: one
Wings: metal cantilever shoulder-wing monoplane
Fuselage: metal semi-monocoque
Tail unit: metal cantilever
Landing gear: hydraulically actuated retractable tricycle unit
Powerplant: one Pratt & Whitney J57-P-20A turbojet, rated at 18,000-lb (8,165-kg) static thrust with afterburning
Fuel capacity: 1,165 gallons (5,296 litres)
Avionics: comprehensive communication and navigation/attack equipment, including APQ-94 search and fire-control radar
Armament: four 20-mm Colt Mark 12 cannon with 84 rounds per gun, plus four AIM-9 Sidewinder air-to-air missiles, and up to 12 Mark 81 bombs or two Bullpup ASMs or eight Zuni rockets on hardpoints under the wings
Dimensions: Span 35 ft 2 in (10.72 m)
Length 54 ft 6 in (16.6 m)
Height 15 ft 9 in (4.8 m)
Wing area: 350 ft² (32.52 m²)
Weights: Empty
Loaded 28,000 lb (12,700 kg)
Maximum 34,000 lb (15,420 kg)

Performance: speed 1,135 mph (1,827 kph) or Mach 1.72 at 36,000 ft (10,973 m); cruising speed 560 mph (901 kph) at 40,000 ft (12,192 m); climb about 21,000 ft (6,400 m) per minute at sea level; climb 6 minutes 30 seconds to 57,000 ft (17,374 m); service ceiling 58,000 ft (17,679 m); range 1,100 miles (1,770 km)
Used also by: Philippines, USA
Notes: The F-8 prototype first flew in 1955, and the type entered service with the US Navy in 1957. The last aircraft was delivered in 1965. Improvements during the years have led to the introduction of improved fighter and fighter-bomber models, able to operate in all weathers, and the RF-8 reconnaissance aircraft, the DF-8 drone-control aircraft and the QF-8 drone aircraft. The specification above applies to the F-8E.

Lockheed Aircraft P-2 Neptune

Type: maritime patrol and anti-submarine aircraft
Crew: nine or ten
Wings: metal cantilever high mid-wing monoplane
Fuselage: metal semi-monocoque
Tail unit: metal cantilever
Landing gear: hydraulically actuated retractable tricycle unit
Powerplant: two Wright R-3350-32W Turbo-Compound radial engines, each rated at 3,700 hp, and two Westinghouse J34-WE-36 turbojets, each rated at 3,400-lb (1,540-kg) static thrust
Fuel capacity: 4,700 gallons (21,366 litres)
Avionics: comprehensive communication and navigation/attack equipment
Armament: up to 8,000 lb (3,629 kg) of bombs, depth charges and torpedoes
Dimensions: Span 103 ft 10 in (31.65 m)
Length 91 ft 8 in (27.94 m)
Height 29 ft 4 in (8.94 m)
Wing area: 1,000 ft² (92.9 m²)
Weights: Empty 49,935 lb (22,650 kg)
Loaded
Maximum 79,895 lb (36,240 kg)
Performance: 403 mph (648 kph) with jet engines; cruising speed 207 mph (333 kph) at 8,500 ft (2,590 m); climb about 1,800 ft (549 m) per minute at sea level with jet engines; service ceiling 22,000 ft (6,706 m); range about 2,500 miles (4,024 km)
Used also by: Japan, Netherlands
Notes: The P-2 series started life as the P2V series, the prototype of which first flew in 1945, and the first production example of which, the P2V-1, entered US service in 1947. Since that time the series has proved a magnificent one, with excellent range and weapons capacity (early models had in addition to their offensive load in the bomb bay eight 20-mm cannon and two 0.5-in/12.7-mm machine-guns). It has proved possible to add to the electronics carried with little difficulty. The last variant, the P2V-7, or P-2H, first flew in 1954, and is the type to which the technical specification above applies. The P-2H is the only model with podded auxiliary jets.

Société Nationale de Constructions Aéronautiques du Nord (SNCAN) 2501 Noratlas

Type: transport aircraft
Crew: five, plus up to 45 passengers
Wings: metal cantilever high-wing monoplane
Fuselage: metal semi-monocoque, with metal monocoque tailbooms
Tail unit: metal cantilever
Landing gear: hydraulically actuated retractable tricycle unit
Powerplant: two Bristol Hercules 738 radial engines, each rated at 2,040 hp and driving a four-blade metal propeller
Fuel capacity:
Avionics: comprehensive communication and navigation equipment
Armament: none
Dimensions: Span 106 ft 7½ in (32.5 m)
Length 72 ft 0¾ in (22.0 m)
Height 19 ft 8¼ in (6.0 m)
Wing area: 1,088.9 ft² (101.16 m²)
Weights: Empty 29,424 lb (13,345 kg)
Loaded
Maximum 47,850 lb (21,705 kg)
Performance: speed 273 mph (440 kph); cruising speed 201 mph (323 kph) at 4,920 ft (1,500 m); climb 1,230 ft (375 m) per minute at sea level; service ceiling 24,600 ft (7,500 m); range 1,553 miles (2,500 km)
Used also by: Angola, Greece, Mozambique, Niger, West Germany
Notes: The Noratlas prototype flew in 1949, under the designation Nord 2500 and powered by a pair of 1,600-hp SNECMA-built Gnôme-Rhône 14R radials. The more powerful Bristol engines, built in France under licence by SNECMA, were selected for the production Noratlas. Maximum payload is 12,125 lb (5,500 kg).

Société Nationale de Constructions Aéronautiques du Sud-Ouest (SNCASO) *Vautour*

Type: attack bomber, bomber and night-fighter aircraft
Crew: one or two, seated in tandem
Wings: metal cantilever high mid-wing monoplane
Fuselage: metal semi-monocoque
Tail unit: metal cantilever
Landing gear: hydraulically actuated retractable bicycle unit, with stabilising outrigger wheels
Powerplant: two SNECMA Atar 101E-3 turbojets, each rated at 7,716-lb (3,500-kg) static thrust
Fuel capacity:
Avionics: comprehensive communication and navigation/attack equipment
Armament: as an attack bomber, four 30-mm DEFA 553 cannon plus 5,300 lb (2,400 kg) of bombs; as a bomber, up to 5,300 lb (2.400 kg) of bombs carried internally and externally; and as a night-fighter, four 30-mm DEFA 553 cannon with 100 rounds per gun, plus two to four Matra R.530, AIM-9 Sidewinder or Matra R.550 Magic air-to-air missiles, and 232 SNEB unguided rockets
Dimensions: Span 49 ft 6½ in (15.1 m)
Length 51 ft 1½ in (15.58 m)
Height 16 ft 2½ in (4.95 m)
Wing area: 484.376 ft² (45.0 m²)
Weights: Empty 22,000 lb (9,979 kg)
Loaded
Maximum 45,635 lb (20,700 kg)
Performance: speed 684 mph (1,100 kph) or Mach 0.9 at sea level; climb 11,800 ft (3,600 m) per minute at sea level; service ceiling 49,200 ft (15,000 m); range about 1,990 miles (3,200 km) on internal fuel
Used only by: France
Notes: For its time, the *Vautour* was an extremely advanced aircraft, the more so as the French had no experience in building such an aircraft in an air industry only just emerging from the ruins of World War II. The prototype made its first flight in 1952, and the first production aircraft appeared in 1956. There are three variants:
1. *Vautour* IIA single-seat attack aircraft, to which the specification above applies
2. *Vautour* IIB two-seat bomber
3. *Vautour* II.1N two-seat night-fighter and all-weather fighter.

Société Nationale Industrielle Aérospatiale SA 316B *Alouette III*

Type: general-purpose helicopter
Crew: one, plus up to six passengers
Rotor: metal cantilever three-blade main rotor; metal cantilever three-blade tail rotor
Fuselage: steel-tube centre fuselage and metal semi-monocoque tailboom
Landing gear: fixed tricycle unit
Powerplant: one Turboméca Artouste IIIB turboshaft, rated at 870 shp but derated to 570 shp
Fuel capacity: 126.5 gallons (575 litres) in one fuselage tank
Avionics: communication and navigation equipment
Armament: one 7.62-mm AA52 machine-gun with 1,000 rounds, or one 20-mm MG151/20 cannon with 480 rounds, or four AS.11 air-to-surface missiles, or two AS.12 air-to-surface missiles, or 68-mm rocket pods

Dimensions: Span 36 ft 1¾ in (11.02 m)
Length (fuselage) 32 ft 10¾ in (10.03 m)
Height 9 ft 10 in (3.0 m)
Rotor disc area: 1,026 ft² (95.38 m²)
Weights: Empty 2,513 lb (1,140 kg)
Loaded
Maximum 4,850 lb (2,200 kg)
Performance: (at maximum take-off weight) speed 130 mph (210 kph) at sea level; cruising speed 115 mph (185 kph) at sea level; climb 850 ft (260 m) per minute at sea level; service ceiling 10,500 ft (3,200 m); hovering ceiling in ground effect 9,450 ft (2,880 m); range 335 miles (540 km)
Used also by: many nations
Notes: Derived from the *Alouette* II, the *Alouette* III features an enlarged cabin, a more powerful engine, improved performance, and enhanced capabilities. The Artouste-engine version described here succeeded the SE 3160 version, which has a lower payload.

Société Nationale Industrielle Aérospatiale/Westland SA 330 Puma

Type: medium transport helicopter
Crew: two, plus accommodation for up to 20
Rotor: metal, carbon fibre and fibreglass cantilever four-blade main rotor; five-blade tail rotor
Fuselage: metal semi-monocoque
Landing gear: hydraulically actuated semi-retractable tricycle unit
Powerplant: two Turboméca Turmo IVC turboshafts, each rated at 1,575 shp
Fuel capacity: 339½ gallons (1,544 litres) in flexible fuselage tanks, plus an optional 418 gallons (1,900 litres) in fuselage ferry tanks, and 154 gallons (700 litres) in external tanks
Avionics: full flight and navigation radar and computer, plus comprehensive radio
Armament: very varied, and including 20-mm cannon, 7.62-mm machine-guns, and a number of missile and rocket combinations
Dimensions: Span 49 ft 2½ in (15.0 m)
Length (fuselage) 46 ft 1½ in (14.06 m)

Height 16 ft 10½ in (5.14 m)
Rotor disc area: 1,905 ft² (177.0 m²)
Weights: Empty (SA 330L) 7,915 lb (3,590 kg)
Loaded
Maximum 16,315 lb (7,400 kg)
Performance: (at 13,230 lb/6,000 kg AUW) speed 182 mph (294 kph); cruising speed 168 mph (271 kph); climb 1,810 ft (552 m) per minute at sea level; service ceiling 19,680 ft (6,000 m); range 355 miles (572 km) at cruising speed
Used also by: Algeria, Cameroon, Chad, Chile, Ecuador, Egypt, Ethiopia, Gabon, Indonesia, Iraq, Ivory Coast, Kenya, Kuwait, Morocco, Nepal, Nigeria, Pakistan, Portugal, South Africa, Spain, Sudan, Togo, Tunisia, UK, Zaire
Notes: The SA 330 was developed to a French Army requirement, and adopted in 1967 by the RAF. The SA 330L is the current military model.

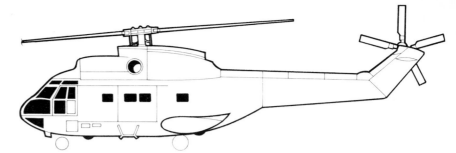

Aérospatiale AM39 *Exocet*

Type: air-to-surface tactical guided missile
Guidance: active radar terminal homing
Dimensions: Span 39⅖ in (1.0 m)
Body diameter 13¾ in (35.0 cm)
Length 15 ft 4¼ in (4.68 m)
Booster: solid-propellant rocket
Sustainer: solid-propellant rocket
Warhead: about 352 lb (160 kg) high explosive
Weights: Launch not more than 1,430 lb (650 kg)
Burnt out
Performance: speed Mach 0.93; range (from helicopter launch) 32¼ miles (52 km), (from an Atlantic aircraft launch) 37¼ miles (60 km), (from a Super *Etendard* aircraft launch) 43 miles (70 km)
Used also by: Iraq
Notes: Derived from the MM38 *Exocet* surface-to-surface anti-shipping missile, the AM39 *Exocet* features a reduced launch weight and a more economical motor, giving greater range. The launch aircraft fires the AM39 using data from a variety of sources. After launch, the missile cruises at about 10 ft (3 m) under gyro and radio altimeter control, before acquiring the target at a range of some 7½ miles (12 km) and then homing automatically, even in an ECM environment.

Aérospatiale AS.11

Type: air-to-surface tactical guided missile
Guidance: command by means of twin wires
Dimensions: Span 19½ in (50.0 cm)
Body diameter 6½ in (16.4 cm)
Length 3 ft 11 in (1.2 m)
Booster: solid-propellant rocket
Sustainer: solid-propellant rocket
Warhead: see Notes below
Weights: Launch 66 lb (29.9 kg)
Burnt out
Performance: speed 360 mph (580 kph); range up to 3,280 yards (3,000 m)
Used by: 27 nations
Notes: Adapted from the SS.11 surface-to-surface battlefield missile, the AS.11 is intended for use by helicopters. There are the following warheads:
1. inert practice head
2. Type 140AC, capable of penetrating 24 in (60.0 cm) of armour plate
3. Type 140AP02, whose 5¾ lb (2.6 kg) of high explosive will penetrate ⅖ in (1.0 cm) of armour at 3,280 yards (3,000 m) and detonate some 7 ft (2.1 m) behind the point of penetration
4. Type 140AP59 anti-personnel fragmentation warhead.

Aérospatiale AS.12

Type: air-to-surface tactical guided missile
Guidance: command to line-of-sight by means of twin wires
Dimensions: Span 25½ in (65.0 cm)
Body diameter 7 in (18.0 cm)
Warhead diameter 8¼ in (21.0 cm)
Length 6 ft 1⅜ in (1.87 m)
Booster: solid-propellant rocket
Sustainer: solid-propellant rocket
Warhead: 62½ lb (28.4 kg) high explosive
Weights: Launch 170 lb (77 kg)
Burnt out
Performance: speed at impact 230 mph (370 kph); range 5 miles (8 km)
Used also by: Netherlands, UK and other nations
Notes: Derived from the SS.12 battlefield missile, the AS.12 arms a number of maritime and military patrol aircraft. Of the same basic design and principle as the AS.11/SS.11, the AS.12/SS.12 carry a far greater punch by virtue of their larger warheads. The OP.3C warhead, for example, penetrates 1½ in (4.0 cm) of armour before exploding on the other side.

Aérospatiale AS.20

Type: air-to-surface tactical guided missile
Guidance: radio command
Dimensions: Span 30⁷⁄₁₀ in (78.0 cm)
Body diameter 9⅘ in (25.0 cm)
Length 8 ft 6 in (2.59 m)
Booster: solid-propellant rocket
Sustainer: solid-propellant rocket
Warhead: 66 lb (30 kg) high explosive
Weights: Launch 315 lb (123 kg)
Burnt out
Performance: speed Mach 1.3; range 2½ miles (4 km)
Used also by: Italy, West Germany and others
Notes: The AS.20 is obsolescent, but is used as a training round for the AS.30. Twin flares at the tail of the missile aid the operator to guide his charge onto the target. The AA.20 is an air-to-air version of the weapon.

Aérospatiale AS.30

Type: air-to-surface tactical guided missile
Guidance: radio command
Dimensions: Span 39⅝ in (1.0 m)
Body diameter 13½ in (34.2 cm)
Length 12 ft 9½ in (3.9 m)
Booster: solid-propellant rocket
Sustainer: solid-propellant rocket
Warhead: 507 lb (230 kg) high explosive
Weights: Launch 1,146 lb (520 kg)
Burnt out
Performance: speed Mach 1.3; range up to 7½ miles (12 km)
Used also by: India, Peru, South Africa, Switzerland, UK, West Germany
Notes: Similar in design to the AS.20, the AS.30 is a much larger weapon, capable of carrying a more powerful warhead over longer ranges. There are two methods of guidance: optically, the operator in the aircraft steering the flares on the missile's tail onto the target, or automatically, with infra-red sensors on the aircraft providing information for computer control. A laser-guided version of the AS.30 is under development with the designation 'Ariel'.

Matra R.511

Type: air-to-air tactical guided missile
Guidance: semi-active radar homing
Dimensions: Span 39⅝ in (1.0 m)
Body diameter 10¼ in (26.0 cm)
Length 10 ft 1⅔ in (3.09 m)
Booster: solid-propellant rocket
Sustainer: solid-propellant rocket
Warhead: high explosive
Weights: Launch 406 lb (184 kg)
Burnt out
Performance: range more than 5 miles (8 km)
Used only by: France
Notes: The R.511 uses radar reflections from the target illuminated by the launch aircraft's radar. The missile is obsolete, and may have been withdrawn from service.

Matra R.530

Type: air-to-air tactical guided missile
Guidance: semi-active radar, or infra-red homing
Dimensions: Span 43¼ in (1.1 m)
Body diameter 10¼ in (26.0 cm)
Length 10 ft 9¼ in (3.28 m)
Booster: Hotchkiss-Brandt/SNPE Marie Antoinette dual-thrust solid-propellant rocket, rated at 18,740-lb (8,500-kg) static thrust
Sustainer: as above
Warhead: 60 lb (27 kg) high explosive
Weights: Launch 430 lb (195 kg)
Burnt out
Performance: speed Mach 2.7; range 11 miles (18 km)
Used also by: Argentina, Australia, Brazil, Colombia, Egypt, Lebanon, Pakistan, Saudi Arabia, South Africa, Venezuela
Notes: The R.530 uses either the EMD AD-26 radar, or SAT AD-3501 infra-red seeker heads, both of them sensitive enough to allow the parent aircraft to attack from any direction. The R.530 can be used from sea level up to an altitude of 68,900 ft (21,000 m).

Matra Super 530

Type: air-to-air tactical guided missile
Guidance: semi-active radar homing
Dimensions: Span 35½ in (90.0 cm)
Body diameter 10¼ in (26.0 cm)
Length 11 ft 7¼ in (3.54 m)
Booster: Thomson/Brandt Angèle dual-thrust solid-propellant rocket
Sustainer: as above
Warhead: high explosive
Weights: Launch 500 lb (227 kg)
Burnt out
Performance: speed Mach 4.5; range up to 21¾ miles (35 km); operating altitude from sea level to above 70,000 ft (21,350 m)
Used also by: Kuwait
Notes: The Super 530 missile is intended to complement the Cyrano IV fire-control system, and introduces improvements to double the range of the R.530. The Super 530 can be used in all weathers, for attacks from any quarter, and has the capability to engage targets 25,000 ft (7,620 m) above or below the firing aircraft. The type is expected to enter service shortly.

Matra R.550 Magic

Type: air-to-air tactical guided missile
Guidance: infra-red homing
Dimensions: Span 26 in (66.0 cm)
Body diameter 6 in (15.0 cm)
Length 9 ft (2.74 m)
Booster: SNPE Romeo solid-propellant rocket
Sustainer: none
Warhead: 27½ lb (12.5 kg), with 13¼ lb (6 kg) of high explosive
Weights: Launch 194 lb (88 kg)
Burnt out
Performance: speed more than Mach 2; range up to 4¼ miles (7 km)
Used also by: Ecuador, Greece, Iraq, Kuwait, Libya, Morocco, Oman, Pakistan, Saudi Arabia, South Africa, Spain
Notes: Designed as a short- and medium-range dogfighting missile, the R.550 Magic has a unique configuration, with cruciform nose and tail surfaces, and an extra set of movable cruciform control surfaces behind, and indexed in line with, the fixed fore-planes. This gives the missile great agility, with turns at up to 30g being possible. The infra-red head is the SAT AD-3601.

SSBS S-2

Type: intermediate-range ballistic missile, silo-launched
Guidance: inertial
Dimensions: Span
Body diameter 4 ft 11 in (1.5 m)
Length 45 ft 11⅖ in (14.0 m)
Booster (1st stage): SEP Type 902 rocket with 15.75 tons (16 tonnes) of solid fuel, delivering 121,253-lb (55,000-kg) thrust
Sustainer (2nd stage): SEP Type 903 rocket with 9.84 tons (10 tonnes) of solid fuel, delivering 99,207-lb (45,000-kg) thrust

Warhead: nuclear, 150 kilotons
Weights: Launch 29.53 tons (30 tonnes) approximately
Burnt out
Performance: range 1,709 miles (2,750 km) approximately
Used only by: France
Notes: Introduced in 1971. Two groups of nine launch areas each are operational on the Plateau d'Albion. Launching needs no human assistance after the sequence is initiated. (SSBS = *Sol-Sol-Balistique-Stratégique* or surface-to-surface strategic ballistic missile.)

SSBS S-3

Type: intermediate-range ballistic missile, silo-launched
Guidance: inertial
Dimensions: Span
Body diameter 4 ft 11 1/10 in (1.5 m)
Length 48 ft 6¾ in (14.8 m)
Booster (1st stage): SEP Type 902 rocket with 15.75 tons (16 tonnes) of solid fuel, delivering 121,253-lb (55,000-kg) thrust
Sustainer (2nd stage): SEP RITA II rocket with 5.91 tons (6 tonnes) of solid fuel, delivering 70,547-lb (32,000-kg) thrust
Warhead: thermonuclear, 1.2 megatons
Weights: Launch
Burnt out
Performance: range 1,864 miles (3,000 km)
Used by: under final development for the French Air Force
Notes: 2nd-generation successor to the SSBS S-2 IRBM, to use the same silos after improvement. The warhead in its re-entry vehicle has special protection against high-altitude ABM nuclear warhead explosions.

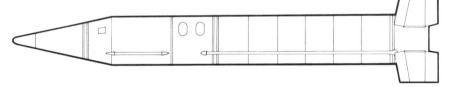

Gabon

200 men.

3 Mirage VG, 2 Mirage V RG FGA.
4 A-1D FGA.
3 C-130, 2 DC-6, 3 C-47, 3 Nord 262, 1 Falcon, 1 Gulfstream transports.
7 light aircraft.
4 *Alouette* III, 3 Puma helicopters.

Ghana

1,400 men and 12 combat aircraft.

1 COIN sqn with 6 M.B.326F, 6 M.B.326K.
2 transport sqns with 8 Islander, 6 Skyvan 3M.
1 comms and liaison sqn with 6 F27, 1 F28.
1 helicopter sqn with 2 Bell 212, 4 *Alouette* III, 3 Hughes 269.
12 Bulldog trainers.

Aeronautica Macchi M.B. 326K

Type: light ground-attack aircraft
Crew: one
Wings: metal cantilever low/mid-wing monoplane
Fuselage: metal semi-monocoque
Tail unit: metal cantilever
Landing gear: hydraulically actuated retractable tricycle unit
Powerplant: one Rolls-Royce Bristol Viper Mark 632-43 turbojet, rated at 4,000-lb (1,814-kg) static thrust
Fuel capacity: 366 gallons (1,660 litres) in three rubber fuselage and two fixed wingtip tanks
Avionics: comprehensive communication and navigation equipment, plus optional attack gear, including a lead-computing gunsight and bombing computer
Armament: two 30-mm DEFA cannon with 125 rounds per gun, plus a wide variety of stores carried on six underwing pylons, the inner four capable of lifting 1,000 lb (454 kg) each, and the outer pair 750 lb (340 kg) each, up to a maximum of 4,000 lb (1,814 kg). Weapons that can be carried include 750- and 500-lb (340- and 227-kg) bombs, napalm tanks, AS.11 or AS.12 missiles, machine-gun pods, Matra 550 air-to-air missiles, a reconnaissance pod, and a variety of air-to-surface rocket pods
Dimensions: Span 35 ft 7 in (10.85 m)
Length 35 ft 0¼ in (10.673 m)
Height 12 ft 2 in (3.72 m)
Wing area: 208.3 ft² (19.35 m²)
Weights: Empty 6,885 lb (3,123 kg)
Loaded 10,240 lb (4,645 kg)
Maximum 13,000 lb (5,897 kg)
Performance: (at a take-off weight of 12,000 lb/5,443 kg) speed 426 mph (686 kph) at 30,000 ft (9,150 m); speed in 'clean' condition 553 mph (890 kph) at 5,000 ft (1,525 m); climb 3,750 ft (1,143 m) per minute at sea level; combat radius with 2,822 lb (1,280 kg) of weapons on a lo-lo-lo mission 167 miles (268 km); combat radius with a camera pod and two auxiliary tanks on a hi-lo-hi photographic reconnaissance mission 644 miles (1,036 km); ferry range 1,323 miles (2,130 km)

Used also by: Argentina, Australia, Bolivia, Brazil, Italy, South Africa, Togo, Tunisia, United Arab Emirates, Zaire, Zambia

Notes: Derived from the M.B. 326GB trainer, the M.B. 326K has only one cockpit, an uprated engine, more fuel capacity and improved weapon carrying capability. There are several versions of the M.B. 326:

1. M.B. 326 initial trainer version for Italy with a Viper 11
2. M.B. 326B trainer for Tunisia with a Viper 11
3. M.B. 326D trainer for Alitalia with a Viper 11
4. M.B. 326E trainer for Italy with a Viper 11
5. M.B. 326F trainer for Ghana with a Viper 11
6. M.B. 326H trainer for Australia with a Viper 11
7. M.B. 326M trainer for South Africa with a Viper 11. The model is also built in South Africa as the Atlas Impala Mark 1
8. M.B. 326GB trainer/attack version with a Viper 20, used by Argentina, Brazil, Togo, Zaire and Zambia. The version is also licence-built in Brazil as the EMBRAER AT-26 *Xavante*
9. M.B. 326K operational trainer/attack version with a Viper 540 engine. The technical specification above relates to this version, which is built in South Africa as the Impala Mark 2
10. M.B. 326L trainer, based on the M.B. 326K but with a two-seat cockpit, used by the United Arab Emirates and Tunisia.

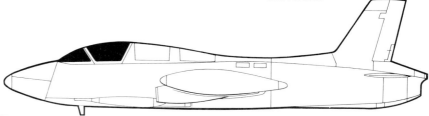

Greece

22,600 men (15,000 conscripts) and 257 combat aircraft, plus about 20,000 reservists.

6 FGA sqns: 2 with 38 F-4E, 8 RF-4E; 3 with 59 A-7H; 1 with 28 F-104G.
5 interceptor sqns: 3 with 45 F-5A/B, 2 with 39 Mirage F1CG.
1 recce sqn with 20 RF-84F.
1 MR sqn with 8 HU-16B Albatross.
OCU with 8 F-5B, 4 TF-104G.
2 transport sqns with 25 C-47, 50 Noratlas, 12 C-130H, 1 Gulfstream, 8 CL-215.
3 helicopter sqns with 14 AB-205, 2 AB-206, 10 Bell 47G, 10 H-19D, 35 UH-1D.
Trainers incl 50 T-33A, 20 T-41A, 18 T-37B, 40 T-2E, 3 TF-104G, 8 F-5B.
Sparrow, Sidewinder, Falcon, R.550 Magic AAM.
1 SAM bn with Nike Hercules.
(18 F-4E FGA, 6 RF-4E recce, 6 TA-7H trainers, 300 Super Sidewinder AAM on order.)
Naval Air Arm
1 sqn with 4 *Alouette* III helicopters.
Army Air Arm
14 army aviation coys.
1 Super King Air, 2 Aero Commander, 20 U-17, 15 L-21 ac; 5 Bell 47G, 20 UH-1D, 42 AB-204/-205 helicopters.

Piper Aircraft L-21 Grasshopper

Type: liaison aircraft
Crew: two, seated in tandem
Wings: metal high-wing braced monoplane
Fuselage: metal tube structure
Tail unit: braced metal structure
Landing gear: fixed tailwheel unit
Powerplant: one Lycoming O-290-11 piston engine rated at 125 hp and driving a metal two-blade propeller
Fuel capacity:
Avionics: communication equipment
Armament: none
Dimensions: Span 35 ft 3 in (10.74 m)
Length 22 ft 7 in (6.88 m)
Height 6 ft 6 in (1.98 m)
Wing area: 179 ft² (16.63 m²)
Weights: Empty 950 lb (431 kg)
Loaded
Maximum 1,580 lb (717 kg)
Performance: speed 123 mph (198 kph); cruising speed 115 mph (185 kph); climb 1,000 ft (305 m) per minute at sea level; service ceiling 21,650 ft (6,600 m); range 770 miles (478 km)
Used by: a number of army air services
Notes: The L-21 entered military service in 1951, and is basically the Piper PA-18. The later L-21B has the 135-hp O-290-D2 engine. The type became the U-7A in US service in 1962.

Guatemala

370 men and 11 combat aircraft.

1 FGA sqn with 11 A-37B.
1 transport sqn with 1 DC-6, 9 C-47, 10 *Arava*.
1 communication sqn with 6 Cessna 172, 3 Cessna 180, 2 Cessna U-206C aircraft, 9 Bell UH-1D helicopters.
2 T-33A trainers.

Cessna Aircraft A-37 Dragonfly

Type: light strike and counter-insurgency aircraft
Crew: two, seated side-by-side
Wings: aluminium alloy cantilever low-wing monoplane
Fuselage: metal semi-monocoque
Tail unit: metal semi-monocoque
Landing gear: hydraulically actuated retractable tricycle unit
Powerplant: two General Electric J85-GE-17A turbojets, each rated at 2,850-lb (1,293-kg) static thrust
Fuel capacity: 422 gallons (1,920 litres) in fuselage, wingtip and wing tanks, plus provision for four underwing 83-gallon (378-litre) auxiliary tanks
Avionics: comprehensive communication and navigation equipment
Armament: one 7.62-mm GAU-2B/A Minigun, plus four underwing pylons on each wing, the inner pair capable of lifting 870 lb

(394 kg) each, the intermediate one 600 lb (272 kg), and the outer one 500 lb (227 kg), up to a maximum of 5,680 lb (2,576 kg). External stores that can be carried include the BLU-1C/B fire bomb, BLU-32/B fire bomb, CBU-12/A, -14/A, or 22/A dispenser and bomb, CBU-19/A canister cluster, CBU-24/B or -25/A dispenser and bomb, LAU-3/A, -32/A, or 59/A rocket pod, M-117 demolition bomb, MK-81 or 82 bombs, SUU-11/A gun pod, SUU-20 bomb and rocket pod, and SUU-25/A flare launcher

Dimensions: Span 35 ft 10½ in (10.93 m)
Length 28 ft 3¼ in (8.62 m)
Height 8 ft 10½ in (2.7 m)
Wing area: 183.9 ft² (17.09 m²)
Weights: Empty 6,211 lb (2,817 kg)
Loaded
Maximum 14,000 lb (6,350 kg)

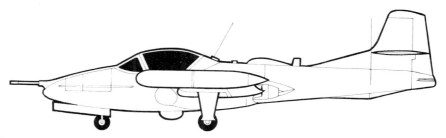

Performance: (at maximum take-off weight) speed 507 mph (816 kph) at 16,000 ft (4,875 m); cruising speed 489 mph (787 kph) at 25,000 ft (7,620 m); climb 6,990 ft (2,130 m) per minute at sea level; service ceiling 41,765 ft (12,730 m); range with a payload of 4,100 lb (1,860 kg) 460 miles (740 km); maximum range 1,012 miles (1,628 km)

Used also by: Chile, Ecuador, Honduras, Peru, Thailand, Uruguay, USA
Notes: Derived from the T-37 trainer, the A-37 is remarkable in the underwing ordnance it can deliver. There are two versions:
1. A-37A, converted from T-37 trainers
2. A-37B, production aircraft. The first prototype flew in 1963.

Guinea - Bissau

500 men.

5 MiG-17 FGA.
4 Il-14, 2 Il-18, 4 An-4 transports.
2 MiG-15, 7 Yak-18, 3 L-29 trainers.
2 Bell 47 helicopters.

Guyana

8 Islander, 1 King Air, 1 Cessna U-206 transports.
2 Bell 206B, 3 Bell 212 and 2 *Alouette* III helicopters.

Bell Helicopter Textron Model 206B JetRanger II

Type: general-purpose light helicopter
Crew: one, plus up to four passengers
Rotors: aluminium and aluminium alloy cantilever two-blade main rotor; aluminium alloy cantilever two-blade tail rotor
Fuselage: aluminium alloy frame, semi-monocoque centre section, and monocoque tailboom
Landing gear: twin metal skids
Powerplant: one Allison 250-C20 turboshaft, rated at 400 shp
Fuel capacity: 63⅓ gallons (288 litres) in a fuselage tank
Avionics: comprehensive communication and navigation equipment
Armament: none
Dimensions: Span 33 ft 4 in (10.16 m)
Length (fuselage) 31 ft 2 in (9.5 m)
Height 9 ft 6½ in (2.91 m)
Rotor disc area: 873 ft² (81.1 m²)

Weights: Empty 1,455 lb (660 kg)
Loaded
Maximum 3,200 lb (1,451 kg)
Performance: speed 140 mph (225 kph) at sea level; cruising speed 138 mph (222 kph) at 5,000 ft (1,525 m); climb 1,260 ft (384 m) per minute at sea level; service ceiling over 20,000 ft (6,095 m); hovering ceiling in ground effect 11,300 ft (3,445 m); range 388 miles (624 km) with maximum payload and maximum fuel at 5,000 ft (1,525 m)
Used also by: Brazil, Brunei, Israel, Malaysia, Mexico, Sri Lanka, Tanzania, Turkey, Uganda, Zambia
Notes: The JetRanger II is the successor to the earlier JetRanger I, and first flew in 1970, entering service the following year. The main difference between the two helicopters is the uprated powerplant of the latter, allowing operations at higher altitudes and in hotter climates.

Haiti

250 men.

8 O-2A COIN.
2 DC-3 transports.
7 light aircraft.
3 H-34, 2 S-58, 4 Hughes 300/500 helicopters.
3 Cessna 150 trainers.

Honduras

1,200 men and 18 combat aircraft.

1 FB sqn with 12 Super *Mystère* B2.
1 COIN sqn with 6 A-37B.
Transports incl 1 C-54, C-45, 1 C-47, 3
   Arava, 1 Westwind, 4 Cessna 180/
   185.
Trainers incl 6 T-6, 4 T-28E, 5 T-41A,
   3 RT-33A.

Avions Marcel Dassault Super *Mystère*

Type: fighter-bomber
Crew: one
Wings: metal cantilever low mid-wing mono-
plane
Fuselage: metal semi-monocoque
Tail unit: metal cantilever
Landing gear: hydraulically actuated retrac-
table tricycle unit
Powerplant: one SNECMA Atar 101G turbo-
jet, rated at 9,920-lb (4,500-kg) static
thrust with afterburning
Fuel capacity:
Avionics: comprehensive communication
and navigation/attack equipment
Armament: two 30-mm DEFA cannon, plus
an internal Matra launcher for thirty-five
SNEB 68-mm rockets, and two underwing
pylons for 2,000 lb (907 kg) of external
stores

Dimensions: Span 34 ft 5¾ in (10.5 m)
Length 46 ft 1¼ in (14.0 m)
Height 14 ft 10¾ in (4.53 m)
Wing area: 377 ft² (35 m²)
Weights: Empty 15,400 lb (6,985 kg)
Loaded
Maximum 22,046 lb (10,000 kg)
Performance: speed 686 mph (1,105 kph) or
Mach 0.9 at sea level; speed 743 mph
(1,200 kph) or Mach 1.125 at high altitude;
climb 17,500 ft (5,333 m) per minute at
sea level; service ceiling 55,750 ft (17,000
m); range 540 miles (870 km) on internal
fuel
Used also by: Ecuador
Notes: The Super *Mystère* is a progressive
development of the *Mystère* IV, as indicated by the designation of its prototype,
the *Mystère* IVB, which first flew late in
1953. This led to the Super *Mystère* B1,
which flew in 1955, and in turn to the definitive Super *Mystère* B2, which took to
the air in 1956. Production examples of the
Super *Mystère* B2 began to come off the
lines in 1957.

Hong Kong

Police air unit: Scottish Aviation Bulldog.

British Aerospace (Scottish Aviation) SA-3-120 Bulldog Series 120

Type: trainer
Crew: two, seated side-by-side
Wings: light alloy cantilever low-wing monoplane
Fuselage: light alloy semi-monocoque
Tail unit: light alloy cantilever
Landing gear: fixed tricycle unit
Powerplant: one Lycoming IO-360-A1B6 piston engine, rated at 200 hp and driving a Hartzell two-blade metal propeller
Fuel capacity: 32 gallons (145.5 litres) in four wing tanks
Avionics: communication and navigation equipment
Armament: provision for four underwing hardpoints capable of lifting a total load of 640 lb (290 kg), including 102-lb (50-kg) bombs, 7.62-mm machine-gun pods, grenade launchers, and guided or unguided air-to-surface projectiles

Dimensions: Span 33 ft (10.06 m)
Length 23 ft 3 in (7.09 m)
Height 7 ft 5¾ in (2.28 m)
Wing area: 129.4 ft² (12.02 m²)
Weights: Empty 1,475 lb (669 kg)
Loaded 2,350 lb (1,066 kg)
Maximum 2,990 lb (1,356 kg)
Performance: (at a take-off weight of 2,350 lb/1,066 kg) speed 150 mph (241 kph) at sea level; cruising speed 138 mph (222 kph) at 4,000 ft (1,220 m); climb 1,034 ft (315 m) per minute at sea level; service ceiling 16,000 ft (4,875 m); endurance 5 hours, range 621 miles (1,000 km)
Used also by: Ghana, Jordan, Kenya, Lebanon, Nigeria, Sweden, UK
Notes: Derived from the Beagle Pup, the Bulldog is designed as a primary trainer and light ground-attack aircraft. The prototype first flew in 1969.

Hungary

23,000 men (8,000 conscripts) and 180 combat aircraft, plus 13,000 reservists.

6 interceptor sqns with 116 MiG-21.
About 20 An-2/-24/-26, 10 Il-14, 10 Li-2 transports.
About 30 Mi-1/-2, 35 Mi-8, Ka-26 helicopters.
53 MiG-15UTI, 11 MiG-21U, Yak-11/-18, 20 L-29/-39 trainers.
AA-2 'Atoll' AAM.
14 SAM bns with SA-2.

Mil Mi-8 'Hip'

Type: transport helicopter
Crew: two or three, plus up to 32 passengers
Rotors: metal cantilever five-blade main rotor; metal cantilever three-blade tail rotor
Fuselage: metal semi-monocoque
Landing gear: fixed tricycle unit
Powerplant: two Isotov TV2-117A turboshafts, each rated at 1,500 shp
Fuel capacity: 411½ gallons (1,870 litres) in one fuselage and two external tanks, plus provision for one or two auxiliary tanks in the fuselage, raising overall fuel capacity to 814 gallons (3,700 litres)
Avionics: comprehensive communication and navigation equipment
Armament: up to eight stores can be carried on external pylons. A typical load consists of eight 57-mm rocket pods, though gun pods and anti-tank missiles can also be carried

Dimensions: Span 69 ft 10¼ in (21.29 m)
Length (fuselage) 60 ft 0¾ in (18.31 m)
Height 18 ft 6½ in (5.65 m)
Rotor disc area: 3,828 ft² (356.0 m²)
Weights: Empty 15,026 lb (6,816 kg)
Loaded 24,470 lb (11,100 kg)
Maximum 26,455 lb (12,000 kg)
Performance: (at normal loaded weight) speed 161 mph (260 kph) at 3,280 ft (1,000 m); cruising speed 155 mph (250 kph); service ceiling 14,760 ft (4,500 m); hovering ceiling in ground effect 6,233 ft (1,900 m); range 298 miles (480 km) at 3,280 ft (1,000 m); ferry range 745 miles (1,200 km)
Used also by: many nations

Notes: Similar in concept and dimensions to the Mi-4, the Mi-8 is turbine powered. The type first flew in 1960, and entered military service before 1967. Maximum internal payload is 8,820 lb (4,000 kg), and maximum external payload 6,614 lb (3,000 kg). There is also an ASW helicopter derived from the Mi-8, known by the NATO reporting name 'Haze'. This has a boat hull and retracting undercarriage, but in all probability the dynamic system of the Mi-8. ASW equipment is carried in a large radome under the nose (surveillance radar) and a towed 'bird' containing a magnetic anomaly detector.

India

100,000 men and about 661 combat aircraft.

3 lt bomber sqns with 50 Canberra B(I).58, B(I).12.
13 FGA sqns: 5 with 100 Su-7B, 4 with 80 HF-24 *Marut* 1A, 4 with 65 Hunter F.56.
11 interceptor sqns with 200 MiG-21F/ PFMA/FL/MF/*bis*.
8 interceptor sqns with 160 Gnat F.1.
1 recce sqn with 6 Canberra PR.57.
10 transport sqns: 1 with 16 HS 748, 2 with 32 C-119G, 2 with 30 An-12, 1 with 29 DHC-3, 3 with 50 C-47, 1 with 20 DHC-4.
12 helicopter sqns: 6 with 100 Mi-4, 3 with 35 Mi-8, 3 with 120 *Chetak* (*Alouette* III); 12 AB-47, 2 S-62.
Comms flts with 1 Tu-124, 6 HS 748, C-47, Devon.
OCU with MiG-21U, 5 Su-7U, Hunter T.66, *Mystère* IVA, Canberra T.13.
Trainers incl 110 *Kiran*, 70 HT-2, 32 HS 748, C-47, 45 *Iskra*, 15 *Marut* ac, *Alouette* III helicopters.
AA-2 'Atoll' AAM; AS.30 ASM.
20 SAM sites with 120 SA-2/-3.
(110 MiG-21MF, 100 *Ajeet* (Gnat), 20 HS 748M, 45 *Marut* Mk 1T, 40 *Iskra* ac, 45 *Chetak* helicopters on order.)

Naval Air Force
2,000
1 attack sqn with 25 Sea Hawk (12 in carrier).
1 MR sqn with 12 *Alizé* (4 in carrier).
3 MR sqns with 5 Super Constellation, 3 Il-38, 5 Defender, 2 Devon.
1 helicopter sqn with 10 *Alouette* III.
3 ASW sqns with 12 Sea King, 8 *Alouette* III helicopters.
7 HJT-16 *Kiran*, 4 Vampire T.55, 4 Sea Hawk ac, 4 Hughes 300 helicopters.
(8 Sea Harrier, 3 Il-38 MR ac, 3 Sea King ASW, 5 Ka-25 helicopters on order.)

Army Air Arm
4 arty obs sqns and independent flts.
40 *Krishak*, 20 Auster AOP9 lt ac; some *Alouette* III, 38 Cheetah helicopters.
(75 Cheetah helicopters on order.)

Auster Aircraft AOP.9

Type: aerial observation post and liaison aircraft
Crew: two or three
Wings: metal braced high-wing monoplane
Fuselage: metal tube
Tail unit: metal cantilever
Landing gear: fixed tailwheel unit
Powerplant: one Blackburn Cirrus Bombardier 203 inline engine, rated at 180 hp and driving a metal two-blade propeller
Fuel capacity:
Avionics: communication and navigation equipment
Armament: none
Dimensions: Span 36 ft 5 in (11.1 m)
Length 23 ft 8½ in (7.21 m)
Height 8 ft 5 in (2.57 m)
Wing area: 197.5 ft² (18.35 m²)
Weights: Empty 1,461 lb (663 kg)
Loaded 2,130 lb (966 kg)
Maximum
Performance: speed 127 mph (204 kph); cruising speed 110 mph (177 kph); climb 930 ft (283 m) per minute at sea level; service ceiling 18,500 ft (5,639 m); range 246 miles (396 km)
Used only by: India
Notes: The AOP.9 first flew in 1954, and was a wholly new design with only superficial resemblances to civil light aircraft. First deliveries were made in 1955.

Fairchild Engine & Airplane C-119 Boxcar

Type: transport aircraft
Crew: four, plus up to 62 passengers
Wings: metal cantilever shoulder-wing inverted gull monoplane

Hawker Siddeley Aviation (Armstrong Whitworth Aircraft) Sea Hawk

Type: carrier-based fighter-bomber
Crew: one
Wings: metal cantilever mid-wing monoplane
Fuselage: metal semi-monocoque
Tail unit: metal cantilever
Landing gear: hydraulically actuated retractable tricycle unit
Powerplant: one Rolls-Royce Nene 103 turbojet, rated at 5,400-lb (2,450-kg) static thrust
Fuel capacity: 395 gallons (1,796 litres) internally

Fuselage: metal semi-monocoque, with metal monocoque booms
Tail unit: metal cantilever
Landing gear: hydraulically actuated retractable tricycle unit
Powerplant: two Wright R-4360-20WA radial engines, each rated at 3,500 hp and driving a Hamilton Standard metal four-blade propeller
Fuel capacity: 2,183 gallons (2,622 litres)
Avionics: comprehensive communication and navigation equipment
Armament: none
Dimensions: Span 109 ft 3 in (34.3 m)
Length 86 ft 6 in (26.36 m)
Height 26 ft 6 in (8.07 m)
Wing area: 1,447 ft² (134.43 m²)
Weights: Empty 39,800 lb (18,053 kg)
Loaded
Maximum 74,000 lb (33,566 kg)
Performance: speed 281 mph (452 kph) at 18,000 ft (5,486 m); climb 1,010 ft (308 m) per minute at sea level; service ceiling 23,900 ft (7,285 m); range 1,770 miles (2,849 km)
Used also by: Egypt, Ethiopia, Italy, Morocco, Taiwan
Notes: The C-119 was a development of the C-82 Packet, with a fuselage nose locating the cockpit ahead of the freight compartment instead of above it. There have been several versions since the C-119B entered service with the USAF in 1949, the most impressive being the AC-119K Stinger gunship, which had the additional power of two 2,850-lb (1,293-kg) General Electric J85-GE-17 turbojets in pods under the wings, an armament of two 20-mm Vulcan and four 7.62-mm Minigun rotary-barrel weapons with 100,000 rounds of ammunition, and forward-looking infra-red and sideways-looking radar. The specification applies to the C-119C.

Avionics: comprehensive communication and navigation equipment
Armament: four 20-mm Hispano cannon with 200 rounds per gun, plus racks for four 500-lb (227-kg) bombs under the wings
Dimensions: Span 39 ft (11.89 m)
Length 39 ft 8 in (12.08 m)
Height 9 ft 9½ in (3.0 m)
Wing area: 278 ft² (25.83 m²)
Weights: Empty 9,720 lb (4,410 kg)
Loaded 13,220 lb (6,000 kg)
Maximum 16,200 lb (7,355 kg)
Performance: speed 599 mph (958 kph) at sea level; 587 mph (939 kph) or Mach 0.83 at high altitude; climb 5,700 ft (1,737 m) per minute at sea level; service ceiling 44,500 ft (13,560 m); range 1,400 miles (2,253 km) with drop tanks

Used only by: India

Notes: The Sea Hawk was of initial Hawker design, the prototype flying in 1947 (land version) and 1948 (naval version). After they had built 35 F.1s for the Fleet Air Arm, Hawker passed control of the type to Armstrong Whitworth, who developed the type further. The technical specification above applies to the FB.5 fighter-bomber. Only the marks F.1 and F.2 were used as fighters, the others being fighter-bombers and ground-attack fighters.

Hawker Siddeley Aviation (Folland Aircraft) Gnat

Type: advanced trainer and light fighter
Crew: one or two, seated in tandem
Wings: metal cantilever shoulder-wing monoplane
Fuselage: metal semi-monocoque
Tail unit: metal cantilever
Landing gear: hydraulically actuated retractable tricycle unit
Powerplant: one Rolls-Royce (Bristol Siddeley) Orpheus 701 turbojet, rated at 4,520-lb (2,050-kg) static thrust

Fuel capacity: 200 gallons (909 litres) internally
Avionics: comprehensive communication and navigation/attack equipment
Armament: two 30-mm Aden cannon with 115 rounds per gun, plus up to 1,000 lb (454 kg) of external stores on four underwing hardpoints
Dimensions: Span 22 ft 2 in (6.75 m)
Length 29 ft 9 in (9.06 m)
Height 8 ft 10 in (2.69 m)
Wing area: 175 ft² (16.26 m²)
Weights: Empty 4,850 lb (2,200 kg)
Loaded 6,650 lb (3,016 kg)
Maximum 8,885 lb (4,030 kg)

Performance: speed 714 mph (1,150 kph); climb 20,000 ft (6,096 m) per minute at sea level; service ceiling over 50,000 ft (15,240 m); range 1,180 miles (1,900 km)
Used also by: UK
Notes: The Gnat was conceived as a lightweight fighter, and first flew in 1954 as the Folland Midge. The type is used as a lightweight fighter, the F.1 to which the technical specification above applies, and as a two-seat advanced trainer.

Hindustan Aeronautics Limited (HAL) *Ajeet*

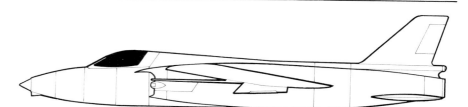

Type: lightweight interceptor and ground-attack fighter
Crew: one
Wings: metal cantilever shoulder-wing monoplane
Fuselage: light alloy semi-monocoque
Tail unit: metal cantilever
Landing gear: hydraulically actuated retractable tricycle unit
Powerplant: one Rolls-Royce Orpheus 701-01 turbojet, rated at 4,500-lb (2,041-kg) static thrust
Fuel capacity: 297 gallons (1,350 litres) in internal tanks in fuselage and wings, plus two optional 33-gallon (150-litre) underwing drop tanks
Avionics: communications equipment
Armament: two 30-mm Aden Mark 4 cannon with 90 rounds per gun, plus four underwing hardpoints capable of lifting two 500-lb (227-kg) bombs (inner stations), four

Arrow Type 122 pods, each with eighteen 68-mm rockets, or two drop tanks (outer stations)
Dimensions: Span 22 ft 1 in (6.73 m)
Length 29 ft 8 in (9.04 m)
Height 8 ft 1 in (2.46 m)
Wing area:
Weights: Empty 5,086 lb (2,307 kg)
Loaded 7,803 lb (3,539 kg)
Maximum 9,195 lb (4,170 kg)
Performance: (at normal loaded weight) speed Mach 0.96 at 39,375 ft (12,000 m); speed 716 mph (1,152 kph) at sea level; climb 6 minutes 2 seconds to 39,375 ft (12,000 m); service ceiling 45,000 ft

(13,720 m); combat radius on a low-level ground-attack raid with two 500-lb (227-kg) bombs 127 miles (204 km)
Used only by: India
Notes: This is basically a Mark II development of the Folland Gnat, which was built under licence by HAL between 1962 and 1974. Design of the *Ajeet* was completed in 1974. Improvements over the basic Gnat include better avionics, the incorporation of integral wing tanks to increase fuel capacity, and increased underwing weapons capacity. A tandem-seat trainer version is under development.

Hindustan Aeronautics Limited (HAL) HF-24 *Marut*

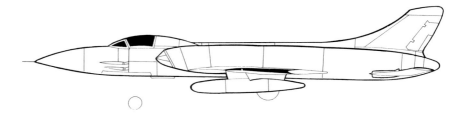

Type: ground-attack fighter
Crew: one
Wings: metal cantilever low-wing monoplane
Fuselage: metal semi-monocoque

73

Tail unit: metal cantilever
Landing gear: hydraulically actuated retractable tricycle unit
Powerplant: two HAL-built Rolls-Royce Bristol Orpheus 703 turbojets, each rated at 4,850-lb (2,200-kg) static thrust
Fuel capacity: 549 gallons (2,491 litres) in fuselage and wing tanks, plus provision for an internal 88-gallon (400-litre) tank in place of the Matra rocket-launcher, and up to four 100-gallon (454-litre) underwing tanks
Avionics: communications and navigation equipment
Armament: four 30-mm Aden Mark 2 cannon with 120 rounds per gun, one Matra Type 103 pack of 50 SNEB 68-mm air-to-air rockets in the lower rear fuselage, and provision under the wings for four 1,000-lb (454-kg) bombs, Type 116 SNEB rocket pods, T10 rocket clusters, napalm tanks or fuel tanks
Dimensions: Span 29 ft 6$\frac{1}{4}$ in (9.0 m)
Length 52 ft 0$\frac{3}{4}$ in (15.87 m)
Height 11 ft 9$\frac{3}{4}$ in (3.6 m)
Wing area: 301.4 ft² (28.0 m²)
Weights: Empty (Mk 1 with ventral tank) 13,658 lb (6,195 kg)
Loaded (Mk 1 with ventral tank) 19,734 lb (8,951 kg)
Maximum (Mk 1) 24,048 lb (10,908 kg)
Performance: (Mk 1) speed Mach 1.02 at 39,375 ft (12,000 m); climb 9 minutes 20 seconds to 40,000 ft (12,200 m); combat radius at low level 148 miles (238 km) for Mk 1T; combat radius for interception mission at 39,375 ft (12,000 m) 246 miles (396 km) for Mk 1T; ferry range 898 miles (1,445 km) at 30,000 ft (9,150 m) for Mk 1T
Used only by: India
Notes: Design of the *Marut* began in 1956 under the control of Dr Kurt Tank, Focke Wulf's chief designer up to 1945. It was originally intended to fit afterburning Orpheus engines in a supersonic Mark II aircraft, but this plan has not seen fruition. The Mark 1T is a tandem-seat trainer.

Hindustan Aeronautics Limited (HAL) HJT-16 Mark I *Kiran*

Type: basic trainer
Crew: two, seated side-by-side
Wings: metal cantilever low-wing monoplane
Fuselage: metal semi-monocoque
Tail unit: metal cantilever
Landing gear: hydraulically actuated retractable tricycle unit
Powerplant: one Rolls-Royce Bristol Viper 11 turbojet, rated at 2,500-lb (1,134-kg) static thrust
Fuel capacity: 250 gallons (1,137 litres) in fuselage and wing tanks, plus provision for 100 gallons (454 litres) in two underwing auxiliary tanks
Avionics: communications and navigation equipment
Armament: from the 116th aircraft, one hardpoint under each wing, capable of taking one 500-lb (227-kg) bomb, a pod fitted with a pair of 7.62-mm FN machine-guns, a pod holding seven 68-mm SNEB rockets, or an auxiliary fuel tank
Dimensions: Span 35 ft 1$\frac{1}{4}$ in (10.7 m)
Length 34 ft 9 in (10.6 m)
Height 11 ft 11 in (3.635 m)
Wing area: 204.5 ft² (19.0 m²)
Weights: Empty 5,644 lb (2,560 kg)
Loaded 7,936 lb (3,600 kg)
Maximum 9,039 lb (4,100 kg)
Performance: (at normal take-off weight) speed 432 mph (695 kph) at sea level; cruising speed 201 mph (324 kph); climb 20 minutes to 30,000 ft (9,850 m); service ceiling 30,000 ft (9,850 m); endurance with internal fuel at 265 mph (426 kph) at 30,000 ft (9,850 m) 1 hour 45 minutes
Used only by: India
Notes: Design began in 1961, with first deliveries being made in 1968. The 116th aircraft was the first *Kiran* Mark IA, with light attack and armament capability. The Mark II, under development, improves on these last two capabilities, and is powered by an Orpheus 701 of 3,400-lb (1,542-kg) static thrust. This improves speed, rate of climb and manoeuvrability. Armament of the *Kiran* Mark II comprises two 7.62-mm machine-guns with 250 rounds per gun, and four underwing hardpoints, capable of lifting 2,000 lb (907 kg) of stores.

Société Nationale Industrielle Aérospatiale SA 315B *Lama*

Type: general-purpose helicopter
Crew: one, with accommodation for four
Rotor: metal cantilever three-blade main rotor; metal cantilever three-blade tail rotor
Fuselage: triangulated metal tube structure and glazed nose
Landing gear: twin metal skids
Powerplant: one Turboméca Artouste IIIB turboshaft, rated at 550 shp
Fuel capacity: 126 gallons (573 litres) in fuselage fuel tank
Avionics: communication and navigation equipment
Armament: none
Dimensions: Span 36 ft 1$\frac{3}{4}$ in (11.02 m)
Length 42 ft 4$\frac{3}{4}$ in (12.92 m)
Height 10 ft 1$\frac{3}{4}$ in (3.09 m)
Rotor disc area: 1,027 ft² (95.4 m²)
Weights: Empty 2,244 lb (1,018 kg)
Loaded 4,300 lb (1,950 kg)
Maximum 5,070 lb (2,300 kg)
Performance: (at 4,850-lb/2,200-kg take-off weight) cruising speed 75 mph (120 kph); climb 820 ft (250 m) per minute at sea level; service ceiling 13,125 ft (4,000 m); endurance 3 hours 20 minutes
Used also by: Argentina, Chile, Ecuador, El Salvador, Peru
Notes: Developed to an Indian armed forces requirement in the late 1960s, using the airframe of the *Alouette* II and the motive system of the *Alouette* III. The *Lama* holds the world helicopter altitude record at 40,820 ft (12,442 m). An external load of 2,500 lb (1,135 kg) can be lifted to 8,200 ft (2,500 m), and among the other roles that can be undertaken by the *Lama* are those of liaison, observation, photography, rescue and training. The type is named Cheetah in Indian service.

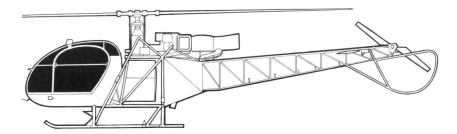

Société Nationale Industrielle Aérospatiale SA 319B *Alouette* III Astazou

Type: general-purpose helicopter
Crew: one, with accommodation for six
Rotor: metal cantilever three-blade main rotor; metal cantilever three-blade tail rotor
Fuselage: steel tube centre section and nose; metal semi-monocoque boom
Landing gear: fixed tricycle unit
Powerplant: one Turboméca Astazou XIV turboshaft, rated at 870 shp
Fuel capacity: 126 gallons (573 litres) in fuselage tank
Avionics: communication and navigation equipment
Armament: (military) one 7.62-mm AA52 machine-gun with 1,000 rounds firing to starboard from the cabin; or one 20-mm MG 151/20 cannon with 480 rounds firing to port from the cabin; or four AS.11 air-to-surface missiles; or two AS.12 air-to-surface missiles; or 68-mm rocket pods
Armament: (naval) two AS.12 air-to-surface missiles; or two Mark 44 torpedoes under the fuselage; or one Mark 44 torpedo and MAD gear in a pod towed behind the helicopter
Dimensions: Span 36 ft 1¾ in (11.02 m)
Length 42 ft 1½ in (12.84 m)
Height 9 ft 10 in (3.0 m)
Rotor disc area: 1.027 ft² (95.4 m²)
Weights: Empty 2,513 lb (1,140 kg)
Loaded Maximum 4,960 lb (2,250 kg)
Performance: (at maximum take-off weight) speed 136 mph (220 kph) at sea level; cruising speed 122 mph (197 kph) at sea level; climb 885 ft (270 m) per minute at sea level; service ceiling 10,500 ft (3,200 m); range with 1,056-lb (480-kg) payload 375 miles (605 km)
Used also by: various countries
Notes: The latest development of the celebrated *Alouette* design of general purpose helicopter, the SA 319B differs from its predecessor, the SA 316B, in having an Astazou XIV instead of an Astazou IIIB turboshaft engine. Although these two units have the same rated power, the Astazou XIV has a fuel consumption 25 per cent less than the Astazou IIIB. In the rescue role, the SA 319B has a winch with a capacity of 500 lb (225 kg). The SA 319B is known as the *Chetak* in Indian service.

Indonesia

28,000 men and 32 combat aircraft.

2 FGA sqns with 16 CA-27 Avon-Sabre.
1 COIN sqn with 16 OV-10F.
Transports incl 11 C-130B, 1 C-140 Jetstar, 12 C-47, 3 Skyvan, 8 F27, 6 CASA C-212, 5 Nomad, 12 Cessna 207/401/402, 7 DHC-3, 18 *Gelatik*.
2 helicopter sqns with 12 UH-34D, 5 Bell 204B, 4 *Alouette* III, 1 S-61A, 46 BO 105, 19 Puma, 16 Bell 47.
Trainers incl 4 T-6, 10 T-33, 31 T-34, Airtourer.
(12 F-5E, 4 F-5F fighters, 16 CASA C-212, 4 F27, 6 Nomad transports, 8 Hawk trg ac; 6 Puma helicopters on order.)
AA-1 'Alkali' AAM.
Some aircraft non-operational for lack of spares. In addition to the aircraft shown above, some 22 Tu-16, 10 Il-28, 40 MiG-15/-17, 35 MiG-19, 15 MiG-21, 10 Il-14, 10 An-12 ac, 20 Mi-4, 9 Mi-6 helicopters are in store.
Naval Air Arm
5 HU-16, 6 C-47, 6 Nomad MR ac; 4 Bell 47G, 6 *Alouette* II/III helicopters. (6 Nomad on order.)
Army Air Arm
2 Aero Commander 680, 1 Beech 18, Cessna 185, 18 *Gelatik* ac; 16 Bell 205, 7 *Alouette* III helicopters.

Commonwealth Aircraft CA-27 Sabre

Type: fighter-bomber
Crew: one
Wings: metal cantilever low-wing monoplane
Fuselage: metal semi-monocoque
Tail unit: metal cantilever
Landing gear: hydraulically actuated retractable tricycle unit
Powerplant: one Commonwealth Aircraft-built Rolls-Royce Avon 26 turbojet, rated at 7,500-lb (3,402-kg) static thrust
Fuel capacity:
Avionics: comprehensive communication and navigation equipment
Armament: two 30-mm Aden cannon, plus two AIM-9 Sidewinder air-to-air missiles or 1,200 lb (544 kg) of bombs on two underwing pylons
Dimensions: Span 37 ft 1¼ in (11.3 m)
Length 37 ft 6 in (11.43 m)
Height 14 ft 4¾ in (4.39 m)
Wing area: 304 ft² (28.24 m²)
Weights: Empty 12,000 lb (5,443 kg)
Loaded 15,990 lb (7,253 kg)
Maximum
Performance: speed 700 mph (1,127 kph) or Mach 0.92 at sea level; speed 672 mph (1,082 kph) or Mach 0.91 at 10,000 ft (3,050 m); climb 12,000 ft (3,660 m) per minute at sea level; service ceiling 50,000 ft (15,240 m); range 1,150 miles (1,850 km)
Used only by: Indonesia
Notes: The North American Sabre was licence-built in Canada by Canadair, and in Australia by Commonwealth Aircraft. The prototype Australian Sabre flew in 1953, and the first production Sabre Mark 30 in 1954. There followed the Sabre Mark 31 with a Commonwealth Aircraft-built Avon 20, compared with the earlier mark's imported engine, and the Sabre Mark 32, to which the technical specification above applies. The Australian Sabre is based on the F-86F mark of the American fighter.

Construcciones Aeronauticas SA (CASA) C-212 Aviocar

Type: STOL light utility transport
Crew: two, plus up to 18 passengers
Wings: light alloy high-wing monoplane
Fuselage: light alloy semi-monocoque
Tail unit: metal cantilever
Landing gear: fixed tricycle unit
Powerplant: two AiResearch TPE 331-5-251C turboprops, each rated at 776 ehp and driving a Hartzell metal four-blade propeller
Fuel capacity: 462 gallons (2,100 litres) in four outer wing tanks
Avionics: communication and navigation equipment

Armament: none
Dimensions: Span 62 ft 4 in (19.0 m)
  Length 49 ft 10½ in (15.2 m)
  Height 20 ft 8 in (6.3 m)
Wing area: 430.56 ft² (40.0 m²)
Weights: Empty 8,609 lb (3,905 kg)
  Loaded
  Maximum 13,889 lb (6,300 kg)
Performance: (at maximum take-off weight)
  speed 230 mph (370 kph) at 12,000 ft
  (3,660 m); cruising speed 223 mph (359
  kph) at 12,000 ft (3,660 m); climb 1,800 ft
  (548 m) per minute at sea level; service
  ceiling 26,700 ft (8,140 m); range with
  maximum fuel at 12,000 ft (3,660 m) with
  2,303-lb (1,045-kg) payload 1,093 miles
  (1,760 km); range with maximum payload
  at 12,000 ft (3,660 m) 298 miles (480 km)
Used also by: Chile, Jordan, Nicaragua,
  Portugal, Saudi Arabia, Spain, Thailand,
  Turkey

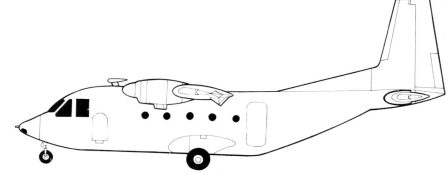

Notes: The prototype of the C-212 first flew
in 1971. There are several versions, including the following military models:
  1. C-212A utility transport

2. C-212AV VIP transport
3. C-212B photographic survey aircraft
4. C-212E navigation trainer.
Maximum payload is 4,410 lb (2,000 kg).

Fokker-VFW F27 Friendship

Type: medium-range transport
Crew: two or three, plus up to 45 (Mark
  400M) or 50 (Mark 500M) passengers
Wings: metal cantilever high-wing monoplane
Fuselage: metal semi-monocoque
Tail unit: metal cantilever
Landing gear: pneumatically actuated retrac-
  table tricycle unit
Powerplant: two Rolls-Royce Dart Mark
  532-7R turboprops, each rated at 2,140
  shp and 525-lb (238-kg) static thrust and
  driving a Dowty Rotol metal four-blade
  propeller
Fuel capacity: 1,130 gallons (5,136 litres) in
  integral outer wing tanks, plus an optional
  503.5 gallons (2,289 litres) in bag tanks
Avionics: comprehensive communication
  and navigation equipment
Armament: none
Dimensions: Span 95 ft 2 in (29.0 m)
  Length 77 ft 3½ in (23.56 m),
  except Mark 500 82 ft 2½ in
  (25.06 m)
  Height 27 ft 11 in (8.5 m),
  except Mark 500 28 ft 7¼ in
  (8.71 m)
Wing area: 753.5 ft² (70.0 m²)
Weights: (Mark 400M, freight)
  Empty 23,947 lb (10,862 kg)
  Loaded
  Maximum 45,000 lb (20,410 kg)
  (Mark 500M, paratroop)
  Empty 25,332 lb (11,491 kg)

Loaded
  Maximum 45,000 lb (20,410 kg)
Performance: cruising speed at 38,000-lb
  (17,237-kg) take-off weight at 20,000 ft
  (6,100 m) 298 mph (480 kph); climb at
  40,000-lb (18,143-kg) take-off weight
  1,620 ft (494 m) per minute at sea level;
  service ceiling at 38,000 lb (17,237 kg)
  take-off weight 30,000 ft (9,145 m); combat radius at maximum take-off weight,
  maximum possible fuel and with cargo payload 1,416 miles (2,278 km); range at
  maximum take-off weight, maximum pos-

sible fuel and with cargo payload 2,727
miles (4,389 km)
Used also by: Algeria, Argentina, Burma,
  Chile, Ghana, Iran, Ivory Coast, Netherlands, Nigeria, Pakistan, Peru, Philippines,
  Senegal, Spain, Sudan, Uruguay
Notes: The Marks 400M and 500M are military versions of the standard airliner, the
  Mark 400M being able to accommodate
  45 paratroops or 13,283 lb (6,025 kg) of
  cargo, and the 500M 50 paratroops or
  14,588 lb (6,617 kg).

Lembaga Industri Penerbangan Nurtanio (LIPNUR) *Gelatik* 32

Type: utility STOL aircraft
Crew: one, plus up to three passengers
Wings: metal cantilever high-wing monoplane
Fuselage: metal semi-monocoque
Tail unit: braced metal structure
Landing gear: fixed tailwheel unit
Powerplant: one Continental O-470-R inline engine, rated at 230 hp and driving a McCauley two-blade metal propeller
Fuel capacity: 42½ gallons (193 litres) in two wing tanks
Avionics: communication and navigation equipment
Armament: none
Dimensions: Span 36 ft 5 in (11.1 m)
Length 26 ft 6¾ in (8.1 m)
Height 8 ft 2½ in (2.5 m)
Wing area: 166.8 ft² (15.5 m²)
Weights: Empty 1,624 lb (737 kg)
Loaded
Maximum 2,711 lb (1,230 kg)
Performance: speed 127 mph (205 kph) at sea level; cruising speed 93 mph (150 kph); climb 866 ft (264 m) per minute at sea level; climb 38 minutes to 12,075 ft (3,680 m); service ceiling 12,075 ft (3,680 m); range 388 miles (625 km) with maximum payload; range 435 miles (700 km) with maximum fuel
Used only by: Indonesia
Notes: The *Gelatik* 32 is the Indonesian-built version of the Polish PZL-104 *Wilga* 32, the first flying in 1964.

Lockheed Aircraft Super Constellation

Type: long-range transport aircraft
Crew: four or five, plus up to 95 passengers
Wings: metal cantilever low-wing monoplane
Fuselage: metal semi-monocoque
Tail unit: metal cantilever
Landing gear: hydraulically actuated retractable tricycle unit
Powerplant: four Wright R-3350-DA3 radial engines, each rated at 3,250 hp and driving a three-blade metal propeller
Fuel capacity:
Avionics: comprehensive communication and navigation equipment
Armament: none
Dimensions: Span 123 ft (37.49 m)
Length 113 ft 7 in (34.62 m)
Height 24 ft 9 in (7.54 m)
Wing area: 1,650 ft² (153.3 m²)
Weights: Empty 73,133 lb (33,173 kg)
Loaded
Maximum 137,500 lb (62,370 kg)
Performance: speed 370 mph (595 kph) at 20,000 ft (6,095 m); cruising speed 355 mph (571 kph) at 22,600 ft (6,888 m); range 5,840 miles (9,400 km)
Used also by: India
Notes: The Super Constellation was the Model 1049 of the Constellation family, and entered service in 1951. It differs from its predecessors principally in having more powerful engines. The USAF still uses the EC-121 AEW version.

Rockwell International (North American) OV-10 Bronco

Type: multi-purpose counter-insurgency aircraft
Crew: two, seated in tandem
Wings: aluminium alloy cantilever shoulder-wing monoplane
Fuselage: aluminium semi-monocoque central pod, and two aluminium semi-monocoque booms
Tail unit: metal cantilever

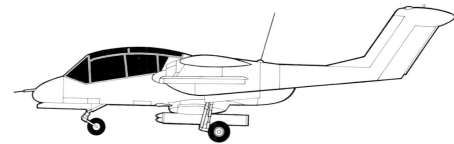

Landing gear: hydraulically actuated retractable tricycle unit

Powerplant: two AiResearch T76-G-416/417 turboprops, each rated at 715 ehp and driving a Hamilton Standard three-blade metal propeller

Fuel capacity: 215 gallons (976 litres) in wing centre-section tank, plus provision for one 125- or 192-gallon (568- or 871-litre) drop tank under the fuselage

Avionics: comprehensive communication and navigation equipment, with provision for low-light sensors and other attack equipment

Armament: four hardpoints, each with a capacity of 600 lb (272 kg), under sponsons on each side of the fuselage, a single under-fuselage hardpoint with a capacity of 1,200 lb (544 kg), two 7.62-mm M60C machine-guns in each sponson, and provision for one AIM-9 Sidewinder air-to-air missile under each wing; with a special kit, the underwing hardpoints can carry rocket pods and bombs. Total external load is 3,600 lb (1,633 kg)

Dimensions: Span 40 ft (12.19 m)
Length 41 ft 7 in (12.67 m)
Height 15 ft 2 in (4.62 m)

Wing area: 291 ft² (27.03 m²)

Weights: Empty 6,969 lb (3,161 kg)
Loaded 9,908 lb (4,494 kg)
Maximum 14,466 lb (6,563 kg)

Performance: speed 281 mph (452 kph) at sea level without weapons; climb 2,650 ft (808 m) per minute at sea level at a weight of 9,908 lb (4,494 kg); service ceiling 30,000 ft (9,145 m); combat radius with maximum ordnance load 228 miles (367 km); ferry range 1,428 miles (2,298 km)

Used also by: South Korea, Thailand, USA, Venezuela, West Germany

Notes: The OV-10 was evolved as a result of the American realisation in Vietnam that they had no aircraft suited to the counter-insurgency role, where good rough field performance and weapons load, delivered accurately at low speed and low altitude, are paramount. The first prototype flew in 1965, and there have been several versions:

1. OV-10A, to which the technical specification above relates, for the US Marine Corps in armed reconnaissance, forward air controller and helicopter escort roles

2. OV-10B for West Germany, basically similar to the OV-10A but equipped for target towing

3. OV-10B(Z), similar to the OV-10B but with a 2,950-lb (1,338-kg) General Electric J85-GE-4 turbojet mounted above the wing to boost speed to 393 mph (632 kph) at 10,000 ft (3,050 m)

4. OV-10C version of the OV-10A for Thailand

5. OV-10D night observation aircraft for the US Navy, with 1,040-shp engines, a 20-mm cannon under the aft fuselage, and forward-looking infrared (FLIR) gear under the nose

6. OV-10E version of the OV-10A for Venezuela

7. OV-10F version of the OV-10A for Indonesia. With the rear seat removed, the OV-10 can carry up to 3,200 lb (1,452 kg) of freight, five paratroops or two litters and one attendant.

Iran

100,000 men and 459 combat aircraft.

10 FB sqns with 32 F-4D, 177 F-4E.
10 FGA sqns with 12 F-5A, 140 F-5E.
3 fighter sqns with 56 F-14A Tomcat.
1 recce sqn with 16 RF-4E.
1 tanker sqn with 13 Boeing 707-320L.
4 medical transport sqns with 64 C-130 E/H, 6 Boeing 747.
4 lt transport sqns with 18 F27, 4 F28, 3 Aero Commander 690, 4 Falcon 20.
10 HH-43F, 6 AB-205, 84 AB-206A, 5 AB-212, 39 Bell 214C SAR, 2 CH-47C, 16 Super *Frelon*, 2 S-61A helicopters.
Trainers incl 9 T-33, 28 F-5F, 49 Bonanza F33A/C.
Phoenix, Sidewinder, Sparrow AAM; AS.12, Maverick, Condor ASM.
5 SAM sqns with Rapier and 25 Tiger-cat.
(5 RF-4E, 24 F-14, 160 F-16A/B fighters, 7 E-3A AWACS ac, 3 F27 transports, 4 Boeing 747 transports, 50 CH-47 helicopters on order.)

Naval Air Arm
1 MR sqn with 6 P-3F Orion.
1 ASW sqn with 12 SH-3D.
1 transport sqn with 6 Shrike Commander, 4 F27.
Helicopters incl 5 AB-205A, 7 AB-212, 6 RH-53D, 10 SH-3D.
(39 P-3C MR ac, 15 SH-3D helicopters on order.)

Army Aviation Command
Aircraft incl 40 Cessna 185, 6 Cessna 310, 10 Cessna O-2, 2 F27; 202 AH-1J, 210 Bell 214A, 21 Huskie, 88 AB-205A, 70 AB-206, 30 CH-47C helicopters.
(163 Bell 214A, 350 Bell 214ST on order.)

Beech Aircraft Bonanza Model F33

Type: trainer and communications aircraft

Crew: one or two, plus up to two passengers

Wings: aluminium alloy cantilever low-wing monoplane

Fuselage: aluminium alloy semi-monocoque

Tail unit: metal cantilever

Landing gear: electrically actuated retractable tricycle unit

Powerplant: one Continental IO-520-BA piston engine, rated at 285 hp and driving a McCauley two-blade metal propeller

Fuel capacity: 36.6 gallons (166.5 litres) in two wing leading-edge tanks, or 61.6 gallons, (280 litres) in two wing leading-edge tanks, plus optional wingtip tanks, each holding 16.6 gallons (75.5 litres)

Avionics: communications and navigation equipment

Armament: none

Dimensions: Span 33 ft 6 in (10.21 m)
Length 26 ft 8 in (8.13 m)
Height 8 ft 3 in (2.51 m)

Wing area: 181 ft² (16.8 m²)

Weights: Empty 2,112 lb (958 kg)
Loaded
Maximum 3,400 lb (1,542 kg)

Performance: (at maximum take-off weight) speed 209 mph (338 kph) at sea level; cruising speed 198 mph (319 kph) at 6,000 ft (1,830 m); climb 1,167 ft (356 m) per minute at sea level; service ceiling 17,860 ft (5,445 m); maximum range 1,023 miles (1,648 km)

Used also by: Mexico, Pakistan, Spain, Switzerland

Notes: Derived from the V-tailed Bonanza V35B of 1945, the conventionally-tailed Bonanza F33 first flew in 1959.

Bell Helicopter Textron Model 214

Type: utility (214A) and search and rescue (214C) helicopter
Crew: two, plus up to 14 passengers
Rotor: metal cantilever two-blade main rotor; metal cantilever two-blade tail rotor
Fuselage: metal semi-monocoque
Landing gear: twin metal skids
Powerplant: one Lycoming LTC4B-8D turboshaft, rated at 2,930 shp
Fuel capacity:
Avionics: comprehensive communication and navigation equipment
Armament: none

Dimensions: Span 50 ft (15.24 m)
　　　　　　　Length
　　　　　　　Height
Rotor disc area: 1,963.5 ft² (182.41 m²)
Weights: Empty
　　　　　　Loaded 13,800 lb (6,260 kg)
　　　　　　Maximum 15,000 lb (6,803 kg)
Performance: cruising speed 150 mph (241 kph); range 299 miles (481 km)
Used also by: Oman, Thailand
Notes: The Bell Model 214 is derived from the Model 214 Huey Plus, with the transmission system of the Bell King Cobra experimental gunship helicopter.

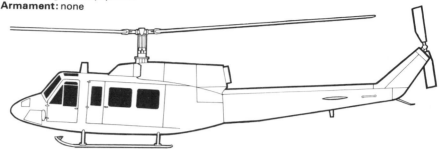

Boeing Vertol CH-47 Chinook

Type: medium transport helicopter
Crew: two or three, plus up to 44 passengers
Rotors: two metal cantilever three-blade main rotors
Fuselage: metal semi-monocoque
Landing gear: fixed tricycle unit
Powerplant: two Lycoming T55-L-11C turboshafts, each rated at 3,750 shp but delivering 7,200 shp through the combined transmission
Fuel capacity: 910 gallons (4,137 litres) in tanks in the fuselage external pods, or 868 gallons (3,944 litres) if the Crashworthy Fuel System is fitted
Avionics: communications and navigation equipment
Armament: none
Dimensions: Span 60 ft (18.29 m) each
　　　　　　　Length (fuselage) 51 ft (15.54 m)
　　　　　　　Height 18 ft 7¾ in (5.68 m)
Rotor disc area: 5,655 ft² (523.3 m²) in all
Weights: Empty 21,464 lb (9,736 kg)
　　　　　　Loaded 33,000 lb (14,968 kg)
　　　　　　Maximum 46,000 lb (20,865 kg)
Performance: (at maximum take-off weight) speed 189 mph (304 kph) at sea level; cruising speed 158 mph (254 kph); climb 2,880 ft (878 m) per minute at sea level; service ceiling 15,000 ft (4,570 m); combat radius with 6,400-lb (2,903-kg) payload 115 miles (185 km); ferry range 1,331 miles (2,142 km)
Used also by: Argentina, Australia, Canada, Italy, Libya, Morocco, Nigeria, Philippines, South Korea, Spain, Syria, UK, USA
Notes: Design of this family of all-weather medium transport helicopters began in 1956, with the first flight being made in 1961. There have been three production variants:
　1. CH-47A, with 2,200-shp Lycoming T55-L-5 or 2,650-shp T55-L-7 turboshafts
　2. CH-47B, with 2,850-shp T55-L-7C turboshafts and improved rotors
　3. CH-47C, to which the specification above relates.
Maximum payload, carried externally, is 25,250 lb (11,453 kg).

Lockheed-Georgia C-130 Hercules

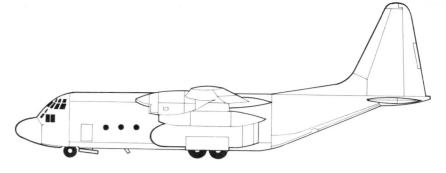

Type: tactical transport aircraft
Crew: four, plus up to 92 passengers
Wings: metal cantilever high-wing monoplane
Fuselage: aluminium and magnesium alloy semi-monocoque
Tail unit: metal cantilever
Landing gear: hydraulically actuated retractable tricycle unit
Powerplant: four Allison T56-A-15 turboprops, each rated at 4,508 ehp and driving a Hamilton Standard four-blade metal propeller, plus provision for eight Aerojet-General 15KS-1,000 JATO units, each rated at 1,000-lb (454-kg) static thrust for 15 seconds
Fuel capacity: 5,795 gallons (26,344 litres) in six integral wing tanks, and 2,264 gallons (10,292 litres) in two underwing pylon tanks
Avionics: comprehensive communication and navigation equipment
Armament: none
Dimensions: Span 132 ft 7 in (40.41 m)
Length 97 ft 9 in (29.78 m)
Height 38 ft 3 in (11.66 m)
Wing area: 1,745 ft² (162.12 m²)
Weights: Empty 75,331 lb (34,169 kg)
Loaded 155,000 lb (70,310 kg)
Maximum 175,000 lb (79,380 kg)
Performance: (at maximum take-off weight) cruising speed 386 mph (621 kph); economical cruising speed 345 mph (556 kph); climb 1,900 ft (579 m) per minute at sea level; service ceiling at a weight of 130,000 lb (58,970 kg) 33,000 ft (10,060 m); range with maximum payload 2,487 miles (4,002 km); range with maximum fuel and a payload of 20,000 lb (9,070 kg) 5,135 miles (8,264 km)

Used also by: many nations

Notes: Designed to a US Air Force requirement of 1951 for a tactical transport, the prototype Hercules first flew in 1954. The type has proved most successful and versatile, and there are numerous variants:

1. C-130A initial production aircraft for the USAF, with 3,750-shp T56-A-1A engines. There were several sub-variants, including the AC-130A gunship and GC-130A drone launcher
2. C-130B, with 4,050-shp T56-A-7A engines, different propellers and greater weights. Sub-variants include the WC-130B weather reconnaissance model and JC-130B air-snatch satellite recovery aircraft
3. C-130E, with more fuel capacity to increase range. Sub-variants include the DC-130E drone director, HC-130E for the Aerospace Rescue and Recovery Service, and WC-130E weather reconnaissance aircraft
4. C-130H, to which the technical specification above applies, with more powerful engines.

Among the prefixes indicating the C-130's functions are DC (drone director), EC (electronics, communications and ECM), HC (search and rescue, helicopter fuelling and spacecraft retrieval), KC (assault transport and probe-drogue refueller), LC (wheel/ski undercarriage) and WC (weather reconnaissance). The AC-130H is a gunship with the formidable armament of one 105-mm howitzer, one 40-mm cannon, two 20-mm or T-171 cannon, two 7.62-mm Miniguns and other optional weapons. The maximum payload of the C-130H is 43,811 lb (19,872 kg).

Lockheed-California P-3 Orion

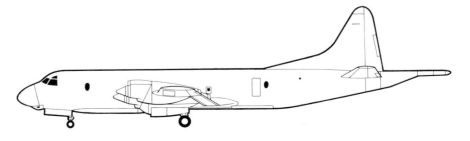

Type: anti-submarine warfare aircraft
Crew: 10
Wings: aluminium alloy cantilever low-wing monoplane
Fuselage: aluminium alloy semi-monocoque
Tail unit: aluminium alloy cantilever
Landing gear: hydraulically actuated retractable tricycle unit

Powerplant: four Allison T56-A-14 turbo-props, each rated at 4,910 shp and driving a Hamilton Standard four-blade metal propeller

Fuel capacity: 7,542 gallons (34,826 litres) in one fuselage and four integral wing tanks

Avionics: comprehensive communication and navigation/attack equipment, including an AN/ASQ-114 general-purpose digital computer, AN/AYA-8 data processing system, AN/ASN-84 inertial navigation system, AN/APN-187 doppler radar, AN/ASA-70 tactical display, AN/ARR-72 sono receivers, AN/ASQ-81 magnetic anomaly detector, AN/ASA-64 submarine anomaly detector, AN/ALQ-78 ECM system, and AN/APS-115 surveillance radar

Armament: weapons bay can accommodate a variety of mines, depth bombs and torpedoes (including the MK-25/39/55/56 2,000-lb/907-kg mine, the MK-36/52 1,000-lb/454-kg mine, the MK-54 and 57 depth bombs, the MK-101 nuclear depth bomb, and the MK-43/44/46 torpedoes), plus 10 hardpoints for external stores (two under the fuselage, each capable of carrying a torpedo or 2,000-lb/907-kg mine, and three under each wing, capable of carrying, from inboard to outboard, a torpedo or 2,000-lb/907-kg mine; a torpedo, 1,000-lb/454-kg mine, single rocket or rocket pod; and a torpedo, 500-lb/227-kg mine, single rocket or rocket pod). Maximum load is 19,252 lb (8,733 kg)

Dimensions: Span 99 ft 8 in (30.37 m)
Length 116 ft 10 in (35.61 m)
Height 33 ft 8½ in (10.29 m)

Wing area: 1,300 ft² (120.77 m²)

Weights: Empty 61,491 lb (27,890 kg)
Loaded 135,000 lb (61,235 kg)
Maximum 142,000 lb (64,410 kg)

Performance: (at maximum take-off weight) speed 473 mph (761 kph) at a weight of 105,000 lb (47,625 kg) at 15,000 ft (4,570 m); cruising speed 378 mph (608 kph) at a weight of 110,000 lb (49,895 kg) at 25,000 ft (7,620 m); patrol speed 237 mph (381 kph) at a weight of 110,000 lb (49,985 kg) at 1,500 ft (457 m); climb 1,950 ft (594 m) per minute at 1,500 ft (457 m); service ceiling 28,300 ft (8,625 m); combat radius with no time on station at normal loaded weight 2,383 miles (3,835 km); combat radius with 3 hours on station at 1,500 ft (457 m) 1,550 miles (2,494 km)

Used also by: Australia, Canada, Japan, Netherlands, New Zealand, Norway, Spain, USA

Notes: Derived from the relatively unsuccessful Electra turboprop airliner, the P-3 family of ASW aircraft has been very successful since the flight of the first prototype in 1958. There are several variants:

1. P-3A, the initial production model with 4,500-ehp T56-A-10W engines. The 110th aircraft onwards are known as Deltic P-3As for their more advanced electronics
2. WP-3A weather reconnaissance model
3. P-3B, the second main production model, with 4,910-ehp T56-A-14 engines, also used by Australia, New Zealand and Norway. US Navy P-3Bs have Bullpup missile capability. A kit to improve the electronics is available
4. P-3C, to which the specification above relates, is an advanced version of the P-3B, with A-NEW system of electronics and sensors. The Update programme introduced better electronics in the mid-1970s, and the Update II programme of the later 1970s again improves electronics, adds an infra-red detection system, and introduces Harpoon air-to-surface missile capability
5. RP-3D research aircraft to map the earth's magnetic field
6. WP-3D atmospheric research aircraft
7. EP-3E early warning aircraft
8. P-3F long-range surveillance aircraft for Iran
9. CP-140 Aurora ASW aircraft for Canada, basically similar to the P-3C, but with special electronics derived from those of the S-3A Viking, Canadian sensors, and improvements from the Update programme.

McDonnell Douglas (McDonnell Aircraft) F-4 Phantom II

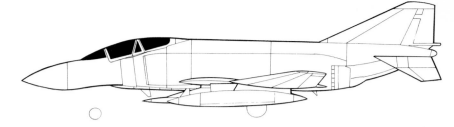

Type: all-weather multi-role fighter
Crew: two, seated in tandem
Wings: metal cantilever low-wing monoplane
Fuselage: metal semi-monocoque
Tail unit: metal cantilever
Landing gear: hydraulically actuated retractable tricycle unit
Powerplant: two General Electric J79-GE-17A turbojets, each rated at 17,900-lb (8,119-kg) static thrust with afterburning
Fuel capacity: 1,545 gallons (7,022 litres) in seven fuselage and two integral wing tanks, plus provision for one 500-gallon (2,270-litre) auxiliary tanks under the fuselage, and two 308-gallon (1,400-litre) tanks under the wings
Avionics: comprehensive communication and navigation/attack equipment, including a CPK-92A/A24G-34 central air data computer, AN/AJB-7 bombing system, AN/ASQ-91 (MOD) weapons release system, AN/ASG-26 (MOD) lead-computing optical sight; AN/ASA-32 automatic fire-control system, AN/APQ-120 fire-control system radar and AN/ARQ-77 AGM-12 control system
Armament: one M61A-1 20-mm multi-barrel cannon, four AIM-7 Sparrow air-to-air missiles semi-recessed under the fuselage, four AIM-9 Sidewinder or two Sparrow air-to-air missiles on two underwing pylons (Falcon, Shrike, Walleye and Bullpup missiles can also be carried on these stations); alternatively, the seven attachment points under the fuselage and wings can carry loads of up to 16,000 lb (7,250 kg) in weight: B-28, 43, 57 and 61 nuclear bombs; BLU-1, 27, 52, and 76 fire bombs; M117, M118, M129, MC-1, Mark 36, 81, 82, 83 and 84 bombs; gun pods; cluster bombs; ECM pods; rocket pods; and other stores.
Dimensions: Span 38 ft 7½ in (11.77 m)
Length 63 ft (19.2 m)
Height 16 ft 5½ in (5.02 m)
Wing area: 530 ft² (49.2 m²)
Weights: Empty 30,328 lb (13,757 kg)
Loaded 41,487 lb (18,818 kg)
Maximum 61,795 lb (28,030 kg)
Performance: (at maximum take-off weight) speed 1,500 mph (2,414 kph) or Mach 2.27 at high altitude with Sparrow missiles

only; speed 920 mph (1,464 kph) or Mach 1.19 at low altitude with Sparrow missiles only; cruising speed 571 mph (919 kph); climb 6,170 ft (1,881 m) per minute at sea level; service ceiling 28,100 ft (8,565 m); service ceiling with Sparrow missiles only more than 60,000 ft (19,685 m); combat radius on interdiction mission 712 miles (1,145 km); ferry range 1,978 miles (3,184 km)
Used also by: Greece, Iran, Israel, Japan, South Korea, Spain, Turkey, UK, USA, West Germany
Notes: Probably the greatest fighter of the post-World War II era, the F-4 originated in a US Navy requirement of 1954 for a long-range all-weather attack fighter. The prototype flew in 1958, and the type began to enter service in 1960, being adopted by the USAF in addition to the US Navy. There have been numerous variants, including:

1. F-4A, with J79-GE-2 engines for the US Navy
2. F-2B, with J79-GE-8 engines, for the US Navy and Marine Corps as an all-weather fighter
3. RF-4B USMC reconnaissance version of the F-4B with multiple sensors
4. F-4C, with J79-GE-15 engines, a version of the F-4B for the USAF and Spain
5. F-4C Wild Weasel defence suppression aircraft for the USAF with ECM warning equipment, jamming pods, chaff dispensers and radiation-homing missiles
6. RF-4C multi-sensor reconnaissance version of the F-4C for the USAF
7. F-4D, with J79-GE-15 engines, a version of the F-4C with improved electronics for the USAF, Iran and South Korea
8. F-4E, to which the above technical specifications apply, a multi-role

fighter for air superiority, close support and interdiction missions, with an inbuilt cannon, improved electronics and advanced engines for the USAF, Greece, Iran, Australia, Israel, West Germany, Turkey and South Korea
9. F-4EJ version of the F-4E for Japan
10. RF-4E multi-sensor reconnaissance model of the F-4E for West Germany, Greece, Iran, Israel, Japan and Turkey
11. F-4F two-seat fighter with improved aerodynamics to increase manoeuvrability, and more advanced electronics, for West Germany
12. F-4G, a limited-production version of the F-4B with data link communications for the US Navy
13. F-4G Wild Weasel version of the F-4E, with special equipment for the suppression of enemy radar guidance systems
14. F-4J, with J79-GE-10 engines, as a development of the F-4B for the US Navy and Marine Corps, with a primary role of interception but with secondary ground-attack capability by virtue of its Westinghouse AN/AWG-10 pulse-doppler fire-control system, and Lear Siegler AJB-7 bombing system
15. F-4K version of the F-4B for the Royal Navy, with the electronics of the F-4J and a powerplant of two Rolls-Royce Spey RB.168-25R Mark 201 turbofans, each rated at 21,250-lb (9,639-kg) static thrust with afterburning
16. F-4M version of the F-4K for the Royal Air Force
17. F-4N, designation of updated F-4Bs
18. F-4S, designation for updated F-4Js with modified J79-GE-10B engines and improved AN/AWG-10A weapons control system.

Iraq

28,000 men, including 10,000 air defence personnel, plus about 339 combat aircraft.

1 bomber sqn with 12 Tu-22.
1 light bomber sqn with 10 Il-28.
4 FGA sqns with 80 MiG-23B.
3 FGA sqns with 60 Su-7B.
3 FGA sqns with 30 Su-20.
2 FGA sqns with 20 Hunter FB.59, FR.10.
5 interceptor sqns with 115 MiG-21.
1 COIN sqn with 12 Jet Provost T.52.
2 transport sqns with 10 An-2, 8 An-12, 8 An-24, 2 An-26, 2 Tu-124, 3 Il-14, 2 Heron.
8 helicopter sqns with 35 Mi-4, 14 Mi-6, 80 Mi-8, 47 *Alouette* III, 8 Super *Frelon*, 40 Gazelle, 3 Puma.

Trainers include MiG-15, MiG-21, MiG-23U, Su-7U, Hunter T.69, 10 Yak-11, 12 L-29, 8 L-39.
AA-2 'Atoll' AAM; AS.11/12 ASM.
SA-2, SA-3 and 25 SA-6 SAM.
(32 Mirage F1C fighters, 4 Mirage F1B trainers, Il-76 transports, R.550 *Magic* AAM, *Exocet* ASM on order.)

Antonov An-12 'Cub'

Type: transport aircraft
Crew: six, and up to 100 passengers
Wings: metal cantilever high-wing monoplane
Fuselage: metal semi-monocoque
Tail unit: metal cantilever
Landing gear: hydraulically actuated retractable tricycle unit
Powerplant: four Ivchenko AI-20K turboprops, each rated at 4,000 ehp and driving a four-blade metal propeller
Fuel capacity: 3,981 gallons (18,100 litres) in 22 bag-type wing tanks
Avionics: comprehensive communication and navigation equipment
Armament: two 23-mm NR-23 cannon in the tail turret

Dimensions: Span 124 ft 8 in (38.0 m)
Length 108 ft 7¼ in (33.1 m)
Height 34 ft 6½ in (10.53 m)
Wing area: 1,310 ft² (121.7 m²)
Weights: Empty 61,730 lb (28,000 kg)
Loaded 121,474 lb (55,100 kg)
Maximum 134,480 lb (61,000 kg)
Performance: speed 482 mph (777 kph); cruising speed 416 mph (670 kph); climb 1,970 ft (600 m) per minute at sea level; service ceiling 33,500 ft (10,200 m); range with maximum payload 2,236 miles (3,600 km); range with maximum fuel 3,540 miles (5,700 km)
Used also by: Algeria, Bangladesh, China, Egypt, Ethiopia, India, Indonesia, Poland, Sudan, Syria, USSR, Yugoslavia
Notes: Derived from the An-10 airliner, the An-12 transport first flew in 1958. The military version is known to NATO as the 'Cub A', and has a maximum payload of 44,090 lb (20,000 kg).

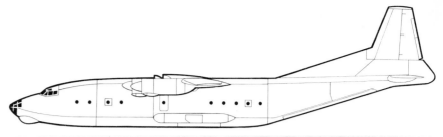

Société Nationale Industrielle Aérospatiale SA 321 Super *Frelon*

Type: heavy-duty helicopter
Crew: up to 5 plus up to 30 passengers
Rotor: metal cantilever six-blade main rotor; metal cantilever five-blade tail rotor
Fuselage: metal semi-monocoque
Landing gear: non-retractable tricycle unit
Powerplant: three Turboméca Turmo IIIC6 (IIIE6 in SA 321H) turboshafts, each rated at 1,550 shp
Fuel capacity: 874 gallons (3,975 litres) in flexible fuselage tanks, plus a variety of optional internal and external tanks in various models
Avionics: full detection, tracking and attack equipment
Armament: four homing torpedoes or *Exocet* anti-ship missiles
Dimensions: Span 62 ft (18.9 m)
Length 75 ft 6¾ in (23.03 m)
Height 21 ft 10¼ in (6.66 m)

Wing area: 3,020 ft² (280.6 m²)
Weights: Empty 15,130 lb (6,863 kg)
Loaded
Maximum 28,660 lb (13,000 kg)
Performance: (at maximum take-off weight) speed 171 mph (275 kph) at sea level; cruising speed 155 mph (250 kph) at sea level; climb 1,312 ft (400 m) per minute at sea level; service ceiling 10,325 ft (3,150 m); range 633 miles (1,020 km) at sea level with 7,716 lb (3,500 kg) payload; A/S endurance 4 hours

Used also by: China, France, Israel, Libya, Pakistan, South Africa, Syria, Zaire
Notes: The SA 321 was developed from the smaller SA 3200 *Frelon*. The main military versions are: SA 320G A/S helicopter; and SA 321H for army and air force use, without external fairings under fuselage or stabilising floats. Maximum payload is 11,023 lb (5,000 kg) carried internally or externally. The rescue hoist has a capacity of 606 lb (275 kg).

Israel

The Israeli Defence Forces/Air Force

Like the *Luftwaffe*, the Israeli Defence Forces/Air Force (IDF/AF) is a modern creation, dating from the creation of the state of Israel in 1948, although it had existed in clandestine form before this date. Since 1948, though, the Israeli Defence Forces in general, and the IDF/AF in particular, have emerged as some of the most efficient and professional in the world, having fought four major wars in the period (1948, 1956, 1967 and 1973), all against Israel's Arab neighbours. The development and maintenance of these forces has been an enormous strain on Israel's economy, but so great have been the external difficulties in obtaining the right weapons from abroad, combined with the cost of such weapons, that Israel has become a major producer of sophisticated weapons, despite her small size, and is now becoming a successful exporter of all types of military equipment. Surrounded by the Mediterranean to the west, and Arab nations on her other flanks, Israel has no real ambitions towards territorial aggrandisement as such, but merely to provide herself with buffer zones against aggression by the Arab states. Her forces, therefore, are based on short, internal lines of communication, with a view to stemming any incursion into Israeli territory, and her air forces are designed to provide tactical support for the armour/infantry forces on the ground, while preventing the Arab air forces from bombing Israel and countering Israeli qualitative and tactical superiority on the ground by the introduction of superior air forces over the battlefield. The IDF/AF has 21,000 men, some 12.8 per cent of the total strength of the standing armed forces, which receive some 23.3 per cent of Israel's gross national product.

For financial reasons, amongst others, Israel is loathe to use specialised aircraft suitable for a single role only, so the majority of Israeli aircraft are used both for interception and for FGA duties. There are 11 squadrons so equipped: one with 25 F/TF-15, five with 170F-4E, three with 30 Mirage IIICJ/BJ, and two with 50 *Kfir/Kfir* C2. There are specialised FGA squadrons, however, for dual-purpose aircraft can never be entirely satisfactory in the FGA role. Thus six FGA squadrons are equipped with 250 A-4E/H/M/N attack aircraft, and it is these that form the real heart of the IDF/AF's tactical support arm.

In the type of land battle preferred by Israel, accurate information of the enemy's dispositions is vital, and here the IDF/AF is well serviced by a reconnaissance squadron equipped with 12 RF-4E, two OV-1 and four E-2C AEW aircraft. Without mobility, though, reconnaissance is of little use, and to allow her forces to react speedily to new tactical information, Israel has relatively effective, if mixed, transport forces: 10 Boeing 707, 24 C-130E/H, six C-97, 18 C-47 and two KC-130H aircraft. With these machines the Israelis are able to move relatively large forces from one end of Israel to the other with some speed. If necessary, some of Israel's 106 light transport and liaison aircraft can also be pressed into this task. Also capable of impressment into offensive duties are some trainers, such as the 24 TA-4E/H and 70 Magister aircraft.

Tactical mobility and support is facilitated by the fact that Israel has some 160 helicopters, including eight Super *Frelon* and 28 CH-53G heavy lift types, 40 Bell 205A and 20 Bell 206 utility helicopters, and 25 UH-1D general-purpose helicopters. Combat in the 1973 war has also persuaded the Israelis, at both the giving and receiving ends, of the importance of SAM missiles, and the IDF/AF has 15 batteries of 90 HAWK missiles, which proved very effective in the 1973 war.

Israel is now producing more aircraft of her own, and indigenously produces spares and replacements for foreign types, but a substantial part of Israel's armoury must still come from abroad. On order at the end of 1977 were 15 F-15 and 75 F-16 fighters, and 30 Hughes 500 helicopter gunships, all of which will help to keep Israel in a strong position *vis-à-vis* her Arab neighbours.

21,000 men (2,000 air defence conscripts), or 25,000 on moblisation, and 543 combat aircraft.

11 FGA/interceptor sqns: 1 with 25 F/TF-15, 5 with 170 F-4E, 3 with 30 Mirage IIICJ/BJ, 2 with 50 *Kfir/Kfir* C2.
6 FGA sqns with 250 A-4E/H/M/N Skyhawk.
1 recce sqn with 12 RF-4E, 2 OV-1, 4 E-2C AEW ac.
Transports incl 10 Boeing 707, 24 C-130E/H, 6 C-97, 18 C-47, 2 KC-130H.
Liaison ac incl 14 *Arava*, 8 Islander, 23 Do 27, 9 Do 28, 25 Cessna U-206, 1 Westwind, 16 Queen Air.
Trainers incl 24 TA-4E/H, 70 Magister, 30 Super Cub.
Helicopters incl 8 Super *Frelon*, 28 CH-53D, 6 AH-1G, 40 Bell 205A, 20 Bell 206, 12 Bell 212, 25 UH-1D, 19 *Alouette* II/III.
Sidewinder, AIM-7E/F Sparrow, *Shafrir* AAM; *Luz* 1, Maverick, Shrike, Walleye, Bullpup ASM.
15 SAM btys with 90 HAWK.
(15 F-15, 75 F-16 fighters, 30 Hughes 500 helicopter gunships on order.)
Naval Air Arm
3 Westwind 1124N MR ac.
(3 Westwind MR ac on order.)

Boeing Airplane KC-97

Type: transport and flight refuelling aircraft
Crew: five, plus 96 passengers or 69 litters in the transport role

Wings: metal cantilever low/mid-wing monoplane
Fuselage: metal semi-monocoque
Tail unit: metal cantilever
Landing gear: hydraulically actuated retractable tricycle unit

Powerplant: four Pratt & Whitney R-4360-59 piston engines, each rated at 3,500 hp and driving a Hamilton Standard metal four-blade propeller
Fuel capacity:
Avionics: comprehensive communication and navigation equipment
Armament: none
Dimensions: Span 141 ft 3 in (43.05 m)
Length 110 ft 4 in (33.63 m)
Height 38 ft 3 in (11.66 m)
Wing area: 1,720 ft² (159.8 m²)
Weights: Empty 82,500 lb (37,422 kg)
Loaded
Maximum 175,000 lb (79,379 kg)

Performance: speed 375 mph (604 kph); cruising speed 300 mph (483 kph); service ceiling 35,000 ft (10,670 m); range 4,300 miles (6,920 km)
Used also by: Spain
Notes: The C-97 Stratofreighter family was derived from the B-29 Superfortress, elements in common being the wings, engines, tail surfaces and lower fuselage. The first C-97 flew in 1944, and the initial production order in 1947 was for the C-97A, which could carry 134 troops or 53,000 lb (24,041 kg) of freight. The first six aircraft built were akin to the B-29, but all subsequent models were related more to the B-50. The next production model was the

C-97C with more powerful engines, strengthened fuselage and casualty evacuation equipment. All future production of the type was of KC tanker/transports, the first production model being the KC-97E, followed by the KC-97F with more powerful engines, and the KC-97G, to which the technical specification above relates. The KC-97G has permanent underwing tanks, and relocated internal tanks, allowing the aircraft to be used as a tanker or as a transport without modification. Some KC-97Gs were modified into KC-97Ls by the addition of General Electric J47-GE-25A turbojet pods removed from surplus KC-50 tankers.

Grumman Aerospace E-2 Hawkeye

Type: airborne early warning aircraft
Crew: five
Wings: metal cantilever high-wing monoplane
Fuselage: metal semi-monocoque
Tail unit: metal and glassfibre cantilever
Landing gear: hydraulically actuated retractable tricycle unit
Powerplant: two Allison T56-A-425 turboprops, each rated at 4,910 eshp and driving a Hamilton Standard four-blade metal propeller
Fuel capacity:
Avionics: comprehensive communication and navigation equipment, plus extensive surveillance equipment, including AN/APS-120 search radar with OL-93/AP radar detector processor (or AN/APS-125 search radar), RT-988/A IFF interrogator with OL-76/AP IFF detector processor, AN/ALR-59 passive detection system, AN/APA-172 control indicator group, OL-77/ASQ computer programmer and other aids
Armament: none

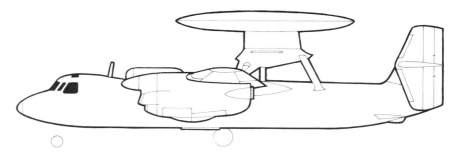

Dimensions: Span 80 ft 7 in (24.56 m)
Length 57 ft 7 in (17.55 m)
Height 18 ft 4 in (5.59 m)
Wing area: 700 ft² (65.03 m²)
Weights: Empty 37,678 lb (17,090 kg)
Loaded
Maximum 51,569 lb (23,391 kg)
Performance: (at maximum take-off weight) speed 361 mph (581 kph); cruising speed 302 mph (486 kph); service ceiling 30,800 ft (9,390 m); ferry range 1,605 miles (2,583 km)
Used also by: Japan, USA

Notes: The prototype of this carrierborne airborne early-warning aircraft flew in 1960, and there are several versions:
1. E-2A, the initial production version, with APS-96 long-range search radar in the 24-ft (7.32-m) diameter AN/APA-171 rotodome
2. E-2B, with a Litton Industries L-304 microelectronic general-purposes computer. All E-2As were retrofitted to E-2B standard by 1971
3. E-2C, with Grumman/GE radar
4. C-2A Greyhound carrier on-board delivery transport, without radome, but up to 39 passengers.

Israel Aircraft Industries *Kfir*

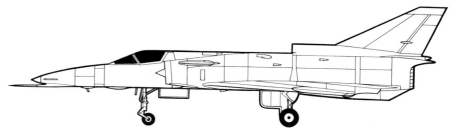

Type: interceptor, patrol and ground-attack fighter

Crew: one

Wings: metal cantilever low-wing delta monoplane, and fixed metal cantilever shoulder-mounted canard plane

Fuselage: metal semi-monocoque

Tail unit: metal cantilever

Landing gear: hydraulically actuated retractable tricycle unit

Powerplant: one General Electric J79 turbojet, rated at 17,900-lb (8,119-kg) static thrust with afterburning

Fuel capacity: probably about 880 gallons (4,000 litres) in internal tanks, plus provision for one or two drop tanks under each wing, of 110-, 132-, 286- or 374-gallon (500-, 600-, 1,300- or 1,700-litre) capacity

Avionics: comprehensive communications and navigation/attack equipment, including MBT Weapons System 2-computer flight control system; Elta Electronics S-8600 multi-mode navigation and weapon delivery system; Tamam central air data computer; Elta EL/M-2001 air-to-air and air-to-surface pulse doppler ranging radar; and Israel Electro-optics head up display and automatic gunsight

Armament: two 30-mm IAI-built DEFA cannon with probably 125 rounds per gun, and seven hardpoints (three under the fuselage and two under each wing) for external stores: for interception these usually comprise two Rafael Shafrir air-to-air missiles; for ground-attack one Luz-1 air-to-surface missile or two 1,000-lb (454-kg) bombs under the fuselage, and two 1,000-lb (454-kg) or four 500-lb (227-kg) bombs under the wings; other stores include rocket pods; napalm tanks; Shrike, Maverick or HOBOS air-to-surface missiles; ECM pods; and drop tanks

Dimensions: Span 26 ft 11½ in (8.22 m)
Length 51 ft 0¼ in (15.55 m)
Height 13 ft 11¼ in (4.25 m)

Wing area: 442 ft² (31.08 m²)

Weights: Empty about 16,060 lb (7,285 kg)
Loaded about 20,701 lb (9,390 kg)
Maximum about 32,188 lb (14,600 kg)

Performance: speed more than 1,516 mph (2,335 kph) or Mach 2.3 at 36,100 ft (11,000 m); climb 45,950 ft (14,000 m) per minute at sea level; climb to 36,100 ft (11,000 m) 1 minute 45 seconds; service ceiling more than 50,000 ft (15,240 m); combat radius as an interceptor with two 132-gallon (600-litre) drop tanks 230-332 miles (370-535 km); combat radius on a lo-lo-lo ground-attack mission 404 miles (650 km); combat radius on a hi-lo-hi ground-attack mission 807 miles (1,300 km)

Used only by: Israel

Notes: Originally a reworked Mirage airframe with Israeli electronics and an improved J79 engine, the original *Kfir* equipped two squadrons before the introduction in 1976 of the *Kfir*-C2, which features fixed canard foreplanes, and a dog-toothed mainplane leading edge. These improvements enhance the type's handling characteristics markedly, especially in the lower range of dogfighting speeds. Weights and performance figures above are for the *Kfir*-C2. The foreplanes, which span 12 ft 9½ in (3.9 m), add only 187 lb (85 kg) to the weight of the aircraft.

Israel Aircraft Industries 1124N Westwind

Type: maritime surveillance

Crew:

Wings: metal cantilever mid-wing monoplane

Fuselage: metal semi-monocoque

Tail unit: metal cantilever

Landing gear: hydraulically actuated retractable tricycle unit

Powerplant: two Garrett-AiResearch TFE 731-3-1G turbofans, each rated at 3,700-lb (1,678-kg) static thrust

Fuel capacity: 1,082 gallons (4,920 litres) in integral wing tanks, wingtips and rear fuselage tanks

Avionics: comprehensive communications and navigation equipment, plus Litton APS-503 search radar. Forward-looking infra-red equipment, low-light TV and MAD gear can also be fitted, as can flare and chaff equipment

Armament: none

Dimensions: Span 44 ft 9½ in (13.65 m)
Length 52 ft 3 in (15.93 m)
Height 15 ft 9½ in (4.81 m)

Wing area: 308.26 ft² (28.64 m²)

Weights: Empty 12,300 lb (5,578 kg)
Loaded
Maximum 22,850 lb (10,364 kg)

Performance: (at maximum take-off weight) speed 542 mph (872 kph) up to 19,400 ft (5,900 m); cruising speed 449 mph (722 kph); climb 7,500 ft (2,285 m) per minute at sea level; service ceiling 45,000 ft (13,725 m); range more than 2,994 miles (4,818 km); endurance 7 hours 30 minutes

Used also by: Honduras

Notes: A development of the IAI-built Rockwell-Standard Westwind, small numbers of the maritime reconnaissance version serve with the Israeli Navy for coastal patrol, electronic reconnaissance and naval tactical support. With the exception of the cruising speed and range figures, the dimensional, weight and performance figures are for the civil Westwind.

Rafael Armament Development Authority *Luz* 1

Type: air-to-surface tactical guided missile
Guidance: probably TV
Dimensions: Span
Body diameter
Length
Booster: probably solid-propellant rocket
Sustainer: probably solid-propellant rocket
Warhead: high explosive, in the region of 441 lb (200 kg)
Weights: Launch
Burnt out
Performance: range about 50 miles (80 km)
Used only by: Israel
Notes: The *Luz* 1 is an Israeli missile for use on F-4E and *Kfir*-C2 aircraft, with the primary task of eliminating the SA-6 and SA-9 missile batteries, ZSU-23-4 self-propelled AA guns, and FROG and 'Scud' battlefield missile systems deployed by the Arab nations surrounding Israel.

Rafael Armament Development Authority *Shafrir*

Type: air-to-air tactical guided missile
Guidance: infra-red homing
Dimensions: Span 20½ in (52.0 cm)
Body diameter 6 3/10 in (16.0 cm)
Length 8 ft 1¾ in (2.47 m)
Booster: solid-propellant rocket
Sustainer: same as above
Warhead: 24¼ lb (11 kg) high explosive

Weights: Launch 205 lb (93 kg)
Burnt out
Performance: range 3 miles (5 km)
Used also by: Chile, Taiwan
Notes: Designed as a simple dogfighting weapon, the *Shafrir* has achieved a 75 per cent kill rate in combat. Electronics have been kept to the minimum, and operation is very simple: when the aircraft's sensors detect a target within range, the pilot is warned by a buzzer, and can fire the missile as soon as its readiness light indicates that it has locked onto the target.

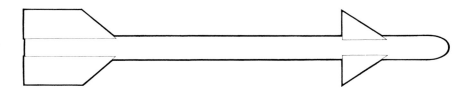

Italy

The Italian Air Force

Like West Germany, Italy has restricted her air force to purely tactical operations, and has no ambitions towards any form of strategic air war. Militarily this is all that Italy needs, which is fortunate in the difficult economic straits in which the country has found herself in recent years. As it is, the air force is neatly tailored to provide the Italian Army with the air support needed for its operations in defence of Italy. The air force numbers 69,000 personnel, about 19 per cent of the total strength of the armed forces, whose budget amounts to 2.6 per cent of the gross national product annually.

Italy's air defence is based on two main combat types, the Lockheed F-104, which is now built in Italy, and the Fiat G91. The single most important element in the air force is the FGA force, made up of one squadron with 18 F-104G, three squadrons with 54 F-104G/S, and two with 36 G91Y aircraft. This main force is supplemented by three reconnaissance and light attack squadrons equipped with 54 G91R, and six all-weather fighter squadrons with 72 F-104S. For high-speed reconnaissance at longer ranges than can be managed by the G91 squadrons, there are two squadrons equipped with the RF-104G. Maritime reconnaissance is also an air force function, and for this there are three squadrons, two of them with 18 Atlantic aircraft, and the other with eight S-2F aircraft. The use of electronic countermeasures features prominently in Italian defence thinking, and for this purpose there is an ECM squadron with eight PD-808, two EC-119G and a miscellany of EC-47, RC-45 and RT-33 aircraft.

For military transport purposes, there are three squadrons, one with 28 C-119, one with 14 G222 and the last with 13 C-130H aircraft. These can be supplemented to a certain extent by aircraft from the five communications squadrons, equipped with 33 P.166M, 32 SIAI 208M, eight PD-808, two DC-9 and two DC-6 aircraft, plus two SH-3D helicopters. Helicopters do not play a great part in the Italian inventory, except in the two SAR squadrons, which have 14 AB-204, seven AB-47J and three HH-3F helicopters in addition to 11 HU-16 aircraft.

Training is the responsibility of one operational conversion unit with 15 TF-104G, and nine training squadrons with 75 G91T, 100 M.B.326, 14 P.166M and 20 SF-260M aircraft, plus 65 AB 47 and 40 AB 204 helicopters. Italy's training programme is perhaps the most impressive single element of her air force, and this will be improved further when the 100 M.B.339 trainers on order are delivered. Also on order are 100 Tornado FGA aircraft, 30 F-104S fighters, 30 G222 transports and 17 HH-3F helicopters, all of which will improve Italy's front-line air strength and mobility quite considerably.

Mobile SAM defence is the responsibility of the army, which deploys four battalions with HAWK missiles in this role. Fixed SAM defences are the province of the air force, however, and to this end there are 96 Nike Hercules missiles deployed in eight air defence groups.

69,000 (23,000 conscripts) and 319 combat aircraft, plus 28,000 reservists.

6 FGA sqns: 1 with 18 F-104G, 3 with 54 F-104S/G, 2 with 36 G91Y.
3 lt attack/recce sqns with 54 G91R/R1/R1A.
6 AWX sqns with 72 F-104S.
2 recce sqns with 36 F/RF-104G.
3 MR sqns: 2 with 18 Atlantic, 1 with 8 S-2F Tracker.
1 ECM recce sqn with 6 PD-808, 2 EC-119G, EC-47, RC-45, RT-33.
3 transport sqns: 1 with 28 C-119, 1 with 14 G222, 1 with 13 C-130H.
5 comms sqns with 33 P.166M, 32 SIAI 208M, 8 PD-808, 2 DC-9, 2 DC-6 ac; 2 SH-3D helicopters.
2 SAR sqns with 11 HU-16 ac; 14 AB-204, 7 AB-47J, 3 HH-3F helicopters.
1 OCU with 15 TF-104G.
9 trg sqns with 75 G91T, 100 M.B.326, 14 P.166M, 20 SF-260M ac; 65 AB-47, 40 AB-204 helicopters.
AIM-7E Sparrow, Sidewinder AAM.
8 SAM groups with 96 Nike Hercules.
(100 Tornado FGA, 30 F-104S fighters, 100 M.B. 339 trg, 30 G222 transports; 17 HH-3F helicopters; *Aspide* AAM on order.)

Naval Air Arm
5 ASW helicopter sqns with 3 SH-34, 24 SH-3D, 32 AB-204AS, 12 AB-212.
(15 AB-212, 9 SH-3D on order.)

Army Aviation
20 units with 40 O-1E, 39 L-21, 80 SM. 1019 lt ac; helicopters incl 70 AB-47G/J, 36 AB-204B, 95 AB-205A, 140 AB-206A/A-1, 26 CH-47C, 5 A-109 (60 A-129 on order).

Aeritalia (Lockheed) F-104S

Type: multi-role combat aircraft
Crew: one
Wings: metal cantilever mid-wing monoplane
Fuselage: metal monocoque
Tail unit: metal cantilever
Landing gear: hydraulically actuated retractable tricycle unit
Powerplant: one General Electric J79-GE-19 turbojet, rated at 17,900-lb (8,119-kg) static thrust with afterburning
Fuel capacity: 746 gallons (3,392 litres) in five bag tanks in the fuselage, plus provision for two 163-gallon (740-litre) tanks on pylons and two 142-gallon (645-litre) wingtip tanks
Avionics: comprehensive communication and navigation/attack equipment, including R21G/H multi-purpose radar for air-to-air interception, ground and contour mapping, and terrain avoidance; fixed-reticule gunsight; bombing computer; air data computer; and dead reckoning navigation devices.
Armament: nine external hardpoints, at wingtips, under the wings and under the fuselage, for a maximum external load of 7,500 lb (3,402 kg). This load can be made up of a variety of weapons, but the normal load is two Sparrow III air-to-air missiles under the wings, two Sidewinder air-to-air missiles under the fuselage, and two Sidewinders or two 142-gallon (645-litre) tanks on the wingtips. A 20-mm M61 multi-barrel cannon can be installed in the fuselage instead of the Sparrow control equipment
Dimensions: Span 21 ft 11 in (6.68 m)
Length 54 ft 9 in (16.69 m)
Height 13 ft 6 in (4.11 m)
Wing area: 196.1 ft² (18.22 m²)
Weights: Empty 14,900 lb (6,760 kg)
Loaded 21,690 lb (9,840 kg)
Maximum 31,000 lb (14,060 kg)
Performance: (at normal loaded weight) speed 1,450 mph (2,330 kph) or Mach 2.2 at 36,100 ft (11,000 m); speed 910 mph (1,464 kph) or Mach 1.2 at sea level; cruising speed 610 mph (981 kph) at 36,100 ft (11,000 m); climb to 35,000 ft (10,670 m) in 1 minute 20 seconds; climb to 56,000 ft (17,070 m) in 2 minutes 40 seconds; service ceiling 58,000 ft (17,680 m); zoom ceiling more than 90,000 ft (27,400 m); radius with maximum fuel 775 miles (1,247 km); ferry range 1,815 miles (2,920 km)
Used also by: Turkey
Notes: This model of the Lockheed F-104 Starfighter is built in Italy for the Italian and Turkish air forces.

89

Aeritalia G91Y

Type: fighter-bomber and reconnaissance fighter

Crew: one

Wings: metal cantilever low-wing monoplane

Fuselage: metal semi-monocoque

Tail unit: metal cantilever

Landing gear: hydraulically actuated retractable tricycle unit

Powerplant: two General Electric J85-GE-13A turbojets, each rated at 4,080-lb (1,850-kg) static thrust with afterburning, and provision for JATO units

Fuel capacity: 703 gallons (3,200 litres) in fuselage and inner wing tanks, and provision for underwing drop tanks

Avionics: comprehensive communications and navigation/attack equipment, including a Computing Devices of Canada 5C-15 position and homing indicator, Sperry SYP-820 2-axis gyro platform, Bendix RDA-12 doppler radar, AiResearch air data computer, Ferranti ISIS B gyro-gunsight and Smiths electronic head up display

Armament: two 30-mm DEFA cannon, and four underwing hardpoints for 1,000-lb (454-kg) bombs, four septuple 2-in (51-mm) rocket pods, four 28x2-in (51-mm) rocket pods, four 5-in (127-mm) rocket containers, or four 750-lb (340-kg) napalm tanks

Dimensions: Span 29 ft 6½ in (9.01 m)
Length 38 ft 3½ in (11.67 m)
Height 14 ft 6 in (4.43 m)

Wing area: 195.15 ft² (18.13 m²)

Weights: Empty 8,598 lb (3,900 kg)
Loaded 17,196 lb (7,800 kg)
Maximum 19,180 lb (8,700 kg)

Performance: (at maximum take-off weight) speed Mach 0.95 at 30,000 ft (9,145 m); speed 690 mph (1,110 kph) at sea level; climb 17,000 ft (5,180 m) per minute at sea level with afterburning; climb 7,000 ft (2,134 m) per minute at sea level without afterburning; time to 40,000 ft (12,200 m) 4 minutes 30 seconds with afterburning, 11 minutes without afterburning; service ceiling 41,000 ft (12,500 m); combat radius with 4,000 lb (1,814 kg) of external stores on a lo-lo-lo mission 230 miles (370 km), on a hi-lo-hi mission 351 miles (565 km); ferry range 2,175 miles (3,500 km)

Used only by: Italy

Notes: Derived from the G91, the G91Y features twin engines in a fuselage based on that of the G91T trainer.

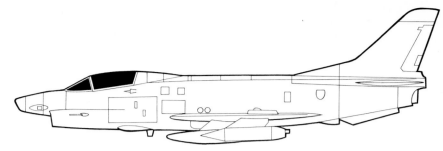

Aeritalia G222

Type: general-purpose transport

Crew: three or four, and up to 44 passengers

Wings: metal cantilever high-wing monoplane

Fuselage: aluminium alloy cantilever

Landing gear: hydraulically actuated retractable tricycle unit

Powerplant: two Fiat-built General Electric T74-GE-P4D turboprops, each rated at 3,400 shp and driving a three-blade metal Hamilton Standard propeller; provision for eight Aerojet General JATO units with a total thrust of 7,937 lb (3,600 kg)

Fuel capacity: 2,638 gallons (12,000 litres) in four wing tanks

Avionics: comprehensive communications and navigation equipment

Armament: none

Dimensions: Span 94 ft 2 in (28.7 m)
Length 74 ft 5½ in (22.7 m)
Height 32 ft 1¾ in (9.8 m)

Wing area: 882.6 ft² (82.0 m²)

Weights: Empty 33,950 lb (15,400 kg)
Loaded 54,013 lb (24,500 kg)
Maximum 58,422 lb (26,500 kg)

Performance: (at maximum take-off weight) speed 336 mph (540 kph) at 15,000 ft (4,575 m); cruising speed 224 mph (360 kph) at 14,750 ft (4,500 m); climb 1,705 ft (520 m) per minute at sea level; climb to 14,750 ft (4,500 m) 8 minutes 35 seconds; service ceiling 25,000 ft (7,620 m); range with maximum payload of 18,740 lb (8,500 kg) at best cruising speed at 19,685 ft (6,000 m) 435 miles (700 km); range with 44 troops 1,380 miles (2,220 km); ferry range 3,075 miles (4,950 km)

Used also by: Argentina, Libya, United Arab Emirates

Notes: The first G222 flew in 1970, with the initial production aircraft taking to the air in 1975. The G222 is an all-weather aircraft, and capable of operating from unprepared strips.

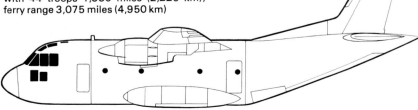

Aeronautica Macchi (Aermacchi) M.B.339

Type: trainer and ground-attack aircraft
Crew: two
Wings: metal cantilever low/mid-wing monoplane
Fuselage: metal semi-monocoque
Tail unit: metal cantilever
Landing gear: hydraulically actuated retractable tricycle unit
Powerplant: one Piaggio-built Rolls-Royce Viper Mark 632-43 turbojet, rated at 4,000-lb (1,814-kg) static thrust
Fuel capacity: 311 gallons (1,413 litres) in two fuselage and two wingtip tanks, plus provision for two 75-gallon (340-litre) drop tanks on the centre underwing hardpoints
Avionics: comprehensive communications and navigation/attack equipment, including Thompson-CSF gyroscopic gunsight and Marconi-Elliott HUDWAC or Astronautics head up display
Armament: provision for one 7.62-mm GAU-2B/A multi-barrel machine-gun with 1,500 rounds, or a 30-mm DEFA cannon with 150 rounds (machine-gun ammunition is stowed in a compartment which can also accept reconnaissance equipment, special electronics, and other loads), plus

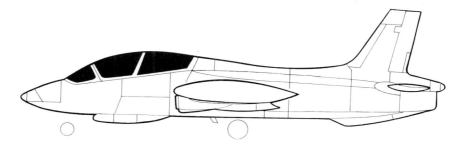

up to 4,000 lb (1,815 kg) of external stores on six underwing hardpoints. Stores that can be carried include AS.11 and AS.12 air-to-surface missiles, Matra 550 air-to-air missiles, 12.7-mm AN/M-3 machine-gun pods, 7.62-mm SUU-11A/A Minigun pods, bombs, napalm tanks, rocket pods, rocket-launchers and drop tanks
Dimensions: Span 35 ft 7½ in (10.858 m)
Length 36 ft (10.972 m)
Height 13 ft 1¼ in (3.994 m)
Wing area: 207.74 ft² (19.3 m²)
Weights: Empty 6,889 lb (3,125 kg)
Loaded 9,700 lb (4,400 kg)
Maximum 13,000 lb (5,895 kg)
Performance: (at normal loaded weight) speed 558 mph (898 kph) at sea level;

speed 508 mph (817 kph) at 30,000 ft (9,150 m); climb 6,600 ft (2,012 m) per minute at sea level; climb to 30,000 ft (9,150 m) in 7 minutes; service ceiling 48,000 ft (14,630 m); range on internal fuel 1,093 miles (1,760 km); ferry range 1,310 miles (2,110 km)
Used only by: Italy
Notes: The M.B.339 was designed in 1973–1974, and is based on the M.B.326K, with an uprated engine, revised forward fuselage and improved electronics.

Breguet Aviation Atlantic

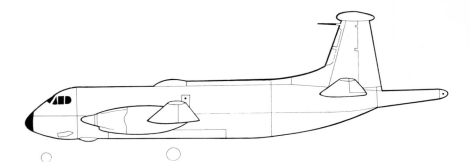

Type: maritime patrol and anti-submarine aircraft
Crew: 12
Wings: metal cantilever low mid-wing monoplane
Fuselage: metal double-bubble semi-monocoque
Tail unit: metal cantilever
Landing gear: hydraulically actuated retractable tricycle unit
Powerplant: two Rolls-Royce Tyne 21 turboprops, each rated at 6,106 ehp and driving a four-blade metal propeller
Fuel capacity: integral wing and tip tanks
Avionics: comprehensive communication and navigation/attack equipment
Armament: all standard bombs, depth charges and mines can be fitted into the bomb bay, as can four homing torpedoes or nine acoustic torpedoes; the four hardpoints under the outer wing panels can each carry a Martel or AS.12 air-to-surface missile, or other stores
Dimensions: Span 119 ft 1 in (36.3 m)
Length 104 ft 2 in (31.75 m)
Height 37 ft 2 in (11.33 m)

Wing area: 1,295 ft² (120.34 m²)
Weights: Empty 52,900 lb (24,000 kg)
Loaded
Maximum 95,900 lb (43,500 kg)
Performance: speed 409 mph (658 kph) at 16,400 ft (5,000 m); patrol speed 199 mph (320 kph); climb 2,450 ft (745 m) per minute at sea level; service ceiling 32,810 ft (10,000 m); range 5,592 miles (9,000 km); endurance on patrol 18 hours
Used also by: France, Netherlands, Pakistan, West Germany

Notes: The Breguet 1150 Atlantic stemmed from a NATO attempt in 1958 to procure a standard maritime patrol replacement for the P-2 Neptune used by many NATO countries. The Breguet 1150 was seemingly the best of the 25 contesting designs, but few of the participant nations bought the end result, the Atlantic, which is a remarkable warplane, and one that is likely to be improved with the introduction of the Atlantic II, with podded jet engines to supplement the turboprops, and allow operations at a weight of 110,000 lb (50,000 kg).

Costruzioni Aeronautiche Giovanni Agusta A 109

Type: general-purpose helicopter
Crew: one, plus seven passengers
Rotor: metal cantilever four-blade main rotor; metal cantilever two-blade tail rotor
Fuselage: aluminium alloy semi-monocoque
Landing gear: fixed tricycle unit
Powerplant: two Allison 250-C20B turboshafts, each rated at 420 shp
Fuel capacity: 121 gallons (550 litres) in fuselage tank
Avionics: comprehensive communication and navigation equipment
Armament: two 7.62-mm machine-guns and two XM-157 rocket launchers, each with seven 2.75-in (70-mm) rockets; or four HOT or TOW anti-tank missiles; or one 7.62-mm Minigun with 1,000 rounds; or one 7.62-mm MG3 machine-gun with 5,000 rounds; or one XM-159C rocket-launcher with nineteen 2.75-in (70-mm) rockets; or one Agusta rocket-launcher with seven 3.2-in (81-mm) rockets; or one 200A-1 rocket-launcher with nineteen 2.75-in (70-mm) rockets

Dimensions: Span 36 ft 1 in (11.0 m)
Length 42 ft 10 in (13.05 m)
Height 10 ft 10 in (3.3 m)
Main rotor disc area: 1,022.6 ft² (95.0 m²)
Weights: Empty 3,120 lb (1,415 kg)
Loaded
Maximum 5,400 lb (2,450 kg)
Performance: (at maximum take-off weight) never-exceed speed 193 mph (311 kph); cruising speed 165 mph (266 kph); climb 1,620 ft (493 m) per minute at sea level; service ceiling 16,300 ft (4,968 m); range 351 miles (565 km) at sea level
Used also by: Venezuela and other nations

Notes: Developed from the civil A 109 general-purpose helicopter, this military version has additional military equipment such as armoured seats, crash-proof fuel tanks, a cargo hook, a rescue hoist, and infra-red emission suppression equipment.

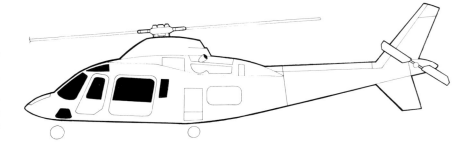

Industrie Aeronautiche e Meccaniche Rinaldo Piaggio P.166

Type: light transport aircraft
Crew: one, plus up to 10 passengers
Wings: metal cantilever high mid-wing gull-wing monoplane
Fuselage: metal semi-monocoque
Tail unit: metal cantilever
Landing gear: hydraulically actuated retractable tricycle unit
Powerplant: two Lycoming GSO-480-B1C6 inline engines, each rated at 340 hp and driving a Hartzell three-blade metal propeller
Fuel capacity: 235 gallons (1,070 litres) in two wing tanks and two wingtip tanks
Avionics: comprehensive communication and navigation equipment
Armament: none
Dimensions: Span 46 ft 9 in (14.25 m)
Length 38 ft 1 in (11.6 m)
Height 16 ft 5 in (5.0 m)
Wing area: 285.9 ft² (26.56 m²)
Weights: Empty 5,070 lb (2,300 kg)
Loaded 8,115 lb (3,680 kg) Maximum
Performance: speed 222 mph (357 kph) at 9,500 ft (2,895 m); cruising speed 207 mph (333 kph) at 12,800 ft (5,800 m); climb 1,240 ft (380 m) per minute at sea level; service ceiling 25,500 ft (7,775 m); range 1,500 miles (2,410 km)
Used also by: South Africa
Notes: The P.166 is derived from the P.136 amphibian, and first flew in 1957. There are two military versions:
1. P.166M, to which the technical specification above applies
2. P.166S surveillance model, with special electronic equipment.

Industrie Aeronautiche e Meccaniche Rinaldo Piaggio PD-808

Type: utility aircraft
Crew: two, plus up to nine passengers
Wings: metal cantilever low-wing monoplane
Fuselage: metal semi-monocoque
Tail unit: metal cantilever
Landing gear: hydraulically actuated retractable tricycle unit
Powerplant: two Rolls-Royce (Bristol) Viper Mark 526 turbojets, each rated at 3,360-lb (1,524-kg) static thrust
Fuel capacity: 819½ gallons (3,727 litres) in fuselage, integral wing, and integral wingtip tanks
Avionics: comprehensive communication and navigation equipment
Armament: none
Dimensions: Span 43 ft 3½ in (13.2 m)
Length 42 ft 2 in (12.85 m)
Height 15 ft 9 in (4.8 m)
Wing area: 225 ft² (20.9 m²)
Weights: Empty 10,650 lb (4,830 kg)
Loaded
Maximum 18,000 lb (8,165 kg)
Performance: (at maximum take-off weight) speed 529 mph (852 kph) at 19,500 ft

(5,945 m); cruising speed 497 mph (800 kph) above 36,000 ft (11,000 m); climb 5,400 ft (1,650 m) per minute at sea level; service ceiling 45,000 ft (13,715 m); range 1,322 miles (2,128 km) with maximum fuel and a payload of 840 lb (381 kg)
Used only by: Italy

Notes: The PD-808 first flew in 1964, and was developed with the aid of the Italian Air Force. There are four military versions:
1. PD-808 VIP with six VIP seats
2. PD-808 TA conventional nine-seat transport
3. PD-808 ECM with special ECM gear
4. PD-808 RM radio calibration model.

93

SIAI-Marchetti SM. 1019E

Type: observation, light ground-attack and utility STOL aircraft
Crew: two, in tandem
Wings: metal braced high-wing monoplane
Fuselage: metal semi-monocoque
Tail unit: metal cantilever
Landing gear: fixed tailwheel unit
Powerplant: one Allison 250-B17 turboprop, rated at 400 shp and driving a metal three-blade Hartzell propeller
Fuel capacity: 70 gallons (320 litres) in four wing tanks, plus provision for underwing auxiliary tanks
Avionics: comprehensive communication and navigation equipment
Armament: two hardpoints under each wing, capable of carrying 2.75-in (70-mm) rocket pods, gun pods, bombs, missiles, auxiliary fuel tanks and reconnaissance pods
Dimensions: Span 36 ft (10.972 m)
Length 27 ft 11½ in (8.52 m)
Height 9 ft 4½ in (2.86 m)
Wing area: 173.95 ft² (16.16 m²)
Weights: Empty 1,609 lb (730 kg)
Loaded 2,866 lb (1,300 kg)
Maximum 3,196 lb (1,450 kg)
Performance: (at maximum take-off weight) never-exceed speed 194 mph (313 kph); cruising speed 175 mph (281 kph) at sea level; climb 1,640 ft (499 m) per minute at sea level; service ceiling 25,000 ft (7,620 m); typical combat radius with two rocket pods at a take-off weight of 3,086 lb (1,400 kg) 69 miles (111 km); range at 9,000 ft (2,745 m) with two auxiliary tanks and a take-off weight of 3,086 lb (1,400 kg) 840 miles (1,352 km)
Used only by: Italy
Notes: This design is currently under production for the Italian Army.

Selenia *Aspide*

Type: air-to-air tactical guided missile
Guidance: semi-active radar homing
Dimensions: Span 39⅖ in (1.0 m)
Body diameter 8 in (20.3 cm)
Length 12 ft 1⁷⁄₁₀ in (3.7 m)
Booster: solid-propellant rocket
Sustainer: none
Warhead: high explosive
Weights: Launch 485 lb (220 kg)
Burnt out
Performance: speed more than Mach 2.5
Used only by: Italy
Notes: Developed as a multi-purpose missile, the *Aspide* is an all-weather missile capable of operating under severe ECM conditions, at both very low and very high altitude. The missile is also used in the Albatros naval point defence missile system, and the Spada army low-level defence system.

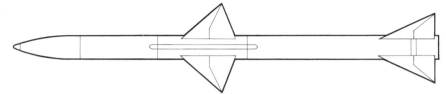

Ivory Coast

200 men.

3 C-47, 2 F27, 2 F28 transports.
3 Cessna F337, 2 Cessna 150 light ac.
5 *Alouette* II/III, 3 Puma helicopters.
(12 Alpha Jet trainers on order.)

Jamaica

2 Islander, 1 DHC-6, 1 King Air, 2 Cessna 185 utility aircraft.
1 Bell 47, 2 Bell 206, 3 Bell 212 helicopters.

Cessna Aircraft U-17

Type: light utility aircraft
Crew: one, plus up to five passengers
Wings: metal braced high-wing monoplane
Fuselage: metal semi-monocoque
Tail unit: metal cantilever
Landing gear: fixed tricycle unit
Powerplant: one Continental IO-520-D piston engine, rated at 300 hp and driving a McCauley two-blade metal propeller
Fuel capacity: 51.7 gallons (235 litres) in two wing tanks, or 67.4 gallons (306.5 litres) in optional long-range wing tanks
Avionics: communication and navigation equipment

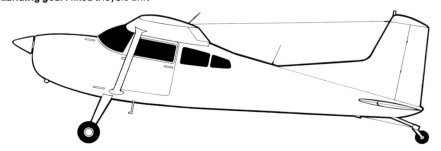

Armament: none
Dimensions: Span 35 ft 10 in (10.92 m)
Length 25 ft 7½ in (7.81 m)
Height 7 ft 9 in (2.36 m)
Wing area: 174 ft² (16.16 m²)
Weights: Empty 1,687 lb (765 kg)
Loaded
Maximum 3,350 lb (1,519 kg)
Performance: (at maximum take-off weight)
speed 178 mph (286 kph) at sea level;
cruising speed 167 mph (269 kph) at
7,500 ft (2,285 m); climb 1,010 ft (308 m)
per minute at sea level; service ceiling
17,150 ft (5,229 m); range with standard
fuel capacity 582 miles (937 km); range
with auxiliary fuel capacity 829 miles
(1,334 km)
Used also by: various nations
Notes: Derived from the civil Model 185 Sky-
wagon, the U-17 has been purchased in
some numbers by the USAF for delivery to
other nations under the military assistance
programme (MAP).

Japan

44,000 men and 358 combat aircraft.
3 FGA sqns with 87 F-86F, 9 F-1.
10 interceptor sqns: 6 with 150 F-104J,
4 with 98 F-4EJ.
1 recce sqn with 14 RF-4E.
3 transport sqns with 13 YS-11, 22
C-1A.
1 SAR wing with 20 MU-2 ac, 22 KV-
107, 26 S-62 helicopters.
Trainers incl 57 T-1A/B, 40 T-2A, 18
T-3, 185 T-33, 82 T-34, F-104DJ, 4
C-46, YS-11E, MU-2J.
AAM-1, Sparrow, Falcon, Sidewinder
AAM.
5 SAM gps with Nike-J (6th forming).
A Base Defence Ground Environment
with 28 control and warning units.
(23 F-15, 14 TF-15, 50 F-4EJ, 59 F-1,
10 T-2, 14 T-3, 7 C-1, 2 MU-2, 2
MU-2J ac, 3 KV-107 helicopters on
order.)
Naval Air Arm
12,000 men, and 600 reservists.
11 MR sqns with 110 P-2J, P2V-7,
S2F-1, 18PS-1.
7 helicopter sqns with 7 KV-107, 61
HSS-2.
1 transport sqn with 4 YS-11M, 1 S2F-
C.
5 SAR flts with 3 US-1 ac, 1-61A, 8
S-62A helicopters.
Trainers incl 6 YS-11T, 5 TC-90, 30B-
65; 8 T-34, 30 KM-2 ac; S-61A, 7
Bell 47, 4 OH-6J helicopters.
(8 P-3C MR, 5 PS-1, 18 KM-2, 2 US-1,
11 P-2J, 1TC-90 ac, 14 HSS-2, 4 SH-
3, 2 S-61A helicopters on order; 1
P2V-7, 6 S2F-1 in store.)
Army Air Arm
1 helicopter wing and 34 aviation sqns.
90 L-19, 20 LM-1/2, 7 LR-1 ac; 50 KV-
107, 40 UH-1H, 80 UH-1B, 70
OH-6J, 50 H-13 helicopters.
(2 LR-1 ac, 3 KV-107, 13 UH-1H, 10
OH-6D, 1AH-1S helicopters on
order.)

Fuji Heavy Industries KM-2B

Type: trainer
Crew: two, seated in tandem
Wings: metal cantilever low-wing monoplane
Fuselage: metal semi-monocoque
Tail unit: metal cantilever
Landing gear: electrically actuated retract-
able tricycle unit
Powerplant: one Lycoming IGSO-480-A1A6
inline engine, rated at 340 hp and driving a
Hartzell three-blade metal propeller
Fuel capacity: 58⅓ gallons (265 litres) in four
wing tanks
Avionics: communication and navigation
equipment
Armament: none
Dimensions: Span 32 ft 10 in (10.0 m)
Length 26 ft 4¼ in (8.04 m)
Height 9 ft 11 in (3.02 m)
Wing area: 177.6 ft² (16.5 m²)
Weights: Empty 2,469 lb (1,120 kg)
Loaded
Maximum 3,329 lb (1,510 kg)
Performance: (at maximum take-off weight)
speed 234 mph (377 kph) at 16,000 ft
(4,875 m); cruising speed 204 mph (328
kph) at 8,000 ft (2,440 m); climb 1,520 ft
(463 m) per minute at sea level; service
ceiling 26,800 ft (8,170 m); range 600
miles (965 km)
Used only by: Japan
Notes: The KM-2B is the latest in a line of
Japanese developments of the Beech
Model 45 (T-34 Mentor). First came the
LM-1 *Nikko* four-seat liaison aircraft, followed in 1956 by the KM-1 Super *Nikko*
with more power and performance. Then
came the KM-1, derived from the T-34A,
and finally the KM-2B, which flew for the
first time in 1974.

Fuji Heavy Industries T1F2 (T-1A)

Type: trainer
Crew: two, seated in tandem
Wings: metal cantilever low mid-wing mono-
plane
Fuselage: metal semi-monocoque
Tail unit: metal cantilever
Landing gear: hydraulically actuated retractable tricycle unit
Powerplant: one Rolls-Royce (Bristol Siddeley) Orpheus B.Or. 4 turbojet, rated at
4,230-lb (1,919-kg) static thrust
Fuel capacity:
Avionics: comprehensive communication
and navigation equipment
Armament: external stores can be carried
on the two pylons under the wings, includ-
ing four 5-in (127-mm) HVAR rockets, two
pods each with seven 2.75-in (70-mm)
rockets, two AIM-9 Sidewinder AAMs, two
750-lb (34-kg) or 500-lb (227-kg) bombs,
or two 0.5-in (12.7-mm) machine-gun
pods
Dimensions: Span 34 ft 4 in (10.46 m)
Length 39 ft 7 in (12.07 m)
Height 13 ft 2 in (4.0 m)
Wing area: 239 ft² (22.2 m²)
Weights: Empty 5,335 lb (2,430 kg)
Loaded 9,150 lb (4,150 kg)
Maximum 11,000 lb (4,990 kg)
Performance: speed 576 mph (927 kph) at
20,000 ft (6,095 m); cruising speed 397
mph (639 kph); climb 7 minutes 30
seconds to 32,820 ft (10,000 m); service
ceiling 39,990 ft (12,190 m); range 806
miles (1,300 km) on internal fuel; range
1,210 miles (1,950 km) with drop tanks
Used only by: Japan
Notes: The Fuji T-1 is Japan's first jet trainer,
and took to the air in 1958. There are two
versions, the other being powered by the
IHI J3 engine and designated T-1B.

Fuji Heavy Industries (Bell) UH-1H (Bell 204B)

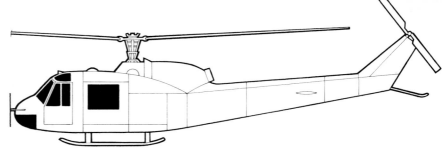

Type: general-purpose helicopter
Crew: one, and up to 14 passengers
Rotor: metal cantilever two-blade main rotor; and metal cantilever two-blade tail rotor
Fuselage: metal semi-monocoque
Landing gear: twin metal skids
Powerplant: one Kawasaki-built Lycoming T53-K-13B turboshaft, rated at 1,400 shp
Fuel capacity: 183 gallons (832 litres) in five fuel cells, plus provision for two auxiliary tanks each holding 125 gallons (568 litres)
Avionics: comprehensive communication and navigation equipment
Armament: none
Dimensions: Span 48 ft (16.63 m)
Length (fuselage) 40 ft 7 in (12.37 m)
Height 14 ft 6 in (4.42 m)
Rotor disc area: 1,809.5 ft² (168.1 m²)

Weights: Empty 5,270 lb (2,390 kg)
Loaded
Maximum 9,500 lb (4,309 kg)
Performance: (at maximum take-off weight) speed 127 mph (204 kph); cruising speed 127 mph (204 kph); climb 1,600 ft (488 m) per minute at sea level; service ceiling 12,600 ft (3,840 m); hovering ceiling in ground effect 9,800 ft (2,985 m); range at sea level 290 miles (467 km)

Used also by: Argentina, Australia, Ethiopia, Indonesia, Kampuchea, Philippines, Singapore, Spain, Taiwan, Thailand, Tunisia, Turkey, Uruguay, Venezuela (Model 204)
Notes: Almost identical with the parent model built by Bell Textron, the Fuji UH-1H has a tractor tail rotor and a Japanese-built engine.

Kawasaki Heavy Industries C-1

Type: medium troop and freight transport
Crew: five, and up to 60 passengers
Wings: aluminium alloy cantilever high-wing monoplane
Fuselage: aluminium alloy semi-monocoque
Tail unit: aluminium alloy cantilever
Landing gear: hydraulically actuated retractable tricycle unit
Powerplant: two Mitsubishi-built Pratt & Whitney JT8D-M-9 turbofans, each rated at 14,500-lb (6,577-kg) static thrust
Fuel capacity: 3,344 gallons (15,200 litres) in four integral wing tanks
Avionics: comprehensive communication and navigation equipment
Armament: none
Dimensions: Span 100 ft 4¾ in (30.6 m)
Length 95 ft 1¾ in (29.0 m)
Height 32 ft 9¼ in (9.99 m)
Wing area: 1,297 ft² (120.5 m²)
Weights: Empty 53,572 lb (24,300 kg)
Loaded 85,320 lb (38,700 kg)
Maximum 99,210 lb (45,000 kg)

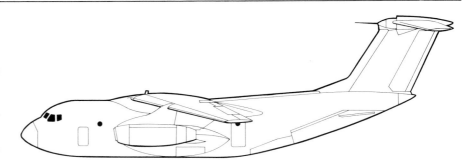

Performance: (at normal take-off weight) speed 501 mph (806 kph) at 25,000 ft (7,620 m) at 78,150 lb (35,450 kg); cruising speed 408 mph (657 kph) at 35,000 ft (10,670 m) at 78,150 lb (35,450 kg); climb 3,500 ft (1,065 m) per minute at sea level; service ceiling 38,000 ft (11,580 m); range on maximum fuel with a payload of 4,850 lb (2,200 kg) 2,084 miles (3,353 km); range with 17,416-lb (7,900-kg) payload 807 miles (1,300 km)

Used only by: Japan
Notes: Design of this medium transport began in 1966, and the first prototype flew in 1970. Currently the Japanese are investigating the possibilities of tanker, minelayer, weather reconnaissance, electronic warfare and tactical transport versions. Maximum payload is 26,235 lb (11,900 kg).

Kawasaki Heavy Industries KH-4

Type: utility helicopter
Crew: one, plus up to three passengers
Rotors: metal cantilever two-blade main rotor; metal cantilever two-blade tail rotor
Fuselage: metal tube structure
Landing gear: twin metal skids
Powerplant: one Lycoming TVO-435-D1A inline engine, rated at 270 hp

Fuel capacity: 46 gallons (209 litres) in a fuselage tank
Avionics: communication and navigation equipment
Armament: none
Dimensions: Span 37 ft 1½ in (11.32 m)
Length (fuselage) 32 ft 7¼ in (9.93 m)
Height 9 ft 3¼ in (2.84 m)
Rotor disc area: 1,083 ft² (100.61 m²)
Weights: Empty 1,890 lb (857 kg)
Loaded
Maximum 2,850 lb (1,292 kg)

Performance: (at maximum take-off weight) speed 105 mph (169 kph); cruising speed 87 mph (140 kph); climb 850 ft (260 m) per minute at sea level; service ceiling 18,500 ft (5,640 m); hovering ceiling in ground effect 18,000 ft (5,485 m); range 214 miles (345 km)
Used also by: Thailand
Notes: The KH-4 is a development of the Bell Model 47G-3B (H-13), with extra seating (for one more passenger) and greater fuel capacity. The first example flew in 1962.

Kawasaki Heavy Industries P-2J

Type: anti-submarine and maritime patrol aircraft
Crew: 12
Wings: metal cantilever mid-wing monoplane
Fuselage: metal semi-monocoque
Tail unit: metal cantilever
Landing gear: hydraulically actuated retractable tricycle unit

Powerplant: two Ishikawajima-built General Electric T64-IHI-10E turboprops, each rated at 3,060 ehp and driving a Sumitomo Precision metal three-blade propeller; plus two Ishikawajima-Harima J3-IHI-7C turbojets, each rated at 3,085-lb (1,400-kg) static thrust

Fuel capacity: 2,848 gallons (12,947 litres) in wing tanks and port wingtip, plus provision for 583 gallons (2,650 litres) in the weapons bay for ferrying

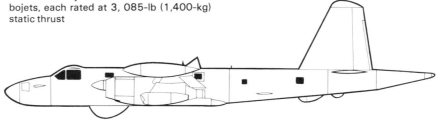

Avionics: comprehensive communication and navigation/attack equipment, including AN/APN 187B-N doppler radar, N-OA-35/HSA tactical plotter, HSA-116 integrated data display system and digital data processor, AN/APS-80-N search radar, AN/APA-125-N radar indicator, HLR-101 ESM, HSQ-101 MAD, HSA-102 AMC, HSA-103 SAD, AN/ASA-20B Julie recorder, AN/AQA-5-N Jezebel recorder, HQA-101 active sonobuoy indicator, AN/ARR-52A(V) sonobuoy receiver, and HSA-1B sonobuoy data display system
Armament: a wide variety of anti-submarine weapons can be carried

Dimensions: Span 97 ft 8½ in (29.78 m)
Length 95 ft 10¾ in (29.23 m)
Height 29 ft 3½ in (8.93 m)
Wing area: 1,000 ft² (92.9 m²)
Weights: Empty 42,500 lb (19,277 kg)
Loaded
Maximum 75,000 lb (34,019 kg)
Performance: (at maximum take-off weight never-exceed speed 403 mph (649 kph); cruising speed 250 mph (402 kph); climb 1,800 ft (550 m) per minute at sea level; service ceiling 30,000 ft (9,150 m); range with maximum fuel 2,765 miles (4,450 km)
Used only by: Japan

Notes: The P-2J is modelled closely on the Lockheed P2V-7 it was designed to replace, and first flew in 1966. The Japanese aircraft is some 4 ft 2 in (1.27 m) longer, an extra section having been added between the wing leading edge and the cockpit to house improved electronics. Early production models did not have as advanced electronics as those detailed here. There is a searchlight in the starboard wingtip.

Kawasaki Heavy Industries (Boeing Vertol) KV-107/II

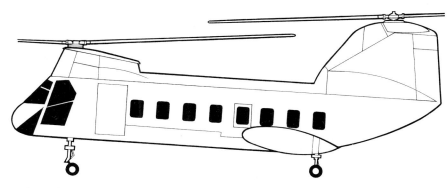

Type: transport and general-purpose helicopter
Crew: two, plus up to 26 passengers
Rotors: steel, aluminium and glassfibre cantilever three-blade main rotor
Fuselage: aluminium alloy semi-monocoque
Landing gear: fixed tricycle unit
Powerplant: two Ishikawajima-Harima-built General Electric CT58-IHI-110-1 turboshafts, each rated at 1,250 shp
Fuel capacity: 291 gallons (1,323 litres) in the sponsons
Avionics: comprehensive communication and navigation equipment
Armament: none
Dimensions: Span 50 ft (15.24 m)
Length (fuselage) 44 ft 7 in (13.59 m)
Height 16 ft 8½ in (5.09 m)
Rotor disc area: (total) 3,925 ft² (364.6 m²)
Weights: Empty 10,732 lb (4,868 kg)
Loaded
Maximum 21,400 lb (9,706 kg)
Performance: (at 19,000-lb/8,618-kg take-off weight) never-exceed speed 168 mph (270 kph); speed 157 mph (253 kph) at sea level; cruising speed 150 mph (241 kph) at

5,000 ft (1,525 m); climb 1,520 ft (463 m) per minute at sea level; service ceiling 15,000 ft (4,570 m); hovering ceiling in ground effect 9,500 ft (2,895 m); range with 6,600-lb (3,000-kg) payload 109 miles (175 km)
Used also by: Burma, Saudi Arabia, Sweden
Notes: Kawasaki Heavy Industries have the exclusive manufacturing and selling rights to the Boeing Vertol Model 107 II transport helicopter, in both military and civil versions. The military models are:
1. KV-107/II-3 mine-countermeasures (MCM) helicopter, with long-range tanks, towing hook and cargo sling

2. KV-107/IIA-3 version of the above, with uprated engines
3. KV-107/II-4 tactical cargo and troop transport, with strengthened floor for carrying vehicles
4. KV-107/IIA-4 version of the above, with uprated engines
5. KV-107/II-5 long-range search and rescue helicopter
6. KV-107/IIA-5 version of the above, with uprated engines.
The figures above are for the basic KV-107/II airline helicopter. Military models differ: the KV-107/IIA-5, for example, has a fuel capacity of 832.6 gallons (3,785 litres).

Mitsubishi Heavy Industries F-1

Type: close-support fighter
Crew: one
Wings: aluminium and aluminium alloy cantilever shoulder-wing monoplane
Fuselage: aluminium alloy semi-monocoque
Tail unit: aluminium and aluminium alloy cantilever
Landing gear: hydraulically actuated retractable tricycle unit
Powerplant: two Ishikawajima-Harima-built Rolls-Royce/Turbomeca Adour (TF40-IHI-801A) turbofans, each rated at 7,070-lb (3,207-kg) static thrust with afterburning
Fuel capacity: 841 gallons (3,823 litres) in seven fuselage tanks, plus provision for three 180-gallon (821-litre) drop tanks under the fuselage and wings
Avionics: comprehensive communication and navigation/attack equipment, including Mitsubishi Electric air-to-air and air-to-surface radar, Mitsubishi Electric (Thompson-CSF) J/AWG-11 head up display, Ferranti 6TNJ-F inertial navigation system, Mitsubishi Electric fire control system and bombing computer, radar homing and warning system, and Lear 5010BL attitude and heading reference system
Armament: one 20-mm Vulcan JM-61 multi-

barrel cannon, plus five hardpoints (one under the fuselage and two under each wing) for external stores. These stores can amount to twelve 500-lb (227-kg) bombs, Mitsubishi ASM-1 air-to-ship missiles, rockets and drop tanks. Two or four Sidewinder, Mitsubishi AAM-1 or other air-to-air missiles can be attached at the wingtips
Dimensions: Span 25 ft 10¼ in (7.88 m)
Length 58 ft 6¾ in (17.85 m)
Height 14 ft 4¾ in (4.39 m)
Wing area: 228 ft² (21.18 m²)
Weights: Empty 14,017 lb (6,358 kg)
Loaded
Maximum 30,146 lb (13,674 kg)
Performance: (at normal take-off weight) speed 1,056 mph (1,699 kph) or Mach 1.6 at 36,100 ft (11,000 m); climb 35,000 ft (10,670 m) per minute at sea level; climb to 36,100 ft (11,000 m) in 2 minutes; service ceiling 50,000 ft (15,240 m); range with eight 500-lb (227-kg) bombs 700 miles (1,126 km)
Used only by: Japan
Notes: The F-1 was derived from the T-2, and the first prototype flew in 1975. Basically similar to the T-2, the F-1 has its 'rear cockpit' area for an electronics bay, housing the bombing computer, inertial navigation system and radar warning system.

Mitsubishi Heavy Industries MU-2

Type: utility transport and maritime reconnaissance/rescue aircraft
Crew: two, plus up to 11 passengers
Wings: metal cantilever high-wing monoplane
Fuselage: aluminium alloy semi-monocoque
Tail unit: aluminium alloy cantilever
Landing gear: electrically actuated retractable tricycle unit
Powerplant: two AiResearch TPE 331-6-251M turboprops, each rated at 724 ehp and driving Hartzell metal three-blade propellers
Fuel capacity: 305 gallons (1,387 litres) in wing and wingtip tanks
Avionics: comprehensive communication and navigation equipment
Armament: none
Dimensions: Span 39 ft 2 in (11.94 m)
Length 33 ft 3 in (10.13 m)
Height 12 ft 11 in (3.94 m)
Wing area: 178 ft² (16.55 m²)

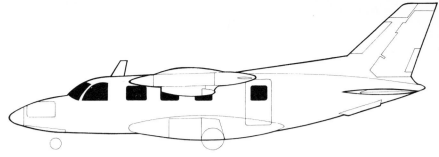

Weights: Empty 5,920 lb (2,865 kg)
Loaded
Maximum 9,920 lb (4,500 kg)
Performance: (at 8,730-lb/3,960-kg take-off weight) cruising speed at 15,000 ft (4,575 m) 365 mph (590 kph); climb 3,100 ft (945 m) per minute at sea level; service ceiling 33,200 ft (10,110 m); range with maximum fuel load and reserves for 30 minutes at 25,000 ft (7,620 m) 1,680 miles (2,700 km)
Used also by: Zaire

Notes: Two versions of this prolific civil transport are used by Japan's armed forces:
1. MU-2E (derived from the MU-2K) for rescue duties
2. MU-2C (derived from the MU-2K) for reconnaissance duties.
The two versions are designated in the Japanese Air Self-Defence Force and the Japanese Ground Self-Defence Force as the MU-2A and LR-1 respectively. The figures quoted above are for the civil MU-2K.

Mitsubishi Heavy Industries T-2

Type: trainer
Crew: two, in tandem
Wings: aluminium and aluminium alloy cantilever shoulder-wing monoplane
Fuselage: aluminium alloy semi-monocoque
Tail unit: aluminium and aluminium alloy cantilever
Landing gear: hydraulically actuated retractable tricycle unit
Powerplant: two Ishikawajima-Harima-built Rolls-Royce/Turbomeca Adour (TF40-IHI-801A) turbofans, each rated at 7,070-lb (3,207-kg) static thrust with afterburning
Fuel capacity: 841 gallons (3,823 litres) in seven fuselage tanks, plus provision for three 183-gallon (833-litre) drop tanks under the fuselage and wings
Avionics: comprehensive communication and navigation/attack equipment, including Mitsubishi Electric search and range radar, Mitsubishi Electric (Thomson-CSF) J/AWG-11 head up display and Lear

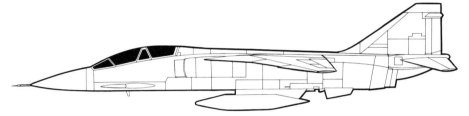

5010BL attitude and heading reference system
Armament: one 20-mm Vulcan JM-61 multi-barrel cannon, plus five hardpoints (one under the fuselage and two under each wing) for fuel tanks and other external stores, and attachments for air-to-air missiles at each wingtip
Dimensions: Span 25 ft 10¼ in (7.88 m)
Length 58 ft 6¾ in (17.85 m)
Height 14 ft 4¾ in (4.39 m)
Wing area: 228 ft² (21.18 m²)
Weights: Empty 13,893 lb (6,301 kg)
Loaded 21,616 lb (9,805 kg)
Maximum 24,750 lb (11,200 kg)

Performance: (at normal take-off weight) speed 1,056 mph (1,699 kph) or Mach 1.6 at 36,100 ft (11,000 m); climb 35,000 ft (10,670 m) per minute at sea level; service ceiling 50,000 ft (15,240 m); range with maximum fuel 1,610 miles (2,593 km)
Used only by: Japan
Notes: The T-2 was Japan's first supersonic aircraft, design of which was begun in 1967. The first prototype flew in 1971. There are two versions:
1. T-2 advanced trainer
2. T-2A combat trainer, with armament.

Nihon Aeroplane Manufacturing Company (NAMC) YS-11

Type: transport aircraft
Crew: four, plus up to 64 passengers
Wings: metal cantilever low-wing monoplane
Fuselage: metal semi-monocoque
Tail unit: metal cantilever
Landing gear: hydraulically actuated retractable tricycle unit
Powerplant: two Rolls-Royce Dart R.Da. 10/1 Mark 542 turboprops, each rated at 3,060 ehp and driving a four-blade metal propeller
Fuel capacity: 1,600 gallons (7,270 litres)
Avionics: comprehensive communication and navigation equipment
Armament: none
Dimensions: Span 105 ft (32.0 m)
Length 86 ft 3 in (26.3 m)
Height 29 ft 6 in (8.99 m)
Wing area: 1,020 ft² (94.8 m²)
Weights: Empty 33,180 lb (15,050 kg)
Loaded
Maximum 54,010 lb (24,500 kg)

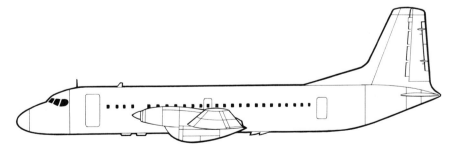

Performance: cruising speed 293 mph (472 kph) at 15,000 ft (4,570 m); range 215 miles (346 km) with maximum payload; range 1,410 miles (2,269 km) with a payload of 7,660 lb (3,475 kg)
Used also by: Philippines
Notes: The YS-11 started life as an airliner, making its first flight in 1962. The specification above is for the YS-11A, which has a maximum payload of 15,320 lb (6,949 kg).

Shin Meiwa Industry PS-1

Type: STOL anti-submarine flying-boat
Crew: 10
Wings: metal cantilever high-wing monoplane
Fuselage: metal semi-monocoque
Tail unit: metal cantilever
Landing gear: boat hull for water operations; hydraulically actuated retractable tricycle unit for beaching
Powerplant: four Ishikawajima-Harima-built General Electric T64-IHI-10 turboprops, each rated at 3,060 ehp and driving a Sumitomo-built Hamilton Standard metal three-blade propeller
Fuel capacity: 4,290 gallons (19,500 litres) in five wing and two fuselage tanks
Avionics: comprehensive communication and navigation/attack equipment, including AN/APN-153 doppler radar, AN/AYK-2 navigation computer, AN/APS-80 search radar, N-OA-35/HSA tactical plotting group, HLR-1 countermeasures device, AN/ARR-52A sonobuoy receiver, AN/ASQ-10A magnetic anomaly detector, HQS-101B dipping sonar, AN/AQA-5 sonobuoy recorder, AN/ASA-16 integrated display, ANA/ASA-50 computer group and HQH-101 sonobuoy data recorder
Armament: two pods are carried under each wing between the engines, each carrying two homing torpedoes, plus a launcher below each wingtip for three 5-in (127-mm) air-to-surface rockets. There is also an upper-deck weapons bay housing AQA-3 Jezebel passive long-range acoustic search equipment and 20 sonobuoys, Julie active acoustic echo ranging system with 12 explosive charges, and four 330-lb (150kg) A/S bombs
Dimensions: Span 108 ft 9 in (33.15 m)
Length 109 ft 9¼ in (33.46 m)
Height 32 ft 2¾ in (9.82 m)
Wing area: 1,462 ft² (135.8 m²)
Weights: Empty 58,000 lb (26,300 kg)
Loaded 79,365 lb (36,000 kg)
Maximum 94,800 lb (43,000 kg)
Performance: (at normal take-off weight) speed 340 mph (547 kph) at 5,000 ft (1,525 m); cruising speed on two engines at 5,000 ft (1,525 m) 196 mph (315 kph); climb 2,264 ft (690 m) per minute at sea level; service ceiling 29,500 ft (9,000 m); endurance 15 hours; normal range 1,347 miles (2,168 km); ferry range 2,948 miles (4,744 km)
Used only by: Japan
Notes: The PS-1 is a remarkable aircraft, the first prototype of which flew in 1967. The excellent design of the hull, combined with STOL devices and the high location of the wings, allows the PS-1 to operate in rough water conditions sufficient to 'ground' other flying-boats. The Japanese Maritime Self-Defence Force also operates an amphibious search and rescue variant, the US-1. This has a proper retractable undercarriage with twin main wheels (the PS-1 has single main wheels, a fuel capacity of 4,950 gallons (22,500 litres), giving an operational radius (including a search of 2 hours 18 minutes) of 1,035 miles (1,665 km), and other specialised improvements). There is also a water-bomber model for fighting forest fires.

Mitsubishi AAM-1

Type: air-to-air tactical guided missile
Guidance: infra-red homing
Dimensions: Span
Body diameter
Length about 8 ft 6⅓ in (2.6 m)
Booster: solid-propellant rocket
Sustainer: as above
Warhead: high explosive
Weights: Launch about 154 lb (70 kg)
Burnt out
Performance: range about 4⅓ miles (7 km)
Used only by: Japan
Notes: Very little is known of this air-to-air missile, which arms F-86 and F-4 fighters of the Japanese Air Self Defence Force.

Jordan

6,650 men and 76 combat aircraft, plus 30,000 reservists.

1 FGA sqn, 1 OCU with 8 F-5A/B, 24 F-5E/F.
2 interceptor sqns with 20 F-104A/B, 24 F-5E/F.
4 C-130B, 1 Boeing 727, 1 Falcon 20, 4 CASA C. 212A *Aviocar* transports.
14 *Alouette* III, 2 S-76 helicopters.
8 T-37C, 12 Bulldog, 1 Dove trainers.
Sidewinder AAM.
(1 C-130H transports; 10 AH-1H, 4 S-76 helicopters on order.)

Lockheed-California F-104 Starfighter

Type: interceptor, strike fighter, all-weather fighter and reconnaissance aircraft
Crew: one
Wings: metal cantilever mid-wing monoplane
Fuselage: metal semi-monocoque
Tail unit: metal cantilever
Landing gear: hydraulically actuated retractable tricycle unit
Powerplant: one General Electric J79-GE-19 turbojet, rated at 17,900-lb (8,119-kg) static thrust with afterburning

Fuel capacity: 746 gallons (3,392 litres) in five fuselage bag-tanks, plus two 163-gallon (740-litre) and two 142-gallon (645-litre) pylon and wingtip tanks
Avionics: comprehensive communication and navigation/attack equipment, including R21G/H air interception, contour mapping and terrain avoidance radar, a bombing computer, APN-198 radar altimeter and APX-46 IFF
Armament: a total weight of 7,500 lb (3,402 kg) of stores can be carried on nine external hardpoints; a typical load might consist of two AIM-7 Sparrow III AAMs under the wings, two Sparrows or AIM-9 Sidewinder AAMs under the fuselage, and two Side-

winders or two 142-gallon (645-litre) tanks on the wingtips. A 20-mm M61 multi-barrel rotary cannon can be fitted in the fuselage, but only if the Sparrow AAM guidance package is omitted

Dimensions: Span 21 ft 11 in (6.68 m)
Length 54 ft 9 in (16.69 m)
Height 13 ft 6 in (4.11 m)

Wing area: 196.1 ft² (18.22 m²)

Weights: Empty 14,900 lb (6,760 kg)
Loaded 21,690 lb (9,840 kg)
Maximum 31,000 lb (14,060 kg)

Performance: (at normal loaded weight) speed 1,450 mph (2,330 kph) or Mach 2.2 at 36,000 ft (10,975 m); speed 910 mph (1,464 kph) or Mach 1.2 at sea level; cruising speed 610 mph (981 kph) at 36,000 ft (10,975 m); climb 50,000 ft (15,240 m) per minute at sea level; climb 1 minute 20 seconds to 35,000 ft (10,670 m); zoom altitude more than 90,000 ft (27,400 m); service ceiling 58,000 ft (17,680 m); radius 775 miles (1,247 km); ferry range 1,815 miles (2,920 km)

Used also by: Canada, Denmark, Greece, Italy, Japan, Netherlands, Norway, Taiwan, Turkey, West Germany

Notes: The F-104 prototype first flew in 1954, and the F-104A entered service in 1956. Since then the type, designed as a day interceptor, has proliferated in the roles it can undertake, and emerged as a first-class combat aircraft. There are several variants:

1. F-104A initial production model, with a 14,800-lb (6,713-kg) J79-GE-3B
2. F-104B two-seat trainer
3. F-104C fighter-bomber, with the 15,800-lb (7,165-kg) J79-GE-7A and a flight refuelling probe
4. F-104D two-seat trainer version of the F-104C
5. F-104DJ Japanese version of the F-104D
6. F-104F West German version of the F-104D
7. F-104G West German tactical strike and reconnaissance aircraft, with a revised structure, manoeuvring flaps, NASARR multi-mode radar, and an inertial navigation system
8. CF-104 Canadair-built version of the F-104G
9. F-104J Japanese-built version of the F-104C
10. F-104RF and F-104RTF West German-built multi-role multi-sensor reconnaissance and trainer models
11. F-104S Italian-built model, to which the specification applies.

Kampuchea

About 10 AU-24 COIN.
About 9 C-47, C-123 transports.
About 15 T-41, 20 T-28 trainers.
About 25 UH-1H helicopters.

Fairchild Engine & Airplane C-123 Provider

Type: transport aircraft
Crew: two, plus up to 61 passengers
Wings: metal cantilever high-wing monoplane
Fuselage: metal semi-monocoque
Tail unit: metal cantilever
Landing gear: hydraulically actuated retractable tricycle unit
Powerplant: two Pratt & Whitney R-2800-99W radial engines, each rated at 2,300 hp and driving a three-blade metal propeller
Fuel capacity:
Avionics: comprehensive communication and navigation equipment
Armament: none
Dimensions: Span 110 ft (33.53 m)
Length 75 ft 9 in (23.1 m)
Height 34 ft 1 in (10.4 m)
Wing area: 1,223 ft² (113.62 m²)

Weights: Empty 29,900 lb (13,563 kg)
Loaded
Maximum 60,000 lb (27,216 kg)
Performance: speed 245 mph (394 kph); cruising speed 205 mph (330 kph); climb 1,150 ft (351 m) per minute at sea level; service ceiling 29,000 ft (8,839 m); range 1,470 miles (2,366 km)
Used also by: Laos, Philippines, South Korea, Taiwan, Thailand, USA, Venezuela
Notes: The C-123 was derived by Chase Aircraft from its 1949 design for a large cargo glider, with provision for power to be added. Financial difficulties led to the production of only five Chase-built C-123As, with twin R-2800-83 radials, and Fairchild then took over the production of the type in 1953. The Fairchild aircraft were C-123B Providers, and differed from their predecessors in having large dorsal fins. The C-123K had one pod-mounted J85-GE-17 turbojet of 2,850-lb (1,293-kg) thrust under each wing to boost performance.

Kenya

1,200 men and 13 combat aircraft.

1 FGA sqn with 4 Hunter FGA.9, 4 F-5E/F.
1 COIN sqn with 5 BAC 167 Strikemaster.
1 trg sqn with 14 Bulldog.
2 lt transport sqns: 1 with 6 DHC-4, 1 with 7 DHC-2, 2 DHC-5, 2 Do 28D.
Other ac incl 1 Turbo Commander, 2 Navajo ac; 2 Puma, 2 Bell 47G and *Alouette* II helicopters.
(8 F-5E/F fighters, 12 Hawk trainers, 4 DHC-5D, 4 Do 28D transports on order.)

Bell Aircraft H-13 (Model 47) Sioux

Type: utility helicopter
Crew: one, plus up to two passengers
Rotor: metal cantilever two-blade main rotor; metal cantilever two-blade tail rotor
Fuselage: metal tube structure
Landing gear: twin metal skids

Powerplant: one Lycoming VO-435 piston engine, rated at 200 hp
Fuel capacity: 50 gallons (227 litres)
Avionics: communication equipment
Armament: none
Dimensions: Span 35 ft 1 in (10.7 m)
Length (fuselage) 27 ft 4 in (8.33 m)
Height 9 ft 6 in (2.9 m)

Rotor disc area: 966.5 ft² (89.8 m²)
Weights: Empty 1,564 lb (709 kg)
    Loaded
    Maximum 2.450 lb (1,111 kg)
Performance: speed 100 mph (161 kph) at sea level; cruising speed 85 mph (137 kph); climb 770 ft (235 m) per minute at sea level; service ceiling 13,200 ft (4,023 m); range 238 miles (383 km)

Used also by: many nations
Notes: The Bell Model 47 was the first Bell helicopter accepted for US service, in 1947, as the H-13. This underwent a series of improvements, and eventually emerged as the H-13J, with 240-hp engine and fully enclosed fuselages for presidential use.

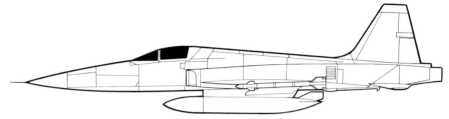

Northrop Corporation Aircraft Group F-5E Tiger II

Type: tactical fighter
Crew: one
Wings: light alloy cantilever low-wing mono-plane
Fuselage: light alloy semi-monocoque
Tail unit: metal cantilever
Landing gear: hydraulically actuated retractable tricycle unit
Powerplant: two General Electric J85-GE-21A turbojets, each rated at 5,000-lb (2,268-kg) static thrust with afterburning
Fuel capacity: 559 gallons (2,540 litres) in fuselage tanks, plus provision for one 229-gallon (1,040-litre) drop tank under the fuselage, and 125- or 229-gallon (568-or 1,040-litre) drop tanks under the wings
Avionics: comprehensive communication and navigation/attack equipment, including AN/APQ-159 lightweight pulse radar for search, tracking and ranging
Armament: two 20-mm M39A2 cannon with 280 rounds per gun, two AIM-9 Sidewinder air-to-air missiles on the wingtips, and up to 7,000 lb (3,175 kg) of stores on one underfuselage and four underwing stations. Stores that can be carried include BLU-1, 27 and 32 fire bombs; CBU-24, 49, 52 and 58 cluster bombs; LAU-3 and 68 2.75-in rocket launchers; MK-36 destructors; MK-82 general-purpose and Snakeye 500-lb (227-kg) bombs; MK-84 2,000-lb (907-kg) bombs; SUU-20 bomb and rocket packs; and SUU-25 flare dispensers. Optional loads include a centreline ejector rack, laser-guided bombs, and the AGM-65 Maverick air-to-surface missile

Dimensions: Span 26 ft 8 in (8.13 m)
    Length 48 ft 2 in (14.68 m)
    Height 13 ft 4 in (4.06 m)
Wing area: 186 ft² (17.3 m²)
Weights: Empty 9,583 lb (4,346 kg)
    Loaded
    Maximum 24,675 lb (11,192 kg)
Performance: (at combat weight of 13,250 lb/6,010 kg) speed 1,060 mph (1,705 kph) or Mach 1.6 at 36,000 ft (10,975 m); cruising speed Mach 0.98 at 36,000 ft (10,975 m); climb 34,500 ft (10,515 m) per minute at sea level; service ceiling 51,800 ft (15,790 m); combat radius with two Sidewinders, 5,200-lb (2,358-kg) load, maximum fuel and 5 minutes of combat at sea level 138 miles (222 km); ferry range 1,831 miles (2,946 km)
Used also by: Brazil, Chile, Egypt, Ethiopia, Indonesia, Iran, Jordan, Malaysia, Philippines, Saudi Arabia, Singapore, South Korea, Sudan, Switzerland, Taiwan, Thailand, USA, Vietnam
Notes: Designed with the T-38 Talon supersonic trainer, the F-5 Freedom Fighter was developed as a private venture as a relatively cheap fighter, with emphasis on dog-fighting ability rather than outright performance. The fighter prototype first flew in 1959, and the type has been an outstanding seller since that time, led by an initial order by the US Department of

Defense, which saw the political and military advantages of supplying the type to anti-communist governments at cheap rates. There have been several versions:

1. F-5 for the USAF with J85-GE-13 engines of 4,080-lb (1,851-kg) thrust
2. RF-5 reconnaissance variant
3. CF-5A for the Canadian Armed Forces
4. NF-5A for the Royal Netherlands Air Force
5. NF-5B twin-seat trainer for the Royal Netherlands Air Force
6. CF-5D twin-seat trainer for the Canadian Armed Forces
7. F-5G and RF-5G single-seat fighter and twin-seat trainer for the Royal Norwegian Air Force
8. C-9 and CE-9 single-seat fighter and twin-seat trainer for the Spanish Air Force
9. F-5E Tiger II, with greatly uprated engines, increasing maximum speed from Mach 1.4 to Mach 1.6. The technical specification above relates to the F-5E
10. F-5F twin-seat version of the F-5E, with the fuselage lengthened by 3 ft 6½ in (1.08 m) and one cannon deleted. Maximum weight of this model is 22.028 lb (9,992 kg).

Société Nationale Industrielle Aérospatiale SA 318C *Alouette II Astazou*

Type: general-purpose helicopter
Crew: one, plus up to three passengers
Rotors: metal cantilever three-blade main rotor; metal cantilever two-blade tail rotor
Fuselage: metal tube structure
Landing gear: twin metal skids
Powerplant: one Turboméca Astazou IIA turboshaft, rated at 530 shp but derated to 360 dhp
Fuel capacity: $127\frac{1}{2}$ gallons (580 litres) in the fuselage tank
Avionics: communication and navigation equipment
Armament: none
Dimensions: Span 33 ft $5\frac{3}{4}$ in (10.2 m)
Length (fuselage) 31 ft $11\frac{3}{4}$ in (9.75 m)
Height 9 ft (2.75 m)
Rotor disc area: 879.5 ft² (81.7 m²)
Weights: Empty 1,961 lb (890 kg)
Loaded
Maximum 3,630 lb (1,650 kg)
Performance: speed 127 mph (205 kph) at sea level; cruising speed 112 mph (180 kph) at sea level; climb 1,300 ft (396 m) per minute at sea level; service ceiling 10,800 ft (3,300 m); hovering ceiling in ground effect 5,085 ft (1,550 m); range 62 miles (100 km) with a payload of 1,322 lb (600 kg); range 447 miles (720 km) with maximum fuel

Used also by: many nations
Notes: The Astazou-powered version of the basic *Alouette* II first flew in 1961, and the type has now entered service with a number of countries. Maximum payload in the flying crane role is 1,322 lb (600 kg), and for rescue work the winch can lift 265 lb (120 kg).

Kuwait

1,000 men and 49 combat aircraft.

2 FB sqns (forming) with 20 A-4KU.
1 interceptor sqn with 20 Mirage F1B/C.
1 COIN sqn with 9 Strikemaster Mk 83.
2 DC-9, 2 L-100-20 transports.
3 helicopter sqns with 30 Gazelle, 12 Puma.
Trainers incl 4 Hunter T.67, 2 TA-4KU.
Red Top, Firestreak, R.550 Magic, Sidewinder, Super 530 AAM.
50 Improved HAWK SAM.
(14 A-4KU, 4 TA-4KU FGA on order.)

Laos

2,000 men and 55 combat aircraft.

1 sqn with 10 MiG-21.
40 T-28A/D COIN ac.
5 AC-47 gunships.
Transports incl 1 Yak-40, 10 C-47, 10 C-123, 6 An-24, 1 Aero Commander, 1 Beaver.
6 T-41D trainers.
4 *Alouette* III, 42 UH-34, 6 Mi-8 helicopters.
AA-2 'Atoll' AAM.

Yakovlev Yak-40 'Codling'

Type: utility transport
Crew: two or three, plus up to 32 passengers
Wings: duralumin cantilever low-wing monoplane
Fuselage: duralumin semi-monocoque
Tail unit: duralumin cantilever
Landing gear: hydraulically actuated retractable tricycle unit
Powerplant: three Ivchenko AI-25 turbofans, each rated at 3,307-lb (1,500-kg) static thrust
Fuel capacity: 860 gallons (3,910 litres) in two integral wing tanks
Avionics: comprehensive communication and navigation equipment
Armament: none
Dimensions: Span 82 ft 0¼ in (25.0 m)
Length 66 ft 9½ in (20.36 m)
Height 21 ft 4 in (6.5 m)
Wing area: 753.5 ft² (70.0 m)
Weights: Empty 20,725 lb (9,400 kg)
Loaded 34,170 lb (15,500 kg)
Maximum 35,275 lb (16,000 kg)

Performance: speed 373 mph (600 kph) at sea level; cruising speed 342 mph (550 kph) at 23,000 ft (7,000 m); climb 1,575 ft (480 m) per minute at sea level; range with maximum payload 900 miles (1,450 km); range with maximum fuel 1,240 miles (2,000 km)
Used also by: Poland, Yugoslavia, Zambia
Notes: Maximum payload is 6,000 lb (2,720 kg).

Lebanon

500 men and 21 combat aircraft.

1 FGA sqn with 9 Hunter F.70, 2 Hunter T.66.
1 interceptor sqn with 10 Mirage IIIEL/BL (not in use).
1 helicopter sqn with 12 *Alouette* II/III, 6 AB-212.
6 Bulldog, 6 Magister and 1 Chipmunk trainers.
1 Dove, 1 Turbo-Commander 690A transports.
R.530 AAM.

Costruzioni Aeronautiche Giovanni Agusta (Bell) 212

Type: utility transport helicopter
Crew: one, plus up to 14 passengers
Rotors: one metal cantilever two-blade main rotor; one metal cantilever two-blade tail rotor
Fuselage: metal semi-monocoque
Landing gear: twin metal skids
Powerplant: one Pratt & Whitney Aircraft of Canada PT6T-3 Turbo Twin Pac turboshaft, derated to 1,290 shp
Fuel capacity: 179 gallons (813 litres) in a fuselage tank
Avionics: comprehensive communication and navigation equipment
Armament: none
Dimensions: Span 48 ft (14.63 m)
Length (fuselage) 46 ft (14.02 m)
Height 14 ft 5 in (4.4 m)
Rotor disc area: 1,809.5 ft² (168.1 m²)
Weights: Empty 5,800 lb (2,630 kg)
Loaded
Maximum 11,200 lb (5,081 kg)

Performance: cruising speed 127 mph (204 kph) at sea level; climb 1,860 ft (567 m) per minute at sea level; service ceiling 17,000 ft (5,180 m); hovering ceiling in ground effect 13,000 ft (3,960 m); range 366 miles (589 km) on one engine at 5,000 ft (1,525 m)
Used also by: Austria, Iran, Malaysia, Morocco, Singapore, Syria, Thailand, Zambia
Notes: The AB 212 is the Agusta-built version of the Bell Model 212. The first was delivered in 1971.

Liberia

2 C-47, 6 Cessna 172/185/207 transports.

Libya

4,000 men and 178 combat aircraft.

1 bomber sqn with 12 Tu-22 'Blinder'.
2 interceptor sqns (1 OCU) with 24 MiG-23 'Flogger'.
4 FGA sqns and OCU with 90 Mirage VD/DE, 10 VDR, 10 VDD.
2 COIN sqns with 32 *Galeb*.
2 transport sqns with 8 C-130H, 1 Boeing 707, 9 C-47, Falcon, 1 JetStar.
Trainers incl 2 *Mystère* 20, 5 MiG-23U, 12 Magister, Falcon ST 2, 20 SF.260, 17 *Galeb*.
4 helicopter sqns with 13 *Alouette* II/III, 6 AB 47, 9 Super *Frelon*, 10 CH-47C.
AA-2 'Atoll', R.550 Magic AAM.
3 SAM regts with 60 *Crotale*, 9 btys with 60 SA-2, SA-3 and SA-6 SAM.
(32 Mirage F1AD/ED fighters, 6 Mirage F1BD trainers, 150 SF.260 trainers, 20 CH-47D helicopters, 1 AS-61A helicopter on order.)

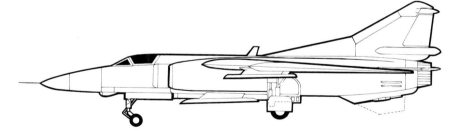

Mikoyan-Gurevich MiG-23 'Flogger'

Type: air combat fighter
Crew: one
Wings: metal cantilever variable-geometry shoulder-wing monoplane
Fuselage: metal semi-monocoque
Tail unit: metal cantilever
Landing gear: hydraulically actuated retractable tricycle unit
Powerplant: one turbojet of unknown type, probably rated at 20,500-lb (9,300-kg) static thrust with afterburning
Fuel capacity:
Avionics: comprehensive communication and navigation/attack equipment, including 'High Lark' airborne interception radar, ECM equipment, doppler radar, and laser rangefinder

Armament: one GSh-23 23-mm twin-barrel cannon in belly pack, plus five pylons for external stores, one under the fuselage, one under each air intake, and one under each inner wing panel, with a total capacity of about 10,000 lb (4,536 kg). Each of these pylons can carry AA-7 'Apex' or AA-8 'Aphid' air-to-air missiles or other stores. The air combat version of the MiG-23 has no gun armament, but provision for four AA-3 'Anab' air-to-air missiles
Dimensions: Span (spread) 46 ft 9 in (14.25 m)
Span (swept) 26 ft 9½ in (8.17 m)
Length 55 ft 1½ in (16.8 m)
Height 15 ft 9 in (4.8 m)
Wing area: 293.4 ft² ¹(27.26 m²)
Weights: Empty about 20,000 lb (9,070 kg)
Loaded about 33,050 lb (15,000 kg)

Maximum about 40,000 lb (18,145 kg)

Performance: (estimated) speed 1,520 mph (2,446 kph) or Mach 2.3 at high altitude; 838 mph (1,348 kph) or Mach 1.1 at sea level; service ceiling 59,050 ft (18,000 m); combat radius 600 miles (960 km)

Used also by: Algeria, Bulgaria, Czechoslovakia, Egypt, Ethiopia, USSR

Notes: The first prototype of the MiG-23 flew in 1965, and the type began to enter service in 1971, though both dates are of necessity estimates. There are several versions of the MiG-23:

1. MiG-23 'Flogger-A' prototype
2. MiG-23S 'Flogger-B' single-seat air combat fighter for the Soviet Air Force, to which the technical specification relates
3. MiG-23U 'Flogger-C' two-seat trainer, with combat capability
4. MiG-23S 'Flogger-E' export version of the MiG-23S 'Flogger-B' with less sophisticated equipment
5. MiG-23 'Flogger-F' export version of the MiG-27 'Flogger-D' interdiction and ground-attack aircraft with the powerplant, air intakes and gun armament of the MiG-23 interceptor.

Malagasy Republic

350 men.

5 C-47, 1 C-53, 1 Defender, 1 Piper Aztec, 7 other utility aircraft.
1 Bell 47, 3 *Alouette* II/III, 2 Mi-8 helicopters.

Britten-Norman Defender

Type: multi-purpose light military aircraft
Crew: one, plus up to nine passengers
Wings: aluminium alloy cantilever high-wing monoplane
Fuselage: aluminium alloy semi-monocoque
Tail unit: aluminium alloy cantilever
Landing gear: fixed tricycle unit
Powerplant: two Lycoming IO-540-K1B6 piston engines, each rated at 300 hp and driving a Hartzell two-blade metal propeller
Fuel capacity: 114 gallons (518 litres) in two integral wing tanks, plus optional tanks in wingtip extensions, each holding 24.5 gallons (111 litres), and two pylon-mounted auxiliary tanks, each holding 50 gallons (227 litres)
Avionics: communication and navigation equipment, plus optional surveillance radar and other sophisticated electronics
Armament: provision for four underwing pylons, the inner pair capable of lifting 700 lb (317.5 kg) each, and the outer pair 450 lb (204 kg) each. Typical loads include twin 7.62-mm machine-gun pods, 500- and 250-lb (227- and 113-kg) bombs, Matra 68-mm rocket pods, SURA rocket clusters, wire-guided missiles, flares, anti-personnel grenades and drop tanks
Dimensions: Span (standard) 49 ft (14.94 m); (extended) 53 ft (16.15 m)
Length 35 ft 7¾ in (10.86 m)
Height 13 ft 8¾ in (4.18 m)
Wing area: (standard) 325 ft² (30.19 m²); (extended) 337 ft² (31.31 m²)
Weights: Empty 3,708 lb (1,682 kg)
Loaded
Maximum 6,600 lb (2,993 kg)
Performance: (at maximum take-off weight) speed 168 mph (270 kph); cruising speed 157 mph (252 kph) at 10,000 ft (3,050 m); climb 1,170 ft (357 m) per minute at sea level; service ceiling 17,000 ft (5,180 m); range with maximum payload 375 miles (603 km); range with maximum fuel 1,723 miles (2,772 km)
Used also by: Angola, Ghana, Guyana, Israel, Jamaica, Malawi, Mauritania, Mexico, Oman, Qatar, Rhodesia, Thailand, Turkey
Notes: Derived from the civil Islander transport, the Defender first appeared in 1971. It was quickly cleared for military service, and can also have machine-guns firing from the cabin doors. There is also the Maritime Defender, a variant designed for search and rescue operations as well as for coastal patrol. The Maritime Defender has a modified nose housing the search radar, increasing length to 36 ft 3¾ in (11.07 m). The specialised equipment carried by the Maritime Defender includes a loudspeaker pod, flares, a parachute dinghy pack and a number of weapon alternatives.

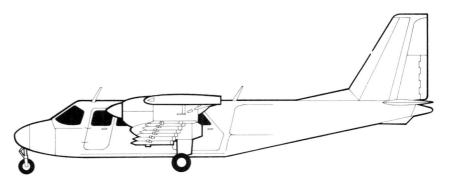

Malawi

4 C-47, 1 Defender, 2 Do 28 and Pembroke utility aircraft.
(4 Do 28 on order.)

Dornier Do 28 D-2 Skyservant

Type: STOL transport and utility aircraft
Crew: one or two, with 13 or 14 passengers
Wings: metal cantilever high-wing monoplane
Fuselage: all-metal stressed skin
Tail unit: metal cantilever
Landing gear: non-retractable tailwheel type
Powerplant: two Lycoming IGSO-540-A1E piston engines, each rated at 380 hp and driving Hartzell three-blade constant-speed propellers
Fuel capacity: 196½ gallons (893 litres) in engine nacelles, plus two optional underwing auxiliary tanks
Avionics: communication and navigation equipment
Armament: none
Dimensions: Span 51 ft 0¼ in (15.55 m)
Length 37 ft 5¼ in (11.41 m)
Height 12 ft 9½ in (3.9 m)
Wing area: 312.2 ft² (29.0 m²)
Weights: Empty 5,080 lb (2,304 kg)
Loaded
Maximum 8,853 lb (4,015 kg)
Performance: (at maximum take-off weight) speed 202 mph (325 kph) at 10,000 ft (3,050 m); cruising speed 170 mph (273 kph) at 10,000 ft (3,050 m); climb 1,050 ft (320 m) per minute at sea level; service ceiling 25,200 ft (7,680 m); range with maximum fuel 1,831 miles (2,950 km)
Used also by: Cameroon, Ethiopia (?), Israel, Kenya, Morocco, Nigeria, Somali Republic, Thailand, Turkey, West Germany, Zambia
Notes: Initial deliveries were made in 1967.

Hunting Percival Aircraft Pembroke

Type: light transport aircraft
Crew: two, plus up to eight passengers
Wings: metal cantilever shoulder-wing monoplane
Fuselage: metal semi-monocoque
Tail unit: metal cantilever
Landing gear: hydraulically actuated retractable tricycle unit
Powerplant: two Alvis Leonides 127 radial engines, each rated at 560 hp and driving a three-blade metal propeller
Fuel capacity:
Avionics: communication and navigation equipment
Armament: none
Dimensions: Span 64 ft 6 in (19.66 m)
Length 46 ft (14.02 m)
Height 16 ft (4.88 m)
Wing area: 400 ft² (37.16 m²)
Weights: Empty 9,589 lb (4,350 kg)
Loaded 13,500 lb (6,124 kg)
Maximum
Performance: speed 224 mph (361 kph) at 2,000 ft (610 m); cruising speed 155 mph (249 kph) at 8,000 ft (2,438 m); climb 1,500 ft (457 m) per minute at sea level; climb 10 minutes 30 seconds to 10,000 ft (3,050 m); service ceiling 22,000 ft (6,706 m); range 1,150 miles (1,850 km)
Used also by: UK
Notes: The Pembroke communications aircraft was evolved from the Prince civil transport, and entered RAF service in 1953. The standard version is the C.1, to which the technical specification above applies.

Malaysia

6,000 men and 36 combat aircraft.

2 FB sqns with 16 F-5E/B.
2 COIN/trg sqns with 20 CL-41G *Tebuan*.
4 transport, 1 liaison sqns with 6 C-130H, 3 Heron, 2 HS 125, 2 F28, 16 DHC-4A, 2 Dove and CL-215.
4 helicopter sqns with 36 S-61A-4, 28 *Alouette* III, 5 Bell 206B, 3 AB-212.
1 trg sqn with 15 Bulldog 120, 12 Cessna 402B ac, 6 Bell 47G, 3 Sioux helicopters.
Sidewinder AAM.
(20 Gazelle helicopters, Super Sidewinder AAM on order.)

Canadair CL-41G

Type: ground-attack aircraft and trainer
Crew: two, seated side-by-side
Wings: metal cantilever low-wing monoplane
Fuselage: metal semi-monocoque
Tail unit: metal cantilever
Landing gear: hydraulically actuated retractable tricycle unit
Powerplant: one Orenda-built General Electric J85-CAN-40 turbojet, rated at 2,825-lb (1,281-kg) static thrust
Fuel capacity: 258 gallons (1,170 litres) in five fuselage tanks, plus provision for two underwing drop tanks, each with a capacity of 40 gallons (181 litres)
Avionics: comprehensive communication and navigation/attack equipment
Armament: a wide variety of stores can be carried on the external hardpoints, including air-to-surface rockets, AIM-9 Sidewinder AAMs, napalm tanks, 500-lb (227-kg) bombs and 0.5-in (12.7-mm) machine-gun pods
Dimensions: Span 36 ft 6 in (11.125 m)
Length 32 ft (9.75 m)
Height 9 ft 3½ in (2.83 m)
Wing area: 220 ft² (20.44 m²)
Weights: Empty 5,296 lb (2,400 kg)
Loaded
Maximum 11,288 lb (5,131 kg)
Performance: speed 488 mph (785 kph) at 30,000 ft (9,145 m); climb 4,250 ft (1,295 m) per minute at sea level; climb 4 minutes 12 seconds to 15,000 ft (4,570 m)
Used only by: Malaysia
Notes: The C1-41G is the ground-attack version of the CL-41A Tutor, the Canadian trainer which first flew in 1963.

Canadair CL-215

Type: multi-purpose amphibian
Crew: two to four, plus up to 19 passengers
Wings: metal cantilever high-wing monoplane
Fuselage: metal boat-hull
Tail unit: metal cantilever
Landing gear: hydraulically actuated retractable tricycle unit
Powerplant: two Pratt & Whitney R-2800-83AM piston engines, each rated at 2,100 hp and driving a Standard Hydromatic metal three-blade propeller
Fuel capacity: 1,300 gallons (5,910 litres) in two wing tanks
Avionics: comprehensive communication and navigation equipment
Armament: none
Dimensions: Span 93 ft 10 in (28.6 m)
Length 65 ft 0½ in (19.82 m)
Height (on land) 29 ft 3 in (8.92 m)
Wing area: 1,080 ft² (100.33 m²)
Weights: Empty 26,600 lb (12,065 kg)
Loaded
Maximum 43,500 lb (19,731 kg) from land; 37,700 lb (17,100 kg) from water
Performance: cruising speed 181 mph (291 kph) at a take-off weight of 41,000 lb (18,595 kg) at 10,000 ft (3,050 m); climb 1,000 ft (305 m) per minute at sea level at

a take-off weight of 43,500 lb (19,731 kg); range 1,405 miles (2,260 km) with a payload of 3,500 lb (1,587 kg)
Used also by: Algeria, Greece, Spain, Thailand

Notes: The CL-215 was designed principally with aerial firefighting in view, and in this capacity is widely used in North America and Europe. The type can also be used for search and rescue, casualty evacuation and supply missions. Maximum payload is 6,260 lb (2,839 kg) in late models.

109

De Havilland Aircraft Dove

Type: light transport aircraft
Crew: two, plus up to eight passengers
Wings: metal cantilever low-wing monoplane
Fuselage: metal semi-monocoque
Tail unit: metal cantilever
Landing gear: hydraulically actuated retractable tricycle unit
Powerplant: two de Havilland DH Gipsy Queen 70 inline engines, each rated at 340 hp and driving a three-blade metal propeller
Fuel capacity:
Avionics: communication and navigation equipment
Armament: none
Dimensions: Span 57 ft (17.38 m)
Length 39 ft 3 in (11.96 m)
Height 13 ft 4 in (4.06 m)
Wing area:
Weights: Empty 5,780 lb (2,622 kg)
Loaded 8,500 lb (3,856 kg)
Maximum

Performance: speed 210 mph (338 kph) at 8,000 ft (2,438 m); cruising speed 179 mph (288 kph); climb 750 ft (229 m) per minute at sea level; service ceiling 20,000 ft (6,096 m); range 500 miles (805 km)
Used also by: Egypt, Eire, Ethiopia, Jordan, Lebanon, Paraguay, Sri Lanka
Notes: The Dove is known in the RAF as the Devon, the first Devon C.1 in fact being the 48th civil Dove converted to military standards on the production line, and handed over in 1948.

De Havilland Aircraft Heron

Type: light transport
Crew: two, plus up to 10 passengers
Wings: metal cantilever low-wing monoplane
Fuselage: metal semi-monocoque
Tail unit: metal cantilever
Landing gear: hydraulically actuated retractable tricycle unit

Powerplant: four de Havilland DH Gipsy Queen 30 inline engines, each rated at 250 hp and driving a two-blade metal propeller
Fuel capacity:
Avionics: communication and navigation equipment
Armament: none
Dimensions: Span 71 ft 6 in (21.79 m)
Length 48 ft 6 in (14.78 m)
Height 15 ft 7 in (4.75 m)
Wing area:
Weights: Empty 8,484 lb (3,848 kg)
Loaded 13,500 lb (6,124 kg)
Maximum
Performance: cruising speed 183 mph (295 kph) at 8,000 ft (2,438 m)
Used also by: Iraq, Sri Lanka
Notes: The Heron is basically a scaled-up version of the Dove, with four engines instead of two. The type entered RAF service in 1955.

Mali

5 MiG-17 FGA.
2 C-47, 2 An-2, 1 An-24 transports.
2 MiG-15 and Yak trainers.
2 Mi-4 helicopters.

Mauritania

150 men.
8 Defender, 1 C-54, 3 C-47, 2 DHC-5D, 1 Caravelle, 2 Skyvan transports.
4 Cessna F337, 1 AL.60 light ac.
(4 IA 58 COIN on order.)

Hughes Helicopter Model 500M-D Defender

Type: multi-role helicopter
Crew: one, plus up to six passengers
Rotor: aluminium cantilever five-blade main rotor; light alloy cantilever two-blade tail rotor
Fuselage: aluminium semi-monocoque
Landing gear: twin metal skids
Powerplant: one Allison Model 250-C20B turboshaft, rated at 420 shp
Fuel capacity: 53 gallons (240 litres) in two fuselage tanks
Avionics: communication and navigation equipment
Armament: a variety of armament options is available, and weapons that can be carried include fourteen 2.75-in rockets, a 7.62-mm Minigun with 2,000 rounds, a 30-mm chain gun with 600 rounds, anti-submarine weapons, and four TOW anti-tank missiles

Dimensions: Span 26 ft 5 in (8.05 m)
Length (fuselage) 23 ft (7.01 m)
Height 8 ft 3½ in (2.53 m)
Rotor disc area: 547.81 ft² (50.89 m²)
Weights: Empty 1,320 lb (598 kg)
Loaded
Maximum 3,000 lb (1,360 kg)
Performance: (at maximum take-off weight) speed 152 mph (244 kph) at 1,000 ft (305 m); cruising speed 135 mph (217 kph) at sea level; climb 1,700 ft (518 m) per minute at sea level; service ceiling 14,400 ft (4,390 m); hovering ceiling in ground effect 8,200 ft (2,500 m); range 366 miles (606 km) at 4,000 ft (1,220 m)
Used also by: Colombia, Finland, India, Israel, South Korea
Notes: This is the military version of the Model 500D civil helicopter, suitable for scouting, trooping, light attack, A/S service, observation, liaison and other military roles. The type has armour protection, an infra-red suppressor and self-sealing fuel tanks.

Mexico

6,000 men and 80 combat aircraft.

1 COIN sqn with 15 AT-33A.
5 COIN/trg sqns with 20 T-6, 45 T-28A.
1 SAR sqn with 18 LASA-60 ac, 9 *Alouette* III, 1 Hiller 12E helicopters.
4 transport sqns with 2 Boeing 727, 1 DC-7, 1 DC-6, 5 C-118, 5 C-54, 1 JetStar, 1 BAC 111, 20 C-47, 3 Skyvan, 12 Islander, 10 *Arava*, Aero Commander.
Helicopters incl 5 Bell 206B, 3 Bell 212, 10 Bell 205.
Trainers incl 20 T-6, 30 T-28, 20 Beech F33-19, 20 Musketeer.
1 para bn.
(12 PC-7 Turbo-Trainer on order.)
Naval Air Force
350 men.
10 HU-16 Albatross MR ac.

Other ac incl 1 Learjet 24D, 4 C-45, 3 DC-3, 1 Beech Baron, 3 Bonanza, 4 Cessna 150.
4 *Alouette* II, 3 Bell 47, 5 Hughes 269A helicopters.

Beech Aircraft AT-11

Type: trainer
Crew: five
Wings: metal cantilever low-wing monoplane
Fuselage: metal semi-monocoque
Tail unit: metal cantilever
Landing gear: electrically actuated retractable tailwheel unit
Powerplant: two Pratt & Whitney R-985-AN-1 piston engines, each rated at 450 hp and driving a metal two-blade propeller
Fuel capacity:
Avionics: communication and navigation equipment
Armament: two 0.3-in (7.62-mm) machine-guns and ten 100-lb (45-kg) bombs
Dimensions: Span 47 ft 8 in (14.53 m)
　　　　　　　 Length 34 ft 2 in (10.41 m)
　　　　　　　 Height 9 ft 8 in (2.95 m)
Wing area: 349 ft² (32.4 m²)
Weights: Empty 6,175 lb (2,801 kg)
　　　　　 Loaded
　　　　　 Maximum 8,727 lb (3,959 kg)
Performance: speed 215 mph (346 kph); climb to 10,000 ft (3,050 m) in 10 minutes 6 seconds; service ceiling 20,000 ft (6,100 m); range 850 miles (1,368 km)
Used also by: Angola, Argentina, Chile, Columbia, Ecuador, Honduras, Nicaragua, Somali Republic, Uruguay
Notes: Derived from the Beech Model 18S light civil transport, the military utility family started with the C-45 transport (six or eight passengers) in 1940, and was then developed into the AT-7 navigation trainer, AT-11 bombing and gunnery trainer, and F-2 photographic reconnaissance aircraft.

Israel Aircraft Industries 201
Arava

Type: STOL light transport
Crew: one or two, and up to 24 troops
Wings: metal high-wing braced monoplane
Fuselage: light alloy semi-monocoque
Tail unit: light alloy cantilever
Landing gear: non-retractable tricycle unit
Powerplant: two Pratt & Whitney Aircraft of Canada PT6A-34 turboprops, each rated at 750 shp and driving a Hartzell 3-blade metal propeller
Fuel capacity: 366 gallons (1,663 litres) in four wing tanks, plus two optional fuselage tanks each holding 225 gallons (1,022 litres) for ferry purposes
Avionics: standard blind-flying equipment and optional communications and navigation equipment
Armament: none
Dimensions: Span 68 ft 9 in (20.96 m)
　　　　　　　 Length 42 ft 9 in (13.03 m)
　　　　　　　 Height 17 ft 1 in (5.21 m)
Wing area: 470.2 ft² (43.68 m²)
Weights: Empty 8,816 lb (3,999 kg)
　　　　　 Loaded
　　　　　 Maximum 15,000 lb (6,803 kg)
Performance: (at maximum take-off weight) 203 mph (326 kph) at 10,000 ft (3,050 m); cruising speed 198 mph (319 kph) at 10,000 ft (3,050 m); climb 1,290 ft (393 m) per minute at sea level; service ceiling 25,000 ft (7,260 m); range with maximum payload 174 miles (280 km) with reserves of fuel for 45 minutes
Used also by: Bolivia, Ecuador, El Salvador, Guatemala, Honduras, Israel, Nicaragua
Notes: This STOL military transport was derived from the civil IAI 101, and the prototype first flew in 1972. Maximum payload is 5,184 lb (2,351 kg). In 1977 IAI offered a maritime reconnaissance version with special search radar.

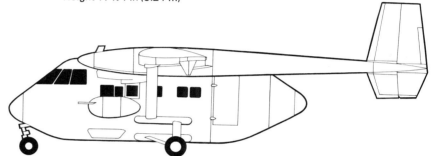

Lockheed-Georgia LASA-60

Type: utility aircraft
Crew: one, plus up to five passengers
Wings: metal high-wing braced monoplane
Fuselage: metal semi-monocoque
Tail unit: metal cantilever
Landing gear: fixed tricycle unit
Powerplant: one Continental TSIO-470 inline engine, rated at 260 hp and driving a two-blade metal propeller
Fuel capacity:
Avionics: communication and navigation equipment
Armament: none
Dimensions: Span 39 ft 4 in (12.0 m)
　　　　　　　 Length 28 ft 1 in (8.56 m)
　　　　　　　 Height 10 ft 8 in (3.25 m)
Wing area: 210 ft² (19.5 m²)
Weights: Empty 2,024 lb (918 kg)
　　　　　 Loaded 3,532 lb (1,602 kg)
　　　　　 Maximum 3,752 lb (1,702 kg)
Performance: speed 167 mph (269 kph) at 15,000 ft (4,570 m); cruising speed 130 mph (209 kph); climb 930 ft (283 m) per minute at sea level
Used only by: Mexico
Notes: The LASA-60 was designed to a Mexican requirement, and first flew in 1959. The type was then produced in Mexico, the first production aircraft flying in 1961.

Mongolia

2,000 men and 10 combat aircraft.

1 FGA sqn with 10 MiG-15.
20 An-2, 6 Il-14, 4 An-24 transports.
10 Mi-1 and Mi-4 helicopters.
Yak-11/-18 trainers.

Morocco

6,000 men and 61 combat aircraft.

2 FB sqns with 34 F/RF-5A, F-5B.
1 COIN sqn with 22 Magister.
1 transport sqn with 12 C-130H, 8 C-119G, 8 C-47, 1 Gulfstream, 6 King Air, 12 *Broussard*.
2 helicopter sqns with 40 AB-205A, 2 AB-206, 2 AB-212, 40 Puma.
12 T-6, 12 T-34C, 10 AS. 201/18 *Bravo* trainers.
Sidewinder AAM.

(50 Mirage F1CH fighters, 24 Alpha Jet trainers, 6 CH-47 helicopters, R.550 Magic AAM on order.)

Costruzioni Aeronautiche Giovanni Agusta (Bell) AB 205

Type: general-purpose utility helicopter
Crew: one, plus up to 14 passengers
Rotor: metal cantilever twin-blade main rotor; metal cantilever twin-blade tail rotor
Fuselage: metal semi-monocoque
Landing gear: twin metal skids
Powerplant: one Lycoming T53-L-13 turboshaft, rated at 1,400 shp
Fuel capacity: 183 gallons (832 litres) in five rubber fuel cells in the fuselage, plus two optional 125-gallon (568-litre) overload tanks in the fuselage
Avionics: comprehensive communication and navigation equipment
Armament: various light armament installations are possible
Dimensions: Span 48 ft 3½ in (14.72 m)
　　　　Length (fuselage) 41 ft 11 in (12.78 m)
　　　　Height 14 ft 8 in (4.48 m)
Rotor disc area: 1,831.6 ft² (170.2 m²)
Weights: Empty 4,800 lb (2,177 kg)
　　　　Loaded 8,500 lb (3,860 kg)
　　　　Maximum 9,500 lb (4,310 kg)
Performance: (at normal loaded weight) speed 138 mph (222 kph) at sea level; cruising speed 132 mph (212 kph); climb 1,800 ft (548 m) per minute at sea level;

hovering ceiling in ground effect 17,000 ft (5,180 m); range with standard tankage 360 miles (580 km)
Used also by: Greece, Indonesia, Iran, Italy, North Yemen, Oman, Saudi Arabia, Spain, Turkey, Uganda, Zambia

Notes: The AB 205 is derived from the Bell UH-1D/UH-1H versions of the Bell 205 family, and is widely used for a number of military applications with optional equipment.

Mozambique

500 men and 47 combat aircraft.

47 MiG-21 fighters.
Transports incl 6 Noratlas, 5 C-47, An-24.
Lt ac incl 7 Zlin.
15 Harvard trainers.
2 *Alouette* II/III, some Mi-8 helicopters.
AA-2 'Atoll' AAM.

Nepal

Army Air Arm:
3 Skyvan, 1 HS 748 transports.
5 *Alouette* III, 2 Puma helicopters.

Netherlands

17,700 men (4,100 conscripts) and 162 combat aircraft, plus about 10,000 reservists.

2 FB sqns with 36 F-104G.
3 FB sqns with 54 NF-5A.
1 FB/trg sqn with 18 NF-5B.
2 interceptor sqns with 36 F-104G.
1 recce sqn with 18 RF-104G.
1 transport sqn with 12 F27.
Sidewinder AAM.
4 SAM sqns with Nike Hercules.
11 SAM sqns with Improved HAWK.
(102 F-16 fighters, Super Sidewinder AAM on order.)
Naval Air Arm
2 MR sqns with 8 Atlantic, 15 P-2 Neptune.
2 ASW helicopter sqns with 6 Lynx, 12 Wasp.
(18 Lynx ASW helicopters on order.)
Army Air Arm
3 army aviation sqns (Air Force crews).
60 *Alouette* III, 30 BO 105 helicopters.

Messerschmitt-Bölkow-Blohm BO 105

Type: light helicopter
Crew: one, and three passengers
Rotor: glassfibre four-blade main rotor; GRP two-blade tail rotor
Fuselage: light alloy semi-monocoque
Landing gear: twin skids
Powerplant: two Allison 250-C20B turboshafts, each rated at 406 shp
Fuel capacity: 127½ gallons (580 litres) in integral fuselage fuel tank, plus optional auxiliary tanks in the freight compartment
Avionics: communications and navigation equipment

Armament: a variety of loads are possible, including six HOT anti-tank missiles
Dimensions: Span 32 ft 3½ in (9.84 m)
　　　　Length 38 ft 11 in (11.86 m)
　　　　Height 9 ft 10 in (3.0 m)
Rotor disc area: 819 ft² (76 m²)
Weights: Empty 2,469 lb (1,120 kg)
　　　　Loaded
　　　　Maximum 5,070 lb (2,300 kg)
Performance: (at normal take-off weight) speed 167 mph (270 kph) at sea level; cruising speed 152 mph (245 kph) at sea level; climb 1,772 ft (540 m) per minute at sea level; service ceiling 17,000 ft (5,180 m); range with auxiliary tanks 621 miles (1,000 km)

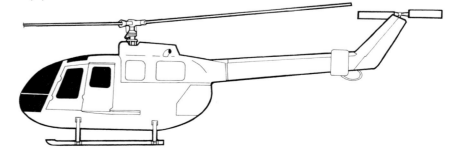

Notes: The design of the BO 105 dates from the early 1960s, and various features were extensively tested on other helicopters before the first BO 105 flew. There are many versions of the BO 105, the most important military variants being the BO 105 PAH 1 anti-tank helicopter, armed with six Euromissile HOT or four BGM-71 TOW missiles, and currently under development; and the BO 105 VBH liaison and light observation helicopter for the German Army.

New Zealand

4,159 men and 34 combat aircraft, plus 713 regular and 160 territorial reservists.

1 FB sqn with 10 A-4K, 3 TA-4K Skyhawk.
1 FB/trg sqn with 16 BAC 167.
1 MR sqn with 5 P-3B Orion.
2 med transport sqns with 5 C-130H, 6 Andover.
1 transport helicopter sqn with 7 Sioux, 3 Wasp, 10 UH-1D/H.
1 comms sqn with 4 Andover, 2 Devon.
Trainers: 8 Devon, 13 Airtrainer, 4 Airtourer ac, 3 Sioux helicopters.
Utility types incl Bristol Freighter.
(6 Airtrainers on order.)
Deployment: Singapore: 1 helicopter flt (3 UH-1).

Bristol Aeroplane Freighter

Type: transport aircraft
Crew: three
Wings: metal cantilever shoulder-wing monoplane
Fuselage: metal semi-monocoque
Tail unit: metal cantilever
Landing gear: fixed tailwheel unit
Powerplant: two Bristol Hercules 734 radial engines, each rated at 1,980 hp and driving a four-blade metal propeller
Fuel capacity:
Avionics: comprehensive communication and navigation equipment
Armament: none
Dimensions: Span 108 ft (32.92 m)
Length 68 ft 4 in (20.83 m)
Height 21 ft 8 in (6.6 m)

Wing area: 1,487 ft² (138.15 m²)
Weights: Empty 27,000 lb (12,247 kg)
Loaded
Maximum 44,000 lb (19,958 kg)
Performance: speed 225 mph (362 kph); cruising speed 193 mph (311 kph); climb 1,380 ft (421 m) per minute at sea level; service ceiling 24,500 ft (7,468 m); range 420 miles (676 km) with a payload of 12,000 lb (5,443 kg); maximum range 820 miles (1,320 k n)
Used only by: New Zealand
Notes: The Bristol Type 170 Freighter was designed as a military transport, with large doors in the nose for the easy loading of *materiel* into the main cargo compartment, 32 ft (9.75 m) long, 8 ft (2.44 m) wide, and 6 ft 8 in (2.03 m) high. The first prototype flew in December 1945.

McDonnell Douglas (Douglas Aviation) A-4 Skyhawk

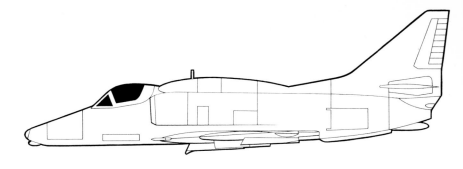

Type: attack bomber

Crew: one

Wings: metal cantilever delta low-wing monoplane

Fuselage: metal semi-monocoque

Tail unit: metal cantilever

Landing gear: hydraulically actuated retractable tricycle unit

Powerplant: one Pratt & Whitney J52-P-408 turbojet, rated at 11,200-lb (5,080-kg) static thrust, plus provision for JATO units

Fuel capacity: 666 gallons (3,028 litres) in fuselage and integral wing tanks, plus provision for one 125-, 250- or 313-gallon (568-, 1,136- or 1,514-litre) tank under the fuselage, and two 125- or 250-gallon (568- or 1,136-litre) tanks under the wings

Avionics: comprehensive communication and navigation/attack equipment, including AN/APG-53A radar, Marconi-Elliott AVQ-24 head up display, electronic counter-measures and others

Armament: two 20-mm Mark 12 cannon with 200 rounds each, plus provision for an external load of up to 9,155 lb (4,153 kg) on hardpoints: one under the fuselage for 3,500 lb (1,588 kg), two under the inner wings, each for 2,250 lb (1,020 kg), and two under the outer wings, each for 1,000 lb (454 kg). Several hundred ordnance variations can be carried, weapons including nuclear and HE bombs, air-to-air and air-to-surface rockets, Sidewinder AAMs, Bullpup ASMs, ECM pods, gun pods and torpedoes

Dimensions: Span 27 ft 6 in (8.38 m)
Length 40 ft 4 in (12.29 m)
Height 15 ft (4.57 m)

Wing area: 260 ft² (24.16 m²)

Weights: Empty 10,800 lb (4,899 kg)
Loaded 24,500 lb (11,113 kg)
Maximum 27,420 lb (12,437 kg)

Performance: (at normal loaded weight) speed with 4,000-lb (1,814-kg) bomb load 646 mph (1,040 kph); climb 10,300 ft (3,140 m) per minute at sea level; service ceiling in 'clean' condition about 49,000 ft (14,935 m); combat radius with 4,000-lb (1,814-kg) bomb load about 460 miles (740 km); ferry range 2,000 miles (3,225 km)

Used also by: Argentina, Australia, Israel, Kuwait, Singapore, USA

Notes: Designed to an attack bomber specification emerging from Korean War experience, the A-4 Skyhawk for the US Navy and Marine Corps amazed all by meeting all its requirements, but at only half the expected take-off weight. The first prototype flew in 1954, and the type entered service in 1956. Since that time the Skyhawk has been updated considerably, and still remains a potent carrier- and land-based attack bomber. There are numerous variants, including:

1. A-4A initial production model with 7,700-lb (3,493-kg) J65-W-4 engine and 5,000 lb (2,268 kg) of weapons for the USN
2. A-4B with detail improvements, a 7,700-lb (3,493-kg) J65-W-16A engine and provision for inflight refuelling for USN and USMC
3. A-4C with limited all-weather capability for the USN and USMC
4. A-4D cancelled variant with Pratt & Whitney J52-P-2 engine
5. A-4E with 8,500-lb (3,856-kg) J52-P-6A engine, longer range, and an external load of 8,200 lb (3,719 kg) for the USN and USMC
6. TA-4E advanced trainer version of the A-4E, with a 9,300-lb (4,218-kg) J52-P-8A engine, produced for the USN and USMC as the TA-4F
7. TA-4F (see TA-4E above)
8. A-4F with a 9,300-lb (4,218-kg) J52-P-8A engine, updated electronics in a 'hump' behind the cockpit, more armour and other improvements
9. A-4G version of the A-4F for the Royal Australian Navy, with provision for Sidewinder AAMs
10. A-4H for Israel, later fitted with Rafael MAHAT lightweight analogue weapons delivery system
11. TA-4H two-seat trainer version of the A-4H for Israel
12. TA-4J simplified version of the TA-4F for the USN, without advanced electronics
13. A-4K version of the A-4F for the Royal New Zealand Air Force
14. A-4KU version of the A-4M for Kuwait
15. TA-4K version of the TA-4F for the Royal New Zealand Air Force
16. TA-4KU version of the TA-4F for Kuwait
17. A-4L uprated version of the A-4C, with electronics 'hump' aft of the cockpit, for the USN
18. A-4M Skyhawk II, derived from the A-4F but with 11,200-lb (5,080-kg) J52-P-408 engine, considerably improved electronics in the 'hump', and increased weapons load. The technical specification above refers to this model
19. A-4N version of the A-4M for Israel
20. A-4P version of the A-4B for the Argentinian Air Force
21. A-4Q version of the A-4B for the Argentinian Navy
22. A-4S updated version of the A-4B for Singapore
23. TA-4S trainer version of the A-4B for Singapore
24. A-4Y advanced attack aircraft for the USMC, with improved head up display, redesigned cockpit and Hughes angle rate bombing system (ARBS). A-4Ms are to be brought up to this standard, and it appears that new A-4Ys will end production of the Skyhawk family.

New Zealand Aerospace Industries Airtrainer CT4

Type: trainer
Crew: two or three
Wings: metal cantilever low-wing monoplane
Fuselage: metal semi-monocoque
Tail unit: metal cantilever
Landing gear: fixed tricycle unit
Powerplant: one Rolls-Royce Continental IO-360-H piston engine, rated at 210 hp and driving a Hartzell metal two-blade propeller

Fuel capacity: 45 gallons (204.5 litres)
Avionics: communication equipment
Armament: none
Dimensions: Span 26 ft (7.92 m)
Length 23 ft 2 in (7.06 m)
Height 8 ft 6 in (2.59 m)
Wing area: 129 ft² (11.98 m²)
Weights: Empty 1,490 lb (675 kg)
Loaded 2,350 lb (1,066 kg)
Maximum 2,400 lb (1,088 kg)
Performance: (at normal take-off weight) speed 178 mph (286 kph) at sea level; cruising speed at 10,000 ft (3,050 m) 144

mph (232 kph); climb 1,350 ft (411 m) per minute at sea level; climb to 10,000 ft (3,050 m) in 11 minutes 40 seconds; service ceiling 17,900 ft (5,455 m); range at 118 mph (190 kph) at sea level 884 miles (1,422 km)

Used also by: Australia, Indonesia, Thailand
Notes: The Airtrainer is based on an Australian civil design, the Victa Aircruiser.

Nicaragua

1,500 men.

4 B-26K bombers.
4 T-33A, 4 T-28D, COIN.
1 HS 125, 5 CASA C.212, 3 C-47, 4 C-45, 2 *Arava*, 4 DHC-3, 10 Cessna 180 transports.
3 CH-34, 4 OH-6A, 1 Hughes 269A helicopters.
4 T-6, 3 Super Cub trainers.

Douglas Aircraft B-26 Invader

Type: attack bomber
Crew: three
Wings: metal cantilever high mid-wing monoplane
Fuselage: metal semi-monocoque
Tail unit: metal cantilever
Landing gear: hydraulically actuated retractable tricycle unit
Powerplant: two Pratt & Whitney R-2800-79 radial engines, each rated at 2,000 hp and driving a metal three-blade propeller
Fuel capacity:
Avionics: comprehensive communication and navigation/attack equipment
Armament: six 0.5-in (12.7-mm) machine-guns, plus up to 4,000 lb (1,814 kg) of bombs

Dimensions: Span 70 ft (21.34 m)
Length 50 ft (15.24 m)
Height 18 ft 6 in (5.64 m)
Wing area: 540 ft² (50.17 m²)
Weights: Empty 22,850 lb (10,365 kg)
Loaded 35,000 lb (15,876 kg)
Maximum 38,500 lb (17,460 kg)
Performance: speed 373 mph (600 kph); cruising speed 284 mph (457 kph); climb 2,000 ft (610 m) per minute at sea level; climb 8 minutes to 10,000 ft (3,050 m); service ceiling 22,100 ft (6,736 m); range 1,400 miles (2,253 km) with maximum bomb load
Used also by: Dominican Republic
Notes: Designed as the A-26, the Invader was conceived and built in quantity during World War II, one of the very few aircraft with this distinction. The prototype first flew in 1942, and the A-36 entered service in 1944. The last aircraft was delivered in 1946, and with the end of World War II, it seemed that the days of the A-26 were limited. The Korean War and Vietnam War showed, however, that the B-26, as the type was redesignated in 1948, was still very useful. The variant most commonly found is the B-26C, to which the specification above applies. The B-26K was rebuilt for Vietnam as the A-26K, and proved a vital night interdiction aircraft, capable of carrying up to 11,000 lb (4,990 kg) of weapons at 350 mph (563 kph), and lingering over the Ho Chi Minh Trail area for two hours, ready to pounce on any signs of activity.

Niger

50 men.

2 C-47, 1 C-54, 3 Noratlas transports.
1 Aero Commander, 2 Cessna 337 light planes.

Nigeria

6,000 men and 24 combat aircraft.

2 FGA/interceptor sqns: 1 with 4 MiG-17, 1 with 20 MiG-21J.
2 transport sqns with 6 C-130H, 2 F27, 1 F28, 1 Gulfstream II and P.149.
1 helicopter sqn with 3 Whirlwind, 4 BO 105, 10 Puma, 10 *Alouette* III.
3 trg/service sqns with 2 MiG-15, 2 Mig-21U, 32 SA Bulldog, 19 Do 27/28, 3 Piper Navajo, 15 L-29.
(6 CH-47, 6 BO 105 helicopters on order.)

Industrie Aeronautiche e Meccaniche Rinaldo Piaggio P.149

Type: liaison and trainer aircraft
Crew: four or five
Wings: metal cantilever low-wing monoplane
Fuselage: metal semi-monocoque
Tail unit: metal cantilever
Landing gear: hydraulically actuated retractable tricycle unit
Powerplant: one Lycoming GO-480 inline engine, rated at 280 hp and driving a three-blade metal propeller
Fuel capacity:
Avionics: communication and navigation equipment
Armament: none

Dimensions: Span 36 ft 5½ in (11.11 m)
Length 25 ft 11¼ in (7.9 m)
Height 9 ft 6 in (2.9 m)
Wing area: 202 ft² (18.8 m²)
Weights: Empty 2,557 lb (1,160 kg)
Loaded
Maximum 3,704 lb (1,680 kg)
Performance: speed 192 mph (309 kph) at sea level; cruising speed 165 mph (265 kph) at 7,500 ft (2,285 m); climb 980 ft (300 m) per minute at sea level; service ceiling 19,685 ft (6,000 m); range 680 miles (1,095 km)
Used only by: Nigeria
Notes: The P.149 was designed as a touring aircraft for civil use, but was converted into a military utility aircraft to meet a German requirement. The P.149 was derived from the P.148 trainer, and was first flown in 1953.

Westland Aircraft Whirlwind

Type: general-purpose helicopter
Crew: three, plus up to eight passengers
Rotors: metal cantilever three-blade main rotor; metal cantilever two-blade tail rotor
Fuselage: metal semi-monocoque
Landing gear: fixed quadricycle unit
Powerplant: one Bristol Siddeley Gnome H.1000 turboshaft, rated at 1,050 shp
Fuel capacity:
Avionics: communication and navigation equipment
Armament: provision for the installation of various weapons, such as machine-guns and air-to-surface missiles
Dimensions: Span 53 ft (16.15 m)
Length (fuselage) 44 ft 2 in (13.46 m)
Height 15 ft 7½ in (4.76 m)
Rotor disc area: 2,206 ft² (204.96 m²)
Weights: Empty 4,694 lb (2,129 kg)
Loaded 8,000 lb (3,629 kg)
Maximum

Performance: Speed 109 mph (175 kph); cruising speed 104 mph (167 kph); climb 1,200 ft (366 m) per minute at sea level at 58 mph (93 kph); hovering ceiling in ground effect 15,800 ft (4,816 m)
Used also by: Brazil, Qatar, UK
Notes: The Westland Whirlwind is basically the Sikorsky S-55 built under licence in the UK, but extensively developed to produce the prolific HAR series for the RAF and Royal Navy. The HAR.10, to which the specification above applies, is the turboshaft-powered model which first flew in 1959. Maximum payload of the HAR.10 is 2,000 lb (907 kg).

North Korea

45,000 men and 655 combat aircraft.

3 lt bomber sqns with 85 Il-28.
13 FGA sqns with 20 Su-7, 320 MiG-15/-17.
10 interceptor sqns with 120 MiG-21 and 110 MiG-19.
250 transports, incl 200 An-2, An-24, 10 Il-14/-18, 1 Tu-154.
Helicopters incl 50 Mi-4, 10 Mi-8.
Trainers incl 50 Yak-18, 60 MiG-15UTI/-21U, Il-28.
AA-1 'Alkali', AA-2 'Atoll' AAM.
3 SAM bdes with 250 SA-2.

North Yemen

1,500 men and about 26 combat aircraft.

1 lt bomber sqn with 14 Il-28.
1 fighter sqn with 12 MiG-17.
3 C-47, 2 Skyvan, 1 Il-14 transports.
4 F-5B, 4 MiG-15UTI, 18 Yak-11 trainers.
1 Mi-4, 2 AB-205 helicopters.
AA-2 'Atoll' AAM.

Norway

10,000 men (5,000 conscripts) and 115 combat aircraft, plus 18,000 reservists.

2 FGA sqns with 32 F-5A.
1 FGA sqn with 22 CF-104G/D.
1 AWX sqn with 27 F-104G, 2 TF-104G.
1 recce sqn with 13 RF-5A.
1 MR sqn with 5 P-3B.

1 OCU with 14 F-5B.
2 transport sqns: 1 with 6 C-130H, 1 with 5 DHC-6, 2 Falcon 20 ECM ac.
1 SAR sqn with 10 Sea King Mk 43 helicopters.
2 helicopter sqns with 32 UH-1B.
17 Saab *Safir* trainers.
Sidewinder AAM; Bullpup ASM.
4 lt AA bns with L/70 40mm guns.
1 SAM bn with Nike Hercules.
(72 F-16 fighters, 1 Sea King helicopter, 40 Roland II SAM on order.)

Saab 91 *Safir*

Type: basic trainer
Crew: two or three
Wings: metal cantilever low-wing monoplane
Fuselage: metal semi-monocoque
Tail unit: metal cantilever
Landing gear: retractable tricycle unit
Powerplant: one Lycoming O-360-A1A piston engine, rated at 180 hp and driving a two-blade metal propeller
Fuel capacity:

Avionics: communication and navigation equipment

Armament: two 8-mm machine-guns and eight 63-mm rockets

Dimensions: Span 34 ft 9 in (10.6 m)
Length 26 ft 4 in (8.03 m)
Height 7 ft 2½ in (2.2 m)

Wing area: 146 ft² (13.56 m²)

Weights: Empty 1,570 lb (712 kg)
Loaded 2,315 lb (1,050 kg)
Maximum 2,660 lb (1,207 kg)

Performance: speed 168 mph (270 kph) at sea level; cruising speed 140 mph (225 kph); climb 985 ft (300 m) per minute at sea level; service ceiling 20,000 ft (6,100 m); range 700 miles (1,125 km)

Used also by: Egypt, Ethiopia, Finland, Sweden

Notes: The prototype Saab 91 was flown in 1945, powered by a 145-hp de Havilland Gipsy Major X. The Saab 91B differs in having the 190-hp Lycoming O-435-A. The Saab 91C differs from the Saab 91B in having accommodation for four, and the Saab 91D, to which the technical specification above applies, has a more powerful Lycoming engine and other improvements.

Oman

2,100 men and 32 combat aircraft.

1 FGA/recce sqn with 12 Hunter.
1 FGA sqn with 12 Jaguar.
1 COIN/trg sqn with 8 BAC 167.
3 transport sqns: 1 with 3 BAC 111, 2 with 10 Defender/Skyvan.
Royal flt with 1 VC10, 1 Gulfstream, 2 AS.202 Bravo trainers.
1 helicopter sqn with 20 AB-205, 2 AB-206, 5 AB-214A/B helicopters.
2 AD sqns with 28 Rapier SAM.
(R.550 Magic AAM on order.)
There is also a police air wing: 1 Learjet light transport, 2 Turbo-Porter transports, 2 Merlin IVA light transports, 4 AB-205, 2 AB-206 helicopters.

British Aerospace BAC 1-11

Type: medium-range transport

Crew: two, plus up to 89 passengers

Wings: aluminium alloy cantilever low-wing monoplane

Fuselage: metal semi-monocoque

Tail unit: metal cantilever

Landing gear: hydraulically actuated retractable tricycle unit

Powerplant: two Rolls-Royce Spey Mark 512 DW turbofans, each rated at 12,550-lb (5,693-kg) static thrust

Fuel capacity: 3,085 gallons (14,024 litres) in centre-section and integral wing tanks, plus provision for two optional tanks holding 1,050 gallons (4,773 litres)

Avionics: comprehensive communication and navigation equipment

Armament: none

Dimensions: Span 93 ft 6 in (28.5 m)
Length 93 ft 6 in (28.5 m)
Height 24 ft 6 in (7.47 m)

Wing area: 1,031 ft² (95.78 m²)

Weights: Empty 51,731 lb (23,464 kg)
Loaded
Maximum 98,500 lb (44,678 kg)

Performance: (at maximum take-off weight) maximum and cruising speed 541 mph (871 kph) at 21,000 ft (6,400 m); climb 2,480 ft (756 m) per minute at sea level; cruising altitude 35,000 ft (10,670 m); range with maximum fuel 2,300 miles (3,700 km); range with typical payload 1,865 miles (3,000 km)

Used also by: Australia, Mexico, Philippines

Notes: Derived from the BAC 1-11 Series 475 airliner, the Omani transport aircraft have a large freight door forward on the port side, and facilities for quick changing from passenger to freight configuration. Maximum payload is 21,269 lb (9,647 kg).

Hawker Aircraft Hunter

Type: fighter, fighter-bomber and fighter-reconnaissance aircraft
Crew: one
Wings: metal cantilever mid-wing monoplane
Fuselage: metal semi-monocoque
Tail unit: metal cantilever
Landing gear: hydraulically actuated retractable tricycle unit
Powerplant: one Rolls-Royce Avon 207 turbojet, rated at 10,150-lb (4,604-kg) static thrust
Fuel capacity: 392 gallons (1,782 litres) internally
Avionics: comprehensive communication and navigation/attack equipment

Armament: four 30-mm Aden cannon with 150 rounds per gun, plus two 1,000-lb (454-kg) bombs and 24 3-in (76-mm) rockets under the wings, as well as two 230-gallon (1,046-litre) drop tanks
Dimensions: Span 33 ft 8 in (10.26 m)
Length 45 ft 10½ in (13.98 m)
Height 13 ft 2 in (4.26 m)
Wing area: 349 ft² (32.42 m²)
Weights: Empty 13,270 lb (6,020 kg)
Loaded 17,750 lb (8,051 kg)
Maximum 24,000 lb (10,885 kg)
Performance: speed 710 mph (1,144 kph) at sea level; 620 mph (978 kph) or Mach 0.94 at 36,000 ft (10,973 m); climb about 8,000 ft (2,438 m) per minute at sea level; climb 7 minutes 30 seconds to 45,000 ft (13,706 m); service ceiling 50,000 ft

(15,240 m); range 1,840 miles 2,965 km) with maximum fuel; combat radius 219 miles (352 km) with 2,000 lb (907 kg) of bombs and drop tanks
Used also by: Chile, India, Iraq, Kenya, Kuwait, Lebanon, Peru, Qatar, Rhodesia, Singapore, Switzerland, Uruguay
Notes: The Hunter is the most successful fighter built in the UK since World War II, the prototype flying in 1951 and the F.1 entering service in 1953. Since that time the Hunter has been produced in a great number of versions for domestic and foreign use, and the type is still widely used as a ground-attack aircraft. The specification above applies to the FGA.9 ground-attack fighter.

Pakistan

18,000 men and 257 combat aircraft, plus 8,000 reservists.

1 lt bomber sqn with 11 B-57B (Canberra).
4 fighter sqns with 21 Mirage IIIEP/DP, 28 VPA.
9 FGA sqns; 7 with 135 MiG-19/F-6, 2 with 40 F-86.
1 recce sqn with 13 Mirage IIIRP, 4 RT-33A.
1 MR sqn with 3 Atlantic, 2 HU-16B.
Transports incl 12 C-130B/E, 1 L-100, 1 Falcon 20, 1 F-27, 1 Super King Air, 1 Bonanza.
10 HH-43B, 4 Super *Frelon*, 12 *Alouette* III, 1 Puma, 12 Bell 47 helicopters.
Trainers incl MiG-15UTI, 45 Saab Supporter, 12 T-33A, 30 T-37, F-86.
Sidewinder, R.530, R.550 Magic AAM.
Naval Air Arm
4 *Alouette* III, 6 Sea King SAR helicopters.
Army Air Arm
40 O-IE lt ac; 12 Mi-8, 6 Puma, 20 *Alouette* III, 12 UH-1, 15 Bell 47G helicopters.
(29 Puma helicopters on order.)

Glenn L. Martin B-57

Type: tactical bomber and strategic reconnaissance aircraft
Crew: two, seated in tandem
Wings: metal cantilever mid-wing monoplane
Fuselage: metal semi-monocoque
Tail unit: metal cantilever
Landing gear: hydraulically actuated retractable tricycle unit
Powerplant: two Pratt & Whitney TF33-P-11A turbofans, each rated at 18,000-lb (8,165-kg) static thrust, and two Pratt & Whitney J60-P-9 turbojets, each rated at 3,300-lb (1,500-kg) static thrust
Fuel capacity:
Avionics: comprehensive communication and navigation equipment
Armament: none
Dimensions: Span 122 ft 5 in (37.32 m)
Length 69 ft (21.03 m)
Height 19 ft (5.79 m)
Wing area:
Weights: Empty about 36,000 lb (16,330 kg)
Loaded
Maximum 63,000 lb (28,576 kg)
Performance: speed over 500 mph (805 kph); climb about 4,000 ft (1,220 m) per minute at sea level; service ceiling 75,000 ft (22,860 m); range about 3,700 miles (5,955 km)

Used also by: USA
Notes: The British Canberra bomber first flew in 1949, and immediately attracted the attention of the USAF, amongst others. A licence production was achieved, and Martin's first production B-57A flew in 1953. Thereafter, there appeared a series of aircraft derived from the Canberra:
1. B-57A preproduction aircraft
2. B-57B production tactical bombers, with 7,220-lb (3,275-kg) Wright J65-W-5 engines, 6,000 lb (2,722 kg) of bombs, and a gun armament of four 20-mm cannon or eight 0.5-in (12.7-mm) machine-guns. The B-57C, E and G had the same weapons and offensive load
3. B-57C trainer with dual controls, based on the B-57B
4. B-57E multi-role (bomber, trainer, reconnaissance aircraft, and target tug) aircraft
5. RB-57D high-altitude reconnaissance aircraft, with 11,000-lb (4,990-kg) J57-P-37A engines and a span of 106 ft (32.3 m)
6. RB-57F, produced by General Dynamics, and intended for the strategic reconnaissance role. The specification above applies to this model, which has a span more than twice the 64 ft (19.5 m) of the early bombers, and additional engines.

Saab-Scania Supporter

Type: training, observation and light ground-attack aircraft
Crew: two, seated side-by-side
Wings: metal braced shoulder-wing monoplane
Fuselage: metal box
Tail unit: metal cantilever
Landing gear: fixed tricycle unit
Powerplant: one Lycoming IO-360-A1B6 piston engine, rated at 200 hp and driving a Hartzell two-blade metal propeller
Fuel capacity: 41.8 gallons (190 litres) in two integral wing tanks
Avionics: communication and navigation equipment
Armament: six underwing hardpoints, capable of lifting a maximum load of 661 lb (300 kg) of external stores (air-to-surface rockets, Bantam anti-tank missiles, or two pods each containing two 7.62-mm machine-guns)
Dimensions: Span 29 ft 0½ in (8.85 m)
Length 22 ft 11½ in (7.0 m)
Height 8 ft 6½ in (2.6 m)
Wing area: 128.1 ft² (11.9 m²)
Weights: Empty 1,424 lb (646 kg)
Loaded 2,480 lb (1,125 kg)
Maximum 2,645 lb (1,200 kg)
Performance: (at normal take-off weight) speed 146 mph (236 kph) at sea level; cruising speed 129 mph (208 kph); climb 807 ft (246 m) per minute at sea level; climb to 6,000 ft (1,380 m) in 9 minutes 18 seconds; service ceiling 13,450 ft (4,100 m); endurance 5 hours 10 minutes
Used also by: Denmark, Sierra Leone, Zambia
Notes: The Supporter, at first designated the MFI 17, is derived from the Safari light utility aircraft, with the addition of six underwing hardpoints. The first prototype flew in 1972.

Panama

Para-military forces: utility aircraft include DHC-6 Twin Otter.

De Havilland Canada DHC-6 Twin Otter

Type: STOL transport
Crew: one or two, plus accommodation for 20
Wings: strut-braced high-wing monoplane
Fuselage: aluminium alloy semi-monocoque
Tail unit: aluminium alloy cantilever
Landing gear: fixed tricycle unit
Powerplant: two Pratt & Whitney Aircraft of Canada PT6A-27 turboprops, each rated at 652 ehp and driving Hartzell three-blade metal propellers
Fuel capacity: 318 gallons (1,446 litres) in two underfloor fuel tanks
Avionics: radio, radar and blind-flying equipment
Armament: none
Dimensions: Span 65 ft (19.81 m)
Length 51 ft 9 in (15.77 m)
Height 19 ft 6 in (5.94 m)
Wing area: 420 ft² (39.02 m²)
Weights: Empty 7,415 lb (3,363 kg)
Loaded
Maximum 12,500 lb (5,670 kg)
Performance: (at maximum take-off weight) cruising speed 210 mph (338 kph) at 10,000 ft (3,050 m); climb 1,600 ft (488 m) per minute at sea level; service ceiling 26,700 ft (8,140 m); range with payload of 2,550 lb (1,156 kg) 892 miles (1,435 km)
Used also by: Argentina, Canada, Chile, Ecuador, Egypt, Ethiopia, Jamaica, Norway, Paraguay, Peru, Sudan, Uganda, USA
Notes: Versatile STOL transport for civilian and military use developed in the early 1960s. It has first-class performance off rough airfields.

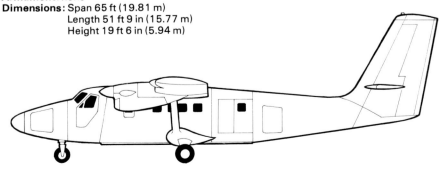

Paraguay

2,500 men and 12 combat aircraft.

1 COIN sqn with 12 T-6 Texan.
Transports incl 5 DC-6B, 2 C-54, 3
   CV-240, 10 C-47, 1 DHC-6, 1 Dove,
   1 DHC-3.
14 Bell UH-13A helicopters.
Trainers incl 8 Fokker S-11, 8 T-23
   Uirapuru, 10 T-6, 1 MS 760, 5
   Cessna 185.
1 para 'regt' (bn).
(10 AT-26 *Xavante* COIN, 10 EMB-
   110 transports on order.)
Naval Air Arm
4 Cessna V206, 2 Cessna 150 ac, 2 Bell
   47G helicopters.
Army Air Arm
2 Bell 47, 3 UH-12E helicopters.

Peru

10,000 men and 163 combat aircraft.

2 lt bomber sqns with 32 Canberra B.2,
   B (I). 8/56, 2 T.4.
4 FB sqns: 2 with 35 Mirage VP, 2 with
   32 Su-20, 4 Su-20UTI.
2 fighter sqns: 1 with 8 F-86F, 1 with
   10 Hunter F.52.
1 trg sqn with 12 MiG-21 (on loan from
   Cuba).
2 COIN sqns with 24 A-37B.
1 MR sqn with 4 HU-16B Albatross.
Transports incl 3 L-100-20, 4 C-130E,
   5 DC-6, 4 C-54, 2 Learjet, 16 An-26,
   2 F27, 4 F28, 7 DHC-6, 16 DHC-5,
18 Queen Air, 3 King Air, 2 Beech
   99, 12 Turbo-Porter, 5 Cessna 185.
Helicopters incl 12 *Alouette* III, 6
   UH-1D, 20 Bell 47G, 14 Bell 212, 6
   Mi-6, 6 Mi-8.
Trainers incl 15 T-6, 6 T-34, 8 T-33A,
   19 T-41, 26 T-37B/C, 4 Cessna 150.
AS.30 ASM.
Naval Air Arm
9 S-2A Tracker ASW.
6 C-47, 2 F27, 1 Aztec transport ac.
6 AB-212 ASW, 5 Bell 47G, 10 Bell
   206, 6 UH-1D/H, 2 *Alouette* III helicopters.
8 T-34 trainers.

Army Air Arm
5 U-10B, 5 Cessna 185 lt ac.
42 Mi-8 (36 in store), 4 *Alouette* III, 5
   Lama helicopters.
(2 Nomad lt transports on order.)

Costruzioni Aeronautiche Giovanni Agusta (Bell) AB 212ASW

Type: ASW and surface strike helicopter
Crew: three or four
Rotor: metal cantilever twin-blade main rotor; metal cantilever twin-blade tail rotor
Fuselage: metal semi-monocoque
Landing gear: twin metal skids
Powerplant: one Pratt & Whitney Aircraft of Canada PT6T-3 Turbo Twin Pac turboshaft, rated at 1,290 shp
Fuel capacity: 179 gallons (814 litres) in main fuselage tank, plus two optional tanks each holding 75 gallons (341 litres)
Avionics: comprehensive all-weather communication and navigation/attack equipment, including SMA/APS search radar, Motorola SST-119X radar transponder, and Bendix AN/AQS-13B variable-depth sonar

Armament: two Mark 44 or Mark 46 homing torpedoes, depth charges or air-to-surface missiles
Dimensions: Span 48 ft (14.63 m)
Length (fuselage) 46 ft (14.02 m)
Height 14 ft 5 in (4.4 m)
Rotor disc area: 1,809.5 ft² (168.1 m²)
Weights: Empty 7,540 lb (3,420 kg)
Loaded Maximum 11,196 lb (5,079 kg)
Performance: (at maximum take-off weight) speed 122 mph (196 kph) at sea level; cruising speed with armament 115 mph (185 kph); climb 1,519 ft (463 m) per minute at sea level; hovering ceiling in ground effect 12,500 ft (3,810 m); search endurance with 50 per cent cruising at 103 mph (166 kph) and 50 per cent hovering out of ground effect 3 hours; range with maximum auxiliary fuel 414 miles (667 km)

Used also by: Argentina, Bangladesh, Brunei, Ghana, Guyana, Israel, Jamaica, Mexico, Saudi Arabia, South Korea
Notes: This is basically the AB 212 airframe modified in the light of experience with the AB 204ASW, and has special strengthening for operations from small ships.

Fokker-VFW F27 Maritime

Type: medium-range maritime patrol aircraft
Crew: seven
Wings: metal cantilever high-wing monoplane

Fuselage: metal semi-monocoque
Tail unit: metal cantilever
Landing gear: pneumatically actuated retractable tricycle unit
Powerplant: two Rolls-Royce Dart Mark 532-7R turboprops, each rated at 2,140

shp and 525-lb (238-kg) static thrust, and driving a Dowty Rotol metal four-blade propeller
Fuel capacity: 2,048 gallons (9,310 litres) in fuselage, wing and pylon tanks

Avionics: comprehensive communication and navigation equipment, including Litton AN/APS-503F search radar, Litton LTN-72 long-range inertial navigation equipment, and optional customer electronics
Armament: none
Dimensions: Span 95 ft 2 in (29.0 m)
Length 77 ft 3½ in (23.56 m)
Height 27 ft 11 in (8.5 m)

Wing area: 753.5 ft² (70.0 m²)
Weights: Empty 27,403 lb (12,430 kg)
Loaded
Maximum 45,000 (20,410 kg)
Performance: (at maximum take-off weight and with pylon tanks) cruising speed at 20,000 ft (6,100 m) at a take-off weight of 40,000 lb (18,150 kg) 265 mph (427 kph); search speed at 2,000 ft (610 m) 168 mph (270 kph);

service ceiling 23,200 ft (7,070 m); range up to 2,547 miles (4,100 km); endurance 12 hours
Used also by: Spain
Notes: Derived from the F27 Friendship, this limited-performance maritime reconnaissance aircraft first flew in 1976. A wide variety of customer-specified electronics are possible.

Sukhoi Su-17 and Su-20 'Fitter'

Type: ground-attack fighter
Crew: one
Wings: metal cantilever variable-geometry mid-wing monoplane
Fuselage: metal semi-monocoque
Tail unit: metal cantilever
Landing gear: hydraulically actuated retractable tricycle unit
Powerplant: one Lyulka AL-21F-3 turbojet, rated at 25,000-lb (11,340-kg) static thrust with afterburning
Fuel capacity: 8,157 lb (3,700 kg) internally, plus provision for external fuel tanks
Avionics: comprehensive communication and navigation/attack equipment, including SRD-5M 'High Fix' ranging radar, ASP-5ND fire-control system, and Sirena 3 radar warning system
Armament: two NR-30 30-mm cannon with 70 rounds per gun, plus a wide variety of external stores on eight pylons, four under the fuselage and four under the wings, for a total load of 11,023 lb (5,000 kg). Weapons that can be carried include bombs, rocket pods and missiles such as the AS-7

'Kerry' air-to-surface missile
Dimensions: Span (spread) about 45 ft 11¼ in (14.0 m)
Span (swept) about 34 ft 9½ in (10.6 m)
Length with probe about 61 ft 6¼ in (18.75 m)
Height about 15 ft 7 in (4.75 m)
Wing area: (spread) about 431.6 ft² (40.1 m²) (swept) about 400.4 ft² (37.2 m²)
Weights: Empty about 22,046 lb (10,000 kg)
Loaded about 30,865 lb (14,000 kg)
Maximum about 41,887 lb (19,000 kg)
Performance: (estimated, at normal loaded weight) speed 1,435 mph (2,309 kph) or Mach 2.17 above 36,100 ft (11,000 m); speed 800 mph (1,288 kph) or Mach 1.05 at sea level; climb 45,275 ft (13,800 m) per minute at sea level; service ceiling 59,050 ft (18,000 m); combat radius with 4,409 lb (2,000 kg) of external stores on a lo-lo-lo mission 224 miles (360 km); combat radius with 4,409 lb (2,000 kg) of external stores on a hi-lo-hi mission 391 miles (630 km)

Used also by: Egypt, Iraq, Poland, USSR
Notes: Derived from the Su-7, the Su-17 and Su-20 feature wings with variable geometry, the outer 13 ft (4.0 m) being hinged to move from a forward position with 28° of sweep to an aft position with 62° of sweep. This gives the Su-17 and Su-20 a good STOL performance, and the uprated engine of the Su-17 increases performance and payload. There are several versions:

1. Su-17 'Fitter-C', to which the technical specification above applies, and which is in service with the Soviet Air Force
2. Su-17 'Fitter-D', also in service with the Soviet Air Force, and distinguishable from the 'Fitter-C' by the small radome under the air intake and the laser marked target seeker in the intake centrebody
3. Su-20 'Fitter-C' is the export version of the Su-17 'Fitter-C', with less advanced electronics and the lower rated Lyulka AL-7F-1 engine of the Su-7 family.

Philippines

16,000 men and 111 combat aircraft, plus 16,000 reservists.

2 FB sqns with 20 F-5A/B, 20 F-86.
1 fighter/trg sqn with 17 T-34A.
3 COIN sqns with 18 SF.260WP, 24 T-28.
1 gunship sqn with 12 AC-47.
1 SAR sqn with 8 HU-16 ac, UH-19, 3 SH-34G, 12 UH-1H, H-13, Hughes 300 helicopters.
1 helicopter sqn with 18 UH-1H.
6 transport sqns with 6 C-130H, 3 L-100-20, 1 Boeing 707, 1 BAC 111, 30 C-47, 10 F27, 4 YS-11, 15 C-123K, 12 Mission Master.
1 liaison sqn with O-1E, Cessna 180, 6 U-17A/B, Cessna 310K, 21 DHC-2.
3 trg sqns with 10 T/RT-33A, 12 T-41A, 8 F-86F, 32 SF.260MP.
Other helicopters incl 12 UH-1D, 8 FH-1100, 5 UH-19, 2 H-34, 2 S-62A.
Sidewinder AAM.
(11 F-5E, 25 F-8H fighters; 38 BO 105, 17 UH-1 helicopters on order.)
Naval Air Arm
1 SAR sqn with 10 Islander.
3 BO 105 helicopters.

Government Aircraft Factories Mission Master

Type: forward area support and surveillance, light transport, and maritime surveillance
Crew: two
Wings: alloy high-wing braced monoplane
Fuselage: alloy semi-monocoque
Tail unit: cantilever metal semi-monocoque
Landing gear: electrically actuated retractable tricycle unit
Powerplant: two Allison 250-B17B turboprops, each rated at 400 shp and driving a three-blade Hartzell metal propeller

Fuel capacity: 1,794 lb (813 kg) in self-sealing fuel cells, plus optional 595 lb (270 kg) in wingtip tanks

Avionics: a variety of search radar, navigation, detection and recording systems to suit customer requirements

Armament: up to 2,000 lb (907 kg) of gun and rocket pods on four underwing hardpoints

Dimensions: Span 54 ft 0 in (16.46 m)
Length 41 ft 2⅔ in (12.56 kg)
Height 18 ft 1½ in (5.52 m)

Wing area: 324 ft² (30.1 m²)

Weights: Empty 4,666 lb (2,116 kg)
Loaded
Maximum 8,500 lb (3,855 kg)

Performance: cruising speed 193 mph (311 kph); climb 1,460 ft (445 m) per minute at sea level; service ceiling 22,500 ft (6,860 m); range 840 miles (1,352 km) at 10,000 ft (3,050 m). (All performance figures at maximum take-off weight unless otherwise specified)

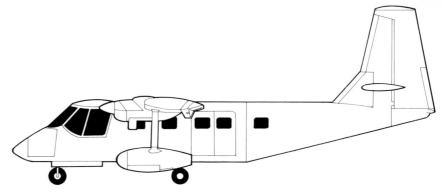

Used also by: Australia, Indonesia

Notes: Basically a STOL transport for civilian users (N22B), converted for military use with extra structural strength, hardpoints, self-sealing tanks and improved avionics. The Search Master is a maritime surveillance adaptation of the Mission Master with 360° search radar and improved navigation equipment. The weight and performance figures quoted above are for the civil N22B model.

Poland

62,000 men (18,000 conscripts) and 725 combat aircraft, plus 60,000 reservists.

1 lt bomber sqn with 6 Il-28.
15 FGA sqns: 14 with 160 MiG-17 and 30 Su-7, 1 with 28 Su-20.
33 interceptor sqns with 80 MiG-17, 340 MiG-21.
6 recce sqns with 72 MiG-15/-21, 5 Il-28, 4 Il-14.
Some 50 transports, incl 22 An-12/-24/-26, 21 Il-14/-18/-62, 4 Tu-134, 5 Yak-40.
165 Mi-1/-2, 19 Mi-4, 26 Mi-8 helicopters.
300 trainers, incl *Iskra*, MiG-15/-17/-21UTI, Il-28.
AA-2 'Atoll' AAM.
36 SA-2, 12 SA-3 SAM bns.

Naval Air Arm
1 Naval Aviation Regt (60 combat aircraft):
1 lt bomber/recce sqn with 10 Il-28.
4 fighter sqns with 12 MiG-15, 38 MiG-17.
2 helicopter sqns with some 25 Mi-1/-2/-4.

Wytwornia Sprzetu Komunikacyjnego Im. Zygmunta Pulawskiego-PZL-Swidnik (Mil) Mi-2

Type: general-purpose light helicopter
Crew: one, plus up to eight passengers
Rotor: duralumin cantilever three-blade main rotor; duralumin cantilever two-blade tail rotor
Fuselage: duralumin semi-monocoque
Landing gear: fixed tricycle unit
Powerplant: two Polish-built Isotov GTD-350P turboshafts, each rated at 400 or 450shp
Fuel capacity: 131 gallons (600 litres) in rubber fuselage tank, plus provision for two auxiliary tanks, one each side of the fuselage, and each holding 52.4 gallons (238 litres)
Avionics: communication and navigation equipment
Armament: rocket pods or air-to-surface missiles on pylons fitted to each side of the fuselage

Dimensions: Span 47 ft 6¾ in (14.5 m)
Length (fuselage) 39 ft 2 in (11.94 m)
Height 12 ft 3½ in (3.75 m)

Rotor disc area: 1,791.11 ft² (166.4 m²)

Weights: Empty 5,229 lb (2,372 kg)
Loaded 7,826 lb (3,550 kg)
Maximum 8,157 lb (3,700 kg)

Performance: (at normal take-off weight) speed 130 mph (210 kph) at 1,640 ft (500 m); cruising speed 124 mph (200 kph) at 1,640 ft (500 m); climb 885 ft (270 m) per minute at sea level; climb to 13,125 ft (4,000 m) in 26 minutes; service ceiling 13,125 ft (4,000 m); hovering ceiling in ground effect 6,550 ft (2,000 m); range with maximum fuel 360 miles (580 km); range with maximum payload 105 miles (170 km)

Used also by: Bulgaria, Syria, USSR

Notes: Although designed in the USSR by the Mil design bureau in the early 1960s, production and marketing was undertaken by the Poles from 1964 onwards.

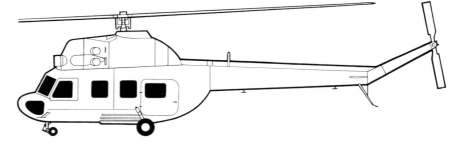

Wytwornia Sprzetu Komunikacyjnego-PZL-Mielec TS-11 *Iskra*

Type: trainer and light ground-attack aircraft
Crew: one or two, in tandem
Wings: metal cantilever mid-wing monoplane
Fuselage: metal semi-monocoque
Tail unit: metal cantilever
Landing gear: hydraulically actuated retractable tricycle unit
Powerplant: one SO-3 turbojet, rated at 2,205-lb (1,000-kg) static thrust

Fuel capacity: 263.5 gallons (1,200 litres) in two-seater, and 308 gallons (1,400 litres) in single-seater, in one fuselage and two integral wing tanks
Avionics: communications and navigation equipment
Armament: (*Iskra* 200 and single-seater) one 23-mm cannon, plus four underwing hardpoints for external stores including bombs up to 220 lb (100 kg) in weight, octuple rocket pods, and 7.62-mm machine-gun pods

Dimensions: Span 33 ft (10.06 m)
Length 36 ft 5 in (11.17 m)
Height 11 ft 5½ in (3.5 m)

Wing area: 188.37 ft² (17.5 m²)

Weights: Empty 5,644 lb (2,560 kg)
Loaded 8,377 lb (3,800 kg)
Maximum 8,465 lb (3,840 kg)
Performance: (at normal take-off weight)
speed 447 mph (720 kph) at 16,400 ft
(5,000 m); cruising speed 373 mph (600
kph); climb 2,913 ft (888 m) per minute at
sea level; climb to 22,975 ft (7,000 m) in
13 minutes 36 seconds; service ceiling
36,100 ft (11,000 m); range for single-
seater 907 miles (1,460 km); range for
two-seater 776 miles (1,250 km)
Used also by: India
Notes: The prototype began flight tests in
1960, and entered large-scale production
in 1962. Current production models are:
  1. *Iskra* 100 with underwing armament
     pods

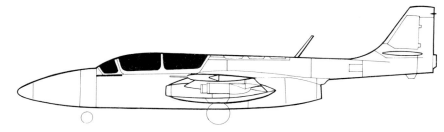

2. single-seat *Iskra* light ground-attack
   aircraft
3. *Iskra* 200, incorporating improvements
4. *Iskra* 200SB improved armament
   trainer.

Portugal

9,500 men, including 1,300 airborne,
and 18 combat aircraft.

1 FGA sqn with 18 G91R-3/-4.
2 transport sqns with 2 C-130H, 24
  CASA C.212 *Aviocar*.
Trainers incl 5 G91T, 10 T-33A, 18
  T-37C, 6 T-38A, 19 Do 27, 25 Chipmunk, 32 Reims-Cessna FTB 337G.
2 helicopter sqns with 30 *Alouette* III
  and 10 Puma.
3 parachute battalions.
(4 C-130H transports on order.)

Qatar

300 men and 4 combat aircraft.

3 Hunter FGA, 1 Hunter T.79.
1 Islander transport.
2 Whirlwind, 4 Commando, 2 Gazelle,
3 Lynx helicopters.
Tigercat SAM.
(30 Mirage F1, 3 Lynx on order.)

Westland Helicopters/Société Nationale Industrielle Aérospatiale Lynx

Type: multi-role military helicopter
Crew: one to four, plus up to 10 passengers
Rotor: steel and glassfibre cantilever four-blade main rotor; light alloy and glassfibre cantilever four-blade tail rotor
Fuselage: light alloy and glassfibre semi-monocoque
Landing gear: twin metal skids (general-purpose version) or fixed tricycle unit (naval version)
Powerplant: two Rolls-Royce BS.360-07-26 Gem turboshafts, each rated at 900 shp maximum contingency rating
Fuel capacity: 202 gallons (918 litres) in five fuselage bag tanks
Avionics: comprehensive communication and navigation/attack equipment, including Avimo-Ferranti 530 lightweight stabilised sight or other acquisition/guidance sights relevant to the weapons being carried
Armament: see breakdown in Notes below
Dimensions: Span 42 ft (12.802 m)
    Length (overall) 49 ft 9 in (15.163 m)
    Height 12 ft (3.66 m)
Rotor disc area: 1,385.4 ft² (128.7 m²)
Weights: Empty (general-purpose) 6,144 lb (2,787 kg)
    Empty (ASW) 7,037 lb (3,192 kg)
    Loaded 9,500 lb (4,309 kg)
    Maximum 10,500 lb (4,763 kg)
Performance: (general-purpose version at normal loaded weight) speed 207 mph (333 kph); cruising speed 175 mph (282 kph); climb 2,180 ft (664 m) per minute at sea level; service ceiling more than 25,000 ft (7,600 m); endurance 3 hours 26 minutes; combat radius about 235 miles (378 km); ferry range 834 miles (1,342 km)
Performance: (naval version at normal loaded weight) speed 200 mph (322 kph); cruising speed 167 mph (269 kph); climb 2,020 ft (616 m) per minute at sea level; service ceiling more than 25,000 m); endurance 3 hours 26 minutes; combat radius 209 miles (336 km); ferry range 650 miles (1,046 km)
Used also by: Argentina, Brazil, Denmark, Egypt, France, Netherlands, UK and others
Notes: The Lynx, designed by Westland but built by Westland and Aérospatiale on a 70/30 basis, is one of the world's outstanding helicopters, being fast, easy to operate, very agile and capable of carrying loads of great weight. The main versions are currently:

1. Lynx AH.1 general-purpose and utility helicopter for the British Army, with tactical troop transport, logistic support, armed escort, anti-tank strike, casualty evacuation, reconnaissance, and search and rescue as its prime missions. Armament can comprise one 20-mm AME 621 cannon with 1,500 rounds, or one 7.62-mm GEC Minigun multi-barrel machine-gun in the cabin or with 3,000 rounds in an Emerson Minitat turret; plus one pylon on each side of the cabin, able to carry two Minigun pods, two rocket pods (of eighteen 68-mm or seven 2.75-in projectiles), or up to six BAC Hawkswing or Aérospatiale AS.11 air-to-surface missiles, or eight Aérospatiale/MBB HOT or Hughes TOW air-to-surface missiles (with six or eight reload rounds carried in the cabin)
2. Lynx HAS.2 anti-submarine helicopter for the Royal Navy. Armament can comprise two Mark 44 or 46 homing torpedoes or two Mark 11 depth charges, operated in conjunction with Alcatel DUAV 4 lightweight dunking sonar; for anti-shipping strike, the Lynx can carry four BAC CL834 Sea Skua, four AS.12 or similar air-to-surface missiles, in conjunction with Ferranti Seaspray search radar
3. Lynx (French Navy), similar to the HAS.2 but with more advanced target acquisition gear
4. Lynx HAR Mark 25/UH-14A for the Royal Netherlands Navy in the SAR and ASW roles respectively.

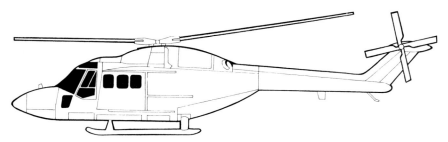

Rhodesia

1,300 men and 84 combat aircraft.

1 lt bomber sqn with 5 Canberra B.2 and 2 T.4.
2 FGA sqns: 1 with 10 Hunter FGA.9, 1 with 18 Vampire FB.9.
1 trg/recce sqn with 8 Provost T.52, 11 Vampire T.55.
1 COIN/recce sqn with 12 AL.60C4, 18 Cessna 337 (Lynx).
1 transport sqn with 10 C-47, 1 Baron 55, 6 Islander.
2 helicopter sqns with 66 *Alouette* II/III.

De Havilland Aircraft Vampire

Type: fighter and fighter-bomber
Crew: one
Wings: metal cantilever mid-wing monoplane
Fuselage: metal semi-monocoque, with metal monocoque tailbooms
Tail unit: metal cantilever
Landing gear: hydraulically actuated retractable tricycle unit
Powerplant: one de Havilland Goblin D.Gn.3 turbojet, rated at 3,350-lb (1,520-kg) static thrust
Fuel capacity:
Avionics: communication and navigation equipment
Armament: four 20-mm Hispano cannon with 150 rounds per gun, plus two 1,000-lb (454-kg) bombs or eight 60-lb (27.2-kg) rockets under the wings
Dimensions: Span 38 ft (11.6 m)
Length 30 ft 9 in (9.37 m)
Height 8 ft 10 in (2.7 m)
Wing area: 262 ft^2 (24.34 m^2)
Weights: Empty 7,200 lb (3,266 kg)
Loaded
Maximum 12,290 lb (5,600 kg)
Performance: speed 548 mph (883 kph) at 30,000 ft (9,144 m); climb 4,800 ft (1,463 m) per minute at sea level; service ceiling 44,000 ft (13,410 m); range 1,400 miles (2,253 km) with drop tanks
Used also by: Chile, Dominican Republic, India, Saudi Arabia, Switzerland
Notes: The Vampire was developed as the DH100, and first flew in 1943. The initial production model, the F.1, entered service in December 1945, and the Vampire was subsequently built in a number of single- and two-seat versions for air forces and navies. A very simple aircraft, the Vampire has no vices and is a delight to fly. Its performance and payload are very limited, however. The technical specification applies to the FB.6 version.

Hunting Percival Aircraft Provost

Type: trainer
Crew: two, seated side-by-side
Wings: metal cantilever low-wing monoplane
Fuselage: metal semi-monocoque
Tail unit: metal cantilever
Landing gear: fixed tailwheel unit
Powerplant: one Alvis Leonides 126 radial engine, rated at 550 hp and driving a three-blade metal propeller
Fuel capacity:
Avionics: communication and navigation equipment
Armament: none
Dimensions: Span 35 ft 2 in (10.72 m)
Length 28 ft 8 in (8.74 m)
Height 12 ft 2½ in (3.72 m)
Wing area: 214 ft^2 (19.88 m^2)
Weights: Empty 3,350 lb (1,520 kg)
Loaded 4,400 lb (1,996 kg)
Maximum
Performance: speed 200 mph (322 kph) at sea level; cruising speed 162 mph (261 kph) at 5,000 ft (1,524 m); climb 2,200 ft (671 m) per minute at sea level; climb 3 minutes 30 seconds to 10,000 ft (3,050 m); service ceiling 25,000 ft (7,620 m); range 648 miles (1,045 km); endurance 4 hours
Used also by: Iraq
Notes: The Provost was introduced into RAF service in 1953 to replace the Percival Prentice as the standard basic trainer. With the introduction of a jet-engined version of the Provost, the Jet Provost, production of the Provost ceased in 1956.

Romania

30,000 men (10,000 conscripts) and 437 combat aircraft, plus 25,000 reservists.

5 FGA sqns with 75 MiG-15/-17, and IAR-93.
12 interceptor sqns with 27 MiG-15/-19, 210 MiG-21.
1 recce sqn with 15 Il-28.
2 transport sqns with some 4 Il-14, 4 Il-18, 1 Il-62, 10 An-24, 2 An-26, 12 Li-2, 1 Boeing 707.
6 Mi-4, 20 Mi-8, 45 *Alouette* III helicopters.
Trainers incl 50 L-29, 50 MiG-15UTl, 10 MiG-21U, 60 IAR-823.
AA-1 'Alkali', AA-2 'Atoll' AAM.
108 SA-2 at about 18 SAM sites.
Naval Air Arm
4 Mi-4 helicopters.

Ilyushin Il-28 'Beagle'

Type: bomber and ground-attack aircraft
Crew: three
Wings: metal cantilever shoulder-wing monoplane
Fuselage: metal semi-monocoque
Tail unit: metal cantilever
Landing gear: hydraulically actuated retractable tricycle unit
Powerplant: two Klimov VK-1 turbojets, each rated at 5,952-lb (2,700-kg) static thrust
Fuel capacity: 1,740 gallons (7,908 litres) in wing tanks, plus extra fuel in wingtip tanks
Avionics: comprehensive communications and navigation equipment
Armament: four 23-mm NR-23 cannon, plus up to 6,613 lb (3,000 kg) of bombs or torpedoes internally and externally
Dimensions: Span (no tip tanks) 70 ft 4¾ in (21.45 m)
Length 57 ft 10¾ in (17.65 m)
Height 22 ft (6.7 m)
Wing area: 654.4 ft² (60.8 m²)
Weights: Empty 28,417 lb (12,890 kg)
Loaded 40,564 lb (18,400 kg)
Maximum 46,297 lb (21,000 kg)

Performance: speed 559 mph (900 kph) at 14,765 ft (4,500 m); climb 2,953 ft (900 m) per minute at sea level; service ceiling 40,355 ft (12,300 m); range 1,355 miles (2,180 km) at 478 mph (770 kph) at 32,800 ft (10,000 m) with a bomb load of 2,205 lb (1,000 kg)
Used also by: Afghanistan, Algeria, China, Egypt, Indonesia, Iraq, North Korea, North Yemen, Poland, Somali Republic, South Yemen, Vietnam
Notes: The Il-28 first flew in 1948, and entered service in 1950. The last aircraft was delivered in Russia during 1960, and in China, where the type was also built, in 1968. Some 10,000 of this seminal bomber were built, in a number of variants:
1. Il-28 initial production model with 5,005-lb (2,270-kg) Klimov RD-45F turbojets
2. Il-28 later production model with 5,952-lb (2,700-kg) Klimov VK-1 turbojets
3. Il-28R with reconnaissance equipment in the bomb bay
4. Il-28T torpedo-bomber
5. Il-28U 'Mascot' trainer, with stepped cockpits for the pupil and instructor.

Vazduhoplovno-Tehnicki Institut & Centrala Industriala Aeronautica Romana *Orao*/IAR-93

Type: ground-attack fighter
Crew: one
Wings: metal cantilever shoulder-wing monoplane
Fuselage: metal semi-monocoque
Tail unit: metal cantilever
Landing gear: hydraulically actuated retractable tricycle unit
Powerplant: two Rolls-Royce Viper Mark 632-41 turbojets, each rated at 4,000-lb (1,814-kg) static thrust, in prototypes; production models may have afterburning Vipers rated at 5,950-lb (2,699-kg) each
Fuel capacity: about 675 gallons (3,070 litres) in internal tanks
Avionics: communications and navigation equipment
Armament: two 30-mm cannon and five hardpoints, one under the fuselage and two under each wing, for external stores up to a maximum weight of 6,615 lb (3,000 kg) approximately

Dimensions: (estimated)
Span 24 ft 9¾ in (7.56 m)
Length 42 ft 3¾ in (12.9 m)
Height 12 ft 4¾ in (3.78 m)
Wing area: (estimate) 193.75 ft² (18.0 m²)
Weights: (estimate)
Empty 10,360 lb (4,700 kg)
Loaded 16,095 lb (7,300 kg)
Maximum 22,700 lb (10,300 kg)
Performance: (estimated, for production aircraft with afterburning engines) speed 1,056 mph (1,699 kph) or Mach 1.6 at high altitude; 762 mph (1,226 kph) or Mach 1.0 at low altitude; climb 39,375 ft (12,000 m) per minute at sea level; time to 36,000 ft (11,000 m) 1 minute 36 seconds; service ceiling 52,500 ft (16,000 m); combat radius with 4,410 lb (2,000 kg) of stores 202 miles (325 km) on a lo-lo-lo raid, 404 miles (650 km) on a hi-lo-hi raid
Used also by: Yugoslavia
Notes: The *Orao* is a joint Romanian and Yugoslav venture, and is known in Romania as the IAR-93. The first prototype flew in 1974, and Romania is currently working on an IAR-93B two-seat variant for training and reconnaissance, as well as interdiction.

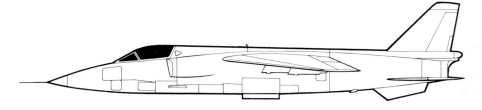

Rwanda

2 C-47, 2 Islander transports.
3 AM.3C liaison aircraft.
1 Magister trainer.
2 *Alouette* III helicopters.

Saudi Arabia

12,000 men and 171 combat aircraft.

3 FB sqns with 60 F-5E.
2 COIN/trg sqns with 35 BAC 167.
1 interceptor sqn with 16 Lightning F.53, 2 T.55.
3 OCU with 24 F-5F, 16 F-5B, 16 Lightning F.53, 2 T.55.
2 transport sqns with 35 C-130E/H.
2 helicopter sqns with 16 AB-206 and 24 AB-205.
Other ac incl 4 KC-130 tankers, 1 Boeing 707, 2 Falcon 20, 2 Jetstar transports; 22 *Alouette* III, 1 AB-206, 1 Bell-212, 2 AS-61A helicopters.
Trainers incl 12 T-41A.
Red Top, Firestreak, Sidewinder, R.530, R.550 Magic AAM; Maverick ASM.
(45 F-15 fighters; 15 TF-15 trainers; 1 Boeing 747, 4 KC-130H transport ac; 6 KV-107 helicopters on order.)

Bell Helicopter Textron AH-1 HueyCobra

Type: armed reconnaissance helicopter
Crew: two, seated in tandem
Rotor: metal cantilever two-blade main rotor; metal cantilever two-blade tail rotor
Fuselage: metal semi-monocoque
Landing gear: twin metal skids
Powerplant: one Lycoming T53-L-13 turbo-shaft, rated at 1,400 shp but derated to 1,100 shp
Fuel capacity: 296 gallons (1,345 litres)
Avionics: comprehensive communication and navigation/attack equipment, including a Univac helmet sight subsystem for weapons aiming in the AH-1Q and S
Armament: one Emerson Electric TAT-102A tactical armament chin turret with one 7.62-mm GAU-2B/A Minigun and 8,000 rounds; or one chin-mounted XM-28 armament subsystem with two Miniguns and 4,000 rounds each, or two XM-129 40-mm grenade launchers with 300 rounds each, or one Minigun and one grenade launcher; plus four hardpoints under the stub wings, for the carriage of four XM-159 packs with 76 2.75-in rockets, or four XM-157 packs with 28 2.75-in rockets, or two XM-18E1 Minigun pods. The port stub wing can also accommodate one XM-35 cannon kit, based on the six-barrel 20-mm cannon and having 1,000 rounds in two ammunition tanks
Dimensions: Span 44 ft (13.41 m)
Length (fuselage) 44 ft 7 in (13.59 m)
Height 13 ft 6¼ in (4.12 m)
Rotor disc area: 1,520.4 ft² (141.2 m²)
Weights: Empty (AH-1G) 6,073 lb (2,754 kg)
Empty (AH-1S) 6,479 lb (2,939 kg)
Loaded (AH-1G) 9,407 lb (4,266 kg)
Loaded (AH-1S) 9,975 lb (4,525 kg)
Maximum (AH-1G) 9,500 lb (4,309 kg)
Maximum (AH-1S) 10,000 lb (4,536 kg)
Performance: (AH-1G at maximum take-off weight) speed 172 mph (277 kph); climb 1,230 ft (375 m) per minute at sea level; service ceiling 11,400 ft (3,475 m); hovering ceiling in ground effect 9,900 ft (3,015 m); maximum range 357 miles (574 km)
Performance: (AH-1S in TOW configuration at maximum take-off weight) speed 141 mph (227 kph); climb 1,620 ft (494 m) per minute at sea level; service ceiling 12,200 ft (3,720 m); hovering ceiling in ground effect 12,200 ft (3,720 m); maximum range 315 miles (507 km)
Used also by: Spain, USA and other nations
Notes: Derived from the UH-1 Iroquois family, the AH-1 armed helicopter keeps the basic powerplant, rotor system and transmission of the UH-1, married to a new fuselage of excellent streamlining, only 38 in (0.965 m) wide. There are the following versions:
1. AH-1G, original US Army version, to which the specification above relates
2. AH-1Q, a modification of the AH-1G with TOW capability for the anti-armour role
3. AH-1R, an uprated AH-1G with the 1,825-shp T53-L-703 but no TOW capability
4. AH-1S, an advanced model of the AH-1G, with 1,825-shp engine and TOW capability, plus improved cockpit and airframe. Later models will have a turreted cannon, improved fire-control equipment and other detail improvements.
See also the Sea Cobra entry.

Senegal

200 men and no combat aircraft.

2 Magister trainers.
6 C-47, 4 F27, 4 *Broussard*, 1 Cessna
    337 transports.
2 *Alouette* II, 1 Gazelle helicopters.

Sierra Leone

2 Saab MFI-15 trainers.
3 Hughes 300/500 helicopters.

Singapore

3,000 men and 103 combat aircraft.

2 FGA/recce sqns with 31 Hunter
    FGA.74, 4 FR.74, 7 T.75.
2 FGA sqns with 40 A-4S, 6 TA-4S.
1 COIN/trg sqn with 15 BAC 167.
1 transport sqn with 2 C-130B, 6
    Skyvan.
1 SAR helicopter sqn with 7 *Alouette*
    III, 3 AB-212.
Helicopters incl 15 UH-1H.
Trainers incl 14 SF.260MS.
2 SAM sqns: 1 with 28 Bloodhound, 1
    with 10 Rapier.
(21 F-5E/F FGA, AIM-9L Super Side-
    winder AAM on order.)

Short Brothers SC.7 Skyvan

Type: STOL utility transport
Crew: one or two, plus up to 19 passengers
Wings: light alloy braced high-wing mono-
plane
Fuselage: light alloy box
Tail unit: metal cantilever
Landing gear: fixed tricycle unit
Powerplant: two Garrett-AiResearch TPE
331-201 turboprops, each rated at 715
shp and driving a Hartzell three-blade
metal propeller
Fuel capacity: 293 gallons (1,332 litres) in
four fuselage roof tanks, plus provision for
an additional 97 gallons (441 litres) in
special fuselage side tanks
Avionics: communication and navigation
equipment
Armament: none

Dimensions: Span 64 ft 11 in (19.79 m)
    Length 41 ft 4 in (12.6 m)
    Height 15 ft 1 in (4.6 m)
Wing area: 373 ft² (34.65 m²)
Weights: Empty 7,620 lb (3,456 kg)
    Loaded 13,700 lb (6,214 kg)
    Maximum 14,500 lb (6,577 kg)
Performance: (at maximum take-off weight)
cruising speed 203 mph (327 kph); climb
1,530 ft (466 m) per minute at sea level;
service ceiling 22,000 ft (6,705 m); range
670 miles (1,075 km)
Used also by: Argentina, Austria, Ecuador,
Ghana, Indonesia, Mauritania, Mexico, Nepal,
North Yemen, Oman, Thailand
Notes: The Skyvan Series 3M is derived from
the civil Series 3, and first flew in 1970. It is
designed for paratrooping, supply dropping, assault landing, transport, casualty
evacuation, and freighting. Maximum payload is 6,000 lb (2,721 kg).

Somali Republic

1,000 men and 25 combat aircraft.

1 lt bomber sqn with 3 Il-28.
2 FGA sqns with 15 MiG-17 and MiG-15UTI.
1 fighter sqn with 7 MiG-21MF.
1 transport sqn with 3 An-2, 3 An-24/-26.
Other aircraft incl 3 C-47, 1 C-45, 6 P. 148, 15 Yak-11, 2 Do 28.
1 helicopter sqn with 5 Mi-4, 5 Mi-8, 1 AB-204.
AA-2 'Atoll' AAM.

South Africa

10,000 men (4,500 conscripts) and 345 combat aircraft, including 70 Citizen Force aircraft and operational trainers, plus 25,000 Active Citizen Force.

2 lt bomber sqns: 1 with 6 Canberra B(I).12, 3 T.4; 1 with 9 Buccaneer S.50.
1 FGA sqn with 32 Mirage F1AZ.
1 fighter/recce sqn with 36 Mirage IIICZ/EZ/RZ/R2Z.
1 interceptor sqn with 16 Mirage F1CZ.
2 MR sqns with 7 Shackleton MR.3, 18 Piaggio P.166S.
3 transport sqns with 7 C-130B, 9 Transall C-160Z, 28 C-47, 5 DC-4, 1 Viscount 781, 4 HS 125, 7 Swearingen Merlin IVA.
4 helicopter sqns: 2 with 40 *Alouette* III, 1 with 19 SA 330 Puma, 1 with 14 SA 321L Super *Frelon*.
1 flt of 11 Wasp with AS.11 (naval assigned), 2 *Alouette* II.
Other helicopters incl 17 *Alouette* III, 40 SA 330 Puma.
4 comms and liaison sqns (army assigned) with 20 Cessna 185A/D/E, 36 AM.3C *Bosbok*, 20 C4M *Kudu*.
Operational trainers incl 16 Mirage IIIBZ/DZ/D2Z, 12 F-86, 120 M.B.326M/K *Impala* I/II; other trg ac incl 110 Harvard (some armed), 5 C-47 ac, 10 *Alouette* III helicopters.
R.530, R.550 Magic AAM; AS.20/30 ASM.
Reserves: 25,000 Active Citizen Force.
5 COIN/trg sqns with 60 *Impala* I/II, 10 Harvard.

Aeritalia AM.3C

Type: utility aircraft
Crew: two, plus up to two passengers
Wings: metal high-wing braced monoplane
Fuselage: metal tube structure and semi-monocoque rear fuselage
Tail unit: metal cantilever
Landing gear: fixed tailwheel unit
Powerplant: one Piaggio-built Lycoming GSO-480-B1B6 inline engine, rated at 340 hp and driving a Piaggio three-blade metal propeller
Fuel capacity: 52½ gallons (238 litres) in four wing tanks
Avionics: communication and navigation equipment
Armament: 750 lb (340 kg) of stores can be carried on two underwing pylons. The stores can include a Matra pod with two 7.62-mm machine-guns and 2,000 rounds, a General Electric Minigun pod with 1,500 rounds, an AS.11 or AS.12 ASM, reconnaissance packs, rockets pods, bombs and other stores
Dimensions: Span 41 ft 5½ in (12.64 m)
Length 29 ft 3¾ in (8.93 m)
Height 8 ft 11 in (2.72 m)
Wing area: 219.16 ft² (20.36 m²)
Weights: Empty 2,380 lb (1,080 kg)
Loaded 3,306 lb (1,500 kg)
Maximum 3,750 lb (1,700 kg)
Performance: speed 173 mph (278 kph) at 8,000 ft (2,440 m); cruising speed 153 mph (246 kph) at 8,000 ft (2,440 m); climb 1,378 ft (420 m) per minute at sea level; service ceiling 27,550 ft (8,400 m); range 615 miles (990 km)
Used only by: South Africa
Notes: The prototype of the AM.3C first flew in 1967.

Arbeitsgemeinschaft Transall C-160

Type: general-purpose transport
Crew: four, plus up to 93 passengers
Wings: metal cantilever high-wing monoplane
Fuselage: aluminium alloy semi-monocoque
Tail unit: aluminium alloy cantilever
Landing gear: hydraulically actuated retractable tricycle unit
Powerplant: two Rolls-Royce Tyne RTy.20 Mark 22 turboprops, each rated at 6,100 ehp and driving a Ratier Figeac-built Hawker Siddeley Dynamics 4-blade propeller
Fuel capacity: 4,179 gallons (19,000 litres) in four wing tanks, plus 71.5 gallons (325 litres) of water-methanol mixture
Avionics: comprehensive communications and navigation equipment
Armament: none
Dimensions: Span 131 ft 3 in (40.0 m)
Length 106 ft 3½ in (32.4 m)
Height 40 ft 6¾ in (12.36 m)
Wing area: 1,722.7 ft² (160.1 m²)
Weights: Empty 63,400 lb (28,758 kg)
Loaded
Maximum 112,435 lb (51,000 kg)
Performance: (at maximum take-off weight) speed 322 mph (518 kph) at 16,000 ft (4,875 m); cruising speed 282 mph (454 kph) at 20,000 ft (6,100 m); climb 1,300 ft (396 m) per minute at sea level; service

ceiling 25,500 ft (7,770 m); range with a payload of 35,274 lb (16,000 kg) 1,056 miles (1,700 km); ferry range 3,915 miles (6,300 km)

Used also by: France, Turkey, West Germany

Notes: The Transall group was formed in 1959 by Messerschmitt-Bölkow-Blohm, Aérospatiale and VFW-Fokker, to design and build the C-160 military transport (for trooping, casualty evacuation, freighting of supplies and vehicles from semi-prepared strips) for France and West Germany. Initial production (90 aircraft for Germany, 60 for France, 20 for Turkey and 9 for South Africa) ended in 1972, but in 1976 it was announced that the production line was to be reopened to build up to 30 more C-160F variants for France, and perhaps for further export. .

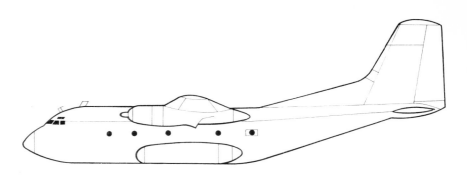

Atlas Aircraft Corporation C4M

Type: light transport aircraft
Crew: two, plus up to six passengers
Wings: metal braced high-wing monoplane
Fuselage: metal stressed skin
Tail unit: metal cantilever
Landing gear: fixed tailwheel unit
Powerplant: one Piaggio-built Lycoming GSO-480-B1B3 piston engine, rated at 340 hp and driving a Hartzell metal three-blade propeller

Fuel capacity: 95 gallons (432 litres) in six wing tanks
Avionics: communication and navigation equipment
Armament: none
Dimensions: Span 42 ft 10¾ in (13.075 m)
Length (tail down) 30 ft 6½ in (9.31 m)
Height (tail down) 12 ft (3.66 m)
Wing area: 225.7 ft² (20.971 m²)
Weights: Empty 2,711 lb (1,230 kg)
Loaded
Maximum 4,497 lb (2,040 kg)

Performance: (at maximum take-off weight) speed 161 mph (259 kph) at 8,000 ft (2,440 m); cruising speed 145 mph (233 kph) at 10,000 ft (3,050 m); climb 800 ft (244 m) per minute at sea level; service ceiling 14,000 ft (4,270 m); range 806 miles (1,297 km)

Used only by: South Africa

Notes: Designed as a passenger or freight carrier, the C4M can be changed from one role to the other very quickly. Maximum payload is 1,235 lb (560 kg).

Avro Shackleton

Type: maritime reconnaissance and anti-submarine aircraft, and airborne early-warning aircraft
Crew: ten
Wings: metal cantilever mid-wing monoplane
Fuselage: metal semi-monocoque
Tail unit: metal cantilever
Landing gear: hydraulically actuated retractable tricycle unit
Powerplant: four Rolls-Royce Griffon 57 inline engines, each rated at 2,455 hp and driving two three-blade metal contra-rotating propellers, plus two Rolls-Royce Viper 203 turbojets, each rated at 2,500-lb (1,134-kg) static thrust
Fuel capacity: 4,248 gallons (19,311 litres)

Avionics: comprehensive communication and navigation/attack equipment, including APS-20 long-range surveillance radar in AEW models
Armament: two 20-mm Hispano cannon, plus up to 10,000 lb (4,536 kg) of bombs, depth charges, mines or torpedoes
Dimensions: Span 119 ft 10 in (36.53 m)
Length 92 ft 6 in (28.19 m)
Height 23 ft 4 in (7.11 m)
Wing area: 1,458 ft² (135.45 m²)
Weights: Empty 57,800 lb (26,218 kg)
Loaded
Maximum 100,000 lb (45,360 kg)
Performance: speed 302 mph (486 kph); cruising speed 253 mph (407 kph); climb 850 ft (260 m) per minute at sea level; service ceiling 19,200 ft (5,852 m); range 4,215 miles (6,780 km)
Used also by: UK

Notes: The design of the Shackleton can be traced back to the Lancaster bomber of World War II, though the prototype first flew in 1949. The MR.1 entered service in 1950, and the maritime version is now used only by South Africa, British aircraft having been converted into AEW.2 models. The technical specification applies to the MR.3.

British Aerospace (Hawker Siddeley Aviation) Buccaneer

Type: strike and reconnaissance aircraft
Crew: two, seated in tandem

Wings: metal cantilever mid-wing monoplane
Fuselage: metal semi-monocoque
Tail unit: metal cantilever
Landing gear: hydraulically actuated retractable tricycle unit

Powerplant: two Rolls-Royce RB.168-1A Spey Mark 101 turbofans, each rated at 11,100-lb (5,035-kg) static thrust
Fuel capacity: 1,560 gallons (7,092 litres) in eight integral fuselage tanks, with the option of an extra 425 gallons (1,932 litres)

in a bomb-door tank, plus provision for an auxiliary tank for 440 gallons (2,000 litres) in the bomb bay, and/or two 250- or 430-gallon (1,136- or 1,955-litre) underwing drop tanks

Avionics: comprehensive communication and navigation/attack equipment, including an air data system, a doppler radar navigation system, a search and fire-control radar incorporating a terrain warning system, and a strike sighting and computing system

Armament: four 1,000-lb (454-kg) Mark 10 bombs on the rotating bomb-bay door, plus four underwing pylons, each capable of carrying loads up to 3,000 lb (1,361-kg) in weight, for a total weapons load of 16,000 lb (7,257 kg). Typical underwing loads one each pylon are one or three 1,000-lb (454-kg) Mark N1 or Mark 10 bombs, two 500- or 540-lb (227- or 250-kg) bombs, six 500-lb (227-kg) bombs, one 18-tube 68-mm rocket pod, one 36-tube 2-in (51-mm) rocket pod, 3-in (76-mm) rockets, and one HSD/Matra Martel air-to-surface missile, up to a maximum of three missiles and one Martel systems pod. The

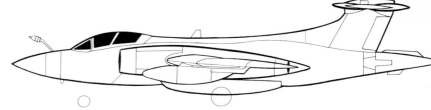

bomb bay can also hold a reconnaissance pack

Dimensions: Span 44 ft (13.41 m)
Length 63 ft 5 in (19.33 m)
Height 16 ft 3 in (4.95 m)
Wing area: 514.7 ft² (47.82 m²)
Weights: Empty about 30,000 lb (13,608 kg)
Loaded 56,000 lb (25,400 kg)
Maximum 62,000 lb (28,123 kg)
Performance: speed 645 mph (1,038 kph) or Mach 0.85 at 200 ft (61 m); climb at 46,000-lb (20,865-kg) weight 7,000 ft (2,134 m) per minute at sea level; service ceiling more than 40,000 ft (9,144 m); combat radius with maximum weapons load 1,150 miles (1,850 km) on a hi-lo-hi strike mission

Used also by: UK
Notes: Designed by the Blackburn company in the late 1950s as an ultra-low level high-speed naval strike aircraft, the Buccaneer prototype first flew in 1958. Current models are:
1. S.2A for the RAF without Martel capability
2. S.2B for the RAF with Martel capability
3. S.2C for the Royal Navy without Martel capability
4. S.2D for the Royal Navy without Martel capability
5. S.50 for South Africa.
All S.2As are being brought up to S.2B standard.

South Korea

30,000 men and 276 combat aircraft, plus 55,000 reservists.

15 FB sqns: 4 with 37 F-4D/E; 9 with 35 F-5A, 126 F-5E; 2 with 48 F-86F.
1 recce sqn with 10 RF-5A.
1 ASW sqn with 20 S-2F.
1 SAR sqn with 2 UH-19, 5 UH-1D, 6 Bell 212 helicopters.
Transports incl 12 C-46, 10 C-54, 10 C-123, 2 HS 748, Aero Commander.
Trainers incl 20 T-28D, 30 T-33A, 20 T-41D, 30 F-5B, 3 F-5F.
4 UH-19, 50 Hughes 500 M-D helicopters.
Sidewinder, Sparrow AAM.
(18 F-4E, 9 F-5F fighters, 24 OV-10G COIN, 6 C-130H transports; 6 CH-47C, 50 Hughes 500M-D helicopters; AIM-9L Super Sidewinder AAM, Maverick ASM on order.)
Army Air Arm
14 O-2A ac; 44 OH-6A, 5 KH-4 helicopters.
(56 OH-6A helicopters on order.)

Sikorsky Aircraft H-19 Chickasaw

Type: utility helicopter
Crew: two, plus up to 10 passengers
Rotors: metal cantilever three-blade main rotor; metal cantilever two-blade tail rotor
Fuselage: metal semi-monocoque
Landing gear: fixed four-wheel unit
Powerplant: one Wright R-1300-3 radial engine, rated at 800 hp
Fuel capacity:
Avionics: communication and navigation equipment
Armament: none
Dimensions: Span 53 ft (16.15 m)
Length (fuselage) 42 ft 3 in (12.88 m)
Height 13 ft 4 in (4.06 m)

Rotor disc area: 2,206 ft² (204.9 m²)
Weights: Empty 5,250 lb (2,381 kg)
Loaded
Maximum 7,900 lb (3,583 kg)
Performance: speed 112 mph (180 kph) at sea level; cruising speed 91 mph (146 kph); climb 1,020 ft (311 m) per minute at sea level; hovering ceiling in ground effect 8,600 ft (2,621 m); range 360 miles (579 km)
Used also by: USA and other nations
Notes: The H-19 is part of the Sikorsky S-55 family, which also includes the British Westland Whirlwind. The S-55 first flew in 1949, and was adopted for service with the US armed forces as the H-19A and B (USAF), H-19C and D (US Army), HOS4S-1 and 2 (USN), HOS4S-2G (USCG), and HRS-1, 2 and 3 (USMC). Known also as the UH-19.

South Yemen

1,300 men and 34 combat aircraft.

1 lt bomber sqn with 7 Il-28.
1 FGA sqn with 15 MiG-17.
1 interceptor sqn with 12 MiG-21F.
1 transport sqn with 4 Il-14, 3 An-24.
1 helicopter sqn with 8 Mi-8, some Mi-4.
3 MiG-15UTI trainers.
AA-2 'Atoll' AAM.

Spain

35,500 men (9,000 conscripts) and 214 combat aircraft, plus 100,000 reservists.

Air Defence Command
5 interceptor sqns: 2 with 34 F-4C(S); 2 with 22 Mirage IIIE, 6 IIID; 1 with 14 Mirage F1C.
1 OCU with 35 T-33A.

Tactical Command
2 FB sqns with 18 F-5A, 2 F-5B, 25 HA-220 Super *Saeta*.
1 recce sqn with 22 RF-4, RF-5A.
1 MR sqn with 10 HU-16B, 2 P-3A.
5 liaison flts with 12 O-1E, 27 Do 27.
Sparrow, Sidewinder, R.550 Magic AAM.

Transport Command
7 sqns with 9 C-130H, 3 KC-97, 12 CASA C.207 *Azor*, 30 CASA C.212 *Aviocar*, 12 DHC-4, 5 Aztec, 1 Navajo.

Training Command
2 OCU with 24 F-5B, 5 sqns with 35 F-33C Bonanza, 45 HA-200A/B *Saeta*, 40 T-33, 25 T-34, 70 T-6, 8 King Air, 10 Baron; 34 AB-47 and AB-205 helicopters.
Other ac incl:
3 SAR sqns with 5 HU-16A, 6 Do 27 ac, 17 AB-205/-206, 4 *Alouette* III helicopters.
1 SAR sqn with 8 CL-215.
(58 Mirage F1, 4 F-4C, 4 RF-4C, 3 F27 MR, 6 CASA 212, 60 CASA C-101; 17 Hughes 300C helicopters; Super Sidewinder AAM on order.)

Naval Air Arm
1 FGA sqn with 5 AV-8A *Matador* (Harrier), 2 TAV-8A.
1 comms sqn with 4 Commanche.
5 helicopter sqns with 10 SH-3D, 11 AB-204/212AS, 12 Bell 47G, 12 Hughes 500HM, 6 AH-1G.
(5 AV-8A FGA; 5 AB-212, 6 SH-3D helicopters on order.)

Army Air Arm
10 CH-47C, 3 Puma, 65 UH-1B/H, 5 *Alouette* III, 1 AB-206A, 15 OH-13, 15 OH-58A helicopters.
(18 OH-58A, 8 UH-1H helicopters on order.)

Construcciones Aeronauticas SA (CASA) C-101

Type: trainer and light tactical aircraft
Crew: two, in tandem
Wings: aluminium alloy cantilever low-wing monoplane
Fuselage: metal semi-monocoque
Tail unit: metal cantilever
Landing gear: hydraulically actuated retractable tricycle unit
Powerplant: one Garrett-AiResearch TFE-731-2-25 turbofan, rated at 3,500-lb (1,588-kg) static thrust
Fuel capacity: 528 gallons (2,400 litres) in one fuselage bag tanks, one centre-section tank and two outer wing integral tanks
Avionics: comprehensive communication and navigation equipment
Armament: hardpoint under the fuselage for various pods and stores, including a 30-mm cannon pod, 12.7-mm machine-gun pod, ECM pod, laser designator pod, or reconnaissance pod; plus six underwing hardpoints for external stores up to a weight of 4,410 lb (2,000 kg). A typical load might be made up of one 30-mm cannon or two 7.62-mm Miniguns under

the fuselage, supplemented by two Sidewinder air-to-air or four Maverick air-to-surface missiles; six LAU-10 5-in (127-mm) rocket pods; six LAU-68 2.75-in (70-mm) rocket pods; six general-purpose, laser-guided or retarded bombs of 250-lb (113-kg) weight; four general-purpose, laser-guided or retarded bombs of 500-lb (227-kg) weight; napalm tanks; or ECM pods

Dimensions: Span 34 ft 9½ in (10.6 m)
Length 40 ft 2¼ in (12.25 m)
Height 14 ft 1¼ in (4.3 m)
Wing area: 215.3 ft² (20.0 m²)
Weights: Empty 6,570 lb (2,980 kg)
Maximum (trainer) 10,140 lb (4,600 kg)
Maximum (ground-attack) 12,345 lb (5,600 kg)
Performance: (estimated, at a take-off weight of 10,140 lb/4,600 kg) speed 460 mph (740 kph) at 20,000 ft (6,100 m);

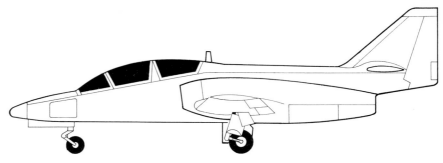

climb 3,660 ft (1,116 m) per minute at sea level; climb to 25,000 ft (7,620 m) in 10 minutes; service ceiling 45,000 ft (13,715 m); combat radius on a lo-lo-lo interdiction mission with 5 minutes of combat 403 miles (648 km); combat radius on a hi-lo-hi close air support mission with 8 minutes of combat and 50 minutes of loiter 150 miles (241 km); ferry range 2,485 miles (4,000 km)

Used only by: Spain

Notes: Developed with aid from Messerschmitt-Bölkow-Blohm in Germany and Northrop in the United States, the CASA 101 made its first flight in 1977, with production machines to enter service in 1979.

Construcciones Aeronauticas SA (CASA) HA 200 *Saeta*

Type: advanced trainer
Crew: two, seated in tandem
Wings: metal cantilever low-wing monoplane
Fuselage: metal semi-monocoque
Tail unit: metal cantilever
Landing gear: hydraulically actuated retractable tricycle unit
Powerplant: two Turboméca Marboré IIA turbojets, each rated at 880-lb (400-kg) static thrust
Fuel capacity: 304 gallons (1,390 litres)
Avionics: communication and navigation equipment
Armament: four 22-lb (10-kg) rockets and four 110-lb (50-kg) bombs on underwing racks
Dimensions: Span 34 ft 2¼ in (10.42 m)
Length 29 ft 1½ in (8.88 m)
Height 10 ft 8 in (3.25 m)
Wing area: 187.2 ft² (17.4 m²)
Weights: Empty 3,697 lb (1,677 kg)
Loaded 5,280 kg (2,395 kg)
Maximum 6,305 lb (2,860 kg)
Performance: speed 435 mph (700 kph) at 22,966 ft (7,000 m); climb 3,484 ft (1,062 m) per minute at sea level; climb 14 minutes to 29,528 ft (9,000 m); service ceiling 41,000 ft (12,500 m); range 557 miles (895 km) on internal fuel; range 977 miles (1,575 km) with tip tanks
Used only by: Spain
Notes: The HA 200 was initially a Hispano aircraft, designed by Professor Willy Messerschmitt and first flown in 1955. It was the first Spanish jet aircraft, and entered service in 1959.

Construcciones Aeronauticas SA (CASA) 207 *Azor*

Type: medium transport aircraft
Crew: four, plus up to 40 passengers
Wings: metal cantilever low-wing monoplane
Fuselage: metal semi-monocoque
Tail unit: metal cantilever
Landing gear: hydraulically actuated retractable tricycle unit
Powerplant: two Bristol Hercules 730 radial engines, each rated at 2,040 hp and driving a four-blade metal propeller
Fuel capacity: 676 gallons (3,070 litres)
Avionics: comprehensive communication and navigation equipment

Armament: none
Dimensions: Span 91 ft 2½ in (27.8 m)
Length 68 ft 5 in (20.85 m)
Height 25 ft 5 in (7.75 m)
Wing area: 924 ft² (85.85 m²)
Weights: Empty 22,213 lb (10,075 kg)
Loaded 34,510 lb (15,655 kg)
Maximum 37,480 lb (17,000 kg)
Performance: speed 285 mph (459 kph) at 6,100 ft (1,860 m); cruising speed 266 mph (428 kph) at 12,340 ft (3,760 m); service ceiling 28,215 ft (8,600 m); range 690 miles (1,110 km) with maximum payload; range 1,840 miles (2,960 km) with a payload of 4,850 lb (2,200 kg)
Used only by: Spain
Notes: The prototype of the CASA 207 first flew in 1955, and the type entered Spanish service in 1960.

Construcciones Aeronauticas SA (CASA) 352-L

Type: utility transport aircraft
Crew: three, plus up to 18 passengers
Wings: metal cantilever low-wing monoplane
Fuselage: metal semi-monocoque
Tail unit: metal cantilever
Landing gear: fixed tailwheel unit
Powerplant: three ENMA Beta B-4 radial engines, each rated at 775 hp and driving a two-blade metal propeller
Fuel capacity:
Avionics: communication and navigation equipment
Armament: none
Dimensions: Span 95 ft 10 in (29.2 m)
Length 62 ft (18.9 m)
Height 14 ft 10 in (4.52 m)
Wing area: 1,189.4 ft² (110.5 m²)
Weights: Empty 14,325 lb (6,498 kg)
Loaded 24,200 lb (10,977 kg)
Maximum
Performance: speed 165 mph (265 kph); cruising speed 132 mph (212 kph); range 800 miles (1,290 km)
Used only by: Spain
Notes: The CASA 352-L is the Spanish-built version of the celebrated Junkers Ju 52/3m, powered by Spanish engines.

Dornier Do 27

Type: general-purpose aircraft
Crew: one, plus up to five passengers
Wings: metal cantilever high-wing monoplane
Fuselage: metal semi-monocoque
Tail unit: metal cantilever
Landing gear: fixed tailwheel unit
Powerplant: one Lycoming GSO-480-B1B6 inline engine, rated at 340 hp and driving a metal three-blade propeller
Fuel capacity: 80 gallons (364 litres)
Avionics: communication and navigation equipment
Armament: none
Dimensions: Span 39 ft 4½ in (12.0 m)
Length 32 ft 5½ in (9.9 m)
Height 8 ft 10¾ in (2.7 m)
Wing area: 208.82 ft² (19.4 m²)
Weights: Empty 2,596 lb (1,177 kg)
Loaded 4,070 lb (1,845 kg)
Maximum
Performance: speed 174 mph (280 kph) at 3,280 ft (1,000 m); cruising speed 146 mph (235 kph) at 8,200 ft (2,500 m); service ceiling about 18,040 ft (5,500 m); range 492 miles (790 km)
Used also by: Angola, Israel, Nigeria, Portugal, South Africa, Switzerland
Notes: The Do 27 was the first West German aircraft to be built in quantity after World War II. It was derived from the experimental Do 25 produced to meet a Spanish requirement, and first flew in 1955, production aircraft being delivered in 1956. The basic model first produced was the Do 27A, with a 275-hp GO-480-B1A6 engine. The Do 27B is a trainer version with dual controls, the Do 27Q is the civil version, and the Do 27H is the up-engined military model to which the technical specification above applies.

Sri Lanka

2,000 men and 8 combat aircraft, plus 1,000 reservists.

1 FGA sqn with 4 MiG-17F, 1 MiG-15UTI, 3 Jet Provost Mk 51.
1 transport sqn with 1 CV-440, 2 DC-3, 2 Riley Heron, 1 HS Heron.
1 comms sqn with 3 Cessna 337.
1 helicopter sqn with 7 AB-206, 6 Bell 47G, 2 SA365 *Dauphin* 2 and Ka-26 'Hoodlum'.
4 Cessna 150, 7 Chipmunk, 5 Dove trainers.

Kamov Ka-26 'Hoodlum'

Type: general-purpose helicopter
Crew: two, plus up to six passengers
Rotors: two plastic cantilever three-blade co-axial contra-rotating main rotors
Fuselage: metal semi-monocoque
Tail unit: fibreglass cantilever
Landing gear: fixed four-wheel unit
Powerplant: two M-14V-26 piston engines, each rated at 325 hp
Fuel capacity:
Avionics: communication and navigation equipment
Armament: none
Dimensions: Span 42 ft 8 in (13.0 m)
Length (fuselage) 25 ft 5 in (7.75 m)
Height 13 ft 3½ in (4.05 m)

Rotor disc area: 2,859.5 ft² (265.66 m²)
Weights: Empty 4,630 lb (2,100 kg)
Loaded 6,780 lb (3,076 kg)
Maximum 7,165 lb (3,250 kg)
Performance: speed 105 mph (170 kph); cruising speed 93 mph (150 kph); service ceiling 9,840 ft (3,000 m); hovering ceiling in ground effect 4,265 ft (1,300 m) at a weight of 6,615 lb (3,000 kg); range with full passenger load 248 miles (400 km); range with auxiliary tanks 745 miles (1,200 km); endurance 3 hours 40 minutes
Used also by: Hungary
Notes: Developed as an agricultural helicopter, the Ka-26 first flew in 1965. Maximum payload is 2,425 lb (1,100 kg) for the flying crane version.

Sudan

1,500 men and 22 combat aircraft.

1 interceptor sqn with 10 MiG-21MF.
1 FGA sqn with 12 MiG-17 (ex-Chinese).
5 BAC 145 and 6 Jet Provost Mk 55 trainers.
1 transport sqn with 6 C-130H, 6 An-12, 5 An-24, 4 F27, 1 DHC-6, 2 DHC-5D, 8 Turbo-Porter and An-2.
1 helicopter sqn with 10 Mi-8, 10 BO-105.
AA-2 'Atoll' AAM.
(10 F-5E, 2 F-5B, 24 Mirage 50 fighters; 6 EMB-111P2, 2 DHC-5D transports; 10 Puma helicopters on order.)

Wytwornia Sprzetu Komuni-kacyjnego-PZL-Mielec (Anton-ov) An-2 'Colt'

Type: general-purpose aircraft
Crew: two, plus up to 14 passengers
Wings: metal and fabric single-bay biplane
Fuselage: metal semi-monocoque
Tail unit: braced metal unit
Landing gear: fixed tailwheel unit
Powerplant: one Shvetsov ASz-62IR piston engine, rated at 1,000 hp and driving an AW-2 metal four-blade propeller
Fuel capacity: 264 gallons (1,200 litres) in six upper wing tanks
Avionics: communication and navigation equipment
Dimensions: Span (upper wing) 59 ft 8½ in (18.18 m); (lower wing) 46 ft 8½ in (14.24 m)
Length 41 ft 9½ in (12.74 m)
Height 20 ft (6.1 m)
Wing area: 770 ft² (71.6 m²)

Weights: Empty 7,605 lb (3,450 kg)
Loaded
Maximum 12,125 lb (5,500 kg)
Performance: (at a weight of 11,574 lb/5,250 kg) speed 160 mph (258 kph) at 5,740 ft (1,750 m); cruising speed 115 mph (185 kph); climb 689 ft (210 m) per minute at sea level; service ceiling 14,425 ft (4,400 m); range with a payload of 1,102 lb (500 kg) 560 miles (900 km)
Used also by: Afghanistan, Albania, Algeria, China, Cuba, East Germany, Egypt, Ethiopia, Hungary, Iraq, Mali, Mongolia, North Korea, Poland, Romania, Somali Republic, Sudan, Syria, Tanzania, Tunisia, USSR, Vietnam
Notes: The first An-2 flew in 1947, and some 5,000 examples were built in Russia before production was switched to Poland in 1960. Another 5,000 or more An-2s have been built in Poland since that date. The technical specification above relates to the An-2P passenger version, whose accommodation includes seats for two children. The An-2T is a general-purpose version capable of carrying 12 passengers or up to 3,306 lb (1,500 kg) of freight.

Sweden

The Royal Swedish Air Force

In a sense caught in a vice between the forces of NATO to the west and south, and those of the USSR to the east and north, Sweden is acutely conscious of the difficulties of her strategic position, and is determined to remain fully neutral, but militarily powerful, as a deterrent to aggression. Almost alone among the neutral states, she relies with very few exceptions on indigenously produced *matériel*, and has thus built up strong armed forces with tailor-made equipment, a strong armaments industry which brings in substantial amounts of foreign currency, and a reputation for total neutrality. The Royal Swedish Air Force is a key element in Sweden's defence policy, with particular

emphasis being placed on hard-hitting strike operations by aircraft that can operate from semi-prepared airstrips, straight lengths of road, and other sites difficult for an aggressor to eliminate entirely. For this reason Swedish aircraft are notable for their STOL performance, ruggedness, easy methods of servicing, and heavy weapons load, combined with sophisticated electronics. The air force has 13,300 personnel, about 20.25 per cent of the total strength of the armed forces, whose budget is some 3.55 per cent of the gross national product.

All aspects of the air defence mechanism are controlled by the STRIL-60 system, a computerised and fully automatic air surveillance and operations control organisation. This co-ordinates the activity of the 15 all-

weather fighter squadrons, 13 of them equipped with 234 J 35F and the other two with 72 J 35D fighters, and the six FGA squadrons, five of them equipped with 72 AJ 37 supersonic strike aircraft, and the last with 18 Saab 105 light strike aircraft. These 21 squadrons are the core of Sweden's air defence system, and operate within a context provided by the STRIL-60's radar stations, and the information provided by four reconnaissance squadrons, two of them operating 36 S 35E aircraft, and the other two 18 SH 37 aircraft.

Other elements of the Swedish air arm are relatively small: two transport squadrons with three C-130, two Caravelle and six C-47 aircraft, and five communications squadrons with 110 Saab 105 and 57 Sk.61 (Bulldog) aircraft. Training, on the other hand, is relatively well provided for, with 150 Saab 105, 78 Sk.61, 20 Sk.35C, 40 Saab *Safir* and 17 Sk.37 aircraft for all stages from primary to advanced training, and operational conversion onto the most sophisticated combat types. There are only 17 helicopters in Sweden's five helicopter groups. Strength will be increased considerably when 97 JA 37 interceptor fighters currently on order are put into service.

Sweden's air force is a formidable one, and based principally on two Mach 2 types, the Saab 35 *Draken* and the Saab 37 *Viggen*. This is clear proof of what can be attained with relatively small financial outlay if the user can specify his needs with accuracy, and be prepared to accept minimal sacrifices in operational efficiency to allow the aircraft to be multi-purpose types. The only parts of the two aircraft which are not of Swedish design are the engines, which have been improved by Swedish designers, and the AAMs.

13,300 men (4,850 conscripts) and 450 combat aircraft.
6 FGA sqns: 5 with 72 AJ 37 *Viggen*, 1 with 18 Sk.60C (Saab 105).

15 AWX sqns: 13 with 234 J 35F *Draken*, 2 with 72 J 35D.
4 recce sqns: 2 with 36 S 35E *Draken*, 2 with 18 SH 37 *Viggen*.
2 transport sqns with 3 C-130E/H, 2 Caravelle, 6 C-47.
5 comms sqns with 110 Sk.60A/B (Saab 105), 57 Sk.61 (Bulldog).
Trainers incl 150 Sk.60, 78 Sk.61, 20 Sk.35C *Draken*, 40 Sk.50 *Safir*, 17 Sk.37 *Viggen*.
5 helicopter gps (3–4 ac each) with 1 HKP-2 (*Alouette* II), 6 HKP-3 (AB-204B), 10 HKP-4B (Vertol 107).
Sidewinder, RB27, RB28, AAM; RB04E, RB05A, RB03 ASM.
A fully computerised, semi-automatic control and air surveillance system, STRIL-60, co-ordinates all air defence components.
(90 JA 37 interceptors, Maverick ASM on order.)

Naval Air Arm
5 HKP-2 (*Alouette* II), 3 HKP-4B (Vertol 107), 7 HKP-4 (KV-107/II), 10 HKP-6 (JetRanger) helicopters.

Army Air Arm
20 Sk.61 (Bulldog), 12 Super Cub ac; 15 HKP-3 (AB-204B), 19 HKP-6 (JetRanger) helicopters.

Saab-Scania 37 *Viggen*

Type: all-weather multi-purpose combat aircraft and operational trainer
Crew: one or two, seated in tandem
Wings: metal cantilever delta low-wing monoplane, with metal cantilever delta mid-wing canard foreplane
Fuselage: metal semi-monocoque
Tail unit: metal cantilever
Landing gear: retractable tricycle unit
Powerplant: one Volvo Flygmotor RM8A (improved version of the Pratt & Whitney JT8D-22) turbofan, rated at 26,015-lb (11,800-kg) static thrust with afterburning in the AJ 37, SF/SH 37, and SK 37; one Volvo Flygmotor RM8B turbofan, rated at 28,108-lb (12,750-kg) static thrust with afterburning in the JA 37 and Saab 37X
Fuel capacity: tanks in each wing, aft of the cockpit, on each side of the fuselage and in a saddle over the engine
Avionics: comprehensive communication and navigation/attack equipment, including Marconi-Elliott (AJ 37) or Smiths (JA 37) head up display, Phillips (AJ 37) or Garrett-AiResearch (JA 37) air data computer, L.M. Ericsson radar, Decca Type 72 doppler radar, SATT radar warning system, Svenska Radio radar display system and electronic counter-measures, and Saab-Scania CK-37 digital computer
Armament: (AJ 37) stores are carried on three underfuselage and four underwing hardpoints, with another two hardpoints

under the wings if desired; typical loads include RB04E anti-ship missile, RB05A air-to-surface missile, pods of Bofors 135-mm air-to-surface rockets, bombs, 30-mm Aden cannon pods, and occasionally RB24 (Sidewinder) and RB28 (Falcon) air-to-air missiles; (JA 37) this model also has seven hardpoints, and a permanent pack with a 30-mm Oerlikon KCA long-range high-velocity cannon, plus medium- and long-range air-to-air missiles (RB24, RB28 and Saab 372), with the following electronics: L.M. Ericsson UAP-1023 pulse-doppler radar, Singer-Kearfott SKC-2037 central digital computer, Garrett-AiResearch LD-5 digital air data computer, Singer-Kearfott KT-70L inertial measuring, and Honeywell/Saab-Scania SA07 digital flight control system

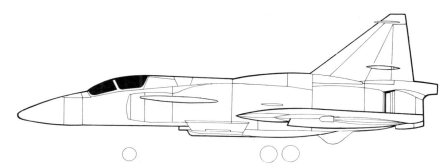

Dimensions: Span 34 ft 9¼ in (10.6 m)
Length (JA 37 and Saab 37X) 51 ft 1½ in (16.4 m)
Length (others) 53 ft 5¾ in (16.3 m)
Height (JA 37) 19 ft 4¼ in (5.9 m)
Height (AJ 37) 19 ft 0¼ in (5.8 m)
Wing area: (main) 495.1 ft² (46.0 m²); (canard) 66.74 ft² (6.2 m²)
Weights: Empty
Loaded (AJ 37) 33,070 lb (15,000 kg)
Loaded (JA 37) 37,478 lb (17,000 kg)

Maximum (AJ 37) 45,195 lb (20,500 kg)
Performance: (JA 37) speed Mach 2 at high altitude; speed above Mach 1.1 at 300 ft (100 m); climb from brakes off to 32,800 ft (10,000 m) less than 1 minute 40 seconds with afterburning; service ceiling over 60,000 ft (18,300 m); combat radius with external stores on a hi-lo-hi mission 620 miles (1,000 km); combat radius with external stores on a lo-lo-lo mission 310 miles (500 km)
Used only by: Sweden
Notes: The first prototype flew in 1967, and the unique configuration immediately proved its worth, the Saab 37 proving to have magnificent STOL characteristics. There are several versions:
1. AJ 37 single-seat all-weather attack aircraft, which entered service in 1971

2. JA 37 single-seat interceptor
3. SF 37 single-seat all-weather armed photographic reconnaissance aircraft, which entered service in 1977 and has comprehensive optical reconnaissance equipment
4. SH 37 single-seat all-weather maritime reconnaissance aircraft, which entered service in 1975 and has a secondary attack capability with the same weapons load as the SF 37
5. SK 37 tandem two-seat trainer, which entered service in 1972 and has a secondary attack capability with the AJ 37
6. Saab 37X projected export version, similar to the JA 37.

Bofors RB 53 Bantam

Type: air-to-surface tactical anti-tank guided missile
Guidance: command by means of wire
Dimensions: Span 15¾ in (40.0 cm)
Body diameter 4⅓ in (11.0 cm)
Length 33½ in (85.0 cm)
Booster: solid-propellant rocket
Sustainer: as above
Warhead: 4⅛ lb (1.9 kg) high explosive
Weights: Launch 16½ lb (7.5 kg)
Burnt out
Performance: cruising speed 190 mph (306 kph); range up to 2,187 yards (2,000 m)
Used also by: Switzerland
Notes: The Bantam was designed as an infantry anti-tank weapon, but can also be used on helicopters and light strike aircraft.

Saab-Scania RB04E

Type: air-to-surface tactical anti-shipping guided missile
Guidance: active radar homing
Dimensions: Span 6 ft 5½ in (1.97 m)
Body diameter 19¾ in (50.0 cm)
Length 14 ft 8 in (4.47 m)
Booster: IMI (Summerfield Research) solid-propellant rocket
Sustainer: as above
Warhead: 661 lb (300 kg) high explosive
Weights: Launch 1,358 lb (616 kg)
Burnt out
Performance: speed Mach 0.9+
Used only by: Sweden
Notes: The RB04E is the latest version of the RB04 family, and is intended for use on the AJ 37 *Viggen*. Once the fighter has acquired the target on radar, the missile's autopilot is locked onto the correct course, the missile is fired, and homes on the target with its own radar in the terminal homing phase of the attack.

Saab-Scania RB05A

Type: air-to-surface tactical guided missile
Guidance: radio command to line-of-sight
Dimensions: Span 32 in (80.0 cm)
Body diameter 12 in (30.0 cm)
Length 11 ft 10 in (3.6 m)
Booster: Volvo Flygmotor VR-35 liquid-propellant rocket
Sustainer: as above
Warhead: high explosive

Weights: Launch about 675 lb (305 kg)
Burnt out
Performance: speed supersonic
Used only by: Sweden
Notes: Intended as a principal weapon for the AJ 37 *Viggen*, the RB05A is an advanced air-to-surface missile capable of operations over land and water, with limited air-to-air capability as well. The missile is controlled by a control stick in the cockpit, and the radio link is virtually immune to jamming. The missile has proved its ability to operate at low level.

Switzerland

45,000 men on mobilisation and 340 combat aircraft.

9 FGA sqns with 142 Hunter F.58.
9 FGA sqns with 145 Venom FB.50 (to be replaced by F-5E).
2 interceptor sqns with 35 Mirage IIIS.
1 recce sqn with 18 Mirage IIIRS.
1 transport sqn with 3 Ju 52/3m.
7 lt ac sqns with 6 Do 27, 12 Porter, 6 Turbo-Porter, 3 Bonanza.
2 helicopter sqns with 30 *Alouette* II/III.
Other ac incl 48 Pilatus P-2, 70 P-3, 65 Vampire FB.6, 35 T.55, 3 Mirage IIIBS, 23 FFA C-3605; 70 *Alouette* II/III helicopters.
Sidewinder, AIM-26B Falcon AAM; AS.30 ASM.
1 para coy.
3 air-base regts.
1 AD bde with 1 SAM regt of 2 bns, each with 32 Bloodhound, and 7 arty regts (22 bns) with 20mm, 35mm and 40mm AA guns.
(66 F-5E, 6 F-5B FGA, 45 Skyguard AA systems on order.)

De Havilland Aircraft Venom

Type: fighter-bomber
Crew: one
Wings: metal cantilever mid-wing monoplane
Fuselage: metal semi-monocoque with metal monocoque tailbooms
Tail unit: metal cantilever
Landing gear: hydraulically actuated retractable tricycle unit
Powerplant: one Rolls-Royce (de Havilland/Bristol Siddeley) Ghost 103 turbojet, rated at 4,850-lb (2,200-kg) static thrust
Fuel capacity:
Avionics: communication and navigation equipment
Armament: four 20-mm Hispano cannon, plus two 1,000-lb (454-kg) bombs and eight 60-lb (27.2-kg) rockets under the wings
Dimensions: Span 41 ft 8 in (12.7 m)
Length 31 ft 10 in (9.7 m)
Height 6 ft 2 in (1.9 m)
Wing area:
Weights: Empty 8,100 lb (3,674 kg)
Loaded
Maximum 15,310 lb (6,945 kg)

Performance: speed 640 mph (1,030 kph); climb 9,000 ft (2,743 m) per minute at sea level; service ceiling 45,000 ft (13,716 m); range 1,075 miles (1,730 km)
Used only by: Switzerland
Notes: Switzerland uses the single-seat version of the Venom fighter, under the designation FB.50. The prototype first flew in 1949, and the type entered British service in 1951, being withdrawn in 1962.

Junkers Flugzeugwerke Ju 52/3m

Type: utility transport aircraft
Crew: two, plus up to 19 passengers
Wings: metal cantilever low-wing monoplane
Fuselage: metal semi-monocoque
Tail unit: braced metal structure
Landing gear: fixed tailwheel unit
Powerplant: three BMW 132T radial engines, each rated at 830 hp and driving a two-blade metal propeller
Fuel capacity:
Avionics: communication and navigation equipment
Armament: none

Dimensions: Span 95 ft 11½ in (29.95 m)
Length 62 ft (18.9 m)
Height 14 ft 9 in (4.5 m)
Wing area: 1,189 ft² (110.5m²)
Weights: Empty 12,346 lb (5,600 kg)
Loaded
Maximum 24,317 lb (11,030 kg)
Performance: speed 190 mph (305 kph); climb 689 ft (210 m) per minute at sea level; service ceiling 18,045 ft (5,500 m); range 808 miles (1,300 km)
Used only by: Switzerland
Notes: The Ju 52 single-engined transport first flew in 1930, and the Ju 52/m three-engined version in 1932. The type served with great distinction in World War II, and has remained in service with several air forces until recently.

Pilatus Flugzeugwerke PC-6 Porter

Type: utility aircraft
Crew: one, plus up to six passengers
Wings: metal high-wing braced monoplane
Fuselage: metal semi-monocoque
Tail unit: metal cantilever
Landing gear: fixed tailwheel unit
Powerplant: one Lycoming GSO-480 inline engine, rated at 340 hp and driving a three-blade metal propeller

Fuel capacity: 88 gallons (400 litres)
Avionics: communication and navigation equipment
Armament: none
Dimensions: Span 49 ft 10 in (15.2 m)
Length 33 ft 5½ in (10.2 m)
Height 10 ft 6 in (3.2 m)
Wing area: 310 ft² (28.8 m²)
Weights: Empty 2,425 lb (1,100 kg)
Loaded 3,970 lb (1,800 kg) Maximum

Performance: speed 145 mph (233 kph); cruising speed 135 mph (217 kph); climb 1,140 ft (347 m) per minute at sea level; service ceiling 23,950 ft (7,300 m); range 400 miles (640 km) with maximum payload; range 750 miles (1,210 km) with maximum fuel
Used also by: Australia, Ecuador
Notes: The Porter first flew in 1959, entering service in 1960. Since that time the aircraft has proved an outstandingly successful machine, very rugged and able to operate from the roughest of strips.

Pilatus Flugzeugwerke PC-6 Turbo-Porter

Type: STOL utility transport
Crew: one, plus up to 11 passengers
Wings: metal braced high-wing monoplane
Fuselage: metal semi-monocoque
Tail unit: metal cantilever
Landing gear: fixed tailwheel unit
Powerplant: one Pratt & Whitney Aircraft of Canada PT6A-27 turboprop, rated at 55° shp and driving a Hartzell metal three-blade propeller

Fuel capacity: 142 gallons (644 litres) in integral wing tanks, plus provision for two 42-gallon (190-litre) optional tanks under the wings
Avionics: comprehensive communication and navigation equipment
Armament: none
Dimensions: Span 49 ft 8 in (15.13 m)
Length 35 ft 9 in (10.9 m)
Height (tail down) 10 ft 6 in (3.2 m)
Wing area: 310 ft² (28.8 m²)

Weights: Empty 2,678 lb (1,215 kg)
　　　　Loaded
　　　　Maximum 6,100 lb (2,770 kg)

Performance: (at a take-off weight of 4,850 lb/2,200 kg) cruising speed 161 mph (259 kph) at 10,000 ft (3,050 m); climb 1,580 ft (482 m) per minute at sea level; service ceiling 30,025 ft (9,150 m); range with external fuel 1,007 miles (1,620 km); endurance with external fuel 6 hours 45 minutes

Used also by: Angola, Argentina, Australia, Austria, Bolivia, Burma, Chad, Ecuador, Oman, Peru, Sudan, Thailand

Notes: The PC-6 is designed for STOL operations in climatic and geographical extremes, and is a very rugged and versatile aircraft.

Syria

25,000 men and about 392 combat aircraft.

6 FGA sqns: 3 with 50 MiG-17, 3 with 60 Su-7.

3 fighter sqns with 50 MiG-23, 12 MiG-27.

12 interceptor sqns with 220 MiG-21PF/MF.

Transports incl 8 Il-14, 6 An-12, 2 An-24, 4 An-26.

Trainers incl Yak-11/-18, 23 L-29, MiG-15UTI, 32 MBB/CASA 223 Flamingo.

Helicopters incl 4 Mi-2, 8 Mi-4, 10 Mi-6, 50 Mi-8, 9 Ka-25 ASW, 15 Super *Frelon*, 6 CH-47C.

AA-2 'Atoll' AAM.

(12 MiG-23 fighters, 18 AB-212, 21 Super *Frelon* helicopters on order.)

Army Air Arm

25 Gazelle helicopters.

(24 Gazelle helicopters on order.)

Army Air Defence Command

24 SAM btys with SA-2/-3, 14 with SA-6, AA arty, interceptor ac and radar.

(SA-6/-8/-9 SAMs on order.)

Construcciones Aeronauticas SA (CASA) 223 Flamingo

Type: aerobatic training aircraft

Crew: two, seated in tandem

Wings: metal cantilever low-wing monoplane

Fuselage: metal semi-monocoque

Tail unit: metal cantilever

Landing gear: fixed tricycle unit

Powerplant: one Lycoming AIO-360-C1B inline engine, rated at 200 hp and driving a Hartzell two-blade metal propeller

Fuel capacity: 48 gallons (220 litres) in integral wing tanks

Avionics: communication and navigation equipment

Armament: none

Dimensions: Span 27 ft 2 in (8.28 m)
　　　　Length 24 ft 4½ in (7.43 m)
　　　　Height 8 ft 10¼ in (2.7 m)

Wing area: 123.64 ft² (11.5 m²)

Weights: Empty 1,510 lb (685 kg)
　　　　Loaded
　　　　Maximum 1,810 lb (821 kg)

Performance: speed 155 mph (249 kph); cruising speed 138 mph (222 kph); climb 1,220 ft (372 m) per minute at sea level; service ceiling 17,390 ft (5,300 m); range 310 miles (500 km)

Used only by: Syria

Notes: The type is used as an aerobatic trainer. The CASA 223 is in fact the Messerschmitt-Bölkow-Blohm 223 Flamingo, and the first Spanish-built aircraft flew in 1972.

Mil Mi-6 'Hook'

Type: heavy transport helicopter

Crew: five, plus up to 65 passengers

Rotors: metal cantilever five-blade main rotor; metal cantilever four-blade tail rotor

Wings: metal cantilever shoulder-wing monoplane

Fuselage: metal semi-monocoque

Landing gear: fixed tricycle unit

Powerplant: two Soloviev D-25V (TV-2BM) turboshafts, each rated at 5,500 shp

Fuel capacity: about 1,700 gallons (7,728 litres) in 11 fuselage tanks and about 940 gallons (4,273 litres) in two external tanks, plus provision for another 940 gallons (4,273 litres) in two auxiliary fuselage tanks

Avionics: comprehensive communication and navigation equipment

Armament: one 12.7- or 14.5-mm (0.5- or 0.57-in) machine-gun in the nose of some aircraft
Dimensions: Span 114 ft 10 in (35.0 m)
Length (fuselage) 108 ft 10½ in (33.18 m)
Height 32 ft 4 in (9.86 m)
Rotor disc area: 10,356 ft² (962.1 m²)
Weights: Empty 60,055 lb (27,240 kg)
Loaded 89,285 lb (40,500 kg)
Maximum 93,700 lb (42,500 kg)
Performance: (at maximum take-off weight) speed 186 mph (300 kph); cruising speed 155 mph (250 kph); service ceiling 14,750 ft (4,500 m); hovering ceiling in ground effect 8,200 ft (2,500 m); range with a payload of 13,228 lb (6,000 kg) 404 miles (650 km); ferry range 900 miles (1,450 km)

Used also by: Algeria, Bulgaria, Egypt, Ethiopia, Indonesia, Iraq, Libya, Peru, USSR, Vietnam
Notes: The largest helicopter in the world in its time, the Mi-6 made its first flight in 1957, and entered service in the late 1950s. The type has established several speed and payload records. Large clamshell doors are provided at the rear of the pod fuselage, and normal loads include up to 26,450 lb (12,000 kg) internally or 19,840 lb (9,000 kg) externally.

Taiwan

70,000 men and 316 combat aircraft, plus 90,000 reservists.

12 fighter sqns with 90 F-100A/F, 165 F-5A/E.
3 interceptor sqns with 44 F-104G.
1 recce sqn with 8 RF-104G.
1 MR sqn with 9 S-2A Tracker.
1 SAR sqn with 8 HU-16A ac.
Transports incl 25 C-46, 40 C-47, 30 C-119, 10 C-123, 1 Boeing 720B.
160 trainers, incl 55 PL-1B *Chienshou*, 32 T-33, 30 T-38, F-5B/F, 3 TF-104G, 6 F-104D, F-100F, T-CH-1.
Helicopters incl 95 UH-1H, 7 UH-19, 10 Bell 47G, OH-6.
Sidewinder AAM, Bullpup ASM.
(25 F-5E fighters, 21 F-5F trg ac, *Shafrir* AAM on order.)
Army Air Arm
80 UH-1H, 2 KH-4, 7 CH-34 helicopters.
(118 UH-IH helicopters on order.)

Aero Industry Development Center (AIDC) Pazmany PL-1B *Chienshou*

Type: trainer
Crew: two, seated side-by-side
Wings: metal cantilever low-wing monoplane
Fuselage: metal semi-monocoque
Tail unit: metal cantilever
Landing gear: fixed tricycle unit
Powerplant: one Lycoming O-320-E2A inline engine, rated at 150 hp and driving a McCauley two-blade metal propeller
Fuel capacity: 20¾ gallons (94 litres) in two wingtip tanks
Avionics: communication equipment
Armament: none

Aero Industry Development Center-Chinese Air Force (AIDC) T-CH-1

Type: trainer and light ground-attack aircraft
Crew: two, seated in tandem

Dimensions: Span 28 ft (8.53 m)
Length 19 ft 8¼ in (5.99 m)
Height 7 ft 4 in (2.24 m)
Wing area: 116 ft² (10.78 m²)
Weights: Empty 950 lb (431 kg)
Loaded
Maximum 1,440 lb (653 kg)
Performance: (at maximum take-off weight) speed 150 mph (241 kph) at sea level; cruising speed 130 mph (209 kph) at sea level; climb 1,600 ft (488 m) per minute at sea level; range 405 miles (650 km)
Used only by: Taiwan
Notes: The Pazmany PL-1 is built under licence in Taiwan by AIDC in the slightly modified PL-1B version, with altered cowling, wider cockpit and other detail changes. The first were delivered in 1970.

Wings: aluminium alloy cantilever low-wing monoplane
Fuselage: aluminium alloy semi-monocoque
Tail unit: aluminium alloy cantilever
Landing gear: hydraulically actuated retractable tricycle unit

Powerplant: one Lycoming T53-L-701 turboprop, rated at 1,450 ehp and driving Hamilton Standard three-blade metal propeller
Fuel capacity: 212 gallons (963 litres) in one fuselage and four wing tanks
Avionics: communication and navigation equipment
Armament:
Dimensions: Span 40 ft (12.19 m)
　　　　　　　Length 33 ft 8 in (10.26 m)
　　　　　　　Height 12 ft (3.66 m)
Wing area: 271 ft² (25.18 m²)
Weights: Empty 5,750 lb (2,608 kg)
　　　　　　Loaded 7,500 lb (3,402 kg)
　　　　　　Maximum 11,150 lb (5,057 kg)
Performance: (at a take-off weight of 7,600 lb/3,447 kg) speed 368 mph (592 kph) at 15,000 ft (4,570 m); cruising speed 253

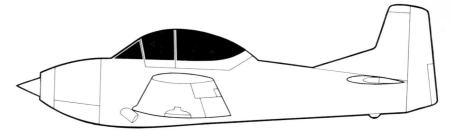

mph (407 kph) at 15,000 ft (4,570 m); climb 3,400 ft (1,036 m) per minute at sea level; service ceiling 32,000 ft (9,755 m); maximum range 1,250 miles (2,010 km)
Used only by: Taiwan
Notes: Design of this aircraft began in 1970, and the first prototype flew in 1973.

Hughes Helicopters OH-6 Cayuse

Type: light observation helicopter
Crew: two, seated side-by-side
Rotor: aluminium cantilever four-blade main rotor; steel and glassfibre cantilever two-blade tail rotor
Fuselage: aluminium semi-monocoque
Landing gear: twin metal skids
Powerplant: one Allison T53-A-5A turboshaft, rated at 317 shp but derated to 252½ shp for take-off and 214½ shp for continuous running
Fuel capacity: 51 gallons (232 litres) in bladder tanks in the rear fuselage
Avionics: communication and navigation equipment
Armament: one XM-27 7.62-mm machine-gun or XM-75 grenade launcher pod
Dimensions: Span 26 ft 4 in (8.03 m)
　　　　　　　Length (fuselage) 23 ft (7.01 m)
　　　　　　　Height 8 ft 1½ in (2.48 m)

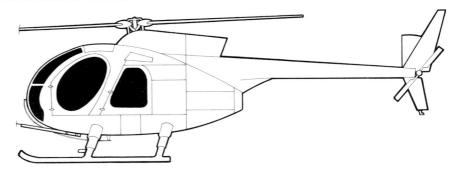

Rotor disc area: 544.63 ft² (50.6 m²)
Weights: Empty 1,229 lb (557 kg)
　　　　　　Loaded
　　　　　　Maximum 2,700 lb (1,225 kg)
Performance: (at 2,400-lb/1,090-kg take-off weight) maximum and cruising speed 150 mph (241 kph) at sea level; climb 1,840 ft (560 m) per minute at sea level; service ceiling 15,800 ft (4,815 m); hovering ceil-

ing in ground effect 11,800 ft (3,595 m); range 380 miles (611 km) at 5,000 ft (1,525 m); ferry range 1,560 miles (2,510 km)
Used also by: Brazil, Colombia, Denmark, Dominican Republic, Japan, Nicaragua, Pakistan, USA
Notes: The first prototype flew in 1963.

Tanzania

1,000 men and 29 combat aircraft.

3 fighter sqns with 11 MiG-21/F-8, 3 MiG-17/F-4, 15 MiG-19/F-6.
1 transport sqn with 1 An-2, 3 HS 748, 12 DHC-4, 6 Cessna 310.
2 MiG-15UTI, 6 Cherokee trainers.
2 Bell 47G, 4 AB-206 helicopters.
(4 DHC-5D transports on order.)

Thailand

43,000 men and 149 combat aircraft.

1 FGA/recce sqn with 12 F-5A, 2 F-5B, 4 RF-5A.
7 COIN sqns with 45 T-28D, 32 OV-10C, 16 A-37B, 31 AU-23A Peacemaker.
1 recce sqn with 4 T-33, 3 RT-33A.
1 utility sqn with 35 O-1 lt ac.
3 transport sqns with 15 C-47, 30 C-123B, 2 HS 748, 1 Islander, 3 Skyvan, 15 AC-47, 2 Merlin IVA, 10 Turbo-Porter.
2 helicopter sqns with 18 S-58T, 30 UH-1H, 40 CH-34C, 13 UH-19, 3 HH-43B.

Trainers incl 10 Chipmunk, 14 T-37B, 15 T-41D, 12 SF.260, 15 CT-4, AT-6.
Sidewinder AAM.
4 bns of airfield defence troops.
(20 F-5E/F FGA, 6 OV-10C COIN, 4 CASA C.212 transports, 18 S-58T, 13 UH-1H helicopters on order.)
Naval Air Arm
1 MR sqn with 10 S-2F Tracker, 2 HU-16B Albatross.
(2 CL-215 transports an order.)
Army Air Arm
5 aviation coys and some flts: 90 O-1 lt ac; 90 UH-IB/D, 4 CH-47, 24 OH-13, 16 FH-1100, 3 Bell 206, 2 Bell

212, 6 OH-23F, 28 KH-4 helicopters.
(3 Merlin IVA transport ac, 2 Bell 214B helicopters on order.)

Fairchild Industries (Pilatus) AU-23A Peacemaker

Type: light attack and utility aircraft
Crew: one or two, plus up to 10 passengers
Wings: metal braced high-wing monoplane
Fuselage: metal semi-monocoque
Tail unit: metal cantilever
Landing gear: fixed tailwheel type
Powerplant: one Garrett TPE 331-1-101F turboprop, rated at 650 shp and driving a Hartzell three-blade metal propeller
Fuel capacity: 142 gallons (644 litres) in integral wing tanks, plus provision for two underwing auxiliary tanks, each with a capacity of 42 gallons (190 litres)
Avionics: comprehensive communication and navigation equipment
Armament: one sidefiring XM-197 20-mm cannon, or two sidefiring 7.62-mm Miniguns, plus up to 1,400 lb (636 kg) of external stores on four underwing hardpoints, the inner pair being able to carry 575 lb (261 kg) each and the outer pair 350 lb (318 kg) each, and 600 lb (272 kg) on a hardpoint under the fuselage. The 2,000 lb (907 kg) of external stores can be made up of a variety of loads, including bombs, canisters, flares, napalm, rockets and smoke grenades
Dimensions: Span 49 ft 8 in (15.14 m)
Length 36 ft 10 in (11.23 m)
Height 12 ft 3 in (3.73 m)
Wing area: 310 ft² (28.8 m²)
Weights: Empty
Loaded
Maximum 6,100 lb (2,767 kg)
Performance: (at maximum take-off weight) speed 174 mph (280 kph); cruising speed 163 mph (262 kph); climb 1,500 ft (457 m) per minute at sea level; service ceiling 22,800 ft (6,950 m); range 558 miles (898 km)
Used only by: Thailand
Notes: The AU-23A Peacemaker is a light counter-insurgency and utility aircraft derived from the Fairchild Porter, itself a licence-built version of the Pilatus Turbo-Porter.

North American Aviation AT-6

Type: advanced trainer
Crew: two, seated in tandem
Wings: metal cantilever low-wing monoplane
Fuselage: metal semi-monocoque
Tail unit: metal cantilever
Landing gear: hydraulically actuated retractable tailwheel unit
Powerplant: one Pratt & Whitney R-1340-49 radial engine, rated at 600 hp and driving a metal two-blade propeller
Fuel capacity:
Avionics: communication and navigation equipment
Armament: one fixed and one flexible 0.3-in (7.62-mm) Browning machine-gun
Dimensions: Span 42 ft (12.8 m)
Length 29 ft (8.84 m)
Height 11 ft 9 in (3.58 m)
Wing area: 254 ft² (23.6 m²)
Weights: Empty 3,900 lb (1,769 kg)
Loaded
Maximum 5,155 lb (2,338 kg)
Performance: speed 210 mph (338 kph); climb 7 minutes 24 seconds to 10,000 ft (3,050 m); service ceiling 24,200 ft (7,376 m); range 629 miles (1,012 km)

Used also by: Bolivia, Chile, Dominican Republic, El Salvador, Honduras, Indonesia, Mexico, Morocco, Nicaragua, Paraguay, Peru, Spain, Tunisia, Zaire
Notes: The AT-6 was developed from the BC-1A in 1940, and is still widely used as a trainer.

Togo

5 Magister and 3 EMB-326GB COIN.
2 C-47, 2 DHC-5D, 1 F28 transports.
4 light planes.
1 Puma helicopter.
(3 EMB-326GB COIN, 5 AlphaJet trainers on order.)

De Havilland Aircraft of Canada DHC-5D Buffalo

Type: STOL utility transport
Crew: three, plus accommodation for 41
Wings: cantilever high-wing monoplane
Fuselage: aluminium alloy semi-monocoque
Tail unit: aluminium alloy cantilever
Landing gear: hydraulically actuated retractable tricycle unit

Powerplant: two General Electric CT64-820-4 turboprops, each rated at 3,133 shp and driving Hamilton Standard constant-speed three-blade propellers

Fuel capacity: 1,754 gallons (7,975 litres) in two inner wing tanks and 20 outer wing rubber tanks

Avionics: radio, radar and blind-flying equipment

Armament: none

Dimensions: Span 96 ft (29.26 m)
Length 79 ft (24.08 m)
Height 28 ft 8 in (8.73 m)

Wing area: 945 ft² (87.8 m²)

Weights: Empty 25,160 lb (11,412 kg)
Loaded
Maximum 49,200 lb (22,316 kg)

Performance: (STOL transport mission from smooth airfield surface) cruising speed 261 mph (420 kph); climb 1,820 ft (555 m) per minute at sea level; service ceiling 27,500 ft (8,380 m); range 691 miles (1,112 km) with 18,000 lb (8,164 kg) payload at 10,000 ft (3,050 m); range 2,038 miles (3,280 km) without payload

Used also by: Brazil, Canada, Ecuador, Kenya, Mauritania, Oman, Peru, Sudan, Tanzania, United Arab Emirates, Zaire, Zambia

Notes: Developed from the Caribou to win a US Army STOL transport requirement issued early in 1962. Its STOL performance includes a take-off to 50 ft (15 m) altitude with a payload of 12,000 lb (5,443 kg) on a STOL assault mission from an unprepared airfield in only 1,250 ft (381 m).

Tunisia

1,700 men (500 conscripts) and 10 combat aircraft.

1 fighter/trg sqn with 10 F-86F.
1 trg sqn with 12 M.B. 326B/K, 2 M.B. 326L.
12 SF.260W, 12 T-6 trainers.
Utility aircraft include *Flamant*.
8 *Alouette* II, 6 *Alouette* III, 4 UH-1H, 1 Puma helicopters.
(6 SF. 260C trainers on order.)

Avions Marcel Dassault *Flamant*

Type: general-purpose aircraft

Crew: one, plus up to five passengers

Wings: metal cantilever low mid-wing monoplane

Fuselage: metal semi-monocoque

Tail unit: metal cantilever

Landing gear: hydraulically actuated retractable tricycle unit

Powerplant: two SNECMA-Renault 12S 02-201 inline engines, each rated at 580 hp and driving a three-blade metal propeller

Fuel capacity:

Avionics: communication and navigation equipment

Armament: none

Dimensions: Span 67 ft 10 in (20.68 m)
Length 41 ft (12.5 m)
Height 14 ft 9 in (4.5 m)

Wing area: 508 ft² (47.2 m²)

Weights: Empty 9,350 lb (4,240 kg)
Loaded 12,760 lb (5,788 kg)
Maximum

Performance: speed 236 mph (380 kph); cruising speed 186 mph (300 kph); climb 984 ft (300 m) per minute at sea level; service ceiling 26,240 ft (8,000 m); range 755 miles (1,215 km)

Used also by: France

Notes: The *Flamant* was designed as a multi-purpose aircraft, the most important variants being:
1. MD-311 bombing and navigation trainer with a glased nose
2. MD-312 utility transport
3. MD-315 10-seat transport.
The prototype MD-303 flew in 1947.

Turkey

50,000 men (30,000 conscripts) and 339 combat aircraft.

13 FGA sqns: 2 with 49 F-4E, 4 with 100 F-5A and 10 F-5B, 2 with 32 F/TF-104G, 2 with 30 F-104S, 3 with 50 F-100C/D/F.
1 interceptor sqn with 30 F-102A, 3 TF-102A.
2 recce sqns with 31 RF-5A, 4 F-5B.
4 transport sqns with 7 C-130E, 20 Transall C-160, 30 C-47, 3 C-54, 3 Viscount 794, 2 Islander, 6 Do 28, 3 Cessna 421 ac; 5 UH-19, 6 HH-1H, 10 UH-IH helicopters.
Helicopters inc AB-206B.
Sidewinder, Sparrow, Falcon AAM; AS.12, Bullpup, Maverick ASM.
8 SAM sqns with Nike Hercules.
Trainers incl 40 T-33A, 30 T-37, 20 T-34, 25 T-41.
(22 F-4E, 8 RF-4E, 56 AlphaJet trainers on order.)

Naval Air Arm
2 ASW sqns with 8 S-2A, I2 S-2E Tracker, 2 TS-2A.
3 AB-204B, 6 AB-212 ASW helicopters.
(10 AB-212 helicopters, 33 Harpoon SSM on order.)

Army Air Arm
2 DHC-2, 18 U-17, 3 Cessna 421, 7 Do 27, 9 Do 28, 20 Beech Baron ac; 100 AB-205/-206, 20 Bell 47G, 48 UH-1D helicopters.
(56 AB-205 helicopters on order.)

Costruzioni Aeronautiche Giovanni Agusta (Bell) AB 206B JetRanger II

Type: general-purpose helicopter
Crew: one, plus up to four passengers
Rotor: aluminium and aluminium alloy cantilever two-blade main rotor; aluminium cantilever two-blade tail rotor
Fuselage: aluminium and aluminium alloy frame, semi-monocoque and monocoque sections
Landing gear: twin metal skids
Powerplant: one Allison 250-C20 turboshaft, rated at 400 shp
Fuel capacity: 63.4 gallons (288 litres) in fuselage tank
Avionics: communication and navigation equipment
Armament: none

Dimensions: Span 33 ft 4 in (10.16 m)
Length (fuselage) 31 ft 2 in (9.5 m)
Height 9 ft 6½ in (2.91 m)
Rotor disc area: 873 ft² (81.1 m²)
Weights: Empty 1,504 lb (682 kg)
Loaded
Maximum 3,350 (1,519 kg)
Performance: (at a take-off weight of 3,200 lb/1,452 kg) speed 140 mph (226 kph) at sea level; cruising speed 133 mph (214 kph); climb 1,358 ft (414 m) per minute at sea level; hovering ceiling in ground effect 11,325 ft (3,450 m); range on standard fuel tankage 418 miles (673 km)
Used also by: Iran, Italy, Morocco, Oman, Saudi Arabia, Spain, Sweden
Notes: Derived from the Bell 206B JetRanger II, the AB 206B features an engine derated to 317 shp to improve operation in hot and high altitude conditions.

General Dynamics (Convair Division) F-102 Delta Dagger

Type: all-weather interceptor fighter
Crew: one
Wings: metal cantilever mid-wing delta monoplane
Fuselage: metal semi-monocoque
Tail unit: metal cantilever
Landing gear: hydraulically actuated retractable tricycle unit
Powerplant: one Pratt & Whitney J57-P-23 turbojet, rated at 17,200-lb (7,802-kg) static thrust with afterburning
Fuel capacity:
Avionics: comprehensive communication and navigation/attack equipment, including a Hughes MG-10 fire-control system
Armament: three AIM-4E Falcon and three AIM-4F Falcon air-to-air missiles
Dimensions: Span 38 ft 1½ in (11.6 m)
Length 68 ft 5 in (20.83 m)
Height 21 ft 2½ in (6.45 m)
Wing area: 661.5 ft² (61.46 m²)
Weights: Empty 19,050 lb (8,630 kg)
Loaded 27,700 lb (12,564 kg)
Maximum 31,500 lb (14,288 kg)
Performance: speed 825 mph (1,328 kph) or Mach 1.25 at 36,000 ft (10,973 m); climb 13,000 ft (3,962 m) per minute at sea level; service ceiling 54,000 ft (16,460 m); range 1,350 miles (2,172 km)

Used only by: Turkey
Notes: The F-102 first flew in 1953, and entered service in 1956, after a lengthy development programme caused by shortfalls in performance. The TF-102A is a subsonic side-by-side trainer.

Vickers-Armstrongs Viscount

Type: transport aircraft
Crew: five, plus up to 43 passengers
Wings: metal cantilever low-wing monoplane
Fuselage: metal semi-monocoque
Tail unit: metal cantilever
Landing gear: hydraulically actuated retractable tricycle unit
Powerplant: four Rolls-Royce Dart 506 (R.Da.3) turboprops, each rated at 1,740 ehp and driving a four-blade metal de Havilland or Rotol propeller

Fuel capacity: 1,950 gallons (8,865 litres)
Avionics: comprehensive communication and navigation equipment
Armament: none
Dimensions: Span 93 ft 8½ in (28.56 m)
Length 81 ft 10 in (24.93 m)
Height 26 ft 9 in (8.15 m)
Wing area: 963 ft² (89.47 m²)
Weights: Empty 38,358 lb (17,399 kg)
Loaded
Maximum 64,500 lb (29,257 kg)

Performance: cruising speed 380 mph (612 kph) at 20,000 ft (6,096 m); ceiling 28,500 ft (8,687 m); range 1,730 miles (2,784 km) with a payload of 11,600 lb (5,262 kg); maximum range 2,000 miles (3,219 km)
Used also by: Brazil, South Africa
Notes: The Viscount was the world's first turboprop-powered airliner. The prototype first flew in 1948 and entered service in 1953. Several military users have Viscounts in their inventories, and the specification above applies to the Series 720.

Uganda

1,000 men and 37 combat aircraft.

2 fighter sqns with 25 MiG-21, 10 MiG-17, 2 MiG-15UTI.
1 transport sqn with 1 L-100-20, 6 C-47, 1 DHC-6.
1 helicopter sqn with 6 AB-205, 4 AB-206.
Trainers incl 5 L-29, 10 Piper Super Cub, 6 AS 202 Bravo.
AA-2 'Atoll' AAM.

Union of Soviet Socialist Republics

The Air Forces of the USSR

Like the United States, the USSR places great importance on the strength of her nuclear deterrent forces, and also like the USA relies on a triad of delivery systems: submarine-launched ballistic missiles, silo-launched intercontinental ballistic missiles, and air-launched missiles and free-fall bombs. Unlike the USA, though, Russia's nuclear forces are operated by different services: the navy has control of 1,015 SLBMs in 90 submarines, the ICBMs and shorter-range missiles are part of the Strategic Rocket Forces, the manned bombers are part of the Long-Range Air Force (part of the Soviet Air Force), and the defence force against nuclear attack is the Air Defence Force, which is independent of the other forces.

The Strategic Rocket Forces have a personnel strength of about 375,000, and control the following forces:
(i) about 1,400 ICBMs
   (a) 190 SS-9, being replaced by SS-18
   (b) 780 SS-11, converting to SS-17 and SS-19
   (c) 60 SS-13
   (d) 60 SS-17
   (e) 110 SS-18
   (f) 200 SS-19
(ii) about 190 IRBMs
   (a) 90 SS-5
   (b) 100 SS-20 mobile IRBMs
(iii) about 500 MRBMs
   (a) 500 SS-4.

It is worth noting that the SS-17, SS-18 and SS-19 ICBMs are capable of use with MIRV or single warheads. There is little doubt that the USSR could deploy more missiles, but is bound by the Interim Agreement of 1972, which fixed a 5-year limit to strategic weapons at the end of the SALT (Strategic Arms Limitation Talks), but which was extended to operate during the period of the SALT II talks. The Russians are also making good progress with the development of improved guidance packages, which will increase the efficiency of Russian missiles against hardened targets.

The Long-Range Air Force is of generally doubtful efficacy against American targets, but nevertheless poses a considerable threat to targets in Europe. There are 135 long-range bombers (100 Tu-95 and 35 M-4), and 491 medium-range bombers (305 Tu-16, 136 Tu-22 and 50 Tu-26 (?)) for a total of 626 offensive aircraft, supported by only 53 air-to-air refuelling tankers (9 Tu-16 and 44 M-4), 94 Tu-16 ECM aircraft, and 36 reconnaissance aircraft (4 Tu-95, 22 Tu-16 and 10 Tu-22).

The *PVO-Strany* is an independent force, with a personnel strength of about 550,000. The force consists of three main elements:

(i) the interceptor force with about 80 MiG-17, 170 MiG-19, 650 Su-9 and Su-11, 350 Yak-28P, 150 Tu-28P, 850 Su-15, 200 MiG-23 and 300 MiG-25 aircraft
(ii) the ABM system, with 64 ABM-1 'Galosh' missiles in four sites surrounding Moscow
(iii) the SAM force, with about 10,000 launchers at 1,000 sites for SA-1, SA-2, SA-3 and SA-5 missiles.
The whole *PVO-Strany* has comprehensive early warning and control systems tied in with the 6,000 early warning and ground control radar stations available.

The Soviet Air Force proper has about 455,000 men, and is deployed in 16 tactical air armies, four with 1,700 aircraft in Eastern Europe, and the other 12 with the other 2,950 combat aircraft in the 12 military districts in Russia. This force is subdivided into the Tactical Air Force and the Air Transport Force, whose detailed composition can be seen from the balance of forces chart.

455,000, excluding Air Defence Force and Long-Range Air Force, and about 4,650 combat aircraft.

Strategic Nuclear Forces
Offensive
(i) *Strategic Rocket Forces* (SRF): (375,000 men).
ICBM (1,400):
   190 SS-9 'Scarp' (converting to SS-18).
   780 SS-11 'Sergo' (converting to SS-17 and SS-19).
   60 SS-13 'Savage'.
   60 SS-17.
   110 SS-18.
   200 SS-19.
IRBM and MRBM: some 690 deployed (most in Western USSR, rest east of Urals).
   90 SS-5 'Skean' IRBM.
   100 SS-20 IRBM (mobile).
   500 SS-4 'Sandal' MRBM.
(ii) *Long-Range Air Force* (LRAF): 756 combat aircraft.
Long-range bombers: 135.
   100 Tu-95 'Bear-A'.
   35 M-4 'Bison'.
Medium-range bombers: 491.
   305 Tu-16 'Badger' with ASM.
   136 Tu-22 'Blinder' with ASM.
   50 Tu-26 (?) 'Backfire-B' with ASM.
Tankers: 53.
   9 Tu-16 'Badger'.
   44 M-4 'Bison'.
ECM: 94.
   94 Tu-16 'Badger'.
Recce: 36.
   4 Tu-95 'Bear'.
   22 Tu-16 'Badger'.
   10 Tu-22 'Blinder'.
Defensive
Air Defence Force (*PVO-Strany*) (550,000 men): Early warning and control systems, with 6,000 early warning and ground control intercept radars; interceptor sqns with SAM units; about 2,720 aircraft:
Interceptors: incl some 90 MiG-17 'Fresco', 170 MiG-19 'Farmer-B/E', 650 Su-9 'Fishpot-B', Su-11 'Fishpot-C', 320 Yak-28P 'Firebar', 150 Tu-28P 'Fiddler', 850 Su-15 'Flagon-A/D/E/F', 200 MiG-23 'Flogger-B', 300 MiG-25 'Foxbat-A'.
Airborne Warning and Control Aircraft: 12 Tu-126 'Moss'.
Trg ac incl 30 Su-7, 40 Su-11, 120 Su-15, 20 MiG-15, 60 MiG-17, 50 MiG-23, 50 MiG-25, 10 Yak-28.
ABM: 64 ABM-1 'Galosh' in 4 sites around Moscow, with 'Try Add' engagement radars; target acquisition and tracking by phased-array 'Dog House' and 'Cat House', early warning by phased-array 'Hen House' radar on Soviet borders. Range of 'Galosh' believed over 200 miles; warheads nuclear, presumably MT range.
SAM fixed-site system: some 10,000 launchers, at over 1,000 sites. SA-1 'Guild', SA-2 'Guideline', SA-3 'Goa', SA-5 'Gammon'.

Air Force
455,000 men with about 4,650 combat aircraft.
Tactical Air Force: aircraft incl 120 Yak-25/-26/-27/-28 'Brewer', 40 MiG-17 'Fresco', 260 Su-7 'Fitter-A', 1,300 MiG-23/-27 'Flogger-B/D', about 1,450 MiG-21 'Fishbed-J/K/L/N', 530 Su-17 'Fitter-C/D', 190 Su-19 'Fencer-A' FGA; about 250 'Beagle', 'Brewer', 150 MiG-25 'Foxbat-B/D', 300 'Fishbed' recce; 60 'Brewer-E', 6 An-12 'Cub' ECM ac; 220 transports; 3,700 helicopters, incl 800 Mi-1/-2 'Hare/Hoplite', 420 Mi-4 'Hound', 500 Mi-6 'Hook', 1,660 Mi-8 'Hip', 10 Mi-10 'Harke', 60 Mi-12 'Homer', 310 Mi-24 'Hind'; 1,100 tac trg ac.
Air Transport Force: about 1,300 aircraft: 50 An-8, 735 An-12 'Cub', 20 An-24/-26 'Coke/Curl', 235 Il-14 'Crate', 15 Il-18 'Coot', 2 Il-62 'Classic', 80 Il-76 'Candid', 100 Li-2 'Cab', 10 Tu-104 'Camel', 8 Tu-134 'Crusty' med, 50 An-22 'Cock' hy.
1,300 Civil *Aeroflot* med- and long-range ac available to supplement military airlift.
Deployment:
16 Tactical Air Armies: 4 (1,700 ac) in Eastern Europe and 1 in each of 12 MD in the USSR.

Naval Air Force
Some 770 combat aircraft.
280 Tu-16 'Badger' med bombers with ASM.
30 Tu-26(?) 'Backfire' med bombers with ASM.

40 Tu-22 'Blinder' med bombers, MR,
ECM ac.
Some 30 Yak-36 'Forger' VTOL FGA,
30 'Fitter-C' FGA.
40 Tu-16 'Badger-E/F' recce, 30 Tu-16
ECM ac.
210 MR ac: 45 Tu-95 'Bear-D', 25 Tu-
95 'Bear-F', 50 Il-38 'May' ac, 90 Be-
12 'Mail' amphibians.
80 Tu-16 'Badger' tankers.
220 ASW helicopters: Mi-4 'Hound',
Mi-14 'Haze', Ka-25A/B 'Hormone'.
280 Misc transports and trainers.

Antonov An-8 'Camp'

Type: transport aircraft
Crew: ?, plus up to 40 troops
Wings: metal cantilever high-wing mono-plane
Fuselage: metal semi-monocoque
Tail unit: metal cantilever
Landing gear: hydraulically actuated retrac-table tricycle unit
Powerplant: two Ivchenko AI-20D turbo-props, each rated at 4,000 ehp and driving a metal four-blade propeller
Fuel capacity:
Avionics: comprehensive communication and navigation equipment
Armament: one 23-mm NR-23 cannon

Dimensions: Span 121 ft 4¾ in (37.0 m)
Length 100 ft 10 in (30.74 m)
Height
Wing area: 1,261 ft² (117.2 m²)
Weights: Empty
Loaded
Maximum 83,775 lb (38,000 kg)
Performance: speed 311 mph (500 kph);
service ceiling 31,500 ft (9,600 m); range
1,860 miles (3,000 km)
Used only by: USSR
Notes: The An-8 preceded the An-10 and An-12 not only in time, but also in ability to operate from short, semi-prepared air-strips. The type first flew in 1955, powered by two 5,100-ehp Kuznetsov NK-2M turbo-props, and entered service in 1957 with the airborne arm.

Antonov An-22 *Antei* 'Cock'

Type: strategic transport
Crew: six, plus up to 29 passengers
Wings: metal cantilever high-wing mono-plane
Fuselage: metal semi-monocoque
Tail unit: metal cantilever
Landing gear: hydraulically actuated retrac-table tricycle unit
Powerplant: four Kuznetsov NK-12MA turbo-props, each rated at 15,000 shp and driving four-blade metal contra-rotating propellers
Fuel capacity: 94,800 lb (43,000 kg)
Avionics: comprehensive communication and navigation equipment
Armament: none

Dimensions: Span 211 ft 4 in (64.4 m)
Length 189 ft 7 in (57.8 m)
Height 41 ft 1½ in (12.53 m)
Wing area: 5,166.6 ft² (480.0 m²)
Weights: Empty 251,325 lb (114,000 kg)
Loaded
Maximum 551,160 lb (250,000 kg)
Performance: speed 460 mph (740 kph);
cruising speed 398 mph (640 kph); range with maximum payload 3,107 miles (5,000 km); range with maximum fuel and a payload of 99,208 lb (45,000 kg) 6,835 miles (11,000 km)
Used also by: Egypt, Ethiopia
Notes: The An-22 first flew in 1965, and has a maximum payload of 176,370 lb (80,000 kg). The rear loading ramp allows bulky items to be loaded into the fuselage, whose main internal measurements are a length of 108 ft 3 in (33.0 m), and a width and height of 14 ft 5 in (4.4 m).

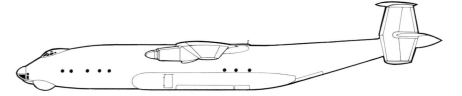

Beriev M-12 Tchaika 'Mail'

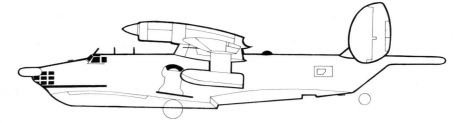

Type: maritime reconnaissance amphibian
Crew:
Wings: metal cantilever high gull-wing monoplane
Fuselage: metal semi-monocoque, with boat hull
Tail unit: metal cantilever
Landing gear: hydraulically actuated retractable tailwheel unit
Powerplant: two Ivchenko AI-20D turboprops, each rated at 4,190 ehp and driving a four-blade metal propeller
Fuel capacity:
Avionics: comprehensive communication and navigation/attack equipment, including a magnetic anomaly detector and sonobuoys
Armament: a minimum of 6,614 lb (3,000 kg) of weapons and/or sonobuoys in an internal weapons bay, plus provision for an unknown weight of stores on up to six hardpoints under the outer wings

Dimensions: Span about 97 ft 6 in (29.7 m)
Length about 107 ft 11¼ in (32.9 m)
Height about 22 ft 11½ in (7.0 m)
Wing area: 1,030 ft² (95.69 m²)
Weights: Empty about 47,950 lb (21,750 kg)
Loaded
Maximum about 65,035 lb (29,500 kg)

Performance: (estimated) speed 379 mph (610 kph); patrol speed 199 mph (320 kph); climb 2,986 ft (910 m) per minute at sea level; service ceiling 37,000 ft (11,280 m); range 2,485 miles (4,000 km)
Used only by: USSR
Notes: The M-12, first known as the Be-12, probably made its first flight in 1960, and entered service in 1962. In four main periods between 1964 and 1973 the type has established a large number of world records, especially in altitude, speed, and payload to altitude.

Ilyushin Il-38 'May'

Type: anti-submarine and maritime patrol aircraft
Crew: 12
Wings: metal cantilever low-wing monoplane
Fuselage: metal monocoque
Tail unit: metal cantilever
Landing gear: hydraulically actuated retractable tricycle unit
Powerplant: four Ivchenko AI-20 turboprops, each rated at about 5,000 ehp and driving a four-blade metal propeller
Fuel capacity: 6,600 gallons (30,000 litres)
Avionics: comprehensive communication and navigation/attack equipment, including a magnetic anomaly detector, surface-search radar and sonobuoys

Armament: weapons bay for a range of torpedoes, depth bombs, mines and other anti-submarine weapons, plus provision (probably) for underwing racks for further stores

Dimensions: Span 122 ft 8½ in (37.4 m)
Length 129 ft 10 in (39.6 m)
Height 33 ft 4 in (10.17 m)

Wing area: 1,507 ft² (140.0 m²)

Weights: Empty about 90,000 lb (40,820 kg)
Loaded
Maximum about 180,000 lb (81,650 kg)

Performance: (estimated) speed 450 mph (724 kph); cruising speed 400 mph (645 kph) at 27,000 ft (8,230 m); range 4,500 miles (7,250 km); endurance 15 hours

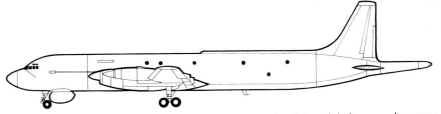

Used also by: India

Notes: Derived from the Il-18 airliner, the Il-38 A/S and maritime patrol aircraft first became known in the west in 1974. Compared with the Il-18, the Il-38 has its wing located farther forward, to maintain the centre of gravity, the long rear fuselage containing lightweight items such as sonobuoys, sensors and crew facilities, and the short forward fuselage containing most of the weapons load, computer equipment and the search radar.

Ilyushin Il-62 'Classic'

Type: long-range passenger transport
Crew: five, plus up to 186 passengers
Wings: metal cantilever low-wing monoplane
Fuselage: metal semi-monocoque
Tail unit: metal cantilever
Landing gear: hydraulically actuated retractable tricycle unit
Powerplant: four Kuznetsov NK-8-4 turbofans, each rated at 23,150-lb (10,500-kg) static thrust
Fuel capacity: 21,998 gallons (100,000 litres) in seven integral wing tanks
Avionics: comprehensive communication and navigation equipment

Armament: none

Dimensions: Span 141 ft 9 in (43.2 m)
Length 174 ft 3½ in (53.12 m)
Height 40 ft 6¼ in (12.35 m)

Wing area: 3,010 ft² (279.6 m²)

Weights: Empty 146,390 lb (66,400 kg)
Loaded
Maximum 357,150 lb (162,000 kg)

Performance: (at maximum take-off weight) cruising speed 560 mph (900 kph) at 39,400 ft (12,000 m); climb 3,540 ft (1,080 m) per minute at sea level; range with a payload of 22,050 lb (10,000 kg) and 176,370 lb (80,000 kg) of fuel 5,715 miles (9,200 km)

Used also by: Poland, Romania

Notes: Capable of moving troops long distances at high speed, the Il-62 has a maximum payload of 50,700 lb (23,000 kg). The type entered service in 1967. There is also an Il-62M version, powered by 25,350-lb (11,500-kg) thrust Soloviev D-30KU turbofans and fitted with an extra fuel tank in the fin. Range of this modified version is 6,215 miles (10,000 km) with a maximum payload of 50,700 lb (23,000 kg).

Ilyushin Il-76T 'Candid'

Type: freight transport
Crew: three
Wings: metal cantilever high-wing monoplane
Fuselage: metal semi-monocoque
Tail unit: metal cantilever
Landing gear: hydraulically actuated retractable tricycle unit
Powerplant: four Soloviev D-30KP turbofans, each rated at 26,455-lb (12,000-kg) static thrust
Fuel capacity: 18,000 gallons (81,825 litres)
Avionics: comprehensive communication and navigation equipment
Armament: two 23-mm NR-23 cannon
Dimensions: Span 165 ft 8 in (50.5 m)
　　　　　　Length 152 ft 10½ in (46.59 m)
　　　　　　Height 48 ft 5 in (14.76 m)
Wing area: 3,229.2 ft² (300.0 m²)

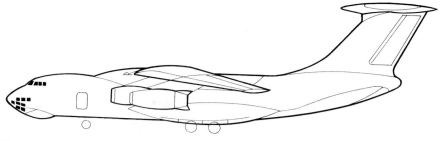

Weights: Empty about 159,000 lb (72,000 kg)
　　　　　Loaded 346,125 lb (157,000 kg)
　　　　　Maximum 374,785 lb (170,000 kg)
Performance: speed 560 mph (900 kph); cruising speed 497 mph (800 kph); maximum cruising height 39,350 ft (12,000 m); range with maximum payload 3,100 miles (5,000 km); range with maximum fuel 4,163 miles (6,700 km)
Used also by: Iraq
Notes: The Il-76T first flew in 1971, and entered service in 1973. The type can operate from semi-prepared strips, and features an advanced loading system, enabling containerised freight to be handled. The Il-76T has STOL capability.

Kamov Ka-15 'Hen'

Type: general-purpose helicopter
Crew: two
Rotors: two metal cantilever three-blade co-axial contra-rotating main rotors
Fuselage: metal frame with plywood and stressed metal skinning
Tail unit: metal cantilever
Landing gear: fixed four-wheel unit
Powerplant: one Ivchenko AI-14V piston engine, rated at 255 hp
Fuel capacity:
Avionics: communication and navigation equipment
Armament: none
Dimensions: Span 32 ft 8 in (9.96 m)
　　　　　　Length (fuselage) 19 ft 4¼ in (5.9 m)
　　　　　　Height 10ft 10in (3.3 m)
Rotor disc area: 1,676.2 ft² (155.73 m²)
Weights: Empty 2,134 lb (968 kg)
　　　　　Loaded 2,500 lb (1,135 kg)
　　　　　Maximum 3,020 lb (1,370 kg)
Performance: speed 93 mph (150 kph); service ceiling 9,840 ft (3,000 m); range 193 miles (310 km)
Used only by: USSR
Notes: Designed as a development of the Ka-10 'Hat', the Ka-15 was intended at first as a spotter aircraft for the Soviet Navy, and first flew in 1953. It has since been adopted by the navy for general-purpose duties.

Kamov Ka-18 'Hog'

Type: general-purpose helicopter
Crew: two, and one passenger
Rotors: two metal cantilever three-blade co-axial contra-rotating main rotors
Fuselage: metal tube framework with duralumin skinning
Tail unit: metal cantilever
Landing gear: fixed four-wheel unit
Powerplant: one Ivchenko AI-14VF piston engine, rated at 280 hp
Fuel capacity: 38.5 gallons (176 litres) in two fuselage tanks, plus provision for two 15.4-gallon (70-litre) auxiliary tanks
Avionics: communication and navigation equipment
Armament: none
Dimensions: Span 32 ft 8 in (9.98 m)
　　　　　　Length (fuselage) 23 ft 0¾ in (7.03 m)
　　　　　　Height 10 ft 11½ in (3.34 m)
Rotor disc area: 1,676.2 ft² (155.73 m²)
Weights: Empty 2,292 lb (1,040 kg)
　　　　　Loaded
　　　　　Maximum 3,218 lb (1,460 kg)
Performance: speed 90 mph (145 kph); service ceiling 11,480 ft (3,500 m)
Used only by: USSR
Notes: Developed from the Ka-15 'Hen', the Ka-18 features the same basic powerplant and rotor system, but has a stretched fuselage to enable a passenger or litter to be carried.

Kamov Ka-25 'Hormone'

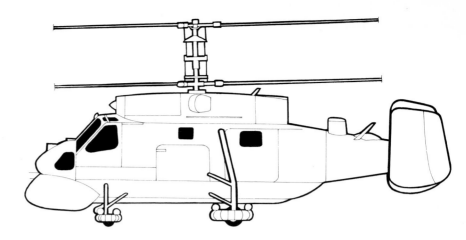

Type: anti-submarine and general-purpose helicopter

Crew: two, plus up to 12 passengers

Rotors: two metal cantilever three-blade co-axial contra-rotating main rotors

Fuselage: metal semi-monocoque

Tail unit: metal cantilever

Landing gear: fixed four-wheel unit

Powerplant: two Glushenkov GTD-3 turbo-shafts, each rated at 900 shp

Fuel capacity:

Avionics: comprehensive communication and navigation/attack equipment, including dipping sonar, magnetic anomaly detector and search radar in the ASW version; and acquisition radar and data link in the missile target-acquisition variant

Armament: one or two 400-mm (15.7-in) torpedoes, conventional or nuclear depth charges and other stores in the weapons bay, plus air-to-surface missiles on the sides of the fuselage on later models

Dimensions: Span 51 ft 8 in (15.74 m)
Length (fuselage) 32 ft (9.75 m)
Height 17 ft 7½ in (5.37 m)

Rotor disc area: 4,193.1 ft² (389.6 m²)

Weights: Empty about 11,023 lb (5,000 kg)
Loaded about 15,652 lb (7,100 kg)
Maximum about 16,535 lb (7,300 kg)

Performance: speed 120 mph (193 kph); service ceiling about 11,000 ft (3,350 m); range about 400 miles (650 km)

Used also by: India, Syria, Yugoslavia

Notes: The Ka-25 was first revealed to the west in 1961, and the type probably entered service in 1965. There are two basic models:

1. 'Hormone-A' ASW version, to which the technical specification above relates

2. 'Hormone-B' target-acquisition version for use with over-the-horizon use of shipborne anti-shipping missiles

There is also a civil version, the KA-25K, with a longer nose, extra rear-looking cockpit under the normal one, and the ability to lift loads of some 4,400 lb (2,000 kg).

Mikoyan-Gurevich MiG-25 'Foxbat'

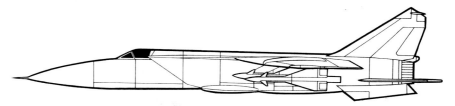

Type: interceptor fighter
Crew: one
Wings: steel and titanium cantilever high-wing monoplane
Fuselage: steel semi-monocoque
Tail unit: light alloy, steel and titanium cantilever
Landing gear: hydraulically actuated retractable tricycle unit
Powerplant: two Tumansky R-31 turbojets, each rated at 24,250-lb (11,000-kg) static thrust with afterburning
Fuel capacity: about 4,100 gallons (18,640 litres) in fuselage, air intakes and integral wing tanks
Avionics: comprehensive communication and navigation/attack equipment, including 'Fox Fire' fire-control radar, Sirena 3 radar warning system, ECM and electronic counter-countermeasures (ECCM) equipment
Armament: four AA-6 'Acrid' air-to-air missiles (two radar and two IR-homing)
Dimensions: Span 45 ft 9 in (13.95 m)
Length 73 ft 2 in (22.3 m)
Height 18 ft 4$\frac{1}{4}$ in (5.6 m)
Wing area: 603 ft² (56.0 m²)

Weights: Empty about 34,000 lb (15,425 kg)
Loaded 68,350 lb (31,000 kg)
Maximum about 79,800 lb (36,200 kg)
Performance: (estimated) speed 2,100 mph (3,380 kph) or Mach 3.2 at high altitude; speed 646 mph (1,040 kph) or Mach 0.85 at low altitude; climb 40,950 ft (12,480 m) per minute at sea level; climb to 36,100 ft (11,000 m) in 2 minutes 30 seconds; service ceiling 80,000 ft (24,400 m); combat radius 700 miles (1,130 km); maximum combat radius 805 miles (1,300 km)
Used also by: Algeria (?), Libya
Notes: The MiG-25 first became known to the west as the E-266 record-breaking aircraft, which flew in 1964. The MiG-25 probably entered service in 1970 after development in fighter and reconnaissance versions, the former at first having priority as a counter to the US North American B-70 supersonic strategic bomber; but with the cancellation of the B-70 in 1961, the reconnaissance aspect of the MiG-25 received higher priority. There are several versions of the MiG-25:

1. MiG-25 'Foxbat-A' interceptor, to which the technical specification applies
2. MiG-25R 'Foxbat-B' reconnaissance aircraft, with a span of 44 ft (13.4 m), five cameras and sideways-looking airborne radar (SLAR)
3. MiG-25U 'Foxbat-C' twin-seat trainer
4. MiG-25R 'Foxbat-D', similar to the 'Foxbat-B' but with improved SLAR capability.

The top speed of the 'Foxbat-A' with four underwing missiles is believed to be 1,850 mph (2,977 kph) at high altitude.

Mikoyan-Gurevich MiG-27 'Flogger-D'

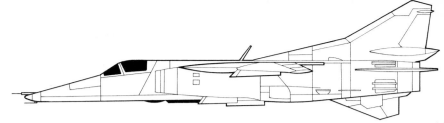

Type: ground-attack aircraft
Crew: one
Wings: metal cantilever variable-geometry shoulder-wing monoplane
Fuselage: metal semi-monocoque
Tail unit: metal cantilever
Landing gear: hydraulically actuated retractable tricycle unit
Powerplant: one turbofan of unknown type, probably rated at 24,250-lb (11,000-kg) static thrust with afterburning
Fuel capacity: in the order of 1,183 gallons (5,380 litres) internally, with provision for external tanks under the fuselage and under the wings
Avionics: comprehensive communication and navigation/attack equipment, including a laser rangefinder and marked target seeker
Armament: one 23-mm multi-barrel cannon, and external stores carried on five pylons. Among the external stores that can be carried are conventional bombs, nuclear bombs, rocket pods, and air-to-surface missiles, including (probably) the AS-7 'Kerry'
Dimensions: Span (spread) 46 ft 9 in (14.25 m)
Span (swept) 26 ft 9½ in (8.17 m)
Length 55 ft 1½ in (16.8 m)
Height 15 ft 9 in (4.8 m)
Wing area: 293.4 ft² (27.26 m²)
Weights: Empty about 20,000 lb (9,070 kg)
Loaded about 33,050 lb (15,000 kg)
Maximum 39,130 lb (17,750 kg)
Performance: (estimated) speed 1,520 mph (2,446 kph) or Mach 2.3 at high altitude; speed 838 mph (1,348 kph) or Mach 1.1 at sea level; service ceiling 59,050 ft (18,000 m); ferry range 1,550 miles (2,500 km) (NB: Compared with other 'Floggers', the 'Flogger-D' has an uprated engine and fixed-geometry air intakes, to ensure maximum transonic performance at lower altitudes.)
Used also by: Bulgaria, Cuba, Egypt, Iraq, Syria
Notes: Derived from the MiG-23, the MiG-27 'Flogger-D' has an uprated engine, extra armour protection for the pilot, and a new nose, its sharper contours holding a laser rangefinder and marked target seeker. The air intakes are also of a fixed-geometry pattern. Maximum weapon load is 4,200 lb (1,900 kg).

Mil Mi-10 'Harke'

Type: flying crane helicopter
Crew: three, plus up to 28 passengers
Rotors: metal cantilever five-blade main rotor; metal cantilever four-blade tail rotor
Fuselage: metal semi-monocoque
Landing gear: fixed four-leg unit
Powerplant: two Soloviev D-25V turboshafts, each rated at 5,500 shp
Fuel capacity: 13,975 lb (6,340 kg) in one fuselage and two external tanks, plus provision for an additional 4,235 lb (1,920 kg) in two auxiliary fuselage tanks
Avionics: comprehensive communication and navigation equipment
Armament: none
Dimensions: Span 114 ft 10 in (35.0 m)
Length (fuselage) 107 ft 9¾ in (32.86 m)
Height 32 ft 2 in (9.8 m)
Rotor disc area: 10,356 ft² (962.1 m²)
Weights: Empty 60,185 lb (27,300 kg)
Loaded 83,775 lb (38,000 kg)
Maximum 96,340 lb (43,700 kg)
Performance: (at maximum take-off weight) speed 124 mph (200 kph); cruising speed 112 mph (180 kph); service ceiling at a weight of 92,594 lb (42,000 kg) 13,120 ft (4,000 m); range with a payload of 33,069 lb (15,000 kg) 19 miles (30 km); range with a payload of 22,046 lb (10,000 kg) 249 miles (400 km); ferry range 391 miles (630 km)
Used only by: USSR
Notes: Designed in the late 1950s as a flying crane derivative of the Mi-6, the Mi-10 first flew in 1960. It has basically the same fuselage as the Mi-6, on high and wide-straddling undercarriage legs. These allow loads up to 12 ft 3½ in (3.75 m) high to be moved into position under the fuselage. Maximum platform payload is 33,069 lb (15,000 kg), and maximum slung payload 17,635 lb (8,000 kg). There is a derivative of the Mi-10 flying crane in the form of the Mi-10K, which has shorter undercarriage legs, and is designed for slung loads. Maximum load is currently 24,250 lb (11,000 kg), but later provision of 6,500-shp Soloviev D-25VF engines will raise this to 30,865 lb (14,000 kg).

Mil Mi-24 'Hind'

Type: combat helicopter
Crew: four, plus up to eight passengers
Rotors: glassfibre and titanium cantilever five-blade main rotor; cantilever three-blade tail rotor
Wings: metal cantilever shoulder-wing monoplane
Fuselage: metal semi-monocoque
Landing gear: hydraulically actuated retractable tricycle unit
Powerplant: two Isotov turboshafts, each rated at 1,500 shp
Fuel capacity:
Avionics: comprehensive communication and navigation/attack equipment
Armament: one 12.7- or 14.5-mm (0.5- or 0.57-in) machine-gun, plus provision for four 'Swatter' anti-tank missiles on the wing endplate pylons, and a variety of rockets and other weapons on four underwing pylons. Each rocket pod holds thirty-two 57-mm rockets. Maximum weapons load is 2,800 lb (1,275 kg)
Dimensions: Span about 55 ft 9 in (17.0 m)
Length (overall) about 55 ft 9 in (17.0 m)
Height about 14 ft (4.25 m)

Rotor disc area: about 2,441 ft² (227.0 m²)
Weights: Empty about 14,300 lb (6,500 kg)
Loaded about 22,046 lb (10,000 kg) Maximum
Performance: (estimated) speed 170 mph (275 kph)
Used only by: USSR
Notes: The existence of the Mi-24 became fully known in the west in 1974, and it seems likely that the type made its first flight in 1971, and entered service in 1973-1974. There are several models of the Mi-24, all using the same basic airframe, powerplant and main rotor:

1. Mi-24 'Hind-A' assault helicopter, with a crew of four, auxiliary wings of considerable anhedral, and six weapon pylons
2. Mi-24 'Hind-B', similar to the 'Hind-A' but with level wings and only the two inner weapons pylons on each wing (the type is believed to be a pre-

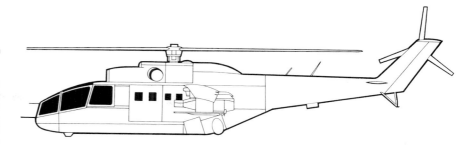

cursor of the 'Hind-A' and built only in small numbers)
3. Mi-24 'Hind-C', similar to the 'Hind-A' but without nose-mounted machine-gun and endplate missile pylons
4. Mi-24 'Hind-D', based on the 'Hind-A', but with the tail rotor on the port

rather than starboard side, and a completely new forward fuselage to suit the type to a primary role as a helicopter gunship. Main armament is a 12.7-mm or a 14.5-mm four-barrel machine-gun in a chin turret allowing large angles of elevation and traverse.

Mil 'Homer'

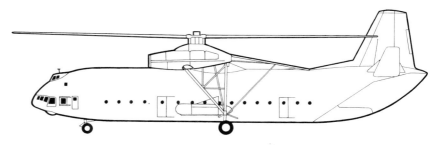

Type: heavy general-purpose helicopter
Crew: six, plus up to some 50 passengers
Rotors: two metal cantilever counter-rotating five-blade main rotors
Wings: metal braced high-wing monoplane
Fuselage: metal semi-monocoque
Tail unit: metal cantilever
Landing gear: fixed tricycle unit
Powerplant: four Soloviev D-25VF turbo-shafts, each rated at 6,500 shp, coupled and each pair driving one main rotor
Fuel capacity:
Avionics: comprehensive communication and navigation equipment
Armament: none
Dimensions: Span (overall) 219 ft 10 in (67.0 m)
Rotor diameter 114 ft 10 in (35.0 m)
Length (fuselage) 121 ft 4½ in (37.0 m)
Height 41 ft (12.5 m)
Rotor disc area: (total) 20,712 ft² (1,924.2 m²)

Weights: Empty about 140,000 lb (63,500 kg)
Loaded 213,850 lb (97,000 kg)
Maximum 231,500 lb (105,000 kg)
Performance: speed 161 mph (260 kph); cruising speed 150 mph (240 kph); service ceiling 11,500 ft (3,500 m); range with a payload of 78,000 lb (35,400 kg) 310 miles (500 km)
Used only by: USSR
Notes: The largest helicopter in the world, the V-12 became known in the west in 1969, when the type captured several load-to-height records, including a load of 88,636

lb (40,204.5 kg) lifted to 7,398 ft (2,255 m). Designed as a VTOL aircraft to carry loads that could be brought in to the nearest airfield by the Antonov An-22, the V-12 was clearly intended to be capable of transporting missiles, its internal measurements being 92 ft 4 in (28.15 m) long, by 14 ft 5 in (4.4 m) wide and high. The rotor system is basically two Mi-6/Mi-10 units, one mounted at the end of each wing and driven by a pair of uprated Soloviev engines. The normal payload with STOL take-off is 66,000 lb (30,000 kg).

Myasishchev M-4 'Bison'

Type: bomber and maritime reconnaissance aircraft
Crew: six
Wings: metal cantilever shoulder-wing monoplane
Fuselage: metal semi-monocoque
Tail unit: metal cantilever
Landing gear: hydraulically actuated bicycle unit, with stabilising wingtip outrigger units
Powerplant: four Mikulin AM-3D turbojets, each rated at 19,180-lb (8,700-kg) static thrust in the 'Bison-A'; four D-15 turbojets, each rated at 28,660-lb (13,000-kg) static thrust in 'Bison-B' and 'Bison-C'
Fuel capacity:
Avionics: comprehensive communication and navigation/attack equipment, plus reconnaissance gear in special models
Armament: (as a bomber) 10 NR-23 23-mm cannon in one manned and four remotely controlled turrets, plus up to 22,046 lb (10,000 kg) of free-fall conventional or nuclear bombs in the internal bomb bay
Armament: (as a reconnaissance aircraft) six NR-23 23-mm cannon in one manned and two remotely controlled turrets, plus at least 9,920 lb (4,500 kg) of internal stores

Dimensions: Span about 167 ft 7½ in (30.48 m)

Length about 154 ft 10 in (47.2 m)

Height about 46 ft (14.1 m)

Wing area: 3,660 ft² (340.0 m²)

Weights: Empty (Bison-A) about 154,320 lb (70,000 kg)

Empty (Bison-B and C) about 176,370 lb (80,000 kg)

Loaded

Maximum (Bison-A) about 350,000 lb (158,750 kg)

Maximum (Bison-B and C) about 374,780 lb (170,000 kg)

Performance: speed 560 mph (900 kph); service ceiling (Bison-A) 42,650 ft (13,000 m); service ceiling (Bison-B and C) 49,200 ft (15,000 m); range with 9,920-lb (4,500-kg) payload 6,835 miles (11,000 km)

Used only by: USSR

Notes: The prototype M-4 or Mya-4 'Bison' probably flew in 1953, and the type prob-

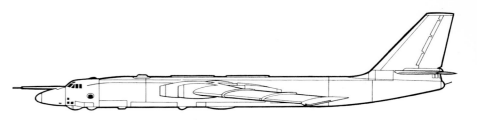

ably entered service in 1955. The need for a large number of defensive gun turrets, an obsolescent design feature, was probably felt because of the type's poor ceiling. There are three versions:

1. M-4 'Bison-A', the USSR's first strategic jet bomber, most of which have now been converted into aerial tankers with fuel and refuelling equipment in the bomb bay. The dimensions above apply to this model

2. M-4 'Bison-B' maritime reconnaissance model, with a solid rather than glazed nose, and a flight refuelling probe. Under the fuselage there are a number of blisters for electronic equipment. On this model the aft dorsal and aft ventral turrets have been deleted

3. M-4 'Bison-C' reconnaissance version with search radar faired into a longer nose, but otherwise similar to the 'Bison-B'.

Sukhoi Su-9 and Su-11 'Fishpot'

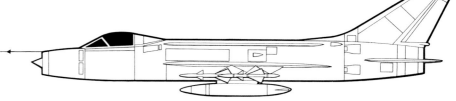

Type: all-weather interceptor fighter

Crew: one

Wings: metal cantilever delta mid-wing monoplane

Fuselage: metal semi-monocoque

Tail unit: metal cantilever

Landing gear: hydraulically actuated retractable tricycle unit

Powerplant: one Lyulka AL-7F-1 turbojet, rated at 22,046-lb (10,000-kg) static thrust with afterburning

Fuel capacity:

Avionics: comprehensive communication and navigation/attack equipment

Armament: two AA-3 'Anab' air-to-air missiles

Dimensions: Span about 27 ft 8 in (8.43 m)

Length with probe about 56 ft (17.0 m)

Height about 16 ft (4.88 m)

Wing area: 260 ft² (24 m²)

Weights: Empty about 20,000 lb (9.072 kg)

Loaded about 27,000 lb (12,250 kg)

Maximum about 30,000 lb (13,600 kg)

Performance: (estimated) speed 1,190 mph (1,915 kph) or Mach 1.8 at 36,100 ft (11,000 m); climb 27,000 ft (8,230 m) per minute at sea level; service ceiling 55,700 ft (17,000 m); maximum range 900 miles (1,450 km)

Used only by: USSR

Notes: Stemming from the same basic design as the Su-7, the Su-9 first flew in late 1955 or early 1956, and entered service in 1959. There are several models:

1. Su-9 'Fishpot-A' prototype with a small cone-shaped radome above the air intake

2. Su-9 'Fishpot-B' initial production version with a 19,840-lb (9,000-kg) Lyulka AL-7F engine, small-diameter air intake and intake centrebody, and an armament of four AA-1 'Alkali' air-to-air missiles

3. Su-11 'Fishpot-C', to which the technical specification above applies. This entered service in 1968, and can be distinguished from the 'Fishpot-B' by its twin-missile armament, longer and less tapered nose, larger intake centrebody, and two thin ducts along the centre fuselage top, as on the Su-7B

4. Su-9U 'Maiden' two-seat trainer version of the Su-9.

Sukhoi Su-15 'Flagon'

Type: all-weather interceptor fighter
Crew: one
Wings: metal cantilever mid-wing mono-plane
Fuselage: metal semi-monocoque
Tail unit: metal cantilever
Landing gear: hydraulically actuated retractable tricycle unit
Powerplant: two afterburning turbojets, possibly Tumansky R-13F-300s, each rated at 14,550-lb (6,600-kg) static thrust with afterburning
Fuel capacity: 1,750 gallons (7,955 litres)
Avionics: comprehensive communication and navigation/attack equipment
Armament: two AA-3 'Anab' air-to-air missiles under the wings, plus further missiles or drop tanks on two pylons under the fuselage
Dimensions: Span about 30 ft (9.15 m)
Length about 68 ft (20.5 m)
Height about 19 ft (5.79 m)
Wing area: 385 ft² (35.75 m²)
Weights: Empty about 23,000 lb (10,435 kg)
Loaded about 35,275 lb (16,000 kg)
Maximum 45,000 lb (20,410 kg)

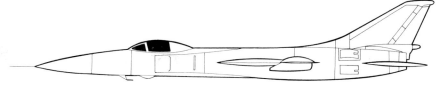

Performance: (estimated) speed 1,650 mph (2,656 kph) or Mach 2.5 in 'clean' condition above 36,100 ft (11,000 m); speed 1,520 mph (2,446 kph) with external stores above 36,100 ft (11,000 m); climb 35,000 ft (10,670 m) per minute at sea level; service ceiling 65,000 ft (19,800 m); combat radius 450 miles (725 km); ferry range 1,400 miles (2,250 km)
Used only by: USSR
Notes: The Su-15 prototype first flew in about 1964, and the type entered service in 1967-1968. There are several models:
1. Su-15 'Flagon-A' initial production version with simple delta wings identical with those of the Su-11. The nose radome is conical. The technical specification above relates to this model, which was built probably in only limited numbers

2. Su-15 'Flagon-B' research STOL version with three lift jets in the fuselage, and wings with compound sweep
3. Su-15 'Flagon-C' two-seat training version of the 'Flagon-D', with limited combat capability
4. Su-15 'Flagon-D' version of the 'Flagon-A' but with wings of compound sweep, spanning 34 ft 6 in (10.53 m). The radome of this first major production version is conical
5. Su-15 'Flagon-E' version of the 'Flagon-D' with updated electronics and more powerful engines to improve performance, to which the specification applies
6. Su-15 'Flagon-F', the latest production version, distinguishable by its ogival nose radome.

Sukhoi Su-17 'Fitter-C' and 'Fitter-D'

Type: variable-geometry fighter
Crew: one
Wings: metal cantilever mid-wing variable-geometry monoplane
Fuselage: metal semi-monocoque
Tail unit: metal cantilever
Landing gear: hydraulically actuated retractable tricycle unit
Powerplant: one Lyulka AL-21F-3 turbojet, rated at 25,000-lb (11,340-kg) static thrust with afterburning
Fuel capacity: 8,157 lb (3,700 kg) internally
Avionics: comprehensive communication and navigation equipment, plus 'High Fix' centrebody interception radar, ASP-5ND fire-control system, and Sirena 3 radar homing and warning system

Armament: two 30-mm NR-30 cannon with 70 rounds per gun, plus a variety of external stores on eight pylons under the fuselage and wings, to a maximum weight of 11,023 lb (5,000 kg)
Dimensions: Span (spread) 45 ft 11¼ in (14.0 m)
Span (swept) 34 ft 9½ in (10.6 m)
Length (minus probe) 50 ft 6¼ in (15.4 m)
Height 15 ft 7 in (4.75 m)
Wing area: (spread) 431.6 ft² (40.1 m²); (swept) 400.4 ft² (37.2 m²)
Weights: Empty about 22,046 lb (10,000 kg)
Loaded about 30,865 lb (14,000 kg)
Maximum about 41,887 lb (19,000 kg)
Performance: (estimated) speed Mach 2.17 at high altitude; speed Mach 1.05 at sea level; climb 45,275 ft (13,800 m) per minute at sea level; service ceiling 59,050

159

ft (18,000 m); combat radius with 4,409 lb (2,000 kg) of external stores 391 miles (630 km) on a hi-lo-hi mission, and 224 miles (360 km) on a lo-lo-lo mission

Used only by: USSR

Notes: The Su-17 is an adaptation of the Su-7 to improve short-field take-off and landing characteristics. The outer 13 ft (4.0 m) of each wing is hinged to allow sweep from 28° to 62°. The basic production model is the 'Fitter-C'. The 'Fitter-D' has a small radome under the nose, and a laser marked target seeker in the intake centrebody.

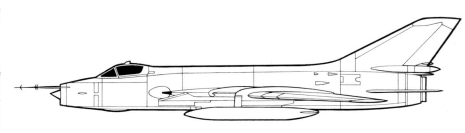

Sukhoi Su-19 'Fencer'

Type: multi-role combat aircraft
Crew: two, seated side-by-side
Wings: metal cantilever variable-geometry shoulder-wing monoplane
Fuselage: metal semi-monocoque
Tail unit: metal cantilever
Landing gear: hydraulically actuated retractable tricycle unit
Powerplant: two turbojets, possibly Lyulka AL-21F-3s, each rated at 25,000-lb (11,340-kg) static thrust with afterburning
Fuel capacity:
Avionics: comprehensive communication and navigation/attack equipment
Armament: one GSh-23 23-mm twin-barrel cannon, and more than 10,000 lb (4,535 kg) of rockets, bombs and guided missiles on six pylons (two under the fuselage, two under the wing-root gloves, and two under the outer wing panels)

Dimensions: Span (spread) about 56 ft 3 in (17.15 m)
Span (swept) about 31 ft 3 in (9.53 m)
Length about 69 ft 10 in (21.29 m)
Height about 21 ft (6.4 m)
Wing area: 430 ft² (39.6 m²)
Weights: Empty about 35,000 lb (15,875 lb) Loaded
Maximum about 68,000 lb (30,850 kg)
Performance: (estimated) speed 1,650 mph (2,655 kph) or Mach 2.5 in 'clean' condition above 36,100 ft (11,000 m); speed 950 mph (1,530 kph) or Mach 1.25 in 'clean' condition at sea level; climb over 40,000 ft (12,200 m) per minute at sea level; service ceiling 60,000 ft (18,290 m);

combat radius on a lo-lo-lo mission over 200 miles (322 km); ferry range over 2,500 miles (4,025 km)

Used only by: USSR

Notes: An advanced variable-geometry ground-attack aircraft similar to the American F-111 family, the Su-19 probably first flew in 1970 and entered service in 1974. Very few details are certain.

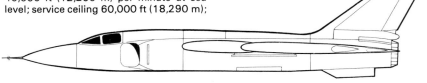

Tupolev Tu-22 'Blinder'

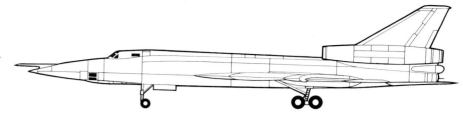

Type: bomber and maritime patrol aircraft
Crew: three
Wings: metal cantilever low mid-wing mono-
plane
Fuselage: metal semi-monocoque
Tail unit: metal cantilever
Landing gear: hydraulically actuated retractable tricycle unit
Powerplant: two turbojets, each rated at
about 27,000-lb (12,250-kg) static thrust
with afterburning
Fuel capacity:
Avionics: comprehensive communication
and navigation/attack equipment, plus reconnaissance gear in maritime versions
Armament: one NR-23 23-mm cannon in a
radar-controlled tail mounting, plus at least
20,000 lb (9,070 kg) of free-fall nuclear or
conventional bombs, or other stores, in the
internal bomb bay, or one AS-4 'Kitchen'
air-to-surface cruise missile semi-recessed
under the fuselage of the 'Blinder-B'
Dimensions: Span about 90 ft 10½ in (27.7
m)
Length about 132 ft 11½ in
(40.53 m)
Height about 17 ft (5.18 m)
Wing area:
Weights: Empty about 85,000 lb (38,600 kg)
Loaded
Maximum about 185,000 lb
(83,900 kg)

Performance: (estimated) speed 920 mph
(1,480 kph) or Mach 1.4 at 40,000 ft
(12,200 m); climb 11,500 ft (3,500 m) per
minute at sea level; service ceiling 60,000
ft (18,300 m); range 1,400 miles (2,250
km)
Used also by: Iraq, Libya
Notes: The Tu-22 was the first operational
Russian supersonic bomber, the prototype
flying in the mid-1950s, and the first production aircraft entering service in 1960.
The Tu-22 is an interesting design, with an
area-ruled fuselage, wings similar to those
of the Tu-28P, engines set on each side of
the fin and rudder, and the main undercarriage legs retracting into fairing behind the
wing trailing edge. There are several versions of the Tu-22:

1. Tu-22 'Blinder-A' medium-range reconnaissance bomber, produced
only in limited numbers because of
its range of only 1,400 miles (2,250
km)
2. Tu-22 'Blinder-B', similar to the
'Blinder-A' but fitted to carry the
460-mile (740-km) range AS-4 'Kitchen' cruise missile. The version also
has a partially retractable flight
refuelling probe
3. Tu-22 'Blinder-C' maritime reconnaissance version for the Soviet
Naval Air Force with cameras in the
bomb bay, and improved radar and
electronics. Electronic countermeasures (ECM) and electronic intelligence (Elint) equipment is probably
carried
4. Tu-22 'Blinder-D' two-seat trainer
5. Tu-22 'Blinder-E' (?), reported to
be a missile-armed long-range interceptor.

Tupolev Tu-26(?) 'Backfire'

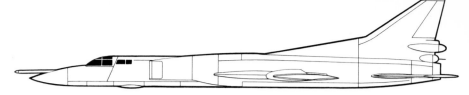

Type: long-range bomber
Crew: probably four
Wings: metal cantilever variable-geometry low mid-wing monoplane
Fuselage: metal semi-monocoque
Tail unit: metal cantilever
Landing gear: hydraulically actuated retractable tricycle unit
Powerplant: two turbofans, possibly military versions of the Kuznetsov NK-144, each rated at 48,501-lb (22,000-kg) static thrust with afterburning
Fuel capacity: fuel tanks take up much of the centre fuselage and fixed inner portions of the wings
Avionics: comprehensive communication and navigation/attack equipment
Armament: the full range of Soviet free-fall nuclear and conventional bombs can be carried internally, and air-to-surface cruise missiles (AS-4 'Kitchen' or AS-6 'Kingfish') can be carried under the fixed glove portion of the wings. The nominal weapon load is 20,800 lb (9,435 kg). There may also be a radar-controlled 23-mm cannon in the tail.

Dimensions: Span (spread) about 113 ft (34.45 m)
Span (swept) about 86 ft (26.21 m)
Length about 132 ft (40.23 m)
Height about 33 ft (10.06 m)
Wing area: 1,785 ft² (165.8 m²)
Weights: Empty about 99,250 lb (45,000 kg)
Loaded
Maximum about 270,000 lb (122,500 kg)
Performance: (estimated) speed between 1,485 mph (2,390 kph) or Mach 2.25 and 1,650 mph (2,655 kph) or Mach 2.5 above 36,100 ft (11,000 m); speed 762+ mph (1,226+ kph) or Mach 1+ at sea level; service ceiling over 60,000 ft (18,300 m); unrefuelled combat radius 3,570 miles (5,745 km)

Used only by: USSR
Notes: Russia's latest supersonic bomber is classified as strategic by the USA, but only tactical by the Russians, its unrefuelled range making it impossible for the 'Backfire' to reach the USA from Russian bases and then return. The prototype flew before 1969, and the first production aircraft entered service in about 1974. There are two versions:
1. Tu-26(?) 'Backfire-A', the original and not very successful initial production variant, with large undercarriage fairings projecting behind the fixed wing-glove trailing edge and causing too much drag
2. Tu-26(?) 'Backfire-B' with redesigned undercarriage retraction system and only vestigial fairings under the wings.

Tupolev Tu-28P 'Fiddler'

Type: long-range all-weather interceptor fighter
Crew: two
Wings: metal cantilever mid-wing monoplane
Fuselage: metal semi-monocoque
Tail unit: metal cantilever
Landing gear: hydraulically actuated retractable tricycle unit
Powerplant: two turbojets of unknown type, each with a probable rating of 27,000-lb (12,250-kg) static thrust with afterburning
Fuel capacity:
Avionics: comprehensive communication and navigation/attack equipment

Armament: two radar-homing and two IR-homing AA-5 'Ash' missiles on pylons under the wings
Dimensions: Span about 65 ft (20.0 m)
Length about 85 ft (26.0 m)
Height about 23 ft (7.0 m)
Wing area:
Weights: Empty about 55,000 lb (25,000 kg)
Loaded
Maximum about 100,000 lb (45,000 kg)
Performance: (estimated) speed 1,150 mph (1,850 kp) or Mach 1.75 at 36,100 ft (11,000 m); climb 25,000 ft (7,500 m) per minute at sea level; service ceiling 65,650 ft (20,000 m); combat radius with internal fuel 900 miles (1,450 km); ferry range 3,100 miles (4,990 km)

Used only by: USSR

Notes: The prototype flew in 1957, and the type entered service in about 1961. The Tu-28P is currently the world's largest fighter. As in other Tupolev designs, the undercarriage main legs retract into large fairings behind the wing trailing edge.

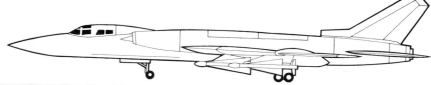

Tupolev Tu-95 'Bear'

Type: long-range bomber and maritime reconnaissance aircraft
Crew: about 10
Wings: metal cantilever mid-wing monoplane
Fuselage: metal semi-monocoque

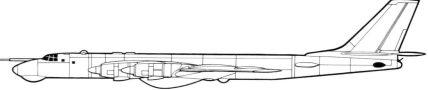

Tail unit: metal cantilever

Landing gear: hydraulically actuated retractable tricycle unit

Powerplant: four Kuznetsov NK-12MV turboprops, each rated at 14,795 ehp and driving a metal eight-blade contra-rotating propeller

Fuel capacity: 16,540 gallons (72,980 litres) in wing tanks

Avionics: comprehensive communication and navigation/attack equipment, including X-band reconnaissance and missile target-acquisition radar in a fairing under the centre fuselage, 'Short Horn' navigation and bombing radar, and 'Bee Hind' tail warning radar

Armament: normally six NR-23 23-mm cannon in manned tail and remotely-controlled dorsal and ventral turrets, plus up to 25,000 lb (11,340 kg) of conventional or nuclear free-fall bombs, and air-to-surface missiles on some versions

Dimensions: Span 159 ft (48.5 m)
Length 155 ft 10 in (47.5 m)
Height 39 ft 9 in (12.12 m)

Wing area:

Weights: Empty about 160,000 lb (72,600 kg)
Loaded
Maximum about 340,000 lb (154,220 kg)

Performance: speed 540 mph (870 kph) in 'clean' condition; service ceiling about 44,000 ft (13,400 m); range with a bomb load of 25,000 lb (11,340 kg) 7,800 miles (12,550 km)

Used only by: USSR

Notes: The prototype of the Tu-95 first flew in 1954, and the type began to enter service in 1956. There are several versions of this huge turboprop-powered aircraft:

1. Tu-95 'Bear-A' strategic bomber for the Soviet Air Force. The technical specification above relates to this model
2. Tu-95 'Bear-B' with an unglazed nose but with additional radar in a large radome under the nose. Used by the Soviet Air Force, the 'Bear-B' at first carried one AS-3 'Kangaroo' air-to-surface missile, but now usually carries an AS-4 'Kitchen'

missile. The type is used mainly for maritime reconnaissance at present, with a large flight refuelling probe

3. Tu-95 'Bear-C', similar to the 'Bear-B' but with a streamlined blister fairing on both (instead of one) sides of the rear fuselage
4. Tu-95 'Bear-D', similar to the 'Bear-C' but with many more electronic systems blisters for the Soviet Naval Air Force. The type has an important role in the acquisition of targets for surface-to-surface and air-to-surface missiles. The avionics details in the technical specification apply to this model
5. Tu-95 'Bear-E' reconnaissance version of the 'Bear-A', with windows in the bomb-bay doors, a refuelling probe above the glazed nose, and the rear fuselage twin blisters of the 'Bear-C'
6. Tu-95 'Bear-F' maritime reconnaissance version with larger aerodynamic fairings behind the inner engine nacelles, and updated electronics.

Tupolev Tu-104 'Camel'

Type: transport aircraft

Crew: four, plus up to 100 passengers

Wings: metal cantilever low-wing monoplane

Fuselage: metal semi-monocoque

Tail unit: metal cantilever

Landing gear: hydraulically actuated retractable tricycle unit

Powerplant: two Mikulin AM-3M-500 turbojets, each rated at 20,945-lb (9,500-kg) static thrust

Fuel capacity: 7,257 gallons (33,150 litres) in seven tank groups in the wings and fuselage

Avionics: comprehensive communication and navigation equipment

Armament: none

Dimensions: Span 113 ft 4 in (34.54 m)
Length 131 ft 5 in (40.06 m)
Height 39 ft 4½ in (12 m)

Wing area: 1,975.2 ft² (183.5 m²)

Weights: Empty 93,696 lb (42,500 kg)
Loaded 167,151 lb (76,000 kg)
Maximum

Performance: speed 590 mph (950 kph) at 32,810 ft (10,000 m); cruising speed 497 mph (800 kph) at 32,810 ft (10,000 m); service ceiling 37,730 ft (11,500 m); range 1,305 miles (2,100 km) with a payload of 26,455 lb (12,000 kg), or 1,926 miles (3,100 km) with a payload of 13,227 lb (6,000 kg)

Used only by: USSR

Notes: The Tu-114 is a high-speed medium-range transport, designed principally for civilian use, but used also for military transport. The maximum payload of the Tu-104B is 26,455 lb (12,000 kg).

Tupolev Tu-126 'Moss'

Type: airborne warning and control system (AWACS) aircraft

Crew:

Wings: metal cantilever low-wing monoplane

Fuselage: metal semi-monocoque

Tail unit: metal cantilever

Landing gear: hydraulically actuated retractable tricycle unit

Powerplant: four Kuznetsov NK-12MV turboprops, each rated at 14,795 ehp and driving a metal eight-blade contra-rotating propeller

Fuel capacity: 16,500 gallons (75,000 litres)

Avionics: comprehensive communication and navigation equipment, plus long-range surveillance radar mounted in a rotating dish, some 36 ft (11 m) in diameter, mounted above the fuselage in front of the fin

Armament: none

Dimensions: Span 167 ft 8 in (51.1 m)
Length 188 ft (57.3 m)
Height 52 ft 8 in (16.05 m)

Wing area: 3,349 ft² (311.1 m²)

Weights: Empty about 198,400 lb (90,000 kg)
Loaded
Maximum about 375,000 lb (170,000 kg)

Performance: (estimated) speed 500 mph (805 kph); operational altitude 40,000 ft (12,200 m); endurance 18 hours; ferry range at least 6,000 miles (9,650 km)

Used only by: USSR

Notes: The Tu-126 AWACS aircraft is derived from the Tu-114 airliner, with a long-range surveillance radar scanner in a saucer-shaped radome above the fuselage. The radar antenna is just under 36 ft (11 m) in diameter. The primary function of the Tu-126 is to operate with advanced fighters cruising at 20,000 ft (6,100 m). The Tu-126 would look for enemy aircraft coming in at low level, and direct the defence fighters to fire their 'snap down' missiles.

Yakovlev Yak-25 'Flashlight'

Type: all-weather fighter
Crew: two, seated in tandem
Wings: metal cantilever shoulder-wing monoplane
Fuselage: metal semi-monocoque
Tail unit: metal cantilever
Landing gear: hydraulically actuated retractable bicycle unit, with stabilising outrigger wheels
Powerplant: two Mikulin AM-9B turbojets, each rated at 5,730-lb (2,600-kg) static thrust
Fuel capacity:
Avionics: comprehensive communication and navigation/attack equipment
Armament: two 37-mm N-37 cannon, plus a ventral pack of 55-mm unguided rockets
Dimensions: Span 36 ft 1 in (11.0 m)
Length 51 ft 4½ in (15.665 m)
Height 15 ft (4.57 m)
Wing area: 311.5 ft² (28.94 m²)
Weights: Empty
Loaded
Maximum more than 19,842 lb (9,000 kg)
Performance: speed in excess of 621 mph (1,000 kph) at 36,090 ft (11,000 m); service ceiling 50,030 ft (15,250 m); range 1,865 miles (3,000 km) with auxiliary tanks
Used only by: USSR
Notes: The Yak-25 first flew in 1952, and entered service as an all-weather interceptor fighter powered by two Mikulin AM-5 turbojets, each rated at 6,710-lb (3,150-kg) with afterburning. These were soon replaced by the more powerful AM-9B engines. There are four variants of the basic aircraft:

1. Yak-25 'Flashlight-A' all-weather interceptor fighter, with two 37-mm cannon but no afterburning. The technical specification applies to this model
2. Yak-25 'Flashlight-B' tactical strike and reconnaissance aircraft, with a glazed and pointed nose, a ventral radome, and extended engine fairings to accommodate afterburning. This was the prototype of the Yak-28
3. Yak-25 'Flashlight-C' two-seat all-weather interceptor version of the 'Flashlight-B', with a solid nose and the armament of the 'Flashlight-A', which had been omitted from the 'Flashlight-B'. This is now known to be the Yak-27P
4. Yak-25 'Flashlight-D' tactical reconnaissance aircraft, with a single 30-mm cannon. This is now known to be the Yak-26.

Yakovlev Yak-28 'Brewer' and 'Firebar'

Type: attack, interceptor and reconnaissance aircraft
Crew: two, seated in tandem
Wings: metal cantilever shoulder-wing monoplane
Fuselage: metal semi-monocoque
Tail unit: metal cantilever
Landing gear: hydraulically actuated retractable bicycle unit, with wingtip stabilising outriggers
Powerplant: two turbojets, probably Tumansky R-11s, each rated at 13,120-lb (5,950-kg) static thrust with afterburning
Fuel capacity:

Yakovlev Yak-26 'Mandrake' and 'Mangrove'

Type: reconnaissance aircraft
Crew: two, seated in tandem
Wings: metal cantilever shoulder-wing monoplane
Fuselage: metal semi-monocoque
Tail unit: metal cantilever
Landing gear: hydraulically actuated retractable bicycle unit, with stabilising outrigger wheels
Powerplant: two Tumansky RD-9 turbojets, each rated at 8,820-lb (4,000-kg) static thrust with afterburning
Fuel capacity:
Avionics: comprehensive communication and navigation equipment, plus specialist reconnaissance equipment
Armament: one 30-mm NR-30 cannon
Dimensions: Span 38 ft 6 in (11.75 m)
Length 62 ft (18.9 m)
Height 14 ft 6 in (4.4 m)
Wing area:
Weights: Empty about 18,000 lb (8,165 kg)
Loaded
Maximum about 26,000 lb (11,800 kg)
Performance: speed 686 mph (1,104 kph) at high altitude; climb about 15,000 ft (4,600 m) per minute at sea level; service ceiling 49,200 ft (15,000 m); range about 1,675 miles (2,700 km) at high altitude
Used only by: USSR
Notes: The Yak-26 was at first known as the Yak-25 'Flashlight-D', and has a glazed nose, and wings extending out from the outrigger wheel housings. There seems to be another aircraft, derived from the same basic airframe, and known in the west only as 'Mandrake'. This is a high altitude reconnaissance aircraft, with straight wings spanning about 71 ft (22.0 m), engines rating only about 6,000-lb (2,720-kg) static thrust, a ceiling of 62,000 ft (19,000 m), and a range of about 2,500 miles (4,000 km).

Yakovlev Yak-27P 'Mangrove'

Type: interceptor fighter
Crew: two, seated in tandem
Wings: metal cantilever shoulder-wing monoplane
Fuselage: metal semi-monocoque
Tail unit: metal cantilever
Landing gear: hydraulically actuated retractable bicycle unit, with stabilising outrigger wheels
Powerplant: two Tumansky RD-9B turbojets, each rated at 8,820-lb (4,000-kg) static thrust with afterburning
Fuel capacity:
Avionics: comprehensive communication and navigation/interception equipment
Armament: two types, one with cannon and unguided rockets, the other with two air-to-air missiles on underwing pylons
Dimensions: Span 38 ft 6 in (11.75 m)
Length about 55 ft (16.75 m)
Height 14 ft 6 in (4.4 m)
Wing area:
Weights: Empty about 18,000 lb (8,165 kg)
Loaded
Maximum about 24,000 lb (10,900 kg)
Performance: speed 686 mph (1,104 kph) or Mach 0.95 at high altitude; climb about 15,000 ft (4.600 m) per minute at sea level; service ceiling 49,200 ft (15,000 m); range 1,000 miles (1,600 km) at high altitude
Used only by: USSR
Notes: The Yak-27P was at first known as the Yak-25 'Flashlight-C'.

Avionics: comprehensive communication and navigation/attack equipment, plus reconnaissance gear in some aircraft
Armament: (attack versions) one NR-30 30-mm cannon, up to 4,409 lb (2,000 kg) of bombs in an internal weapons bay, and rocket pods on two underwing pylons
Armament: (interceptor) two AA-3 'Anab' air-to-air missiles and, optionally, two K-13A (AA-2) 'Atoll' air-to-air missiles
Dimensions: Span about 42 ft 6 in (12.95 m)
Length (Yak-28) about 70 ft 0½ in (21.65 m)
Height about 12 ft 11½ in (3.95 m)
Wing area:
Weights: Empty about 24,250 lb (11,000 kg)
Loaded
Maximum about 35,000–41,000 lb (15,875–18,600 kg)
Performance: (estimated) speed 733 mph (1,180 kph) or Mach 1.1 at 35,000 ft (10,670 m); cruising speed 571 mph (920 kph); climb 27,900 ft (8,500 m) per minute at sea level; service ceiling 55,000 ft (16,750 m); combat radius 575 miles (925 km); ferry range 1,600 miles (2,575 km)

Used only by: USSR
Notes: The prototype of the Yak-28 flew before 1961, and the type was in service by the middle of 1962. There are several versions of the basic aircraft:

1. Yak-28 'Brewer-A, B and C', initial production attack versions, with glazed noses and short engine intakes on some examples
2. Yak-28 'Brewer-D' reconnaissance version with cameras in the bomb bay
3. Yak-28 'Brewer-E' ECM escort aircraft
4. Yak-28P 'Firebar' two-seat interceptor, with the bomb bay deleted, and the glazed nose replaced by a dielectric radome housing the scanner for the 'Skip Spin' radar, and increasing length to about 74 ft (22.56 m)
5. Yak-28U 'Maestro' trainer version of the 'Firebar', with two separate cockpits.

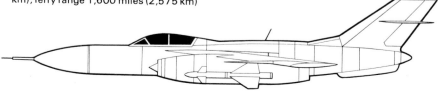

Yakovlev Yak-36 'Forger'

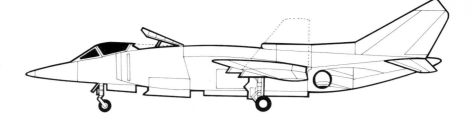

Type: V/STOL attack and reconnaissance aircraft

Crew: one

Wings: metal cantilever mid-wing monoplane

Fuselage: metal semi-monocoque

Tail unit: metal cantilever

Landing gear: hydraulically actuated retractable tricycle unit

Powerplant: one vectored-thrust main turbojet, rated at about 17,031-lb (7,725-kg) static thrust, and two auxiliary lift jets, each rated at about 5,600-lb (2,540-kg) static thrust

Fuel capacity: 640 gallons (2,900 litres)

Avionics: comprehensive communication and navigation/attack equipment

Armament: a wide variety of stores can be carried on four underwing pylons

Dimensions: Span about 23 ft (7.0 m)
Length about 49 ft 3 in (15.0 m)
Height 13 ft 3 in (4.0 m)

Wing area: 170 ft² (15.8 m²)

Weights: Empty about 12,000 lb (5,450 kg)
Loaded
Maximum about 22,046 lb (10,000 kg)

Performance: (estimated) speed about 859 mph (1,382 kph) or Mach 1.3 at above 36,100 ft (11,000 m)

Used only by: USSR

Notes: Designed for operation from the Soviet Navy's new aircraft-carriers, the Yak-36 appears to have been developed from the Yakovlev 'Freehand' experimental VTOL type, which featured a mixture of vectored-thrust and direct-lift engines. The Yak-36 has so far been seen in two forms:

1. Yak-36 'Forger-A' combat aircraft, to which the technical specification above applies

2. Yak-36 'Forger-B' two-seat trainer, which has an extra cockpit and a counterbalancing rear fuselage extension, increasing overall length to about 58 ft (17.66 m).

166

AA-1 'Alkali'

Type: air-to-air tactical guided missile
Guidance: semi-active radar homing
Dimensions: Span 22¾ in (58.0 cm)
　　　　　　　Body diameter 7 in (17.8 cm)
　　　　　　　Length 6 ft 2 in (1.88 m)
Booster: solid-propellant rocket
Sustainer: none
Warhead: high explosive
Weights: Launch about 198 lb (90 kg)
　　　　　　Burnt out
Performance: speed between Mach 1 and 2;
　　range from 3¾ to 5 miles (6 to 8 km)
Used by: same nations that use Su-9 and all-
　　weather versions of the MiG-19
Notes: Used on the Sukhoi Su-9, Mikoyan-
　　Gurevich MiG-17, and Mikoyan-Gurevich
　　MiG-19 fighters, with the target illumi-
　　nated by 'Spin Scan' and 'Scan Odd' radars.

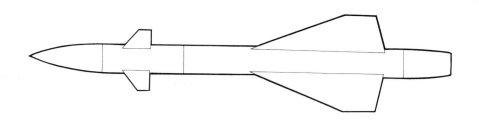

AA-2 'Atoll' (or K-13A)

Type: air-to-air tactical guided missile
Guidance: infra-red homing in 'Atoll', or
　　semi-active radar homing in 'Advanced
　　Atoll'
Dimensions: Span 20¾ in (53.0 cm)
　　　　　　　Body diameter 4¾ in (12.0 cm)
　　　　　　　Length 9 ft 2 in (2.8 m)
Booster: solid-propellant rocket
Sustainer: none
Warhead: high explosive
Weights: Launch 154 lb (70 kg)
　　　　　　Burnt out
Performance: speed Mach 2+; range be-
　　　　　　tween 3 and 4 miles (5 and 6.5
　　　　　　km)
Used also by: Afghanistan, Algeria, Angola,
　　Bangladesh, Bulgaria, Cuba, Czecho-
　　slovakia, East Germany, Egypt, Finland,
　　Hungary, India, Iraq, Laos, Libya, Mozam-
　　bique, North Korea, North Yemen, Poland,
　　Romania, Somali Republic, South Yemen,
　　Sudan, Syria, Uganda, Vietnam, Yugoslavia
Notes: There are two versions of the AA-2,
　　the infra-red 'Atoll' and the semi-active
　　radar 'Advanced Atoll'. The design, size and
　　performance of the AA-2 is very similar to
　　that of the AIM-9B Sidewinder.

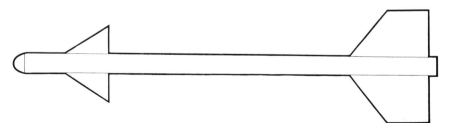

AA-3 'Anab'

Type: air-to-air tactical guided missile
Guidance: infra-red or semi-active radar homing
Dimensions: Span 4 ft 3 in (1.3 m)
    Body diameter 11 in (28.0 cm)
    Length (IR version) 13 ft 5 in (4.1 m); (radar version) 13 ft 1 in (4.0 m)
Booster: solid-propellant rocket
Sustainer: none
Warhead: high explosive
Weights: Launch 606 lb (275 kg)
    Burnt out
Performance: range between 5 and 6 miles (8 and 10 km)
Used only by: USSR
Notes: The AA-3 is a standard air-to-air missile for the forces of the Warsaw Pact, and is used in conjunction with 'Skip Spin' radar.

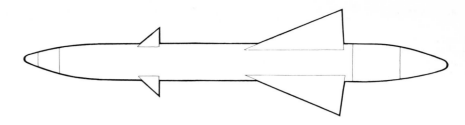

AA-5 'Ash'

Type: air-to-air tactical guided missile
Guidance: infra-red or semi-active radar homing
Dimensions: Span about 4 ft 3 in (1.3 m)
    Body diameter 11 in (28.0 cm)
    Length (IR version) 18 ft (5.5 m); (radar version) 17 ft (5.2 m)
Booster: solid-propellant
Sustainer: none
Warhead: high explosive
Weights: Launch about 441 lb (200 kg)
    Burnt out
Performance: range perhaps $18\frac{1}{2}$ miles (30 km)
Used only by: USSR
Notes: Used on the Tupolev Tu-28P and possibly on the Mikoyan-Gurevich MiG-25, the AA-5 is used in conjunction with 'Big Nose' radar.

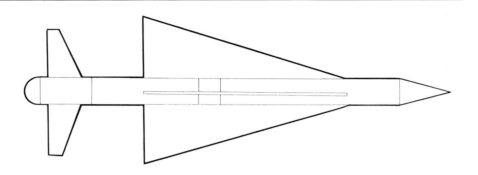

AA-6 'Acrid'

Type: air-to-air tactical guided missile
Guidance: infra-red or semi-active radar homing
Dimensions: Span 7 ft $4\frac{3}{8}$ in (2.25 m)
    Body diameter $15\frac{3}{4}$ in (40.0 cm)
    Length (IR version) 19 ft (5.8 m); (radar version) 20 ft (6.1 m)
Booster: solid-propellant rocket
Sustainer: none
Warhead: about 220 lb (100 kg) high explosive
Weights: Launch (IR version) 1,433 lb (550 kg); (radar version) 1,874 lb (750 kg)
    Burnt out
Performance: speed Mach 2.2; range 23 miles (37 km)
Used only by: USSR
Notes: The AA-6 is basically a scaled up AA-3, and is associated with the Mikoyan-Gurevich MiG-25's 'Fox Fire' radar. The wingtip fairings of the 'Foxbat-A' version of the MiG-25 are believed to contain continuous-wave illuminating radar for the semi-active homing head of the two AA-6s usually carried on the outboard pylons.

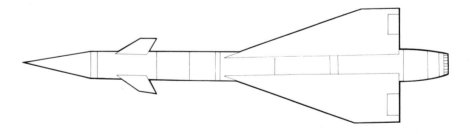

AA-7 'Apex'

Type: air-to-air tactical guided missile
Guidance: infra-red or semi-active radar homing
Dimensions: Span about 3 ft 5½ in (1.05 m)
Body diameter about 9⅝ in (24.0 cm)
Length (radar version) about 14 ft 1¼ in (4.3 m)
Booster: solid-propellant rocket
Sustainer: none
Warhead: high explosive, up to 88 lb (40 kg) in weight
Weights: Launch up to 772 lb (350 kg)
Burnt out
Performance: range (IR version) about 9⅓ miles (15 km); range (radar version) about 18⅔ miles (30 km)
Used only by: USSR

Notes: The AA-7 has similarities to the AA-3, but is clearly a more advanced missile, its manoeuvrability attested by the multiple control surfaces. The infra-red homing version is slightly shorter than the semi-active radar homing model. The AA-7 is used on the Mikoyan-Gurevich MiG-21 and 23. The associated fire-control radar is 'High Lark' on the MiG-23.

AA-8 'Aphid'

Type: air-to-air tactical guided missile
Guidance: infra-red or (perhaps) semi-active radar homing
Dimensions: Span
Body diameter about 5⅒ in (13.0 cm)
Length about 6 ft 6¾ in (2.0 m)
Booster: solid-propellant rocket
Sustainer: none
Warhead: 13¼ lb (6 kg) high explosive
Weights: Launch 121 lb (55 kg)
Burnt out
Performance: range between 3½ and 5 miles (5.5 and 8 km)
Used only by: USSR
Notes: Probably derived from the AA-2, the AA-8 is a short-range dogfighting missile, with good acceleration and manoeuvrability.

ABM-1 'Galosh'

Type: anti-ballistic missile missile
Guidance: radar command
Dimensions: Body diameter 8 ft 10³⁄₁₀ in (2.75 m) approximately
Length 65 ft 7⅝ in (20.0 m) approximately
Booster: solid-propellant rocket
Sustainer: solid-propellant rocket (in presumed 2nd and possible 3rd stages)

Warhead: nuclear, 2–3 megatons, and suitable for operation outside the atmosphere
Weights: Launch 72,000 lb (32,660 kg)
Burnt out
Performance: slant range 186+ miles (300+ km)
Used only by: USSR
Notes: In service at four sites (64 launchers) round Moscow. Thought to be inferior to the US Spartan ABM. It has been seen in 'detail' only in a closed, ribbed container, so dimensions and other data must be treated with caution.

AS-1 'Kennel'

Type: air-to-surface tactical anti-shipping guided missile

Guidance: beam-riding or radio command are the two most likely guidance methods, plus active or passive radar terminal homing

Dimensions: Span about 15 ft 9 in (4.8 m)
Body diameter
Length about 27 ft 8¼ in (8.44 m)

Booster: none

Sustainer: turbojet

Warhead: about 1,984-lb (900-kg) high explosive

Weights: Launch about 6,614 lb (3,000 kg)
Burnt out about 5,511 lb (2,500 kg)

Performance: speed about Mach 0.9; range about 93 miles (150 km) with a high flight profile, or 56 miles (90 km) with a low flight profile

Used also by: Egypt

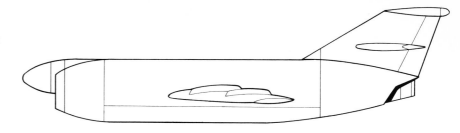

Notes: Usually carried in pairs below the wings of the Tu-16, the AS-1 is assumed to be the maritime version of the SSC-2B 'Samlet' coast defence missile. It was first seen in 1961 and entered service in 1963.

AS-2 'Kipper'

Type: air-to-surface tactical anti-shipping guided missile

Guidance: radio command, with infra-red terminal homing

Dimensions: Span about 15 ft 1 in (4.6 m)
Body diameter about 35⅜ in (90.0 cm)
Length about 30 ft 10 in (9.4 m)

Booster: none

Sustainer: probably turbojet

Warhead: high explosive or nuclear

Weights: Launch about 13,228+ lb (6,000+ kg)
Burnt out about 10,362 lb (4,700 kg)

Performance: speed Mach 1.2; range up to 130 miles (210 km)

Used only by: USSR

Notes: The AS-2 missile is carried by the Tupolev Tu-16 'Badger-C' bomber. It was first seen in 1961 and entered service in 1965.

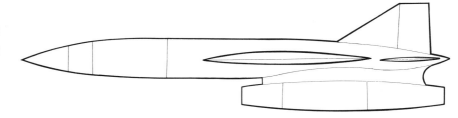

AS-3 'Kangaroo'

Type: air-to-surface strategic guided missile

Guidance: probably autopilot, with mid-course radio command corrections

Dimensions: Span about 30 ft (9.15 m)
Body diameter about 6 ft 1 in (1.85 m)
Length about 49 ft (14.96 m)

Booster: none

Sustainer: probably turbojet

Warhead: probably thermonuclear, or at least 5,071-lb (2,300-kg) high explosive

Weights: Launch about 24,250 lb (11,000 kg)
Burnt out about 16,094 lb (7,300 kg)

Performance: speed Mach 2; range estimates vary between 115 miles (185 km) and 404 miles (650 km), but in the absence of any information on the fuel/weapon ratio, it is impossible to be more precise

Used only by: USSR

Notes: The AS-3 is the largest Russian air-to-surface missile, and is carried by the Tupolev Tu-95 bomber. The primary objective of the missile is probably area targets such as cities. It was first seen in 1961 and entered service in 1963.

AS-4 'Kitchen'

Type: air-to-surface strategic guided missile
Guidance: probably inertial, plus mid-course radio command corrections and IR terminal homing
Dimensions: Span about 7 ft 10½ in (2.4 m)
Body diameter about 35⅝ in (90.0 cm)
Length about 37 ft (11.3 m)
Booster: none
Sustainer: probably liquid-propellant rocket
Warhead: thermonuclear or high explosive, about 2,204 lb (1,000 kg)
Weights: Launch 13,228+ lb (6,000+ kg)
Burnt out about 7,496 lb (3,400 kg)
Performance: speed Mach 2.5; range about 185 miles (298 km) at low level, or 447 miles (720 km) with a high flight profile
Used only by: USSR
Notes: The AS-4 is carried semi-recessed under the fuselage of the Tupolev Tu-22 'Blinder', and under the wings of the Tu-95 'Bear' and Tu-26 'Backfire'. The Tu-95 'Bear-B' is probably used for mid-course corrections for this advanced high-speed missile. The AS-4 was first seen in 1961 and entered service in 1967.

AS-5 'Kelt'

Type: air-to-surface tactical and anti-shipping missile
Guidance: autopilot, plus active or passive radar homing
Dimensions: Span about 15 ft (4.57 m), though some reports suggest 14 ft 1¼ in (4.3 m)
Body diameter about 35 in (90.0 cm)
Length about 31 ft (9.45 m), though some reports suggest 28 ft 2⅝ in (8.59 m)
Booster: none
Sustainer: liquid-propellant rocket
Warhead: high explosive, about 2,204 lb (1,000 kg)
Weights: Launch about 10,580 lb (4,800 kg)
Burnt out about 8,157 lb (3,700 kg)
Performance: speed Mach 0.95; range 199 miles (320 km) with a high mission profile, or 100 miles (160 km) with a low mission profile
Used also by: Egypt
Notes: The AS-5 bears a strong similarity to the AS-1 'Kennel' in its configuration, but has a solid nose and rocket propulsion. The AS-5 is carried under the wing of a Tupolev Tu-16. The nose section of the missile appears identical with that of the SS-N-2 'Styx', which may mean that the 'Kelt' has a similar anti-shipping guidance and capability. The AS-5 entered service in 1966.

AS-6 'Kingfish'

Type: air-to-surface strategic guided missile
Guidance: inertial, plus active radar homing
Dimensions: Span about 10 ft 6 in (3.2 m)
Body diameter about 35⅝ in (90.0 cm)
Length about 29 ft 6⅓ in (9.0 m)
Booster: none
Sustainer: probably liquid-propellant rocket
Warhead: thermonuclear or high explosive, weighing about 992 lb (450 kg)
Weights: Launch about 10,580 lb (4,800 kg)
Burnt out about 6,393 lb (2,900 kg)
Performance: speed about Mach 2.5; range about 497 miles (800 km) at high altitude, and about 135+ miles (220+ km) at low altitude
Used only by: USSR
Notes: Very little is known of this advanced cruise missile, carried by the Tupolev Tu-26 'Backfire'. The guidance combination would appear to be very accurate, and the AS-6 may also be used as an anti-shipping weapon. It was first seen in 1975 and entered service during 1976.

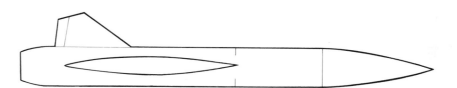

AS-7 'Kerry'

Type: air-to-surface tactical guided missile
Guidance: probably radio command, with possibly an anti-radiation homing head
Dimensions: Span
                Body diameter
                Length
Booster:
Sustainer:
Warhead: high explosive
Weights: Launch about 2,650 lb (1,200 kg)
            Burnt out
Performance: range about $6\frac{1}{4}$ miles (10 km)
Used only by: USSR
Notes: Virtually nothing is known of this tactical missile, believed to be carried by the Sukhoi Su-7, Su-17, and Su-19.

AS-8

Type: air-to-surface tactical guided missile
Guidance: possible laser-seeking
Dimensions: Span
                Body diameter
                Length
Booster: probably solid-propellant rocket
Sustainer: none
Warhead: high explosive
Weights: Launch
            Burnt out
Performance: range about 5 miles (8 km)
Used only by: USSR
Notes: Virtually nothing is known of this tactical missile, which forms the primary armament of the Mil Mi-24 'Hind-A' and 'Hind-C' helicopters.

AS-X-9

Type: air-to-surface tactical guided missile
Guidance: anti-radiation homing
Dimensions: Span
                Body diameter
                Length
Booster: probably solid-propellant rocket
Sustainer:
Warhead: high explosive
Weights: Launch
            Burnt out
Performance: range up to 48 miles (90 km)
Used only by: USSR
Notes: Virtually nothing is known of this anti-radiation missile which is carried by the Sukhoi Su-19.

SA-5 'Gammon'

Type: long-range air defence missile
Guidance: radio command, with semi-active radar homing
Dimensions: Span 11 ft $11\frac{3}{4}$ in (3.65 m)
            Body diameter (booster) 3 ft $3\frac{2}{5}$ in (1.0 m); (2nd stage) 2 ft $7\frac{1}{2}$ in (0.8 m)
            Length 54 ft $1\frac{3}{8}$ in (16.5 m)
Booster: solid-propellant rocket
Sustainer: solid-propellant rocket (it has been suggested that there is a solid-propellant rocket in the warhead, making this a 3rd stage)
Warhead: high explosive or nuclear
Weights: Launch 22,046 lb (10,000 kg) approximately
            Burnt out
Performance: range 155 miles (250 km) approximately; ceiling 95,143 ft (29,000 m) approximately; slant range 100+ miles (160+ km)
Used only by: USSR
Notes: Introduced in 1967, and Russia's main high-altitude air defence missile, it is deployed in some numbers for protection of important sites and cities. Performance is generally thought to be inferior to that of the US Nike Zeus, and although a limited ABM role is claimed for the SA-5, the fact that it is manoeuvred aerodynamically means that this capability must be very small.

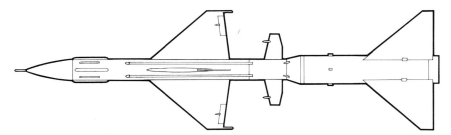

SS-4 'Sandal'

Type: medium-range ballistic missile, trailer-launched, single stage
Guidance: inertial (earlier models had radio guidance)
Dimensions: Body diameter 5 ft 3 in (1.6 m) approximately
            Length 68 ft $10\frac{3}{4}$ in (21.0 m) approximately
Booster: none
Sustainer: liquid-propellant rocket (nitric acid/kerosene fuel)
Warhead: high explosive or nuclear, 1 megaton
Weights: Launch 26.57 tons (27 tonnes) approximately
            Burnt out
Performance: speed at burn-out Mach 6-7; range 1,118 miles (1,800 km); throw-weight 1,000 lb (454 kg); CEP 1.2 miles (1.93 km)
Used only by: USSR

Notes: A development of the SS-3 'Shyster', itself a development of the wartime V2, the SS-4 was introduced in 1959, and is now most widely deployed in the Central Asian Military District, targeted on Chinese objectives.

SS-5 'Skean'

Type: intermediate-range ballistic missile, silo-launched, single stage
Guidance: probably inertial
Dimensions: Body diameter 8 ft 0 in (2.44 m) approximately
            Length 82 ft 0 in (25.0 m) approximately
Booster: none
Sustainer: probably two RD-216 liquid-propellant rockets
Warhead: nuclear, 1 megaton
Weights: Launch
            Burnt out
Performance: 2,175 miles (3,500 km); throw-weight 1,000 lb (454 kg); CEP 1.75 miles (2.78 km)
Used only by: USSR
Notes: Introduced in 1961. There are only about 100 deployed in IRBM fields.

SS-9 'Scarp'

Type: intercontinental ballistic missile, silo-launched, three stages
Guidance: inertial
Dimensions: Diameter 9 ft 10$\frac{1}{10}$in (3.0 m) maximum
Length 114 ft 9$\frac{4}{5}$ in (35.0 m) approximately
Booster: liquid-propellant rocket
Sustainer: liquid-propellant rockets (2nd and 3rd stages)

Warhead: Model 1 nuclear, 20–25 megatons
Model 2 nuclear, 18 megatons
Model 3 nuclear, either FOBS or depressed trajectory delivery
Model 4 nuclear, 3×5-megaton MRVs
Weights: Launch
Burnt out

Performance: range 7,450 miles (12,000 km) for Models 1 and 2; range unlimited for Model 3 in FOBS role; 4,660 miles (7,500 km) for Model 4; throw-weight 12–15,000 lb (5,443–6,804 kg); CEP 0.6 mile (0.97 km)
Used only by: USSR
Notes: Introduced in 1965 (Models 1 and 2). It is uncertain if the Models 3 and 4 are operational.

SS-11 'Sego'

Type: intercontinental ballistic missile, silo-launched, two stages
Guidance: inertial
Dimensions: Base diameter 8 ft 2$\frac{2}{5}$ in (2.5 m) approximately
Length 65 ft 7$\frac{2}{5}$ in (20.0 m) approximately
Booster: liquid-propellant rocket

Sustainer: liquid-propellant rocket
Warhead: Model 1 nuclear, 1–2 megatons
Model 2 nuclear, 1–2 megatons, with penetration aids
Model 3 nuclear, 3 × 100/300-kiloton MRVs
Weights: Launch
Burnt out
Performance: range 6,525 miles (10,000 km); throw-weight 1,500 lb (680 kg) for

Models 1 and 2; throw-weight 2,000 lb (907 kg) for Model 3; CEP 0.6 mile (0.97 km) for Models 1 and 2; CEP 0.5 mile (0.8 km) for Model 3
Used only by: USSR
Notes: Models 1 and 2 introduced in 1966, Model 3 in 1973. The SS-11 'Sego' is the most widely deployed Russian ICBM.

SS-13 'Savage'

Type: intercontinental ballistic missile, silo-launched, three stages
Guidance: presumed inertial
Dimensions: Body diameter 5 ft 6$\frac{4}{5}$ in (1.7 m) approximately
Length 65 ft 7$\frac{2}{5}$ in (20.0 m) approximately
Booster: solid-propellant rocket
Sustainer: solid-propellant rockets (2nd and 3rd stages)
Warhead: nuclear, 1 megaton
Weights: Launch
Burnt out
Performance: range 5,000–6,200 miles (8–10,000 km); throw-weight 1,000 lb (454 kg); CEP 0.8 mile (1.3 km)
Used only by: USSR
Notes: Russian equivalent to the US Minuteman. Introduced in 1968. It has 3-stage structure, the stages separated by unfaired trusses. The top two stages may be in service in a mobile role.

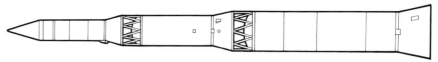

SS-14 'Scapegoat'

Type: intermediate-range ballistic missile, ground-launched after erection from a trailer, two stages
Guidance: presumed inertial
Dimensions: Body diameter 4 ft 7$\frac{1}{10}$ in (1.4 m)
Length 34 ft 9$\frac{3}{10}$ in (10.6 m)
Booster: solid-propellant rocket
Sustainer: solid-propellant rocket
Warhead: nuclear, up to 1 megaton
Weights: Launch
Burnt out

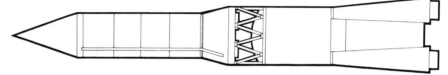

Performance: range 2,485 miles (4,000 km); CEP 1.25 miles (2.0 km)
Used only by: USSR
Notes: Upper two stages of the SS-13 'Savage' ICBM, part of the 'Scamp' weapon system. Introduced in 1968. To launch, the 'iron maiden' housing on the tracked carrier is elevated, this lowering the braced structure at the rear onto the ground; the 'iron maiden' is then opened, lowered and then closed, leaving the missile on the braced platform for firing.

SS-X-16

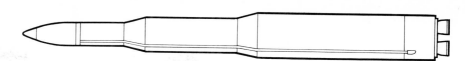

Type: intercontinental ballistic missile, silo- or mobile-launched, three stages
Guidance: inertial
Dimensions: Body diameter 6 ft 6¾ in (2.0 m) approximately
Length 65 ft 7⅖ in (20.0 m) approximately
Booster: solid-propellant rocket
Sustainer: solid-propellant rocket (2nd and 3rd stages)
Warhead: nuclear, single RV possibly exceeding 1 megaton; MIRV is believed possible with the use of a post-boost vehicle
Weights: Launch
Burnt out
Performance: range 5,000+ miles (8,000+ km); throw-weight 2,000 lb (907 kg); CEP 0.33 mile (0.54 km)
Used by: under final development for the Russian Strategic Rocket Forces
Notes: 2nd-generation 'light' ICBM, about to be deployed. MIRV capability is present, but may not be implemented as a result of SALT limitations. The top two stages are used for the SS-X-20 IRBM.

SS-17

Type: intercontinental ballistic missile, cold-launched from a silo, two stages
Guidance: inertial, with computer-controlled re-entry vehicle
Dimensions: Base diameter 8 ft 2⅖ in (2.5 m) approximately
Length 78 ft 8 9/10 in (24.0 m) approximately
Booster: liquid-propellant rocket
Sustainer: liquid-propellant rocket
Warhead: Model 1 nuclear, MIRV system with 4×900-kiloton warheads
Model 2 nuclear, single 5-megaton RV (?)
Weights: Launch
Burnt out
Performance: range 6,200+ miles (10,000+ km); throw-weight 6,000 lb (2,721 kg); CEP 0.33 mile (0.54 km)
Used only by: USSR
Notes: Replacement, with SS-19, for the SS-11. Introduced in 1975. Deployed in modernised SS-11 silos.

SS–X–Z 'Scrooge'

Type: mobile strategic weapon system, tube-launched, two or three stages
Guidance: presumed inertial
Dimensions: Tube diameter 6 ft 6¾ in (2.0 m) approximately
Tube length 65 ft 7⅖ in (20.0 m) approximately
Booster: solid-propellant rocket
Sustainer: solid-propellant rocket in the presumed 2nd and possible 3rd stages
Warhead: nuclear, possibly 1 megaton
Weights: Launch
Burnt out
Performance: range 3,110 miles (5,000 km) minimum
Used only by: USSR
Notes: Introduced in 1977. The missile, possibly an SS-13 derivative, is launched from the tube, which is raised to a vertical position for firing. Details are 'guesstimates'.

'Swatter'

Type: air-to-surface tactical guided missile
Guidance: radio command to line-of-sight, plus possible terminal homing
Dimensions: Span 26 in (65.0 cm)
Body diameter 5 9/10 in (15.0 cm)
Length 35½ in (90.0 cm)
Booster: solid-propellant rocket
Sustainer: none
Warhead: armour-piercing high explosive
Weights: Launch 58 lb (26.5 kg)
Burnt out
Performance: speed 335 mph (540 kph); range from 328 to 2,406 yards (300 to 2,200 m)
Used only by: USSR
Notes: The Mil Mi-24 attack helicopter has rails for air-to-surface missiles, though no missiles have yet been revealed on these in photographs seen in the west. Pending the development of the AS-8 missile, therefore, it seems likely that a derivative of the AT-2 'Swatter' anti-tank missile is probably used, as there appear to be no provisions for launching a wire-guided missile, and the AT-2 is the only radio command tactical missile operated by the Russians.

SS-18

Type: intercontinental ballistic missile, cold-launched from a silo, two stages
Guidance: inertial, with computer-controlled re-entry vehicle
Dimensions: Span
Base diameter 9 ft 10 1/10 in (3.0 m) approximately
Length 78 ft 8 1/10 in (24.0 m) approximately
Booster: liquid-propellant rocket
Sustainer: liquid-propellant rocket
Warhead: Model 1 nuclear, 18–25 megatons
Model 2 nuclear, 8×2+ megaton MIRV
Model 3 nuclear, 10–15 megatons (?)
Weights: Launch
Burnt out

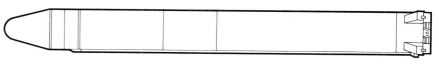

Performance: range 6,525 miles (10,500 km) for Models 1 and 3; range 5,750 miles (9,250 km) for Model 2; throw-weight 16–20,000 lb (7,258–9,072 kg); CEP 0.4 mile (0.64 km) for Models 1 and 2; CEP 0.33 mile (0.48 km) for Model 3
Used only by: USSR
Notes: Introduced in 1974, in modernised SS-9 silos. Most deployed SS-18s are thought to be Model 1s.

SS-19

Type: intercontinental ballistic missile, silo-launched, two stages

Guidance: inertial, with computer-controlled re-entry vehicle

Dimensions: Base diameter 9 ft 0 in (2.75 m) approximately
Length 82 ft 0 in (25.0 m) approximately

Booster: liquid-propellant rocket

Sustainer: liquid-propellant rocket

Warhead: Model 1 nuclear, 6 × 400/500-kiloton MIRV (other estimates claim 6 × 1/2-megaton) megaton MIRV
Model 2 nuclear, 5+ megaton

Weights: Launch
Burnt out

Performance: range 6,990+ miles (11,250+ km) for Model 1; range 6,200+ miles (10,000+ km) for Model 2; throw-weight 7,000 lb (3,175 kg); CEP 0.4 mile (0.64 km) for Model 1; CEP 0.33 mile (0.46 km) for Model 2

Used only by: USSR

Notes: Introduced in 1974 to replace the SS-11, whose silos are re-used after modernisation. Only the Model 1 is known to have entered service.

SS–X–20

Type: intermediate-range ballistic missile, mobile-launched, two stages

Guidance: inertial

Dimensions: Body diameter 6 ft 6¾ in (2.0 m) approximately
Length 55 ft 1⅝ in (16.8 m) approximately

Booster: solid-propellant rocket

Sustainer: solid-propellant rocket

Warhead: nuclear, 3×150+ kiloton MIRV or single RV

Weights: Launch
Burnt out

Performance: range 3,480 miles (5,600 km) with MIRV; range 4,600 miles (7,400 km) with single RV

Used by: under final development for the Russian Strategic Rocket Forces

Notes: Replacement for the SS-4 and SS-5, using the first two stages of the SS-16.

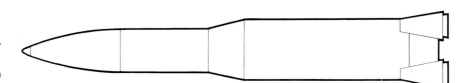

United Arab Emirates

1,800 men and 46 combat aircraft.

2 interceptor sqns with 32 Mirage VAD/DAD/RAD.

1 FGA sqn with 7 Hunter FGA.76, 2 T.77.

1 COIN sqn with 4 M.B. 326KD/LD, 1 SF.260WD.

Transports incl 2 C-130H, 1 Boeing 720-023B, 1 G-222, 4 Islander, 1 Falcon, 3 DHC-4, 1 DHC-5D, 1 Cessna 182.

Helicopters incl 8 AB-205, 6 AB-206, 3 AB-212, 10 *Alouette* III, 10 Puma.

R.550 Magic AAM; AS.11/12 ASM.

(1 G-222, 3 DHC-5D transports, Lynx helicopter on order.)

United Kingdom

The Royal Air Force

All too unfortunately, the history of the Royal Air Force since World War II has been similar to those of the Royal Navy and British Army: just about adequate financial support overall, but far too much meddling in equipment programmes, and a succession of strategic and tactical reviews that have led to much waste of time and effort, let alone money, combined with mistaken procurement policies. The problem is basically twofold: firstly, no clear continuous policy of Britain's long-term aims in the period in which she has withdrawn from all pretensions of world power; and secondly, too much government control of the armed forces' technical decisions on grounds of politics and finance, rather than of military necessity. The net result is that although the RAF remains a large and formidable force, it is neither as large nor as formidable as the situation warrants or as the money spent on it should have produced. RAF personnel number 84,646, about 27 per cent of the total strength of the armed forces, which receive about 4.95 per cent of the country's gross national product.

The Royal Air Force consists of three main commands: Strike Command and Support Command in the UK, and RAF Germany to provide tactical air support for the British Army in Germany. Strike Command is responsible for the UK Air Defence Region, as well as the vestigial forces in the Middle East and the Far East. For operations in and around the UK, Strike Command has four groups. No 1 Group (Strike) has six bomber squadrons equipped with 48 Vulcan B.2, two strike squadrons with 25 Buccaneer S.2, one photographic reconnaissance squadron with 11 Canberra PR.9, one target-towing squadron with Canberra TT.17, two squadrons with Canberra target, one strategic reconnaissance squadron with eight Vulcan SR.2, and two tanker squadrons with 16 Victor K.2. No 11 Group (Air Defence) has two interceptor squadrons with 24 Lightning F.6, one interceptor squadron with 10 Phantom FG.1, four interceptor squadrons with 40 Phantom FGR.2, one AEW squadron with 11 Shackleton AEW.2 (to be replaced by Nimrod AEW), one SAM squadron with Bloodhound 2, plus a number of Hunter fighters and a squadron of 12 Phantom FGR.2 to be added in 1979. No 18 Group (Maritime) consists of four maritime reconnaissance squadrons with 28 Nimrod MR.1, two Wessex helicopter squadrons, and several Whirlwind helicopter SAR flights. No 38 Group (Air Transport and Offensive Support) has one close-support squadron with 16 Harrier GR.3, two attack and close-support squadrons with 24 Jaguar GR.1, four medium transport squadrons with 40 C-130, one strategic transport squadron with 11 VC10, one helicopter squadron with 14 Wessex tactical transports, and two helicopter squadrons with 24 Puma tactical transports.

Support Command controls flying training for the most part, and has a large number of trainers and operational conversion aircraft: Jet Provosts at the RAF College, and the 1st and 6th Flying Training Schools; Gnats at the 4th Flying Training School; Hawks at the 4th Flying Training School; Bulldogs at the 3rd Flying Training School and various university air squadrons; Jetstreams at the 3rd Flying Training School; Chipmunks with various AEFs; Hunters at the 4th Flying Training School; Dominies at the 6th Flying Training School; and Whirlwind, Gazelle and Sioux helicopters at the Central Flying School (H).

RAF Germany has two squadrons with 20 Phantom FGR.2, two strike squadrons with 25 Buccaneer S.2, five close-support and attack squadrons with 60 Jaguar Gr.1, two close-support squadrons with 32 Harrier GR.3, one Wessex tactical transport squadron with 13 helicopters, one Bloodhound 2 SAM squadron, and four Rapier SAM squadrons. Other units of small size are detached from the UK and German forces for service in other areas.

In some respects the RAF is fully up-to-date, with adequate numbers of first-class aircraft; but in other respects equipment has lagged behind the times, and the considerable re-equipment programme the RAF is undergoing is none too early. Among the equipment on order are 24 Harriers, 11 Nimrod AEW aircraft, nine VC10 tankers, 175 Hawk trainers and light ground-attack aircraft, substantial quantities of Bulldog trainers, Bloodhound 2 SAMs, and 30 CH-47 Chinook lift helicopters. It is also planned that the RAF acquires some 385 Tornado multi-role aircraft, 220 of them for FGA duties and the other 165 for air defence duties.

The arrival of these new types will materially improve the RAF, but the force must still in the near future take careful thought for the next generation of aircraft, bearing in mind the changing objectives of the RAF as part of the British defence force.

84,646, including 4,906 women and 300 enlisted outside UK, and about 511 combat aircraft, plus 30,300 regular and 300 volunteer reservists.

6 strike sqns with 48 Vulcan B.2.
4 strike sqns with 50 Buccaneer S.2.
3 close support sqns with 48 Harrier GR.3.
6 attack and close support sqns with 72 Jaguar GR.1.
9 interceptor sqns: 2 with 24 Lightning F.6, 7 with 72 Phantom FG.1/FGR.2.
5 recce sqns: 1 with 8 Vulcan SR.2, 2 with 24 Jaguar GR.1, 2 with 22 Canberra PR.9 and TT.17.
1 AEW sqn with 11 Shackleton AEW.2 (to be replaced by Nimrod).
4 MR sqns with 28 Nimrod MR.1.
1 ECM sqn with 3 Nimrod R.1, 4 Canberra B.6.
2 tanker sqns with 16 Victor K.2.
1 strategic transport sqn with 11 VC10.
4 tac transport sqns with 40 C-130.
3 lt comms sqns with HS 125, Andover, Pembroke, Devon aircraft and Whirlwind helicopter.
Operational Conversion Units with about 97 combat aircraft, including 9 Vulcan, 11 Buccaneer, 7 Canberra, 21 Phantom, 24 Jaguar, 7 Lightning, 15 Harrier, 3 Nimrod, Jetstream and a number of Andover and Hercules transport aircraft.
Training units with Hunter, Hawk, Gnat, Bulldog, Jet Provost, C-130, Victor, Dominie ac; Wessex, Whirlwind, Puma, Gazelle helicopters.
8 helicopter sqns: 5 tac transport (2 with 24 Puma HC.1, 3 with 40 Wessex HC.2), 3 SAR with 17 Whirlwind HAR.10, 8 Wessex.
Sidewinder, Sparrow, Red Top, Firestreak AAM; Martel, AS.12, AS.30 ASM.
2 SAM sqns with Bloodhound 2.
(24 Harrier FGA, 11 Nimrod AEW, 9 VC10 tankers, 175 Hawk, Bulldog trg ac, 30 Chinook helicopters; Bloodhound SAM; Super Sidewinder, Sky Flash AAM, Hawkswing ASM on order; 385 Tornado MRCA (220 FGA, 165 AD) planned.)

Royal Air Force Regiment:
7 fd and 5 AD sqns with Rapier SAM.
1 flt with Tigercat SAM.

Deployment:
The Royal Air Force includes an operational home command (Strike Command), responsible for the UK Air Defence Region and the Near and Far East, and 1 overseas command (RAF Germany: 8,600). Sqns are deployed overseas as follows:
Germany: 2 Phantom FGR.2, 2 Buccaneer, 5 Jaguar, 2 Harrier, 1 Wessex, 1 Bloodhound, 4 Rapier, 1 fd sqn of RAF Regt.
Gibraltar: Hunter detachment.
Cyprus: 1 Whirlwind (with UNFICYP) and 1 sqn RAF Regt.
Malta: 1 Canberra PR.7.
Hong Kong: 1 Wessex.
Belize: Harrier (6ac), Puma and 1 sqn RAF Regt.

Fleet Air Arm
1 strike sqn with 14 Buccaneer S.2.
1 FGA sqn with 14 Phantom FG.1.

1 AEW sqn with 7 Gannet AEW3, 1 COD.4, 3 T.5.
7 ASW helicopter sqns: 5 with 29 Sea King (4 sqns embarked), 1 of 39 Wasp flts, 1 of 6 Wessex 3 flts, 4 Lynx flts.
1 cdo assault sqn with 16 Wessex 5.
3 SAR flts: 2 with Wessex HAS.1, 1 with Wessex 5.
1 utility helicopter sqn with Wessex 5.
5 trg sqns with Sea King, Wasp, Wessex 3/5, Lynx.
(35 Sea Harrier VTOL ac, 21 Sea King, 60 Lynx helicopters on order.)

Army Air Arm

6 aviation regts.
100 Scout, 7 *Alouette* II, 20 Sioux, 150 Gazelle, 20 Lynx helicopters.

British Aerospace (BAC) Lightning

Type: all-weather interceptor fighter
Crew: one
Wings: metal cantilever high mid-wing monoplane
Fuselage: metal semi-monocoque
Tail unit: metal cantilever
Landing gear: hydraulically actuated retractable tricycle unit
Powerplant: two Rolls-Royce Avon 301 turbojets, each rated at 16,360-lb (7,421-kg) static thrust with afterburning
Fuel capacity:
Avionics: comprehensive communication and navigation/attack equipment
Armament: two Red Top or Firestreak air-to-air missiles, plus two optional 30-mm Aden cannon. Export models have provision for 6,000 lb (2,722 kg) of external stores above and below the wings
Dimensions: Span 34 ft 10 in (10.6 m)
Length 53 ft 3 in (16.25 m)
Height 19 ft 7 in (5.95 m)
Wing area: 460 ft² (42.74 m²)
Weights: Empty about 28,000 lb (12,700 kg)
Loaded
Maximum about 50,000 lb (22,680 kg)
Performance: speed 1,500 mph (2,415 kph) or Mach 2.27 at 40,000 ft (12,192 m); cruising speed 595 mph (958 kph); climb 50,000 ft (15,240 m) per minute at sea level; service ceiling over 60,000 ft

(18,290 m); range 800 miles (1,290 km) with ventral tanks but no overwing tanks
Used also by: Saudi Arabia
Notes: The Lightning was Britain's first truly supersonic fighter, and resulted from the development of the English Electric P.1A research aircraft, which was redesigned to emerge as the P.1B fighter prototype in 1957. After much development work, this finally became the Lightning Mach 2 fighter, which entered RAF service in 1959. Since then there have been several variants:

1. Lightning F.1 initial production model with a relatively primitive afterburner, but Ferranti Airpass interception radar in the intake centrebody for the control of the two Firestreak missiles
2. Lightning F.2 with a fully variable afterburner and improved all-weather capabilities
3. Lightning F.3 definitive interceptor model, with the Avon 301 series instead of the Avon 210 series, Red Top as well as Firestreak AAMs, a larger, flat-topped fin, and provision for two overwing ferry tanks
4. Lightning T.4 side-by-side operational trainer, based on the F.1A
5. Lightning T.5 side-by-side operational trainer, based on the F.3
6. Lightning F.6 development of the F.3, and at first known as the F.3A. The specification applies to this model.

British Aerospace (BAC) VC10

Type: long-range strategic transport aircraft
Crew: four, plus up to 150 passengers
Wings: metal cantilever low-wing monoplane
Fuselage: metal semi-monocoque
Tail unit: metal cantilever
Landing gear: hydraulically actuated retractable tricycle unit
Powerplant: four Rolls-Royce Conway 301 turbofans, each rated at 22,500-lb (10,206-kg) static thrust
Fuel capacity:
Avionics: comprehensive communication and navigation equipment
Armament: none
Dimensions: Span 146 ft 2 in (44.55 m)
Length 133 ft 8 in (40.74 m)
Height 40 ft (12.19 m)
Wing area: 2,932 ft² (272.4 m²)
Weights: Empty 146,000 lb (66,225 kg)
Loaded
Maximum 323,000 lb (146,512 kg)

Performance: speed 580 mph (933 kph) at 30,000 ft (9,144 m); cruising speed 518 mph (834 kph) at 38,000 ft (11,583 m); range 3,668 miles (5,903 km) with a payload of 59,000 lb (26,762 kg); range 5,370 miles (8,642 km) with a payload of 24,000 lb (10,886 kg)

Used also by: Oman
Notes: The RAF's VC10 C.1 is derived from the civil Standard VC10, with features from the Super VC10, such as uprated engines and extra fuel tankage in the fin. The first military VC10 flew in 1965.

British Aerospace (Hawker Siddeley Aviation) 125

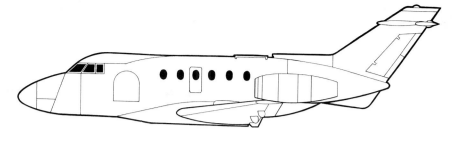

Type: navigation trainer, light transport and utility aircraft
Crew: two to four, plus two pupils or up to eight passengers
Wings: metal cantilever low-wing monoplane
Fuselage: metal semi-monocoque
Tail unit: metal cantilever
Landing gear: hydraulically actuated retractable tricycle unit
Powerplant: two Rolls-Royce Bristol Viper Mark 520 turbojets, each rated at 3,310-lb (1,501-kg) static thrust
Fuel capacity: 1,018 gallons (4,628 litres) in integral wing tanks
Avionics: comprehensive communication and navigation equipment
Armament: none
Dimensions: Span 47 ft (14.33 m)
Length 47 ft 5 in (14.45 m)
Height 16 ft 6 in (5.03 m)

Wing area: 353 ft² (32.8 m²)
Weights: Empty
Loaded 20,500 lb (9,299 kg)
Maximum
Performance: (at normal take-off weight) maximum cruising speed 472 mph (760 kph) at 25,000 ft (7,620 m); climb to 25,000 ft (7,620 m) in 13 minutes; service ceiling 40,000 ft (12,200 m); range 1,338 miles (2,153 km)

Used also by: Brazil, Malaysia, Nicaragua, South Africa
Notes: Based on the Hawker Siddeley (de Havilland) 125 business jet, the HS 125 has appeared in three military versions:
  1. Dominie T.1 advanced navigation trainer, based on the Series 2 aircraft
  2. CC.1 communications aircraft, based on the Series 400 civil machine
  3. CC.2 communications aircraft, based on the Series 600 civil machine.

British Aerospace (Hawker Siddeley Aviation) Harrier

Type: V/STOL close-support and reconnaissance aircraft
Crew: one
Wings: metal cantilever shoulder-wing monoplane
Fuselage: aluminium alloy and titanium semi-monocoque
Tail unit: metal cantilever
Landing gear: hydraulically actuated bicycle unit, with hydraulically actuated retractable wingtip-mounted outrigger wheels
Powerplant: one Rolls-Royce Bristol Pegasus Mark 103 vectored thrust turbofan, rated at 21,500-lb (9,752-kg) static thrust
Fuel capacity: 630 gallons (2,865 litres) in five fuselage and two wing integral tanks, plus provision for two underwing 100-gallon (454-litre) combat drop tanks or two 330-gallon (1,500-litre) ferry tanks

Avionics: comprehensive communication and navigation/attack equipment, including Ferranti FE 541 inertial navigation and attack system (INAS), Smiths electronic head up display, Smiths air data computer, and Ferranti laser ranger and marked target seeker (LRMTS)
Armament: all armament is carried on five pylons, one under the fuselage and two under each wing, the fuselage and inner wing pylons being capable of carrying 2,000 lb (910 kg) of stores each, and the outer wing pylons 650 lb (295 kg) each, up to a current maximum of 5,000 lb (2,270 kg), though 8,000 lb (3,630 kg) can be car-

ried. In addition, the strakes under the fuselage can each be replaced by a 30-mm Aden cannon pod. A typical load might consist of two 30-mm cannon pods, one 1,000-lb (454-kg) bomb under the fuselage, two 1,000-lb (454-kg) bombs on the inner wing pylons, and two Matra 155 rocket pods, each with nineteen 68-mm SNEB rockets, on the outer pylons
Dimensions: Span 25 ft 3 in (7.7 m)
Length 45 ft 7¾ in (13.91 m)
Height 11 ft 3 in (3.43 m)

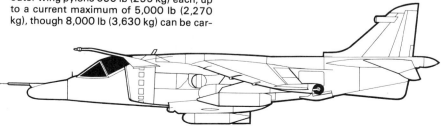

179

Wing area: 201.1 ft² (18.68 m²)

Weights: Empty 12,200 lb (5,533 kg)

Loaded

Maximum over 25,000 lb (11,340 kg)

Performance: speed 737 mph (1,186 kph) or Mach 0.972 at low level; dive speed Mach 1.3; climb (VTOL) 50,000 ft (15,240 m) per minute at sea level; service ceiling more than 50,000 ft (15,240 m); combat radius on a hi-lo-hi strike mission without drop tanks 260 miles (418 km); ferry range 2,070 miles (3,330 km); range with one inflight refuelling more than 3,455 miles (5,560 km)

Used also by: Spain, USA

Notes: The vectored-thrust Harrier prototype, the P.1127 Kestrel, first flew in 1960, and production aircraft entered service in 1969. There are several models:

1. Harrier GR.1, 1A and 3, single-seat close-support aircraft
2. Harrier T.2, 2A and 4, two-seat combat trainer with full combat capability, 55 ft 9½ in (17.0 m) in length, some 10 ft 3½ in (3.13 m) longer than single-seaters as a result of its extra forward fuselage section and tail boom
3. Sea Harrier FRS.1 single-seat fighter, reconnaissance and strike aircraft under development for the Royal Navy
4. Harrier Mark 50, or AV-8A single-seat close-support and tactical reconnaissance model for the US Marine Corps, whose aircraft are armed with a pair of AIM-9 Sidewinder air-to-air missiles
5. Harrier Mark 54, or TAV-8A two-seat operational trainer.

All RAF Harriers are retrofitted or are being retrofitted with laser rangefinders and marked target seekers in a 'chisel' nose.

British Aerospace (Hawker Siddeley Aviation) Hawk

Type: trainer and close-support aircraft
Crew: two, seated in tandem
Wings: metal cantilever low-wing monoplane
Fuselage: metal semi-monocoque
Tail unit: metal cantilever
Landing gear: hydraulically actuated retractable tricycle unit
Powerplant: one Rolls-Royce/Turboméca RT.172-06-11 Adour 151 turbofan, rated at 5,340-lb (2,422-kg) static thrust
Fuel capacity: 365 gallons (1,659 litres) in integral wing and fuselage bag tanks, plus provision for one 100-gallon (454-litre) drop tank under each wing
Avionics: comprehensive communication and navigation equipment
Armament: (trainer) one 30-mm Aden cannon pod under the fuselage, plus one hardpoint under each wing, capable of carrying external stores of 1,000-lb (454-kg) weight, though normal training is limited to a maximum of 1,500 lb (680 kg); (close-support) one underfuselage and four underwing hardpoints, each capable of carrying 1,000 lb (454 kg) of external stores, up to a maximum weight of 5,660 lb (2,567 kg)
Dimensions: Span 30 ft 9¾ in (9.39 m)
Length 36 ft 7¾ in (11.17 m)
Height 13 ft 5 in (4.09 m)
Wing area: 179.6 ft² (16.69 m²)
Weights: Empty 8,040 lb (3,647 kg)
Loaded 12,284 lb (5,572 kg)
Maximum 17,097 lb (7,755 kg)
Performance: speed 620 mph (997 kph); climb to 30,000 ft (9,145 m) in 6 minutes 6 seconds; service ceiling 48,000 ft (14,630 m); endurance as a trainer in 'clean' condition about 2 hours; ferry range with drop tanks 1,923 miles (3,095 km)

Used also by: Finland, Indonesia, Kenya (?)
Notes: A useful and attractive little aircraft, the Hawk is capable of development into a number of other roles. The first two examples were delivered in 1976.

British Aerospace (Hawker Siddeley Aviation) Nimrod

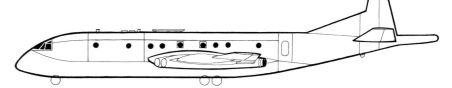

Type: maritime patrol aircraft
Crew: 12
Wings: metal cantilever low/mid-wing monoplane
Fuselage: metal semi-monocoque
Tail unit: metal cantilever
Landing gear: hydraulically actuated retractable tricycle unit
Powerplant: four Rolls-Royce RB.168-20 Spey Mark 250 turbofans, each rated at 12,140-lb (5,507-kg) static thrust
Fuel capacity: 10,730 gallons (48,780 litres) in fuselage, integral wing and wing leading-edge tanks, plus six optional tanks for a further 1,887.5 gallons (8,580 litres) in the weapons bay
Avionics: comprehensive communication and navigation/attack equipment, including a Marconi-Elliott navigation/attack system based on a Marconi-Elliott 920 ATC computer, EMI Searchwater long-range air-to-surface vessel search radar with a Ferranti FM 1600D digital computer controlling the inbuilt data processing subsystem, AQS 901 acoustics processing and display system operating with the aid of two Marconi-Elliott 920 ATC computers and a variety of active and passive sonobuoys, and Emerson Electronics ASQ-10A magnetic anomaly detector (avionics data are for MR.2)

Armament: a large weapons bay can accommodate up to nine torpedoes, or depth charges, mines or bombs in six lateral rows, plus two underwing hardpoints for the carriage of cannon pods, rocket pods, mines, or air-to-surface missiles, though this last capability is not currently available; sonobuoys are carried aft
Dimensions: Span 114 ft 10 in (35.0 m)
Length 126 ft 9 in (38.63 m)
Height 29 ft 8½ in (9.08 m)
Wing area: 2,121 ft² (197.0 m²)
Weights: Empty 92,000 lb (41,730 kg)
Loaded 177,500 lb (80,510 kg)
Maximum 192,000 lb (87,090 kg)
Performance: (MR.1) speed 575 mph (926 kph); cruising speed 547 mph (880 kph); patrol speed on two engines 230 mph (370 kph); service ceiling 42,000 ft (12,800 m); endurance 12 hours; ferry range 5,755 miles (9,265 km)
Used only by: UK

Notes: Derived from the same basic airframe as the Comet airliner, the Nimrod is an excellent maritime reconnaissance aircraft, with long range, high transit speed, good patrol endurance, advanced sensors and first-class weapons capability. There are four versions:

1. Nimrod MR.1 maritime reconnaissance variant, which is described in the technical section above, with the exception of the avionics subsection, which refers to the MR.2. In the MR.1, tactical navigation/attack is the task of an 8K Marconi-Elliott 920B digital computer.
2. Nimrod R.1 electronic reconnaissance variant, which has no MAD tailboom and is thus only 118 ft (35.97 m) long.
3. MR.2 maritime reconnaissance variant, basically the MR.1 refitted with more advanced sensor and navigation equipment, and new communications gear, for delivery during 1978–80.
4. Nimrod AEW.3 airborne early warning variant, described separately.

British Aerospace (Hawker Siddeley Aviation) Nimrod AEW. 3

Type: airborne early warning aircraft
Crew:
Wings: metal cantilever low/mid-wing monoplane

Fuselage: metal semi-monocoque
Tail unit: metal cantilever
Landing gear: hydraulically actuated retractable tricycle unit
Powerplant: four Rolls-Royce RB.168-20 Spey Mark 250 turbofans, each rated at 12,140-lb (5,507-kg) static thrust

Fuel capacity: probably in the order of 12,000 gallons (54,552 litres) in fuselage and wing tanks

Avionics: comprehensive communication and navigation equipment, plus Marconi-Elliott Avionics pulsed-doppler radar for ship and aircraft surveillance, with advanced automatic data processing

Armament: none

Dimensions: Span 115 ft 1 in (35.08 m)
Length 137 ft 5½ in (41.76 m)
Height 33 ft (10.06 m)

Wing area: 2.121 ft² (197.0 m²)

Weights: Empty
Loaded
Maximum

Performance: classified, but endurance is more than 10 hours

Used only by: UK

Notes: Derived from the Nimrod MR series, the Nimrod AEW.3 is an advanced early warning platform, suitable for operations at sea or over central Europe. The location of the two main radar scanners at each end of the fuselage rather than in a rotating radome offers a number of technical advantages, the benefits of which are enhanced by the excellent communications and tactical data systems. Electronic support measures (ESM) equipment is located in the fairings on top of the fin and on each wing leading edge.

British Aerospace (Hawker Siddeley Aviation) Sea Harrier

Type: carrierborne V/STOL fighter, strike and reconnaissance aircraft

Crew: one

Wings: metal cantilever shoulder-wing monoplane

Fuselage: metal semi-monocoque

Tail unit: metal cantilever

Landing gear: hydraulically actuated retractable bicycle unit, with stabilising outrigger wheels

Powerplant: one Rolls-Royce (Bristol) Pegasus 104 vectored-thrust turbofan, rated at 21,500-lb (9,752-kg) static thrust

Fuel capacity: 630 gallons (2,865 litres) in five integral fuselage and two integral wing tanks, plus provision for two 330-gallon (1,500-litre) ferry tanks, or two 100-gallon (455-litre) drop tanks

183

Avionics: comprehensive communication and navigation/attack equipment, including Ferranti Blue Fox multi-mode radar, Smiths head up display, and Decca doppler radar

Armament: two optional 30-mm Aden cannon under the fuselage, plus a variety of armament installations on one underfuselage and four underwing pylons, the three inner pylons being able to lift 2,000 lb (907 kg) each, and the outer pair 650 lb (295 kg) each, up to a maximum external load of 5,000 lb (2,270 kg), though 8,000 lb (3,630 lb) have been carried. The pylons can carry stores similar to those of the Harrier GR.3, with the addition of a pair of AIM-9 Sidewinder AAMs

Dimensions: Span 25 ft 3¼ in (7.7 m)
Length 47 ft 7 in (14.5 m)
Height 12 ft 2 in (3.71 m)

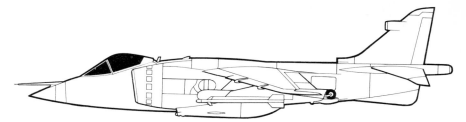

Wing area: 201.1 ft² (18.68 m²)
Weights: Empty
Loaded
Maximum
Performance: classified, but comparable with that of the Harrier GR.3
Used only by: UK

Notes: The Sea Harrier first flew in 1978, for entry into service in 1978. The Sea Harrier differs from the Harrier basically in having a raised cockpit, new electronics, and a folding nose. Two versions are envisaged for the present:

1. FRS. 1 combat aircraft, to which the specification above applies
2. T.4 two-seat trainer.

British Aerospace (Hawker Siddeley Aviation) Vulcan

Type: bomber and strategic reconnaissance aircraft
Crew: five
Wings: metal cantilever mid-wing delta monoplane
Fuselage: metal semi-monocoque
Tail unit: metal cantilever
Landing gear: hydraulically actuated retractable tricycle unit
Powerplant: four Rolls-Royce (Bristol Siddeley) Olympus 301 turbojets, each rated at 20,000-lb (9,072-kg) static thrust
Fuel capacity:
Avionics: comprehensive communication and navigation/attack equipment

Armament: up to 21,000 lb (9,526 kg) of conventional or nuclear bombs (bomber versions only)
Dimensions: Span 111 ft (33.83 m)
Length 105 ft 6 in (32.15 m)
Height 27 ft 2 in (8.26 m)
Wing area: 3,964 ft² (368.27 m²)
Weights: Empty
Loaded
Maximum about 250,000 lb (113,399 kg)
Performance: speed 640 mph (1,030 kph) or Mach 0.97 at high altitude; service ceiling about 65,000 ft (19,810 m); range about 4,600 miles (7,400 km)
Used only by: UK
Notes: The prototype Vulcan flew in 1952, and the bomber entered service in 1955, the second of the three British 'V' strategic

nuclear bombers of the 1950s. There are four variants:

1. Vulcan B.1 with 11,000-lb (4,990-kg) Olympus 101 turbojets, and inferior performance compared with later models. Later models were up-engined, eventually with 13,500-lb (6,124-kg) Olympus 104 engines
2. Vulcan B.1A with a bulged rear fuselage containing ECM equipment
3. Vulcan B.2, with a larger and thinner wing, the ability to carry the Blue Steel stand-off nuclear missile, and initially the 17,000-lb (7,711-kg) Olympus 201
4. Vulcan SR.2 strategic reconnaissance version, without armament but fitted with a variety of sensors.

British Aerospace (Scottish Aviation) Jetstream

Type: aircrew trainer and light transport aircraft
Crew: two, plus up to 12 passengers
Wings: aluminium alloy cantilever low-wing monoplane
Fuselage: aluminium alloy semi-monocoque
Tail unit: aluminium alloy cantilever
Landing gear: hydraulically actuated retractable tricycle unit
Powerplant: two Turboméca Astazou XVI D turboprops, each rated at 996 ehp and driving a Hamilton Standard three-blade metal propeller
Fuel capacity: 384 gallons (1,745 litres) in two integral wing tanks
Avionics: comprehensive communication and navigation equipment
Armament: none
Dimensions: Span 52 ft (15.85 m)
Length 47 ft 1½ in (14.37 m)
Height 17 ft 5½ in (5.32 m)

Wing area: 270 ft² (25.08 m²)
Weights: Empty 7,683 lb (3,485 kg)
Loaded
Maximum 12,566 lb (5,700 kg)
Performance: (at maximum take-off weight) speed 282 mph (454 kph) at 10,000 ft (3,050 m); cruising speed 269 mph (433 kph) at 15,000 ft (4,575 m); climb 2,500 ft (762 m) per minute at sea level; service ceiling 25,000 ft (7,620 m); range 1,380 miles (2,224 km)

Used only by: UK
Notes: Derived from the Handley Page HP 137 Jetstream, the Scottish Aviation machine appears in both civil and military guises, the two main military models being:
1. Jetstream T.1 for the RAF in the multi-engine pilot training scheme
2. Jetstream T.2 for the Royal Navy in the observer training programme, with MEL E 190 weather and terrain mapping radar in a 'thimble' nose.

British Aerospace (Scottish Aviation) SA-3-200 Bulldog Series 200

Type: flying and weapons training, and observation, liaison, reconnaissance and light strike aircraft
Crew: two, seated side-by-side
Wings: light alloy cantilever low-wing monoplane
Fuselage: light alloy semi-monocoque
Tail unit: light alloy cantilever
Landing gear: electro-mechanically actuated retractable tricycle unit

Powerplant: one Lycoming AEIO-360-A1B6 piston engine, rated at 200 hp and driving a Hartzell two-blade metal propeller
Fuel capacity: 32 gallons (145.5 litres) in four wing tanks
Avionics: communication and navigation equipment
Armament: provision for four underwing hardpoints, capable of accepting a maximum weapons load of 640 lb (290 kg), including light bombs, rockets, grenade launchers, and machine-gun pods
Dimensions: Span 33 ft 9 in (10.29 m)
Length 24 ft 11 in (7.59 m)
Height 8 ft 4 in (2.54 m)
Wing area:

Weights: Empty 1,810 lb (821 kg)
Loaded 2,304 lb (1,045 kg)
Maximum 2,601 lb (1,179 kg)
Performance: (at normal loaded weight) speed 173 mph (278 kph) at sea level; cruising speed 162 mph (260 kph) at 4,000 ft (1,220 m); climb 1,160 ft (353 m) per minute at sea level; service ceiling 18,500 ft (5,640 m); endurance 5 hours; range 621 miles (1,000 km)

Used only by: UK
Notes: Derived from the Series 120 Bulldog, the Series 200 has a retractable undercarriage, higher-mounted tailplane, better nose lines, an improved cockpit canopy, and improved performance and weights.

Handley Page Victor

Type: air-refuelling tanker and strategic reconnaissance aircraft
Crew: four or five
Wings: metal cantilever mid-wing monoplane
Fuselage: metal semi-monocoque
Tail unit: metal cantilever
Landing gear: hydraulically actuated retractable tricycle unit
Powerplant: four Rolls-Royce Conway 201 turbofans, each rated at 20,600-lb (9,344-kg) static thrust

Fuel capacity:
Avionics: comprehensive communication and navigation equipment, plus special reconnaissance gear in the SR.2
Armament: none
Dimensions: Span 120 ft (36.58 m)
Length 114 ft 11 in (35.05 m)
Height 30 ft 1½ in (9.2 m)
Wing area: 2,597 ft² (241.27 m²)
Weights: Empty 91,000 lb (41,277 kg)
Loaded
Maximum 233,000 lb (101,150 kg)
Performance: speed about 640 mph (1,030 kph) or Mach 0.92 at 36,000 ft (10,973

m); service ceiling 60,000 ft (18,290 m); range 4,600 miles (7,400 km)
Used only by: UK
Notes: The Victor was the third of the RAF's strategic nuclear bombers to enter service, the prototype having flown in 1952, and the initial production B.1 being taken into service in 1956. Their only defence is in ECM, which will not provide sufficient protection at high altitude in present conditions, so as the type cannot readily be converted to low-level penetration raids, the surviving aircraft have been converted into tankers and strategic reconnaissance aircraft.

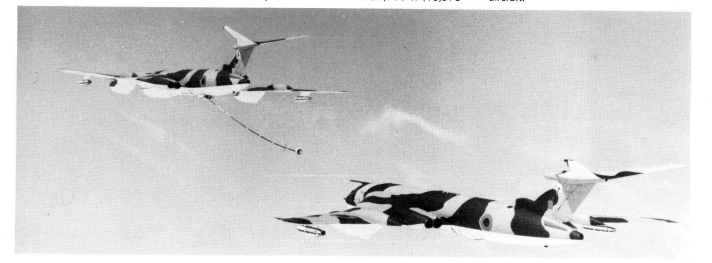

Panavia Aircraft Tornado

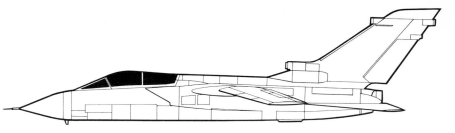

Type: multi-role combat aircraft
Crew: two, in tandem
Wings: variable-geometry metal cantilever shoulder-mounted monoplane
Fuselage: metal semi-monocoque
Tail unit: metal cantilever
Landing gear: hydraulically actuated retractable tricycle unit
Powerplant: two Turbo-Union RB.199-34R-4 turbofans, each rated at 16,000-lb (7,258-kg) static thrust with afterburning
Fuel capacity: internal self-sealing fuel tanks in the fuselage and wings, plus provision for underwing auxiliary fuel tanks
Avionics: comprehensive communications and navigation equipment; the primary attack/navigation system comprises a Texas Instruments multi-mode forward-looking radar (Marconi-Elliott multi-mode airborne interception radar in RAF air defence model), Ferranti 3-axis digital inertial navigation system, Decca Type 72 doppler radar, Microtecnica air data computer, Litef Spirit 3 16-bit central digital computer, Aeritalia radio-radar altimeter, Smiths/Teldix/OMI head up display, Ferranti nose-mounted laser rangefinder and marked-target receiver, Marconi-Elliott TV tabular display, Astronautics bearing distance heading indicator and contour map display, Siemens or Cossor SSR-3100 IFF transponder, Elettronica warning radar, and MSDS/Plessey/Decca passive ECM system

Armament: two 27-mm IWKA-Mauser cannon, and a variety of non-nuclear stores on three underfuselage hardpoints and four underwing hardpoints. The hardpoints can carry Sidewinder, Sky Flash, Sparrow and *Aspide* 1A air-to-air missiles; AS.30, Martel, *Kormoran* and Jumbo air-to-surface missiles; napalm tanks; BL-755 600-lb (272-kg) cluster bombs; Mk 83 or other 1,000-lb (454-kg) bombs; 'smart' and retarded bombs; Lepus flare bombs; reconnaissance pods; and active or passive ECM pods. The maximum external load is more than 15,000 lb (6,804 kg)
Dimensions: Span (spread) 45 ft 7¼ in (13.9 m); Span (swept) 28 ft 2½ in (8.6 m)
Length 54 ft 9½ in (16.7 m)
Height 18 ft 8½ in (5.7 m)
Wing area:
Weights: Empty 22,000–23,000 lb (9,980-10,430 kg)
Loaded
Maximum 38,000–40,000 lb (17,240–18,145 kg)

Performance: speed more than 1,320 mph (2,125 kph) or Mach 2 at 36,000 ft (11,000 m); speed about 910 mph (1,465 kph) or Mach 1.2 at low altitude; service ceiling over 50,000 ft (15,240 m); range about 1,000 miles (1,610 km) at high altitude with wings spread and on internal fuel; ferry range more than 3,000 miles (4,830 km) with external auxiliary tanks
Used also by: Italy, West Germany
Notes: Design of the 3-nation Tornado was completed in 1972, and the first prototype flew in 1974. First service deliveries should take place during 1979. The basic design had to fulfil six operational requirements:
1. close air support and battlefield interdiction
2. interdiction and counter-air strike
3. air superiority
4. interception
5. naval strike
6. reconnaissance.

There is also to be a trainer variant. The details given above are for the basic interdiction and strike model.

Société Européenne de Production de l'Avion ECAT (SEPECAT) Jaguar

Type: strike fighter and trainer
Crew: one or two, in tandem
Wings: metal cantilever shoulder-wing monoplane
Fuselage: metal semi-monocoque
Tail unit: metal cantilever
Landing gear: hydraulically actuated retractable tricycle unit
Powerplant: two Rolls-Royce/Turboméca Adour 102 turbofans, each rated at 7,305-lb (3,314-kg) static thrust with afterburning
Fuel capacity: 924 gallons (4,200 litres) in four fuselage and two wings tanks, plus provision for three 264-gallon (1,200-litre) drop tanks, one under the fuselage and two under the wings
Avionics: comprehensive communication and navigation/attack equipment, including in the British versions Marconi-Elliott digital/inertial navigation and weapon aiming subsystem with an MCS 920M digital computer, E3R 3-gyro inertial platform, inertial velocity sensor, navigation control unit and projected map display; Marconi-Elliott air data computer; Smiths electronic head up display; Smiths FS6 horizontal situation indicator; Sperry C2J gyro amplifier master unit, compass controller and magnetic detector; Plessey weapon control system; and in the Jaguar S a Ferranti laser rangefinder and marked target seeker
Armament: (Jaguar A and S) two 30-mm cannon (DEFA 553 in Jaguar A, Aden in Jaguar S), plus five external hardpoints (one under the fuselage and two under each wing, the fuselage and inner wing points stressed to take loads of up to 2,205 lb (1,000 kg), and the outer wing points up to 1,102 lb (500 kg), to a maximum of 10,000 lb (4,535 kg) carried externally. The hardpoints can carry nuclear weapons, bombs, reconnaissance pods, missiles, rockets and fuel tanks
Dimensions: Span 28 ft 6 in (8.69 m)
Length 55 ft 2½ in (16.83 m)
Height 16 ft 0½ in (4.89 m)
Wing area: 258.33 ft² (24.0 m²)
Weights: Empty 15,432 lb (7,000 kg)
Loaded 24,000 lb (11,000 kg)
Maximum 34,000 lb (15,500 kg)
Performance: speed 990 mph (1,593 kph) or Mach 1.5 at 36,000 ft (11,000 m); speed 840 mph (1,350 kph) or Mach 1.1 at sea level; attack radius on internal fuel 507 miles (815 km) on a hi-lo-hi raid, 357 miles (575 km) on a lo-lo-lo raid; attack radius with external fuel tanks 818 miles (1,315 km) on a hi-lo-hi raid, 518 miles (835 km) on a lo-lo-lo raid; ferry range 2,614 miles (4,210 km) with maximum external fuel
Used also by: Ecuador, France, India, Oman
Notes: Evolved from the Breguet Br121, the Jaguar resulted from a British Aircraft Corporation and Breguet Aviation liaison to meet similar French and British air force requirements for an advanced trainer and attack aircraft. There are the following versions:
1. Jaguar A is a French single-seat tactical support aircraft
2. Jaguar B (Jaguar T.2) is a British two-seat operational trainer, with one 30-mm Aden cannon and a length of 53 ft 10½ in (16.42 m)
3. Jaguar E is a French two-seat advanced trainer, with two 30-mm

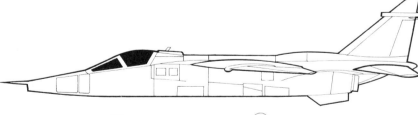

DEFA 553 cannon and a length of 53 ft 10½ in (16.42 m)
4. Jaguar S (Jaguar GR.1) is a British single-seat tactical support model, similar to the Jaguar A but with superior navigation/attack systems
5. Jaguar International is the export version, based on the Jaguar S with more powerful Adour RT.172-26 engines, rated at 8,600-lb (3,900-kg) static thrust each with afterburning. There are various armament options, including a pair of overwing pylons for dogfighting missiles such as the Magic.

Société Nationale Industrielle Aérospatiale/Westland SA341/342 Gazelle

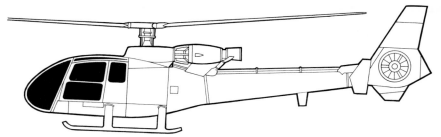

Type: light utility helicopter
Crew: one or two, plus three passengers
Rotor: plastic and glassfibre three-blade main rotor; 13-blade shrouded fan tail rotor
Fuselage: welded metal frame and metal semi-monocoque
Landing gear: twin steel tube skids
Powerplant: (SA 341) one Turboméca Astazou IIIA turboshaft, rated at 590 shp
Fuel capacity: 161 gallons (735 litres) in main, auxiliary and ferry tanks
Avionics: navigation and communication equipment
Armament: loads that can be carried include two 36-mm rocket pods, four AS.11 or HOT wire-guided missiles, two AS.12 missiles, four TOW missiles, two forward-firing 7.62-mm machine-guns, plus cabin- or chin-mounted 7.62-mm machine-guns
Dimensions: Span 34 ft 5½ in (10.5 m)
Length (fuselage) 31 ft 3¼ in (9.53 m)
Height 10 ft 2¾ in (3.15 m)
Rotor disc area: 931 ft² (86.5 m²)

Weights: Empty (SA 341H) 2,002 lb (908 kg)
Empty (SA 342) 2,105 lb (955 kg)
Maximum (SA 341H) 3,970 lb (1,800 kg)
Maximum (SA 342) 4,190 lb (1,900 kg)
Performance: (at maximum take-off weight) speed 193 mph (310 kph) at sea level; cruising speed 164 mph (264 kph) at sea level; climb 1,770 ft (540 m) per minute at sea level for SA 341; climb 2,010 ft (612 m) per minute at sea level for SA 342; service ceiling 16,400 ft (5,000 m) for SA 341; service ceiling 14,100 ft (4,300 m) for SA 342; range 469 miles (755 km) for SA 342 with maximum fuel at economical cruising speed (144 mph/233 kph)

Used also by: Egypt, France, Iraq, Kuwait, Malaysia, Qatar, Senegal, Yugoslavia
Notes: A joint Anglo-French helicopter resulting from a 1967 programme. There are 10 versions:
SA 341 B for British Army (Gazelle AH.1)
SA 341 C for Royal Navy (Gazelle HT.2)
SA 341 D for RAF (Gazelle HT.3)
SA 341 E project for RAF communications (Gazelle HCC.4)
SA 341 F for French Army
SA 341 G civil version
SA 341 H military export version
SA 342 J civil version of SA 342L
SA 342 K military version with 870 shp Astazou XIVH
SA 342 L military version with improved tail rotor.

Westland Aircraft Wessex

Type: multi-role helicopter
Crew: two or three, plus up to 16 passengers
Rotors: metal cantilever four-blade main rotor; metal cantilever four-blade tail rotor
Fuselage: metal semi-monocoque
Landing gear: fixed tailwheel unit
Powerplant: one Rolls-Royce Coupled Gnome 110/111 turboshaft, rated at 1,350 shp

Fuel capacity:
Avionics: comprehensive communication and navigation equipment
Armament: installations include flexible machine-guns and ASMs
Dimensions: Span 56 ft (17.07 m)
Length (fuselage) 48 ft 4½ in (14.74 m)
Height 16 ft 2 in (4.93 m)
Main rotor disc area: 2,463 ft² (228.82 m²)

Weights: Empty 8,304 lb (3,767 kg)
Loaded
Maximum 13,500 lb (6,120 kg)
Performance: speed 132 mph (212 kph) at sea level; cruising speed 121 mph (195 kph); climb 1,650 ft (503 m) per minute at sea level; service ceiling 14,000 ft (4,300 m); range 478 miles (769 km)
Used also by: Australia, Bangladesh
Notes: The Wessex is basically the Sikorsky S-58 built under licence in Britain, with a variety of turboshaft engines. The Royal Navy's HAS.1 and 3 have Rolls-Royce (Napier) Gazelles, the RAF's HC.2 (to which the technical specification above applies), the coupled Gnomes, the engines used in most other versions.

Westland Aircraft (Fairey Aviation) Gannet

Type: carrierborne anti-submarine and airborne early warning aircraft
Crew: three
Wings: metal cantilever mid-wing inverted gull monoplane
Fuselage: metal semi-monocoque
Tail unit: metal cantilever
Landing gear: hydraulically actuated retractable tricycle undercarriage
Powerplant: one Rolls-Royce (Armstrong Siddeley/Bristol Siddeley) Double Mamba 102 turboprop, rated at 3,875 ehp and driving two four-blade metal contra-rotating propellers

Fuel capacity:
Avionics: comprehensive communication and navigation/attack equipment, including a MAD sting on A/S versions, and APS-20 surveillance radar in AEW versions
Armament: two torpedoes, or 2,000 lb (907 kg) of bombs, depth charges or mines in the bomb bay, and sixteen 5-in (127-mm) or twenty-four 3-in (76-mm) rockets under the wings (A/S versions only)
Dimensions: Span 54 ft 6 in (16.61 m)
Length 44 ft (13.41 m)
Height 16 ft 10 in (5.13 m)
Wing area: 490 ft² (45.52 m²)

Weights: Empty 16,960 lb (7,693 kg)
Loaded
Maximum 24,000 lb (10,886 kg)
Performance: speed 250 mph (402 kph); climb 2,200 ft (670 m) per minute at sea level; service ceiling 25,000 ft (7,620 m); range about 800 miles (1,287 km)
Used only by: UK
Notes: The Gannet prototype first flew in 1949, and the initial production AS.1 in 1953. The last aircraft was delivered in 1961. There have been several A/S versions, but the technical specification above, with the exception of the armament section, applies to the Gannet AEW.3.

Westland Helicopters Sea King

Type: anti-submarine helicopter, with secondary search and transport roles

Crew: four, and up to 22 passengers

Rotor: metal cantilever five-blade main rotor; metal cantilever six-blade tail rotor

Fuselage: light alloy stressed skin

Landing gear: hydraulically actuated retractable tailwheel unit

Powerplant: two Rolls-Royce Gnome H.1400-1 turboshafts, each rated at 1,660 shp

Fuel capacity: 800 gallons (3,636 litres) in fuselage bag tanks, plus provision for an internal auxiliary tank

Avionics: comprehensive communication and navigation/attack equipment, including a fully integrated all-weather hunter-killer weapons system, based on Plessey Type 195 dipping sonar, Bendix AN/AQS-13B Mark 50 dipping sonar, Marconi-Elliott AD 580 doppler navigation system, and AW 391 search radar

Armament: four Mark 44 homing torpedoes or four Mark 11 depth charges

Dimensions: Span 62 ft (18.9 m)
Length (fuselage) 55 ft 9¾ in (17.01 m)
Height 16 ft 10 in (5.13 m)

Rotor disc area: 3,019 ft² (280.5 m²)

Weights: Empty about 13,000 lb (5,896 kg)
Loaded
Maximum 21,000 lb (9,525 kg)

Performance: (at maximum take-off weight) speed 143 mph (230 kph); cruising speed 129 mph (208 kph) at sea level; climb 2,020 ft (616 m) per minute at sea level; service ceiling 10,000 ft (3,050 m); hovering ceiling in ground effect 5,000 ft (1,525 m); range with maximum load about 350 miles (563 km); range with maximum fuel 937 miles (1,507 km)

Used also by: Australia, Belgium, Brazil, Egypt, India, Libya, Norway, Pakistan, Saudi Arabia, West Germany

Notes: The Sea King is derived from the Sikorsky S-61 series, much altered by Westland. The type is capable of various missions (ASW, search and rescue, tactical troop transport, casualty evacuation, and freighting), and the following versions are in service:

1. Sea King HAS.1 ASW helicopter for the Royal Navy
2. Sea King HAS.2 ASW and SAR helicopter for the Royal Navy, with uprated engine
3. Sea King HAR.3 SAR helicopter for the RAF, with uprated engine
4. Sea King Mark 41 SAR helicopter for West Germany
5. Sea King Mark 42 ASW helicopter for the Indian Navy
6. Sea King Mark 43 SAR helicopter for the Royal Norwegian Air Force
7. Sea King Mark 45 ASW helicopter for the Pakistan Navy
8. Sea King Mark 47 ASW helicopter for the Egyptian Navy, ordered by Saudi Arabia
9. Sea King Mark 48 SAR helicopter for the Belgian Air Force
10. Sea King Mark 50 ASW helicopter for the Royal Australian Navy.

The technical details above refer to the HAS.2/HAR.3/Mark 50 series. Maximum payload is 6,500 lb (2,948 kg).

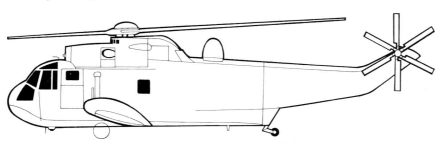

British Aerospace (BAC) Hawkswing

Type: air-to-surface tactical anti-tank guided missile
Guidance: command by means of wire
Dimensions: Span 15¾ in (40.0 cm)
Body diameter 6 in (17.0 cm)
Length 3 ft 8 in (1.17 m)
Booster: solid-propellant rocket
Sustainer: as above
Warhead: hollow-charge high explosive
Weights: Launch
Burnt out
Performance: range up to 4,374 yards (4,000 m)
Used only by: UK
Notes: The Hawkswing is the helicopter-launched version of the Swingfire anti-tank missile, with a very powerful warhead and excellent range characteristics. The Lynx helicopter can carry up to six Hawkswings, three on each side of the fuselage.

British Aerospace (BAC) Sea Skua

Type: helicopter-launched air-to-surface anti-shipping missile
Guidance: semi-active radar homing
Dimensions: Span about 23⅜ in (60.0 cm)
Body diameter about 7 9⁄16 in (20.0 cm)
Length about 9 ft 3⅝ in (2.83 m)
Booster: solid-propellant rocket
Sustainer: as above
Warhead: high explosive, with a weight of about 44 lb (20.0 kg)

Weights: Launch about 463 lb (210 kg)
Burnt out
Performance: classified
Used by: under development for UK
Notes: The Sea Skua is designed as an anti-shipping missile for the defence of frigates against missile-armed fast attack craft, and larger vessels as well. The target is illumined by the launch helicopter's Ferranti Seaspray radar, and the missile then homes automatically. The range of the missile will probably be great enough for the helicopter to be immune from the target's AA defences. Sea Skua is a wave-skimming missile.

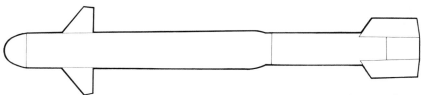

British Aerospace (HSD) Firestreak

Type: air-to-air tactical guided missile
Guidance: infra-red homing
Dimensions: Span 29½ in (74.9 cm)
Body diameter 8¾ in (22.225 cm)
Length 10 ft 5½ in (3.19 m)
Booster: solid-propellant rocket

Sustainer: as above
Warhead: about 50 lb (22.7 kg) high explosive
Weights: Launch about 300 lb (136 kg)
Burnt out
Performance: speed more than Mach 2; range between 0¾ and 5 miles (1.2 and 5 km)
Used also by: Kuwait, Saudi Arabia
Notes: The Firestreak is a pursuit-course missile used on the Lightning fighter.

British Aerospace (HSD) Red Top

Type: air-to-air tactical guided missile
Guidance: infra-red homing
Dimensions: Span 35¾ in (90.8 cm)
Body diameter 8¾ in (22.225 cm)
Length 10 ft 8¾ in (3.27 m)
Booster: solid-propellant rocket
Sustainer: as above
Warhead: 68 lb (31 kg) high explosive
Weights: Launch
Burnt out
Performance: speed about Mach 3; range at least 7½ miles (12 km)
Used also by: Kuwait, Saudi Arabia
Notes: Originally known as the Firestreak Mark IV, the Red Top maintains the basic design of the earlier missile, but is far more advanced electronically, has a larger warhead, and is powered by an improved motor. The Red Top can engage the target from virtually any direction.

British Aerospace (HSD) Sky Flash

Type: air-to-air tactical guided missile
Guidance: semi-active radar homing
Dimensions: Span 39⅝ in (1.0 m)
Body diameter 8 in (20.0 cm)
Length 12 ft (3.66 m)
Booster: Aerojet General solid-propellant rocket
Sustainer: none
Warhead: 66 lb (30 kg) high explosive
Weights: Launch 441 lb (200 kg)
Burnt out
Performance: speed more than Mach 2.25; range about 15½ miles (25 km)
Used only by: UK
Notes: Based on the Raytheon AIM-7E Sparrow III, the Sky Flash uses a different guidance package specially designed by Marconi, and offering a very high hit probability with all-round attack capability.

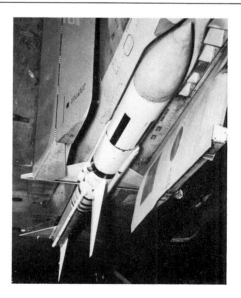

Matra/British Aerospace (HSD) AS.37/AJ.168 Martel

Type: air-to-surface tactical guided missile

Guidance: passive radar homing, or TV guidance

Dimensions: Span 3 ft $11\frac{1}{4}$ in (1.2 m)
Body diameter $15\frac{3}{4}$ in (40.0 cm)
Length (AS.37) 13 ft $6\frac{1}{4}$ in (4.12 m); (AJ.168) 12 ft $8\frac{1}{2}$ in (3.87 m)

Booster: Hotchkiss-Brandt/SNPE Basile solid-propellant rocket

Sustainer: Aérospatiale/SNPE Cassandre solid-propellant rocket

Warhead: 331 lb (150 kg) high explosive

Weights: Launch (AS.37) 1,168 lb (530 kg); (AJ.168) 1,213 lb (550 kg)
Burnt out

Performance: speed below Mach 1; range perhaps $37\frac{1}{4}$ miles (60 km) maximum, or $18\frac{1}{2}$ miles (30 km) when launched at Mach 1 at low altitude

Used also by: France

Notes: There are two versions of the Martel (Missile Anti-Radar and TELevision):

1. AS.37 anti-radar version made by Matra, which homes onto radar antennae
2. AJ.168 TV-homing version made by British Aerospace, which is guided onto the target by the aircraft's weapons operator, who watches the image transmitted by the TV camera in the missile's nose.

United States of America

The United States Air Force is by far the largest air force in the western alliance, and dominates strategic and tactical considerations in Europe partially by its presence in that theatre, but partially by its numerical strength in the continental United States, its ability to reinforce Europe quickly in the event of a crisis, and to supply allied air forces with large numbers of replacement aircraft, missiles and other offensive stores. For strategic nuclear offence, the United States has a triad of delivery systems: submarine-launched ballistic missiles, silo-launched intercontinental ballistic missiles, and air-launched missiles and free-fall bombs. The USAF, in the form of the Strategic Air Command (SAC), controls both the ICBM and aircraft forces in the USA's nuclear arsenal. USAF personnel strength is 570,800, some 27.6 per cent of the total manpower strength of the US armed forces, which receive an annual allocation of about 6.1 per cent of the gross national product.

The USA's main deterrents are the strategic nuclear forces, which comprise elements of the US Navy (656 SLBMs in 41 SSBNs), and the Strategic Air Command of the USAF. This has 1,054 ICBMs: 550 Minuteman III each with three MIRV, 450 Minuteman II with a single warhead each, and 54 Titan II with a single warhead each. The Minuteman III missiles are currently being upgraded in warhead yield and reduced CEP by the introduction of the 370-kiloton Mark 12A MIRV warhead, the improved NS-20 guidance system, and modifications to the associated software. These are thought to reduce the CEP of the missile from 1,500 ft (457 m) to 700 ft (213 m), and so materially improve the missile force's chances of destroying hardened targets in the USSR. Improving the basic missile development of the MARV warhead has continued, and preliminary hardware design for the new MX tunnel-mobile ICBM has started. This last is intended to move on a special train through subterranean tunnels, and so present a virtually untraceable target, and be launched by elevation through the crust of the tunnel and subsequent standard surface firing. Progress is also being made with the air-launched cruise missile (ALCM).

The SAC system also controls some 382 manned bombers (four squadrons of FB-111 with 66 aircraft, 15 squadrons of B.52G/H with 241 aircraft, and five squadrons of B-52D with 75 aircraft) for operation use with 1,250 SRAMs, plus 50 B-52D/F for training purposes; 125 bombers (mostly B-52D/F) in reserve; 487 KC-135 tankers in 30 squadrons; and

strategic reconnaissance and command forces in the form of two squadrons of SR-71A (10 aircraft), 10 U-2C/K, four E-4A/B and 19 RC/EC-135. HQ is Omaha, Nebraska.

For defence against strategic attack, the US and Canada operate the North American Air Defense Command (NORAD), with its headquarters at Colorado Springs. The US forces under command of NORAD are the Aerospace Defense Command (ADCOM), with the following components:
1. Safeguard anti-ballistic missile system, with its missiles deactivated.
2. Interceptor force, with 141 F-106A of six USAF squadrons, 60 F-101B of three Air National Guard (ANG) squadrons, 40 F-4D of two ANG squadrons, and 90 F-106A of five ANG squadrons (331 interceptors in all).
3. Airborne early warning force, with 10 EC-121 AEW aircraft of one Reserve squadron.
4. Warning systems, comprising
    (i) satellite-based early-warning system
    (ii) Space Detection and Tracking System (SPADATS)
    (iii) Ballistic Missile Early Warning System (BMEWS)
    (iv) Distant Early Warning (DEW) Line
    (v) Pinetree Line
    (vi) 474N SLBM detection and warning network
    (vii) Perimeter Acquisition Radar Attack Character System (PARCS)
    (viii) Cobra Dane Radar
    (ix) Back-Up Interceptor Control (BUIC)
    (x) Semi-Automatic Ground Environment (SAGE) tracking system
    (xi) ground radar stations, some 51 in number and manned by the ANG.

The rest of the USAF is made up of tactical elements for world-wide deployment, and consists of large numbers of squadrons for a variety of tasks:
48 FGA squadrons with 1,100 F-4.
2 FGA squadrons with 48 F-105G (Wild Weasel).
2 FGA squadrons with 48 F-4G (Wild Weasel).
13 FGA squadrons with 282 F-111E/F.
9 FGA squadrons with 216 F-15.
4 FGA squadrons with 96 A-7D.
3 FGA squadrons with 48 A-10A.
9 tactical reconnaissance squadrons with 192 RF-4C.
1 AWACS squadron with 3 E-3A (with 19 more on order).
1 defence evaluation squadron with 21 EB-57, soon to be supplemented by 2 more squadrons with 40 EF-111A.
6 tactical air control squadrons with 88 OV-10A and O-2E.
1 tactical air control squadron with 7 EC-130E.
1 tactical air control squadron with 11

EC-135.
3 tactical air control squadrons with 27 CH-3 helicopters.
4 special operations squadrons with 20 AC-130.
1 special operations squadron with CH-3 and UH-1 helicopters.
4 aggressor training squadrons with 55 F-5E.
7 operational conversion units with F-4.
1 operational conversion unit with F-5.
2 operational conversion units with F-15.
2 operational conversion units with F-101 and F-106.
3 operational conversion units with A-10.
1 operational conversion unit with RF-4C.
1 tactical drone squadron with 7 DC-130A.
15 tactical airlift squadrons with 234 C-130.
13 heavy transport squadrons with 234 C-141.
4 heavy transport squadrons with 70 C-5A.
5 SAR squadrons with 30 HC-130 aircraft, plus 76 HH-3 and HH-53, and 11 HH-1 helicopters.
3 weather reconnaissance squadrons with 14 WC-130 and 29 WC-135.
Helicopter squadrons with 138 UH-1N, 21 HH-3E and 51 HH/CH-53.
28 training squadrons.
The deployment of these squadrons is detailed in the balance of forces chart.

570,800, including 39,000 women, and about 3,400 combat aircraft.

Strategic Nuclear Forces
Strategic Air Command (SAC): some 600 combat aircraft.

Offensive:
ICBM (1,054):
    450 Minuteman II, 550 Minuteman III, 54 Titan II.
Aircraft (432 combat bombers):
    66 FB-111A in 4 sqns ⎫ with
    241 B-52G/H in 15 sqns ⎬ 1,250
    75 B-52D in 5 sqns. ⎭ SRAMs
    Training: 50 B-52D/F.
    Storage or reserve: 125, incl B-52D/F.
    Tankers: 487 KC-135 in 30 sqns.
    Strategic reconnaissance and command: 10 SR-71A in 2 sqns; 10 U-2C/K; 4 E-4A/B; 19 RC/EC-135.
Defensive:
North American Air Defense Command (NORAD), HQ at Colorado Springs, is a joint American-Canadian organisation. US forces under NORAD are in Aerospace Defense Command (ADCOM).
ABM: Safeguard system (msls deactivated).
Aircraft (excluding Canadian and tac units):
    Interceptors (331 ac):
        (i) Regular: 6 sqns with 141 F-106A.

(ii) Air National Guard (ANG): 3 sqns with 60 F-101B, 2 with 40 F-4D, 5 with 90 F-106A.

AEW aircraft: 1 reserve sqn with 10 EC-121.

Warning Systems:

(i) Satellite-based early-warning system: 3 DSP satellites, 1 over eastern hemisphere, 2 over western; surveillance and warning system to detect launchings from SLBM, ICBM and Fractional Orbital Bombardment Systems (FOBS).

(ii) Space Detection and Tracking System (SPADATS): USAF Spacetrack (7 sites), USN SPASUR and civilian agencies. Space Defense Center at NORAD HQ: satellite tracking, identification and cataloguing control.

(iii) Ballistic Missile Early Warning System (BMEWS): 3 stations (Alaska, Greenland, England); detection and tracking radars with ICBM and IRBM capability.

(iv) Distant Early Warning (DEW) Line: 31 stations roughly along the 70° N parallel.

(v) Pinetree Line: 24 stations in Central Canada.

(vi) 474N: 3 stations on US east, 1 on Gulf, 3 on west coast (to be replaced by Pave Paws phased-array radars: 1 on east, 1 on west coast); SLBM detection and warning net.

(vii) Perimeter Acquisition Radar Attack Characterization System (PARCS): 1 north-facing phased-array 2,000-mile (3,219-km) system at inactive ABM site in North Dakota.

(viii) Cobra Dane Radar: phased-array system at Shemya, Aleutians.

(ix) Back-up Interceptor Control (BUIC): system for AD command and control (all stations but 1 semi-active).

(x) Semi-Automatic Ground Environment (SAGE): 6 locations (2 in Canada); combined with BUIC and Manual Control Centre (MCC) in Alaska (to be replaced by Joint Surveillance System (JSS) with 7 Region Operations Control Centres, 4 in US, 1 in Alaska, 2 in Canada); system for coordinating surveillance and tracking of objects in North America airspace.

(xi) Ground radar stations: some 51 stations manned by Air National Guard, augmented by the Federal Aviation Administration (FAA) stations (to be replaced as surveillance element of JSS).

Air Force

81 FGA sqns: 48 with 1,100 F-4, 2 with 48 F-105G (Wild Weasel), 2 with 48 F-4G (Wild Weasel), 13 with 282 F-111E/F, 9 with 216 F-15, 4 with 96 A-7D, 3 with 48 A-10A.

9 tac recce sqns with 192 RF-4C.

1 AWACS sqn with 3 E-3A (19 on order).

1 defence system evaluation sqn with 21 EB-57 (2 with 40 EF-111A due).

11 tac air control sqns: 6 with 88 OV-10 and O-2E, 1 with 7 EC-130E, 1 with 11 EC-135 ac, 3 with 27 CH-3 helicopters.

5 special operations sqns: 4 with 20 AC-130 ac, 1 with CH-3, UH-1 helicopter.

4 aggressor trg sqns with 55 F-5E.

16 OCU: 7 with F-4, 1 with F-5, 2 with F-15, 2 with F-101/-106, 3 with A-10, 1 with RF-4C.

1 tac drone sqn with 7 DC-130A.

15 tac airlift sqns with 234 C-130.

17 hy transport sqns: 4 with 70 C-5A, 13 with 234 C-141.

5 SAR sqns with 30 HC-130 ac, 76 HH-3/-53, 11 HH-1 helicopters.

3 medical transport sqns with 17 C-9.

3 weather recce sqns with 14 WC-130, 29 WC-135.

Helicopters incl 138 UH-1N, 21 HH-3E, 51 HH/CH-53.

28 trg sqns with 113 T-33, 700 T-37, 900 T-38, 135 T-39, 50 T-41, 20 T-43, C-5A, C-130E, C-141A, U-3, C-140.

Deployment:

Continental United States (incl Alaska):

(i) Tactical Air Command (82,000 men): 9th and 12th Air Forces with 43 fighter sqns, 5 tac recce sqns.

(ii) Military Airlift Command (MAC) (64,500 men): 21st and 22nd Air Forces.

Europe: US Air Force, Europe (USAFE) (76,000 men): 3rd Air Force (Britain), 16th Air Force (Spain; units in Italy, Greece and Turkey), 17th Air Force (Germany and Netherlands) with 1 AD sqn in Iceland; 25 fighter sqns (plus 4 in US on call) with 312 F-4C/D/E, 20 F-5E, 72 F-15, 156 F-111E/F; 3 tac recce sqns (plus 3 in US on call) with 60 RF-4C; 2 tac airlift sqns (plus 6 in US on call) with 32 C-130.

Pacific Air Forces (PACAF) (31,000 men): 5th Air Force (Japan, Okinawa, 1 wing in Korea), 13th Air Force (Philippines, Taiwan) with 9 fighter sqns, 1 tac recce sqn.

Reserves (139,900 men):

(i) Air National Guard (92,500 men) with about 1,000 combat aircraft:

10 interceptor sqns (under ADCOM); 29 fighter sqns (11 with 283 F-100C/D, 3 with 84 F-105B/D, 2 with 40 F-4C, 11 with 256 A-7, 2 with 49 A-37B); 8 recce sqns (1 with 20 RF-101, 7 with 135 RF-4C); 19 tac transport sqns (18 with 150 C-130A/B/C, 1 with 16 C-7); 6 tac air spt sqns with 120 O-2A; 13 tanker sqns with 104 KC-135, 1 ECM sqn with 10 C/EC-121; 1 defence system evaluation sqn with 20 EB-57B; 2 SAR sqns with 8 HC-130

(ii) Air Force Reserve (47,400 men) with about 190 combat aircraft:

3 fighter sqns with 69 F-105D; 4 attack sqns with 91 A-37B; 17 tac transport sqns (11 with 121, C-130 A/B, 4 with 63 C-123K, 2 with 31 C-7); 1 AEW sqn with 10 EC-121 (ADCOM), 3 tanker sqns with 24 KC-135; 2 special operations sqns with 10 AC-130, 7 CH-3; 4 SAR sqns (2 with 13 HC-130, 2 with 20 HH-3E, HH-1H); 1 weather recce sqn with 4 WC-130. 18 Reserve Associate Military Airlift sqns (personnel only): 4 transport for C-5A, 13 transport for C-141A, 1 aero medical for C-9A.

(iii) Civil Reserve Air Fleet: 220 long-range commercial ac (124 cargo/convertible, 96 passenger).

Marine Corps

3 Air Wings (364 combat aircraft):

12 FGA sqns with 144 F-4N/S.

13 FGA sqns: 3 with 80 AV-8A Harrier, 5 with 60 A-4F/M, 5 with 60A-6A/E.

1 recce sqn with 10 RF-4B.

1 ECM sqn with 10 EA-6B.

2 observation sqns with 36 OV-10A.

3 assault transport/tanker sqns with 36 KC-130F.

3 attack helicopter sqns with 54 AH-1J.

4 lt helicopter sqns with 96 UH-1E/N.

9 med helicopter sqns with 162 CH-46F.

6 hy helicopter sqns with 126 CH-53D.

Sparrow and Sidewinder AAM.

Reserves:

1 Air Wing: 2 fighter sqns with 24 F-4N, 5 attack sqns with 60 A-4E/F, 1 observation sqn with 18 OV-10A, 1 transport/tanker sqn with 12 KC-130, 7 helicopter sqns (1 attack with 18 AH-1G, 2 hy with 24 CH-53, 3 med with 54 CH-46, 1 lt with 21 UH-1E).

Naval Air Arm

12 attack carrier air wings about 1,100 combat aircraft):

26 fighter sqns: 14 with 168 F-14A, 12 with 144 F-4.

36 attack sqns: 11 with 110 A-6E, 25 with 300 A-7E.

10 recce sqns with 30 RA-5C and RF-8.

24 land-based MR sqns with 280 P-3B/C.

13 ASW sqns each with 10 S-3A.

13 AEW sqns each with 4 E-2B/C.

12 ASW helicopter sqns each with 8 SH-3A/D/G/H.

17 misc support sqns with 12 C-130F/LC-130, 7 C-118, 12 C-9B, 12 CT-39, 13 C-131, 6 C-117, 20 C-1, 15 C-2, 36 EA-6A/B ac; 30 RH-53D, CH-46, SH-3, SH-2B/C helicopters.

1 aggressor trg sqn with 13 F-5E/F.

Reserves:

2 carrier wings: 6 A-7A/B attack, 4 F-4N fighters, 2 RF-8G recce, 3 EA-6A and EKA-3 ECM, 2 E-2B AEW sqns.

13 MR sqns with P-3A.

2 tac spt sqns with C-9B, C-118B.

2 composite sqns with TA-4J.

7 helicopter sqns: 4 ASW with SH-3A/G, 2 lt attack with HH-1K, 1 SAR with HH-3A.

Army Air Arm

Aircraft/helicopters: about 500 ac, incl 300 OV-1/-10, 200 U-8/-21, 40 C-12; 9,000 helicopters, incl 1,000 AH-1G/Q/S, 4,000 UH-1/-19, 15 UH-60A, 700 CH-47/-54, 3,600 OH-6A/-58A, H-13.

Trainers incl 310 T-41/-42 ac; 700 TH-55A helicopters.

(148 AH-1S helicopters on order).

Beech Aircraft C-12A Huron

Type: communications aircraft
Crew: one or two, plus up to 13 passengers
Wings: light alloy cantilever low-wing mono-plane
Fuselage: light alloy semi-monocoque
Tail unit: light alloy cantilever
Landing gear: electrically actuated retract-able tricycle unit
Powerplant: two Pratt & Whitney Aircraft of Canada PT6A-38 turboprops, each rated at 750 shp and driving a Hartzell three-blade metal propeller
Fuel capacity: 453 gallons (2,059 litres) in wing bladder tanks
Avionics: comprehensive communication and navigation equipment
Armament: none
Dimensions: Span 54 ft 6 in (16.61 m)
Length 43 ft 9 in (13.34 m)
Height 15 ft (4.57 m)
Wing area: 303 ft² (28.15 m²)
Weights: Empty 7,334 lb (3,327 kg)
Loaded
Maximum 12,500 lb (5,670 kg)
Performance: (at maximum take-off weight) speed 301 mph (484 kph) at 14,000 ft (4,267 m); cruising speed 262 mph (421 kph) at 30,000 ft (9,140 m); climb 2,450 ft (747 m) per minute at sea level (civil version); service ceiling 30,900 ft (9,420 m); range at maximum cruising speed 1,824 miles (2,935 km)
Used also by: Algeria, Bolivia. Eire, Pakistan
Notes: Based on the Super King Air 200, the C-12A communications aircraft entered US military service in 1975. One model is operated by the Irish Army Air Corps in the coastal fishery protection role.

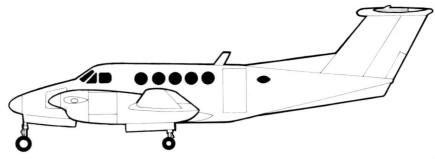

Beech Aircraft T-34C

Type: trainer and light tactical strike aircraft
Crew: two, seated in tandem
Wings: light alloy cantilever low-wing mono-plane
Fuselage: light alloy semi-monocoque
Tail unit: light alloy cantilever
Landing gear: electrically actuated retract-able tricycle unit
Powerplant: one Pratt & Whitney Aircraft of Canada PT6A-25 turboprop, rated at 715 shp, but torque-limited to 400 shp, and driving a Hartzell three-blade metal propeller
Fuel capacity: 107 gallons (488 litres) in four wing tanks, plus an optional 17.6 gallons (80 litres)
Avionics: comprehensive communication and navigation equipment
Armament: (T-34C-1) four underwing hard-points, the two inner ones capable of carry-ing 600 lb (272 kg) each, and the outer ones 300 lb (136 kg) each, to a maximum of 1,200 lb (544 kg) of external stores, which can include 7.62-mm Minigun pods, light bombs, AGM-22A anti-tank missiles, and LAU-32 or LAU-59 rocket pods
Dimensions: Span 33 ft 4 in (10.16 m)
Length 28 ft 8½ in (8.75 m)
Height 9 ft 11 in (3.02 m)

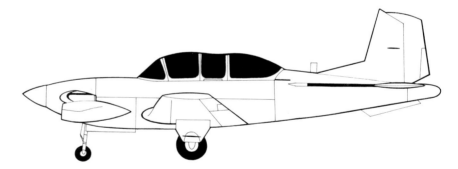

Wing area: 179.9 ft² (16.71 m²)
Weights: Empty 2,630 lb (1,193 kg)
Loaded 4,274 lb (1,938 kg)
Maximum 5,500 lb (2,495 kg)
Performance: (T-34C-1 at maximum take-off weight) speed 198 mph (318 kph) at 18,000 ft (5,500 m); climb 560 ft (170 m) per minute at sea level; combat radius at a take-off weight of 5,373 lb (2,437 kg) on a strike mission 345 miles (555 km)
Used also by: Algeria, Argentina, Ecuador, Indonesia, Morocco, Peru

Notes: Derived from the 1953 Beechcraft T-34A and T-34B Mentor piston-engined trainer for the USAF and USN respectively, the turboprop-powered T-34C stems from a 1973 USN inquiry into the possibility of upgrading the type. Tests of converted examples proved highly successful, and new production aircraft entered US Navy service early in 1978. The T-34C-1 is an ar-maments trainer, well able to act in the for-ward air controller (FAC) and light tactical strike mission roles, as which it has been ordered by several air forces.

Beech Aircraft T-42A Cochise

Type: instrument trainer
Crew: four or five
Wings: aluminium alloy cantilever low-wing monoplane
Fuselage: aluminium alloy semi-monocoque
Tail unit: metal cantilever
Landing gear: electrically actuated retract-able tricycle unit
Powerplant: two Continental IO-470-L piston engines, each rated at 260 hp and driving a Hartzell two-blade metal propeller

Fuel capacity: 83 gallons (378 litres) in two wing leading-edge tanks, or 113 gallons (515 litres) in wing leading-edge tanks
Avionics: comprehensive communication and navigation equipment
Armament: none
Dimensions: Span 37 ft 10 in (11.53 m)
Length 28 ft (8.53 m)
Height 9 ft 7 in (2.92 m)
Wing area: 199.2 ft² (18.5 m²)
Weights: Empty 3,226 lb (1,463 kg)
Loaded
Maximum 5,100 lb (2,313 kg)

Performance: (at maximum take-off weight) speed 231 mph (372 kph) at sea level; cruising speed 216 mph (348 kph) at 6,000 ft (1,830 m); climb 1,693 ft (516 m) per minute at sea level; service ceiling 19,300 ft (5,880 m); maximum range 1,141 miles (1,836 km)
Used only by: USA
Notes: Derived from the civil Model 95-55, the T-42B was selected for US instrument training service in 1965.

200

Beech Aircraft U-21F

Type: light transport
Crew: two, plus up to 13 passengers
Wings: aluminium alloy cantilever low-wing monoplane
Fuselage: metal semi-monocoque
Tail unit: metal cantilever
Landing gear: electrically actuated retractable tricycle unit
Powerplant: two Pratt & Whitney Aircraft of Canada PT6A-28 turboprops, each rated at 680 ehp and driving a Hartzell metal four-blade propeller
Fuel capacity: 391 gallons (1,779 litres) in rubber fuel cells in the wings
Avionics: comprehensive communication and navigation equipment
Armament: none
Dimensions: Span 45 ft 10½ in (13.98 m)
Length 39 ft 11½ in (12.18 m)
Height 15 ft 4¼ in (4.68 m)
Wing area: 280 ft² (26.0 m²)
Weights: Empty 6,767 lb (3,069 kg)
Loaded
Maximum 11,500 lb (5,216 kg)
Performance: (at maximum take-off weight) cruising speed 285 mph (459 kph) at a weight of 10,500 lb (4,762 kg) at 10,000 ft (3,050 m); climb 1,963 ft (598 m) per minute at sea level; service ceiling 24,850 ft (7,575 m); range 1,542 miles (2,483) at long-range cruising power at 21,000 ft (6,400 m)
Used also by: Algeria, Chile, Eire, Guyana, Israel, Jamaica, Morocco, Peru, Uruguay, Venezuela
Notes: The US Army bought its first four Beech Aircraft Twin Bonanza communications and transport machines in 1952, designating them L-23. Large numbers of Beech aircraft were then bought in the L-23 series, which was redesignated U-8 Seminole in 1962. The introduction of

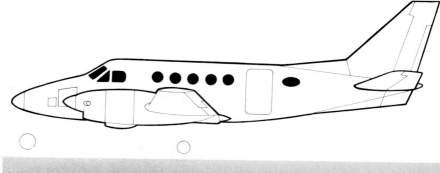

Pratt & Whitney turboprops produced the Beech Queen Air Model 65-90T, tested by the US Army as the NU-8F. The Queen Air was in turn developed into the King Air Model 65-90, which was adopted as the U-21A. The type was widely used in the Vietnam war for special electronic reconnaissance duties, specific models of the King Air being designated RU-21A, B, C, D and E. The Beech Aircraft B99 airliner is basically similar, but has a fuselage 4 ft 2 in (1.27 m) shorter, and is used by Chile for search and rescue missions, and for navigation training.

Beech Aircraft VC-6B

Type: liaison and instrument training aircraft
Crew: two, plus up to four passengers
Wings: aluminium alloy cantilever low-wing monoplane
Fuselage: aluminium alloy semi-monocoque
Tail unit: metal cantilever
Landing gear: electrically actuated retractable tricycle unit
Powerplant: two Pratt & Whitney Aircraft of Canada PT6A-21 turboprops, each rated at 550 ehp and driving a Hartzell three-blade metal propeller
Fuel capacity: 320 gallons (1,454 litres) in two nacelle tanks and auxiliary tanks in the outer wings
Avionics: comprehensive communication and navigation equipment
Armament: none
Dimensions: Span 50 ft 3 in (15.32 m)
Length 35 ft 6 in (10.82 m)
Height 14 ft 4½ in (4.33 m)
Wing area: 293.94 ft² (27.31 m²)
Weights: Empty 5,717 lb (2,593 kg)
Loaded
Maximum 9,650 lb (4,377 kg)
Performance: (at maximum take-off weight) cruising speed 256 mph (412 kph) at 12,000 ft (3,660 m); climb 1,955 ft (596 m) per minute at sea level; service ceiling 28,100 ft (8,565 m); maximum range 1,229 miles (1,979 km)
Used also by: Spain
Notes: Derived from the King Air Model C90, the VC-6B was adopted as a VIP light transport in 1976. The same basic type

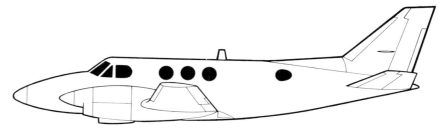

was adopted by the US Navy as an advanced trainer under the designation T-44A. This has 680-ehp Pratt & Whitney Aircraft of Canada PT6A-28 turboprops, increased operating weights and superior performance, maximum cruising speed being 287 mph (462 kph) at 12,000 ft (3,660 m). A modified version, company designation King Air A100, serves with the USAF as the U-21F utility aircraft. This is 4 ft 2 in (1.27 m) longer, and can carry up to 13 passengers in a pressurised fuselage.

Bell Helicopter Textron AH-1G HueyCobra

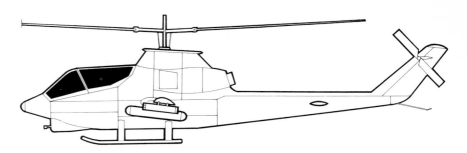

Type: attack helicopter
Crew: two, seated in tandem
Rotors: metal cantilever two-blade main rotor; metal cantilever two-blade tail rotor
Fuselage: aluminium alloy frame forward fuselage, semi-monocoque centre section, and monocoque tailboom
Landing gear: twin metal skids
Powerplant: one Lycoming T53-L-13 turbo-shaft, rated at 1,400 shp but derated to 1,100 shp for continuous running
Fuel capacity:
Avionics: comprehensive communication and navigation/attack equipment
Armament: one 7.62-mm GAU-28/A Mini-gun and one XM-129 40-mm grenade-launcher in the chin turret, plus a variety of weapons on four hardpoints under the wings. These can carry four XM-159 or XM-157 2.75-in (70-mm) FFAR rocket pods, the first with 76 and the second with 28 rockets each, or two BGM-71 TOW anti-tank missiles, or one XM-35 20-mm 6-barrel cannon with 1,000 rounds under

the port inner pylon, or two XM-18E1 Mini-gun pods
Dimensions: Span 44 ft (13.41 m)
Length (fuselage) 44 ft 7 in (13.59 m)
Height 13 ft 6¼ in (4.12 m)
Rotor disc area: 1,520.4 ft² (141.2 m²)
Weights: Empty 6,073 lb (2,754 kg)
Loaded
Maximum 9,500 lb (4,309 kg)
Performance: speed 172 mph (277 kph); climb 1,230 ft (375 m) per minute at sea level; service ceiling 11,400 ft (3,475 m);

hovering ceiling in ground effect 9,900 ft (3,015 m); range 357 miles (574 km)
Used also by: Israel, Spain
Notes: The Model 209 HueyCobra was developed from the UH-1B/C Iroquois to provide the US Army with a proper gunship helicopter. The prototype first flew in 1965, and the type immediately showed that the combination of the UH-1's dynamic system with a new streamlined, slim fuselage was a winner. From the AH-1G initial production model have been derived a number of more advanced models.

Bell Helicopter Textron AH-1J SeaCobra

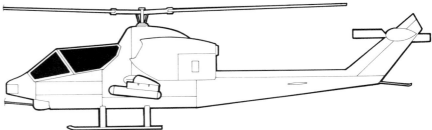

Type: attack helicopter
Crew: two, seated in tandem
Rotor: Metal cantilever two-blade main rotor; metal cantilever two-blade tail rotor
Fuselage: metal semi-monocoque
Landing gear: twin metal skids
Powerplant: one Pratt & Whitney Aircraft of Canada T400-CP-400 (two coupled engines) turboshaft, rated at 1,800 shp, but flat-rated to 1,100-shp continuous power, with 1,250 shp available for take-off and emergencies
Fuel capacity:
Avionics: comprehensive communication and navigation/attack equipment
Armament: one General Electric chin-mounted turret mounting a 20-mm XM-197 three-barrel cannon with 750 rounds, plus four hardpoints under the stub wings, able to accommodate a wide variety of external stores, including XM-18E1 7.62-mm Minigun pods, XM-157 packs with seven 2.75-in (70-mm) rockets, and XM-159 packs with nineteen 2.75-in rockets
Dimensions: Span 44 ft (13.41 m)
Length (fuselage) 44 ft 7 in (13.59 m)
Height 13 ft 8 in (4.15 m)
Rotor disc area: 1,520.4 ft² (141.2 m²)
Weights: Empty 7,261 lb (3,294 kg)
Loaded 9,972 lb (4,523 kg)
Maximum 10,000 lb (4,535 kg)
Performance: (at maximum take-off weight) speed 207 mph (333 kph); climb 1,090 ft (332 m) per minute at sea level; service ceiling 10,550 ft (3,215 m); hovering ceil-

ing in ground effect 12,450 ft (3,794 m); maximum range 359 miles (577 km)
Used also by: Iran
Notes: Developed from the AH-1G series for the US Marine Corps, the SeaCobra features a twin-engined coupled powerplant, with strengthened transmission and larger tail rotor. There is also an improved version of the SeaCobra, designated the AH-1T

SeaCobra. This uses the Pratt & Whitney Aircraft of Canada T400-WV-402 coupled engine, rated at 1,970 shp, driving a rotor system based on that of the Bell Helicopter Textron Model 214. Main rotor span is 48 ft (14.63 m), fuselage length is 48 ft 2 in (14.68 m), and maximum take-off weight 14,000 lb (6,350 kg). The AH-1T is in production for the US Marine Corps.

Bell Helicopter Textron AH-1T SeaCobra

Type: attack helicopter
Crew: two, seated in tandem
Rotors: metal cantilever two-blade main rotor; metal cantilever two-blade tail rotor
Fuselage: metal semi-monocoque
Landing gear: twin metal skids
Powerplant: one Pratt & Whitney Aircraft of Canada T400-WV-402 coupled turbo-shaft, rated at 1,970 shp

Fuel capacity:
Avionics: comprehensive communication and navigation/attack equipment
Armament: one 20-mm XM-197 three-barrel rotary cannon, plus a wide variety of external stores, including guided and unguided missiles
Dimensions: Span 48 ft (14.63 m)
Length (fuselage) 48 ft 2 in (14.68 m)
Height
Rotor disc area: 1,809.6 ft² (168.1 m²)

Weights: Empty 8,014 lb (3,635 kg)
Loaded
Maximum 14,000 lb (6,350 kg)
Performance:
Used only by: USA
Notes: The AH-1T SeaCobra is a combination of the dynamic system of the Bell Model 214, the airframe of the AH-1J, and an improved engine, the whole package giving the AH-1T formidable performance and an excellent payload. First deliveries were made in 1976 to the US Marine Corps.

Bell Helicopter Textron UH-1 and HH-1 Iroquois

Type: general-purpose helicopter
Crew: one, plus up to 14 passengers
Rotor: metal cantilever two-blade main rotor; metal cantilever two-blade tail rotor
Fuselage: metal semi-monocoque
Landing gear: twin metal skids
Powerplant: one Lycoming T53-L-13 turboshaft, rated at 1,400 shp
Fuel capacity: 183 gallons (832 litres) in five rubber fuel cells, or an overload capacity of 433 gallons (1,968 litres) by the addition of two 125-gallon (568-litre) auxiliary tanks
Avionics: communication and navigation equipment
Armament: none on the UH-1H, but the UH-1B carries an armament of four side-mounted 7.62-mm machine-guns or two packs of 2.75-in (70-mm) rockets, each pack holding 24 projectiles
Dimensions: Span 48 ft (14.63 m)
Length (fuselage) 41 ft 10¾ in (12.77 m)
Height 14 ft 6 in (4.42 m)
Rotor disc area: 1,809 ft² (168.06 m²)
Weights: Empty 4,667 lb (2,116 kg)
Loaded 9,039 lb (4,100 kg)
Maximum 9,500 lb (4,309 kg)
Performance: (at maximum take-off weight) maximum and cruising speed 127 mph (204 kph); climb 1,600 ft (488 m) per minute at sea level; service ceiling 12,600 ft (3,840 m); hovering ceiling in ground effect 13,600 ft (4,145 m); range with maximum fuel 318 miles (511 km)
Used also by: many nations
Notes: This prolific family of general-purpose helicopters is based on the Bell Model 204 and 205 series, the UH-1A, B and C being based on the Model 204, with the early Lycoming T53-L turboshaft and a capacity for nine passengers, and the later variants on the Model 205, which is larger and more powerfully engined. The basic types are:

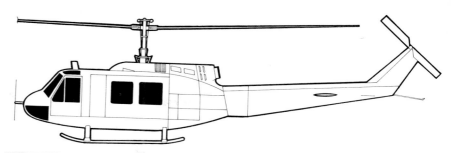

1. UH-1A with 700-shp T53-L-1A, deliveries beginning in 1959
2. UH-1B with 960- or 1,100-shp T53-L-5 or 11
3. UH-1C with the 1,100-shp T53-L-11 but improved rotor and fuel capacity
4. UH-1H with the 1,400-shp T53-L-13. There is also the UH-1F missile support

helicopter, based on the Model 204 but powered by one General Electric T58-GE-3 turboshaft of 1,000 shp, and capable of lifting loads of up to 4,000 lb (1,814 kg). The UH-1P psychological warfare model was derived from the UH-1F. The HH-1H is a base rescue helicopter derived from the UH-1H. The specification is for the UH-1H.

Bell Helicopter Textron UH-1N

Type: general-purpose helicopter
Crew: one, plus up to 14 passengers
Rotor: aluminium and laminates cantilever two-blade main rotor; metal cantilever two-blade tail rotor
Fuselage: metal semi-monocoque
Landing gear: twin metal skids
Powerplant: one Pratt & Whitney Aircraft of Canada PT6T-3 Turbo Twin Pac coupled turboshaft, rated at 1,800 shp but flat-rated to 1,130 shp for continuous operation and 1,290 shp for take-off and emergencies
Fuel capacity: 179 gallons (814 litres) in five rubber fuel cells, plus auxiliary tanks for an additional 150 gallons (681 litres)
Avionics: comprehensive communication and navigation equipment
Armament: none
Dimensions: Span 48 ft 2¼ in (14.69 m)
Length (fuselage) 42 ft 4¾ in (12.92 m)
Height 14 ft 10¼ in (4.53 m)
Rotor disc area: 1,809 ft² (168.06 m²)
Weights: Empty (civil version) 6,070 lb (2,753 kg)
Loaded
Maximum 10,500 lb (4,762 kg)
Performance: (at maximum take-off weight) maximum and cruising speed 115 mph (185 kph) at sea level; climb 1,420 ft (433

m) per minute at sea level; service ceiling 15,000 ft (4,570 m); hovering ceiling in ground effect 12,900 ft (3,930 m); range 248 miles (400 km)

Used also by: Canada, Colombia
Notes: Deliveries to the US forces began in 1970. Maximum payload is 3,383 lb (1,534 kg).

Boeing Airplane
B-52 Stratofortress

Type: strategic bomber
Crew: six
Wings: metal cantilever shoulder-wing monoplane
Fuselage: metal semi-monocoque
Tail unit: metal cantilever
Landing gear: hydraulically actuated bicycle unit, with stabilising outriggers
Powerplant: eight Pratt & Whitney TF33-P-3 turbofans, each rated at 17,000-lb (7,711-kg) static thrust
Fuel capacity:
Avionics: comprehensive communication and navigation/attack equipment
Armament: one 20-mm ASG-21 six-barrel cannon, plus up to 27,000 lb (12, 247 kg) of bombs carried internally, or two AGM-28B Hound Dog air-to-surface missiles under the wings, or 20 AGM-69A SRAM air-to-surface missiles, 12 carried under the wings on four triple launchers and the remaining eight carried on a rotary dispenser internally
Dimensions: Span 185 ft (56.4 m)
Length 157 ft 7 in (48.03 m)
Height 48 ft 3 in (14.75 m)
Wing area: 4,000 ft² (371.6 m²)
Weights: Empty 193,000 lb (87,100 kg)
Loaded
Maximum 505,000 lb (229,000 kg)
Performance: speed about 630 mph (1,014 kph) over 24,000 ft (7,315 m); service ceiling in the order of 55,000 ft (16,765 m); range 12,500 miles (20,150 km)
Used only by: USA
Notes: First visualised as a straight-winged piston-engined strategic bomber, the B-52 became a jet aircraft with the development of the 10,000-lb (4,536-kg) General Electric J57 turbojet. The first prototype flew in 1952, but the first production aircraft did not reach the users, the Strategic Air Command, until 1957. There have been several models of this still powerful bomber:
1. B-52A development model with J57-P-9W engines
2. B-52B and RB-52B, powered by J57-P-19 or 29 engines, and fitted

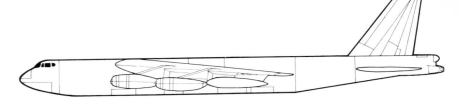

with full operational equipment as a multi-role bomber (B-52B) or as a reconnaissance aircraft (RB-52B) with cameras or electronic reconnaissance equipment. Underwing tanks with a capacity of 833 gallons (3,800 litres) were standard, and the normal bomb load was 10,000 lb (4,536 kg) over a range of 8,000 miles (12,875 km)
3. B-52C with J57-P-29W engines
4. B-52D with J57-P-29W engines, intended for long-range strategic bombing
5. B-52E with J57-P-29W engines, but completely new navigation and attack equipment
6. B-52F with J57-P-43W engines, but otherwise similar to the B-52E
7. B-52G with J57-P-43W engines and a 'wet' wing to hold far more fuel

than had been possible on earlier models, and so increase range significantly. The fin and rudder assembly was shortened but increased in chord, a remotely controlled rear turret was fitted, and provision was made for the carriage of AGM-28 Hound Dog attack missiles and Quail decoy missiles
8. B-52H with TF33-P-3 turbofans for greater performance, especially in range, a 20-mm multi-barrel cannon in the tail in place of earlier models' four .5-in (12.7-mm) machine-guns, and vastly improved sensors and electronics.

The B-52D, E and F have been used for tactical missions in Vietnam, while the B-52G and H have remained front-line SAC bombers with SRAM armament. Production ended in 1963.

Boeing Aerospace E-3A Sentry

Type: airborne warning and control system (AWACS) aircraft
Crew: 17
Wings: aluminium alloy cantilever low-wing monoplane
Fuselage: metal semi-monocoque
Tail unit: metal cantilever
Landing gear: hydraulically actuated retractable tricycle unit
Powerplant: four Pratt & Whitney TF33-PW-100A turbofans, each rated at 21,000-lb (9,525-kg) static thrust
Fuel capacity: 19,864 gallons (90,299 litres) in one integral centre-section, four integral wing and two reserve integral wing tanks
Avionics: comprehensive communication and navigation equipment, with Westinghouse AN/APY-1 downward-looking radar and IBM 4 Pi CC-1 computer as the core of the AWACS system
Armament: none
Dimensions: Span 145 ft 9 in (44.42 m)
Length 152 ft 11 in (46.61 m)
Height 42 ft 5 in (12.93 m)
Wing area: 3,050 ft² (283.4 m²)
Weights: Empty about 175,000 lb (79,380 kg)

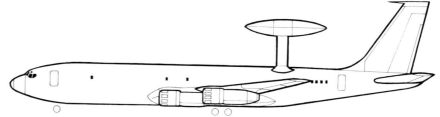

Loaded
Maximum about 350,000 lb
(158,760 kg)
Performance: speed about 600 mph (966 kph) at high altitude; operating altitude in excess of 40,000 ft (12,200 m); endurance more than 12 hours
Used also by: NATO
Notes: Developed from the Boeing 707-320 airliner, the E-3A AWACS aircraft first flew in 1972 under the designation EC-137D, with prototype Hughes and Westinghouse surveillance radars. The Westinghouse radar was selected for production E-3As. The radar is located in a radome 30 ft (9.14 m) in diameter, which rotates at six revolutions per minute above the fuselage of the E-3A. The radar scans to a range of 230 miles (370 km) for aircraft flying close to the ground, and farther for aircraft operating at higher altitudes. The E-3A has two main functions:

1. as an airborne surveillance, command and control centre for Tactical Air Command, to allow quick-reaction tactical decisions in forward military areas
2. as a surveillance and tracking airborne and early warning command and control centre for Aerospace Defense Command.

The first production E-3A was delivered in 1977, and the type has been selected for NATO use in Europe.

A VIP transport version of the Boeing 707 is also used by the USAF under the designation VC-137. Among these is the 'flying White House', known as Air Force One.

Boeing Aerospace E-4

Type: airborne command post
Crew: between 28 and 60
Wings: aluminium alloy cantilever low-wing monoplane
Fuselage: aluminium alloy semi-monocoque
Tail unit: aluminium alloy cantilever
Landing gear: hydraulically actuated retractable tricycle unit
Powerplant: four General Electric F103-GE-100 turbofans, each rated at 52,500-lb (23,814-kg) static thrust
Fuel capacity: 42,833 gallons (194,715 litres) in one centre-section integral and six wing integral tanks
Avionics: massively comprehensive communication and navigation equipment
Armament: none
Dimensions: Span 195 ft 8 in (59.64 m)
Length 231 ft 4 in (70.5 m)
Height 63 ft 5 in (19.33 m)
Wing area: 5,500 ft² (511 m²)
Weights: Empty about 380,000 lb (172,370 kg)
Loaded
Maximum 803,000 lb (364,230 kg)
Performance: speed 608 mph (978 kph) at 30,000 ft (9,150 m); service ceiling about 45,000 ft (13,715 m); range about 6,500 miles (10,460 km)
Used only by: USA
Notes: Intended as an Advanced Airborne National Command Post, the Boeing E-3 is derived from the Boeing 747 airliner. The

first two had Pratt & Whitney JT9D engines, but have now been retrofitted with General Electric engines, to bring them up to the standard of the third and fourth aircraft. The first three machines were E-4As, with 4,620 ft² (429.2 m²) of floor area and electronic equipment transferred from EC-135 Airborne Command Post aircraft. The fourth and subsequent aircraft will be E-4Bs, with highly sophisticated communication and decision-taking equipment provided by Boeing, Computer Services Corporation, Electrospace Systems Inc, and E-Systems Inc. The improved electronics will later be retrofitted to the E-4As, the first of which entered service in 1974.

Boeing Commercial T-43A

Type: navigation trainer
Crew: two, plus 12 students, four advanced students and three instructors
Wings: aluminium alloy cantilever low-wing monoplane
Fuselage: aluminium alloy semi-monocoque
Tail unit: aluminium alloy cantilever
Landing gear: hydraulically actuated retractable tricycle unit
Powerplant: two Pratt & Whitney JT8D-9A turbofans, each rated at 14,500-lb (6,575-kg) static thrust
Fuel capacity: 4,300 gallons (19,547 litres) in one integral centre-section and two integral wing tanks, plus an optional 666 gallons (3,027 litres) in a rear fuselage tank
Avionics: comprehensive communication and navigation equipment, including a complete instrument and systems station for each student
Armament: none
Dimensions: Span 93 ft (28.35 m)
Length 100 ft (30.48 m)
Height 37 ft (11.28 m)
Wing area: 980 ft² (91.05 m²)
Weights: Empty about 62,000 lb (28,123 kg)
Loaded
Maximum 115,500 lb (52,390 kg)

Performance: speed 586 mph (943 kph) at 23,500 ft (7,165 m); cruising speed 576 mph (927 kph) at 22,600 ft (6,890 m); climb 3,750 ft (1,143 m) per minute at sea level; endurance 6 hours; range 2,995 miles (4,820 km)

Used only by: USA

Notes: Derived from the Boeing 737-200 airliner, the T-43A is the world's most advanced navigation trainer. The 737 is used by Brazil, Egypt and Venezuela.

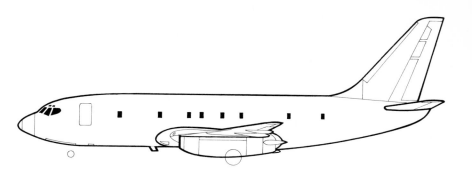

Boeing Vertol CH-46D Sea Knight

Type: combat assault helicopter

Crew: three, plus up to 25 passengers

Rotors: two metal cantilever three-blade main rotors

Fuselage: metal semi-monocoque

Landing gear: fixed tricycle unit

Powerplant: two General Electric T58-GE-16 turboshafts, each rated at 1,870 shp

Fuel capacity: 833 gallons (3,785 litres) in sponsons

Avionics: comprehensive communication and navigation equipment

Armament: none

Dimensions: Span 50 ft (15.24 m)
Length (fuselage) 33 ft 4 in (10.16 m)
Height 16 ft 8 in (5.08 m)

Rotor disc area: (total) 3,925 ft² (364.64 m²)

Weights: Empty 11,585 lb (5,240 kg)
Loaded
Maximum 21,400 lb (9,706 kg)

Performance: (at maximum take-off weight) speed 165 mph (266 kph) at sea level; cruising speed 155 mph (249 kph); climb 1,890 ft (576 m) per minute at sea level; service ceiling 13,100 ft (3,993 m); range 230 miles (370 km)

Used only by: USA

Notes: The military version of the Boeing Vertol Model 107, the CH-46 serves with US Marine Corps and US Navy units. Initial

models were powered by the 1,250-shp T58-GE-8B, but this was changed to the 1,400-shp T58-GE-10 in the CH-46D, and the US Marine Corps is at present updating its CH-46s to CH-46E standard by the

installation of 1,870-shp T58-GE-16 engines, and the incorporation of other modifications. The type is built in Japan as the Kawasaki KV-107, and serves in Sweden as the HKP-4. Payload 4,000 lb (1,814 kg).

Cessna Aircraft O-2

Type: forward air controller and psychological warfare aircraft

Crew: two, plus up to two passengers

Wings: metal braced high-wing monoplane

Fuselage: metal semi-monocoque

Tail unit: metal cantilever

Landing gear: hydraulically actuated retractable tricycle unit

Powerplant: two Continental IO-360-C piston engines, each rated at 210 hp and driving a McCauley two-blade metal propeller

Fuel capacity: 73 gallons (333 litres) in four wing tanks, plus provision for two more wing tanks, each of 25-gallon (113.5-litre) capacity

Avionics: comprehensive communication and navigation equipment

Armament: an external load of weapons pods can be carried on four underwing hardpoints

Dimensions: Span 38 ft 2 in (11.63 m)
Length 29 ft 9 in (9.07 m)
Height 9 ft 2 in (2.79 m)

Wing area: 202.5 ft² (18.81 m²)

Weights: Empty 2,848 lb (1,292 kg)
Loaded
Maximum 5,400 lb (2,449 kg)

Performance: (at maximum take-off weight) speed 199 mph (320 kph) at sea level; cruising speed 144 mph (232 kph) at

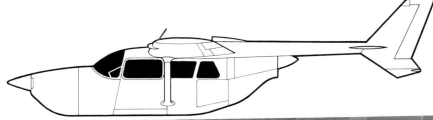

10,000 ft (3,050 m); climb 1,180 ft (360 m) per minute at sea level; service ceiling 19,300 ft (5,883 m); range 1,060 miles (1,706 km)

Used also by: Haiti, Iran, Ivory Coast, Mauritania, Niger, Portugal, Rhodesia, Senegal, Sri Lanka, Zaire

Notes: Derived from the civil Model 337 Skymaster, the O-2 is current in four military versions:

1. O-2A for forward air controller missions, fitted with visual reconnais-

sance, target identification, target marking, damage assessment and communication equipment

2. O-2B for psychological warfare missions, with a high powered loudspeaker system

3. O-2E for tactical air control with specialised command equipment

4. Reims Cessna 337. French produced counter-insurgency version (F 337, FA 337, FT 337P, FTB 337G).

Cessna Aircraft T-37

Type: trainer
Crew: two, seated side-by-side
Wings: aluminium alloy cantilever low-wing monoplane
Fuselage: metal semi-monocoque
Tail unit: metal cantilever
Landing gear: hydraulically actuated retractable tricycle unit
Powerplant: two Continental J69-T-25 turbojets, each rated at 1,025-lb (465-kg) static thrust
Fuel capacity: 257 gallons (1,170 litres) in one main fuselage and 12 wing tanks, plus provision for two 54-gallon (245-litre) wingtip tanks on the T-37C only
Avionics: communication and navigation equipment
Armament: provision on the T-37C only for two 250-lb (113-kg) bombs or four Sidewinder air-to-air missiles
Dimensions: Span 33 ft 9$\frac{1}{3}$ in (10.3 m)
Length 29 ft 3 in (8.92 m)
Height 9 ft 2$\frac{2}{3}$ in (2.8 m)
Wing area: 183.9 ft² (17.09 m²)
Weights: Empty 3,870 lb (1,755 kg)
Loaded
Maximum (T-37B) 6,600 lb (2,993 kg)
Maximum (T-37C) 7,500 lb (3,402 kg)
Performance: (T-37B at maximum take-off weight) speed 426 mph (685 kph) at 25,000 ft (7,620 m); cruising speed 380 mph (612 kph) at 25,000 ft (7,620 m); climb 3,020 ft (920 m) per minute at sea level; service ceiling 35,100 ft (10,700 m); normal range 604 miles (972 km); maximum range 663 miles (1,067 km)
Performance: (T-37C at maximum take-off weight) speed 402 mph (647 kph) at 25,000 ft (7,620 m); cruising speed 357 mph (574 kph) at 25,000 ft (7,620 m); climb 2,390 ft (728 m) per minute at sea level; service ceiling 29,900 ft (9,115 m); normal range 850 miles (1,367 km); maximum range 943 miles (1,517 km)
Used also by: Burma, Chile, Colombia, Greece, Jordan, Pakistan, Peru, Portugal, Thailand, Turkey
Notes: The T-37 was the USAF's first all-jet trainer, and the prototype made its maiden flight in 1954. There have been three versions:
1. T-37A with 920-lb (417-kg) thrust J69-T-9 engines
2. T-37B with 1,025-lb (465-kg) J69-T-25 engines
3. T-37C, basically similar to the T-37B, but with tip tanks and armament.

Cessna Aircraft T-41A Mescalero

Type: trainer
Crew: two, seated side by side, and up to two passengers
Wings: metal braced high-wing monoplane
Fuselage: metal semi-monocoque
Tail unit: metal cantilever
Landing gear: fixed tricycle unit
Powerplant: one Lycoming 0-320-H piston engine, rated at 160 hp and driving a two-blade metal propeller
Fuel capacity: 31.6 gallons (143.8 litres) in two wing tanks, plus provision for auxiliary tanks raising total fuel capacity to 40 gallons (182 litres)
Avionics: communication and navigation equipment
Armament: none
Dimensions: Span 35 ft 10 in (10.92 m)
Length 26 ft 11 in (8.2 m)
Height 8 ft 9$\frac{1}{2}$ in (2.68 m)
Wing area: 174 ft² (16.17 m²)
Weights: Empty 1,379 lb (626 kg)
Loaded
Maximum 2,300 lb (1,043 kg)
Performance: (at maximum take-off weight) speed 144 mph (232 kph) at sea level; cruising speed 140 mph (225 kph) at 8,000 ft (2,440 m), climb 770 ft (235 m) per minute at sea level; service ceiling 14,200 ft (4,330 m); maximum range 864 miles (1,390 km)
Used also by: Bolivia, Chile, Colombia, Dominican Republic, El Salvador, Greece, Guatemala, Honduras, Kampuchea, Laos, Liberia, Peru, Philippines, Saudi Arabia,

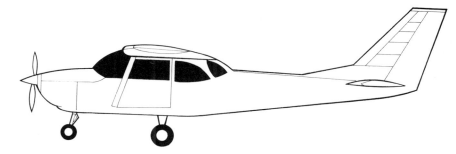

South Korea, Thailand, Turkey, Uruguay
Notes: Derived from the Cessna Model 172 lightplane, the T-41A Mescalero is used for basic training before successful pilot applicants move on to more sophisticated aircraft. There are also four slightly improved variants:
1. T-41B Mescalero for the US Army, for training and installation support

duties, and based on the civil Model R172E with a fuel-injected engine of 210 hp
2. T-41C for the US Air Force, for cadet training at the USAF Academy, with fixed-pitch propellers
3. T-41D for the Ecuadorean Air Force, with constant-speed propellers and altered electrical system.

Cessna Aircraft U-3

Type: utility transport
Crew: one, plus up to five passengers
Wings: metal cantilever low-wing monoplane
Fuselage: metal semi-monocoque
Tail unit: metal cantilever
Landing gear: electro-mechanically actuated retractable tricycle unit
Powerplant: two Continental 0-470-M inline engines, each rated at 240 hp and driving a three-blade metal propeller
Fuel capacity: 85 gallons (386 litres) in two wingtip tanks, plus six optional wing tanks
to raise maximum fuel capacity to 169 gallons (768 litres)
Avionics: communication and navigation equipment
Armament: none
Dimensions: Span 36 ft 11 in (11.25 m)
Length 29 ft 3 in (8.92 m)
Height 10 ft 6 in (3.2 m)
Wing area: 179 ft² (16.63 m²)
Weights: Empty 3,251 lb (1,474 kg)
Loaded
Maximum 5,500 lb (2,494 kg)
Performance: (at maximum take-off weight) speed 238 mph (383 kph) at sea level;
cruising speed 223 mph (359 kph) at 7,500 ft (2,285 m); climb 1,662 ft (507 m) per minute at sea level; service ceiling 19,750 ft (6,020 m); range 1,804 miles (2,903 km)
Used also by: Bolivia, Philippines, Tanzania, Zaire
Notes: The U-3 is the military version of the Model 310, and was at first designated L-27. The prototype flew in 1953. The U-3A entered service in 1957. The U-3B modified version has a swept fin, a longer nose and more cabin windows.

Douglas Aircraft A-3 Skywarrior

Type: reconnaissance and electronic warfare aircraft
Crew: three
Wings: metal cantilever shoulder-wing monoplane
Fuselage: metal semi-monocoque
Tail unit: metal cantilever
Landing gear: hydraulically actuated retractable tricycle unit
Powerplant: two Pratt & Whitney J57-P-10

turbojets, each rated at 12,400-lb (5,625-kg) static thrust

Fuel capacity:

Avionics: comprehensive communication and navigation equipment, and special electronic equipment in ECM aircraft

Armament: none

Dimensions: Span 72 ft 6 in (22.1 m)
Length 76 ft 4 in (23.3 m)
Height 23 ft 6 in (7.16 m)

Wing area: 812 ft² (75.44 m²)

Weights: Empty about 39,400 lb (17,872 kg)
Loaded
Maximum about 80,000 lb (36,288 kg)

Performance: speed 610 mph (982 kph) at 10,000 ft (3,050 m); climb 3,600 ft (1,100 m) per minute at sea level; service ceiling 43,000 ft (13,110 m); range 2,000 miles (3,220 km) with maximum fuel

Used only by: USA

Notes: The A-3 Skywarrior was initially designated A3D, and its prototype first flew in 1952. Deliveries to the US Navy of the A3D-1 bomber (with a bomb load of 12,000 lb/5,443 kg) began in 1954. The Skywarrior was the world's first carrier-borne strategic bomber, but in service the Westinghouse J40-WE-3 proved near to useless, and it was not until 1956 that the re-engined A3D-2 entered service. Later, however, the US Navy's missile programme removed the need for strategic bombers, and the A3D/A-3 was modified to fill other roles:

1. RA-3B reconnaissance aircraft
2. EA-3B electronic countermeasures (ECM) aircraft
3. TA-3B radar and navigation trainer
4. KA-3B tanker aircraft
5. EKA-3B tanker and ECM aircraft.

The USAF's B-66 Destroyer is basically the same aircraft, and is powered by the 10,000-lb (4,536-kg) Allison J71-A-13 engine:

1. RB-66A night photographic reconnaissance and indoctrination
2. RB-66B reconnaissance aircraft
3. B-66B bomber
4. RB-66C electronic reconnaissance aircraft
5. WB-66D weather reconnaissance aircraft
6. EB-66E jamming aircraft.

Fairchild Republic A-10A Thunderbolt II

Type: close-support aircraft

Crew: one

Wings: aluminium alloy cantilever low-wing monoplane

Fuselage: aluminium alloy semi-monocoque

Tail unit: aluminium alloy cantilever

Landing gear: hydraulically actuated retractable tricycle unit

Powerplant: two General Electric TF34-GE-100 turbofans, each rated at 9,065-lb (4,112-kg) static thrust

Fuel capacity: 1,337.5 gallons (6,080 litres) in two centre-section and two fuselage fuel cells, plus provision for three drop tanks, each of 500-gallon (2,271-litre) capacity

Avionics: comprehensive communication and navigation/attack equipment, including a Kaiser head up display, a radar homing and warning (RHAW) system, Pave Penny laser target designation system, ALR-46 radar alarm system, Westinghouse ALQ-119 and -131 ECM, and other systems

Armament: one General Electric GAU-8/A Avenger 30-mm seven-barrel cannon with 1,350 rounds, plus external stores up to a weight of 16,000 lb (7,257 kg) carried on 11 pylons (three under the fuselage, two under the centre section, and three under each wing; the fuselage centreline pylon can carry 5,000 lb/2,268 kg, the two fuselage outer and centre-section pylons 3,500 lb/1,587 kg each, the two inner wing pylons 2,500 lb/1,134 kg each, and the four outer wing pylons 1,000 lb/454 kg each). Among the stores that can be carried are twenty-eight 500-lb (227-kg) MK-82 LDGP or retarded bombs; six 2,000-lb (907-kg) MK-84 general-purpose bombs; six BLU-1 or 27/B incendiary bombs; 20 Rockeye II cluster bombs; 16 CBU-52/71, 10 CBU-38 or 16 CBU-70 dispenser weapons; four SUU-25 flare launchers; six AGM-65A Maverick air-to-surface missiles; MK-82 and -84 laser-guided bombs; MK-84 optically-guided bombs; two SUU-23 gun pods; drop tanks; and ECM equipment pods

Dimensions: Span 57 ft 6 in (17.53 m)
Length 53 ft 4 in (16.26 m)
Height 14 ft 8 in (4.47 m)

Wing area: 506 ft² (47.01 m²)

Weights: Empty 23,611 lb (10,710 kg)
Loaded 31,400 lb (14,243 kg)
Maximum 47,400 lb (21,500 kg)

Performance: (at maximum take-off weight) speed 449 mph (722 kph) in 'clean' condition at sea level; cruising speed 394 mph (634 kph) at 5,000 ft (1,525 m); climb 6,000 ft (1,828 m) per minute at sea level

at basic design weight; climb 1,000 ft (328 m) per minute at maximum take-off weight; combat radius with maximum weapons load, loiter of 2 hours and 20 minutes' reserve fuel, 288 miles (463 km); ferry range 2,647 miles (4,200 km)
Used only by: USA
Notes: One of the most important aircraft in

the USAF's inventory, the A-10A results from a 1970 requirement for a new generation of close-support aircraft, in which weapons load and the ability to operate close to the front line at low altitudes predominated over sheer performance. The resulting A-10A is a fascinating aircraft, with its pilot enclosed in a 'bathtub' of titanium

armour, multiply redundant systems and structure, and the two engines pod-mounted on pylons above the fuselage and between the wings and tailplane. Here the engines are less vulnerable to ground fire, and their giveaway heat emission (IR signature) partially shielded by the wings and tailplane.

General Dynamics (Convair Division) C-131

Type: transport aircraft
Crew: four, plus 48 passengers
Wings: metal cantilever low-wing monoplane
Fuselage: metal semi-monocoque
Tail unit: metal cantilever
Landing gear: hydraulically actuated retractable tricycle unit
Powerplant: two Pratt & Whitney R-2800-99W radial engines, each rated at 2,500 hp and driving a metal three-blade propeller
Fuel capacity:
Avionics: comprehensive communication and navigation equipment
Armament: none
Dimensions: Span 105 ft 4 in (32.1 m)
　　　　　　Length 79 ft 2 in (24.13 m)
　　　　　　Height 28 ft 2 in (8.59 m)
Wing area: 920 ft² (85.47 m²)
Weights: Empty 29,248 lb (13,267 kg)
　　　　　Loaded
　　　　　Maximum 47,000 lb (21,319 kg)
Performance: speed 293 mph (472 kph); cruising speed 254 mph (409 kph); climb 1,410 ft (430 m) per minute at sea level; service ceiling 24,500 ft (7,468 m); range 450 miles (724 km)
Used only by: USA
Notes: The C-131 is one of a series of military aircraft developed from the Convair 240/340/440 family of civil airliners:

　　1. T-29A navigator trainer, based on

the Convair 240
2. T-29B with a pressurised fuselage and detail improvements
3. T-29C with 2,500-hp R-2800-99W engines replacing the earlier -77 and -97 models
4. T-29D bombardier trainer with a new nose
5. VT-29D executive transport
6. ET-29D electronic warfare officer trainer
7. C-131A Samaritan, a version of the Convair 240, for 27 litters or 37

passengers
8. C-131B, based on the Convair 340, was an electronic test bed and transport, to which the specification above applies
9. C-131D and VC-131D transports, based on the Convair 340 and 440
10. C131E electronic countermeasures (ECM) trainers
11. RC-131F charting aircraft
12. RC-131G airline aids checker
13. VC-131H turboprop-powered executive transport.

General Dynamics (Fort Worth Division) F-16

Type: air combat fighter
Crew: one
Wings: aluminium alloy cantilever mid-wing monoplane
Fuselage: metal semi-monocoque
Tail unit: aluminium alloy, glassfibre and laminate cantilever
Landing gear: hydraulically actuated retractable tricycle unit
Powerplant: one Pratt & Whitney F100-PW-100(3) turbofan, rated at about 25,000-lb (11,340-kg) static thrust with afterburning
Fuel capacity: about 870 gallons (3,955 litres) in wing and fuselage fuel cells, plus provision for drop tanks
Avionics: comprehensive communication and navigation/attack equipment, including Westinghouse pulse-doppler ranging and tracking radar, Dalmo Victor ALR-46 radar warning system, Sperry Flight Systems air data computer, Singer-Kearfott improved SKN-2400 inertial navigation system, National Security Agency KIT-2A/TSEC cryptographic system, Marconi-Elliott head up display, and Delco fire-control computer
Armament: one General Electric M61A-1 20-mm multi-barrel cannon with 500 rounds, two wingtip stations for infra-red homing air-to-air missiles up to 250 lb (113 kg) in weight, and seven external hardpoints (one under the fuselage rated at

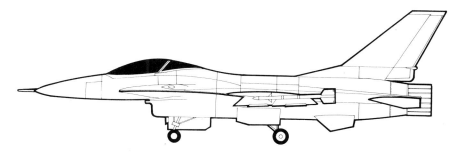

2,200 lb/998 kg, two under the inner wings and rated at 3,500 lb/1,587 kg each, two under the middle portion of the wings and rated at 2,500 lb/1,134 kg each, and two under the outer wings and rated at 250 lb/113 kg each, for a maximum external weapons and fuel load of 15,200 lb/6,894 kg if a reduced internal fuel load is carried, or an

external load of about 10,500 lb/4,763 kg if full internal fuel is carried). A typical load might consist of six AIM-9J/L Sidewinder AAMs on the wingtip and two outer underwing stations, two 308-gallon (1,400-litre) drop tanks on the centre underwing stations, bomb clusters or missiles on the four inner underwing stations, and a 250-gallon (1,136-litre) drop tank or 2,200-lb (998-kg) bomb under fuselage

Dimensions: Span 31 ft (9.45 m)
  Length 47 ft 7¾ in (14.52 m)
  Height 16 ft 5¼ in (5.01 m)
Wing area: 300 ft² (27.87 m²)
Weights: Empty (F-16A) 14,567 lb (6,607 kg)
  Empty (F-16B) 15,141 lb (6,868 kg)
  Loaded
  Maximum (F-16A) 33,000 lb (14,968 kg)
Performance: speed more than Mach 2 at 40,000 ft (12,200 m); service ceiling more than 50,000 ft (15,240 m); combat radius more than 575 miles (925 km); range with drop tanks more than 2,303 miles (3,705 km)
Used also by: Belgium, Denmark, Israel, Netherlands, Norway

Notes: Perhaps the most important Western combat aircraft of the late 1970s, the F-16 started life as a technology demonstrator to see how much smaller than the F-15 it was possible to build a useful lightweight fighter. The YF-16 was so encouraging that in 1974 it was chosen for production under the Air Combat Fighter programme. Considerable potential for 'growth' is built into the design, to accommodate improved electronics, more powerful variants of the F100 engine (with variable-geometry air intakes as opposed to the F-16A's fixed-geometry intakes), and radar-homing missiles. The F-16B is a tandem-seater training version with reduced fuel capacity.

General Dynamics (Convair Division) F-106 Delta Dart

Type: interceptor fighter
Crew: one
Wings: metal cantilever low mid-wing delta monoplane
Fuselage: metal semi-monocoque
Tail unit: metal cantilever
Landing gear: hydraulically actuated retractable tricycle unit
Powerplant: one Pratt & Whitney J75-P-17 turbojet, rated at 24,500-lb (11,130-kg) static thrust with afterburning
Fuel capacity:
Avionics: comprehensive communication and navigation/attack equipment, including the Hughes MA-1 electronic guidance and fire-control system
Armament: one 20-mm M-61 cannon, plus a variety of missiles in an internal bay, a typical load consisting of one AIR-2A Genie, one AIR-2G Genie, and two AIM-4E, 4F or 4G Falcons

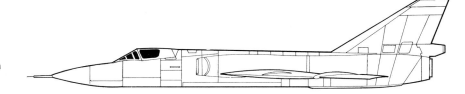

Dimensions: Span 38 ft 3½ in (11.67 m)
  Length 70 ft 8¾ in (21.55 m)
  Height 20 ft 3¼ in (6.15 m)
Wing area: 631.3 ft² (58.65 m²)
Weights: Empty 23,646 lb (10,725 kg)
  Loaded
  Maximum 38,250 lb (17,350 kg)
Performance: speed 1,525 mph (2,455 kph) or Mach 2.31 at 40,000 ft (12,192 m); climb about 30,000 ft (9,144 m) per minute at sea level; service ceiling 57,000 ft (17,375 m); combat radius 600 miles (966 km)

Used only by: USA
Notes: The F-106 is derived from the not altogether successful F-102, and first flew in 1956. The engine is far more powerful, and the drag of the fuselage has been considerably reduced. At the same time a more sophisticated weapons system has been fitted, capable of operating with the SAGE (Semi-Automatic Ground Environment) system. The single-seater is the F-106A, and the two-seater the F-106B operational trainer.

Grumman Aerospace A-6 Intruder

Type: all-weather attack aircraft
Crew: two, seated side-by-side
Wings: metal cantilever mid-wing monoplane
Fuselage: metal semi-monocoque
Tail unit: metal cantilever
Landing gear: hydraulically actuated retractable tricycle unit
Powerplant: two Pratt & Whitney J52-P-8A turbojets, each rated at 9,300-lb (4,218-kg) static thrust
Fuel capacity: about 1,990 gallons (9,046 litres) in fuselage and wing tanks, plus provision for five 250-gallon (1,136-litre) drop tanks
Avionics: comprehensive communication and navigation/attack equipment, including Norden AN/APC-148 multi-mode radar for ground mapping, terrain-clearing and following, and target acquisition, tracking and rangefinding (both moving and static targets), IBM AN/ASQ-133 solid-state digital computer, Conrac armament control unit (ACU), and Kaiser AN/AVA-1 multi-mode display
Armament: all weapons are carried on five external hardpoints, each with a capacity of 3,600 lb (1,633 kg), up to a maximum load of 15,000 lb (6,804 kg). A typical load consists of thirty 500-lb (227-kg) bombs in five

210

clusters of six bombs each, or three 2,000-lb (917-kg) bombs and two 250-gallon (1,135-litre) auxiliary drop tanks
Dimensions: Span 53 ft (16.15 m)
Length 54 ft 7 in (16.64 m)
Height 16 ft 2 in (4.93 m)
Wing area: 528.9 ft² (49.1 m²)
Weights: Empty 25,630 lb (11,625 kg)
Loaded
Maximum 60,400 lb (27,397 kg)
Performance: (without external stores) speed 643 mph (1,035 kph) at sea level; cruising speed 476 mph (766 kph); climb 9,200 ft (2,804 m) per minute at sea level; service ceiling 46,800 ft (14,265 m); range with maximum payload 1,924 miles (3,096 km); combat range with maximum external fuel 2,723 miles (4,382 km); combat range with full combat load 1,077 miles (1,733 km)

Used only by: USA
Notes: The original specification for the A-6 was for an all-weather, day/night, low-level, carrierborne attack bomber capable of delivering nuclear or conventional bombs, and the A-6 is notable for all these abilities, plus extreme range and heavy weapons capability. The first prototype flew in 1960, and there are several variants:
1. A-6A, the original production model, which entered service in 1963
2. EA-6A, with a partial strike capability, but intended for the support of strike aircraft and ground forces by suppressing enemy electronic activity and gathering tactical electronic information over the battlefield. Special equipment on the fin and under the wings detects, locates, classifies, records and jams enemy radio and radar
3. EA-6B Prowler, described separately
4. A-6B, with Standard ARM missile capability
5. A-6C, similar to the A-6A but with an underfuselage turret fitted with forward-looking infra-red (FLIR) sensors and low-light TV, to improve night capability
6. KA-6D tanker aircraft, with a capacity for 2,925 gallons (11,933 litres) of transferable fuel
7. A-6E, to which the specification above applies.

Grumman Aerospace EA-6B Prowler

Type: ECM aircraft
Crew: four
Wings: metal cantilever mid-wing monoplane
Fuselage: metal semi-monocoque
Tail unit: metal cantilever
Landing gear: hydraulically actuated retractable tricycle unit
Powerplant: two Pratt & Whitney J52-P-408 turbojets, each rated at 11,200-lb (5,080-kg) static thrust
Fuel capacity: about 1,990 gallons (9,046 litres) in fuselage and wing tanks, plus provision for five 250-gallon (1,136-litre) drop tanks
Avionics: comprehensive communication and navigation equipment, plus ALQ-99 advanced ECM system, allowing the EA-6B to undertake tactical ECM missions by detecting, locating, identifying and jamming enemy radio and radar semi-automatically
Armament: none
Dimensions: Span 53 ft (16.15 m)
Length 59 ft 5 in (18.11 m)
Height 16 ft 2 in (4.93 m)
Wing area: 528.9 ft² (49.1 m²)
Weights: Empty 32,162 lb (14,588 kg)
Loaded
Maximum 65,000 lb (29,483 kg)
Performance: (with five tactical jamming system pods) speed 623 mph (1,002 kph); cruising speed 605 mph (973 kph); service ceiling 38,000 ft (11,580 m); ferry range 2,022 miles (3,254 km)

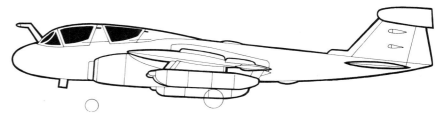

Used only by: USA
Notes: Derived from the Grumman EA-6A, the Prowler has highly sophisticated electronics, the heart of which is the AN/ALQ-99 tactical jamming system, the operation of part of which is entrusted to the additional two crew members. Their presence has made necessary the lengthening of the fuselage. The Prowler carries 8,000 lb (3,629 kg) of electronics internally, and up to another 4,750 lb (2,155 kg) in four pods under the wings and one under the fuselage.

Grumman Aerospace F-14 Tomcat

Type: multi-role fighter
Crew: two, seated in tandem
Wings: metal cantilever variable-geometry mid-wing monoplane
Fuselage: metal box and semi-monocoque
Tail unit: metal and composite cantilever
Landing gear: hydraulically actuated retractable tricycle unit
Powerplant: two Pratt & Whitney TF30-P-412A turbofans, each rated at 20,900-lb (9,480-kg) static thrust with afterburning
Fuel capacity: 16,200 lb (7,348 kg) internally and 3,800 lb (1,724 kg) externally
Avionics: comprehensive communication and navigation/attack equipment, including a Hughes AN/AWG-9 weapons control system and Kaiser AN/AVG-12 vertical and head up display system

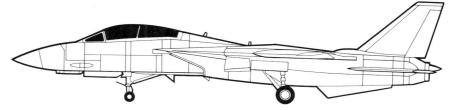

Armament: one General Electric M61A-1 Vulcan 20-mm multi-barrel cannon, four AIM-7 Sparrow air-to-air missiles partially submerged in the underfuselage, and two underwing pylons for four AIM-9 Sidewinder air-to-air missiles, or two Sidewinders with two Sparrows or two AIM-54 Phoenix air-to-air missiles. Alternatively, six Phoenix and two Sidewinder missiles can be carried, or a combination of missiles and bombs up to a maximum weight of 14,500 lb (6,577 kg)

Dimensions: Span (spread) 64 ft 1½ in (19.45 m)
Span (swept) 38 ft 2½ in (11.65 m)
Span (overswept) 33 ft 3½ in (10.15 m)
Length 61 ft 2 in (18.89 m)
Height 16 ft 10 in (4.88 m)
Wing area: (unswept) 565 ft² (52.49 m²)
Weights: Empty 38,930 lb (17,659 kg)
Loaded 58,539 lb (26,553 kg)
Maximum 74,348 lb (33,724 kg)

Performance: speed 1,564 mph (2,517 kph) or Mach 2.34 at high altitude; speed 910 mph (1,470 kph) or Mach 1.2 at sea level; climb more than 30,000 ft (9,150 m) per minute at sea level; service ceiling more than 50,000 ft (15,240 m); range more than 2,000 miles (3,200 km)

Used also by: Iran

Notes: The prototype of this important naval fighter first flew in 1970. The F-14 has three main missions:
  a. fighter sweep and escort, to clear airspace of enemy aircraft and so allow friendly strike aircraft to operate
  b. protection of carrier task forces
  c. tactical strike, with the support of escort and ECM aircraft.

The combination of the highly sophisticated AWG-9 weapons control system and AIM-54 Phoenix missiles has proved particularly successful, even with the simultaneous launch of four missiles at numerous long-range targets. There are currently three variants of the Tomcat:
  1. F-14A, described in the technical specification
  2. F-14B, similar to the F-14A but powered by 28,090-lb (12,741-kg) Pratt & Whitney F401-400 turbofans to improve performance, especially in acceleration. Cost has prevented the widespread introduction of the type
  3. F-14C, a development of the F-14B with new weapons and electronics.

Grumman American Aviation VC-11A Gulfstream II

Type: transport aircraft
Crew: two or three, plus up to 19 passengers
Wings: metal cantilever low-wing monoplane
Fuselage: metal semi-monocoque
Tail unit: metal cantilever
Landing gear: hydraulically actuated retractable tricycle unit
Powerplant: two Rolls-Royce Spey Mark 511-8 turbofans, each rated at 11,400-lb (5,171-kg) static thrust
Fuel capacity: 23,300 lb (10,568 kg)
Avionics: comprehensive communication and navigation equipment
Armament: none
Dimensions: Span 68 ft 10 in (20.98 m)

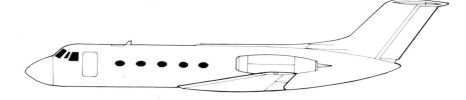

Length 79 ft 11 in (24.36 m)
Height 24 ft 6 in (7.47 m)
Wing area: 809.6 ft² (75.21 m²)
Weights: Empty 37,186 lb (16,687 kg)
Loaded
Maximum 65,500 lb (29,711 kg)
Performance: (at maximum take-off weight) cruising speed 581 mph (936 kph) at

25,000 ft (7,620 m); climb 4,350 ft (1,325 m) per minute at sea level; service ceiling 43,000 ft (13,100 m); range 4,117 miles (6,625 km)

Used also by: Gabon, Greece, Morocco, Nigeria, Oman

Notes: The prototype of the Gulfstream II first flew in 1966, and entered service in 1968.

Hughes Helicopters AH-64

Type: armed helicopter
Crew: two, seated in tandem
Rotors: metal cantilever four-blade main rotor; metal cantilever four-blade tail rotor
Fuselage: aluminium alloy semi-monocoque
Landing gear: hydraulically actuated retractable tailwheel unit
Powerplant: two General Electric T700-GE-700 turboshafts, each rated at 1,536 shp but derated for normal operations
Fuel capacity: 300 gallons (1,366 litres) in two fuselage fuel cells, plus provision for external auxiliary tanks
Avionics: comprehensive communication and navigation/attack equipment
Armament: one 30-mm Hughes XM-230 chain gun with 1,200 rounds, plus a variety of loads on four underwing hardpoints. Loads can include 16 Hellfire anti-tank missiles, or 76 2.75-in (70-mm) rockets, or a combination of both
Dimensions: Span 48 ft (14.63 m)
Length (fuselage) 49 ft 5 in (15.06 m)
Height 12 ft 6¾ in (3.83 m)

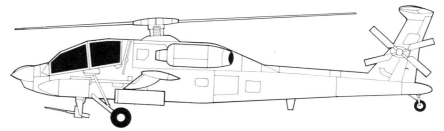

Rotor disc area: 1,809 ft² (168.06 m²)
Weights: Empty 9,500 lb (4,309 kg)
Loaded 13,200 lb (5,987 kg)
Maximum 17,400 lb (7,892 kg)
Performance: (at normal loaded weight, estimated) speed 191 mph (307 kph); cruising
speed 180 mph (289 kph); climb 3,200 ft
(975 m) per minute at sea level; service
ceiling 20,500 ft (6,250 m); hovering ceiling in ground effect 14,600 ft (4,450 m);
range 359 miles (578 km) on internal fuel;
range 1,168 miles (1,880 km) with maximum internal and external fuel

Used by: under development for USA
Notes: The prototype of the AH-64 first flew
in 1965, and the type was selected in 1976
as the winner of the Advanced Attack Helicopter programme. The AH-64 will probably enter service in 1980.

Hughes Helicopters TH-55A Osage

Type: training helicopter
Crew: two, seated side-by-side
Rotor: metal cantilever three-blade main
rotor; metal cantilever two-blade tail rotor
Fuselage: metal frame and monocoque
Landing gear: twin metal skids

Powerplant: one Lycoming HIO-360 piston
engine, rated at 180 hp
Fuel capacity:
Avionics: communication equipment
Armament: none
Dimensions: Span 25 ft 3½ in (7.71 m)
Length 28 ft 10¾ in (8.81 m)
Height
Rotor disc area: 502.4 ft² (46.7 m²)
Weights: Empty
Loaded
Maximum 1,670 lb (758 kg)

Performance: speed 86 mph (138 kph);
climb 1,450 ft (442 m) per minute at sea
level; service ceiling 6,000 ft (1,829 m)
range 195 miles (314 km)
Used also by: Algeria, Ghana, Nicaragua
Notes: The prototype flew in 1956, and the
TH-55 entered service with the US Army in
1964. The basic helicopter is the Hughes
Model 269A.

Kaman Aerospace SH-2 Seasprite

Type: anti-submarine and anti-missile helicopter, with utility capability
Crew: three
Rotor: aluminium and glassfibre cantilever
four-blade main rotor; aluminium and
glassfibre cantilever four-blade tail rotor
Fuselage: metal semi-monocoque
Landing gear: tailwheel type, with retractable
main wheels
Powerplant: two General Electric T58-GE-8F
turboshafts, each rated at 1,350 shp
Fuel capacity: 230 gallons (1,044.4 litres) internally, and provision for 100 gallons
(454.6 litres) in external auxiliary tanks
Avionics: comprehensive communication
and navigation/attack equipment, including Canadian Marconi LN-66HP surveillance radar, ASQ-81 magnetic anomaly
detector, ALR-54 passive radiation
detector, SSQ-41 passive sonobuoys,
SSQ-47 active sonobuoys, APN-182
doppler radar, and Teledyne ASN-123 tactical navigation system with computer and
CRT display
Armament: one or two Mark 44 or Mark 46
homing torpedoes
Dimensions: Span 44 ft (13.41 m)
Length (fuselage) 40 ft 6 in
(12.3 m)
Height 13 ft 7 in (4.14 m)
Rotor disc area: 1,520.5 ft² (141.25 m²)
Weights: Empty 7,040 lb (3,193 kg)
Loaded 12,800 lb (5,805 kg)
Maximum 13,300 lb (6,033 kg)
Performance: (at normal loaded weight)
speed 165 mph (265 kph) at sea level;
cruising speed 150 mph (241 kph); climb
2,440 ft (744 m) per minute at sea level;
service ceiling 22,500 ft (6,860 m); hover-
ing ceiling in ground effect 18,600 ft
(5,670 m); range 422 miles (679 km)
Used only by: USA

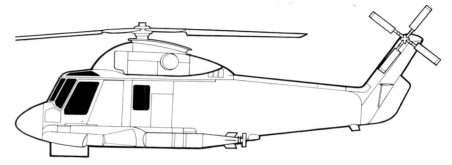

Notes: The prototype of the Kaman UH-2
family first flew in 1969, and the type has
since served the US Navy in a number of
capacities:
1. UH-2A with one 1,250-shp T58-GE-
8B engine
2. UH-2B simplified version with one
T58
3. UH-2C, UH-2As and UH-2Bs improved by being re-engined with two
T58s
4. HH-2D for survey work

5. SH-2D light airborne multi-purpose
system (LAMPS) helicopter with ASW
capability in the form of two Mark 44
or Mark 46 torpedoes, LN-66 surveillance radar, ASQ-81 MAD and
sonobuoy facility
6. SH-2F, to which the specification
above applies, with increased ASW
capability, more powerful engines
and an improved rotor system.

Ling-Temco-Vought (Vought Systems Division) A-7 Corsair II

Type: tactical fighter
Crew: one
Wings: metal cantilever high-wing mono-
plane
Fuselage: metal semi-monocoque
Tail unit: metal cantilever
Landing gear: hydraulically actuated retrac-
table tricycle unit
Powerplant: one Allison TF41-A-2 (Rolls-
Royce Spey) turbofan, rated at 15,000-lb
(6,804-kg) static thrust

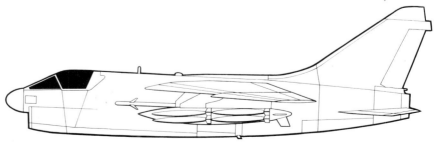

Fuel capacity: 1,249 gallons (5,678 litres) in
internal tanks, plus provision for 999 gallons (4,542 litres) carried externally

Avionics: comprehensive communication
and navigation/attack equipment, including a Texas Instruments AN/APQ-126

navigation and weapons delivery radar, AN/ASN-91 digital navigation and weapons delivery computer, Marconi-Elliott AN/AVQ-7 head up display, CP-953/A air data computer, and AN/APN-190 doppler radar

Armament: one 20-mm M61A-1 Vulcan multi-barrel cannon with 1,000 rounds, plus a weapons load of up to 15,000 lb (6,805 kg) on eight weapons stations: two under the fuselage, each for 500 lb (227 kg); two under the inner wings, each for 2,500 lb (1,134 kg); and four under the outer wings, each for 3,500 lb (1,587 kg). The hardpoints can carry air-to-air missiles, air-to-surface missiles, rocket pods, gun pods, general-purpose bombs, incendiary bombs, Pave Penny AN/AAS-35 laser target-designator pod, and drop tanks

Dimensions: Span 38 ft 9 in (11.8 m)
Length 46 ft 1½ in (14.06 m)
Height 16 ft 0¾ in (4.9 m)

Wing area: 375 ft² (34.83 m²)

Weights: Empty 19,403 lb (8,800 kg)
Loaded
Maximum 42,000 lb (19,050 kg)

Performance: speed 691 mph (1,112 kph) in 'clean' condition at sea level; climb and ceiling not known, and not relevant; combat radius with weapon load about 715 miles (1,150 km); ferry range 3,224 miles (5,188 km)

Used also by: Greece

Notes: Although its configuration was derived from the F-8 Crusader fighter, the A-7 Corsair II has a completely new structure to suit it to the heavy weapon carrying role at low altitude and at high speed. Designed for the US Navy as a carrierborne attack aircraft, the A-7 made its first flight in 1965, and entered service in 1966. It has been adopted by the USAF as well as by the US Navy. There are several models:
1. A-7A initial production variant with

an 11,350-lb (5,148-kg) Pratt & Whitney TF30-P-6 for the USN
2. A-7B with a 12,200-lb (5,534-kg) TF30-P-8 for the USN
3. A-7C, first 67 of the A-7E type with the TF30-P-8
4. TA-7C twin-seat trainer adaptation of the A-7B and A-7C
5. A-7D tactical fighter for the USAF with the 14,250-lb (6,465-kg) Allison

TF41-A-1 engine
6. A-7E attack/close air support/interdiction model for the USN with the TF41-A-2 engine, to which the technical specification above relates
7. RA-7E, a reconnaissance variant of the A-7E, currently under development
8. YA-7E project for a two-seat trainer and tactical aircraft
9. A-7H version of the A-7E for Greece.

Lockheed Aircraft C-121 Constellation

Type: transport aircraft and airborne early warning aircraft

Crew: five, plus up to 72 passengers (27 crew in EC-121)

Wings: metal cantilever low-wing monoplane

Fuselage: metal semi-monocoque

Tail unit: metal cantilever

Landing gear: hydraulically actuated retractable tricycle unit

Powerplant: four Wright R-3350-34 radial engines, each rated at 3,250 hp and driving a three-blade metal propeller

Fuel capacity:

Avionics: comprehensive communication and navigation equipment, plus a WS214M radar and electronics package in the EC-121

Armament: none

Dimensions: Span 126 ft 2 in (38.46 m)
Length 116 ft 2 in (35.41 m)
Height 27 ft (8.23 m)

Wing area: 1,653.6 ft² (153.6 m²)

Weights: Empty 80,611 lb (36,565 kg)
Loaded
Maximum 143,600 lb (65,137 kg)

Performance: speed 321 mph (517 kph) at 20,000 ft (6,096 m); climb 845 ft (258 m) per minute at sea level; service ceiling 20,600 ft (6,279 m); range 4,600 miles (7,403 km)

Used also by: India

Notes: The Lockheed Constellation was designed before World War II as a civil airliner, but the design was immediately seized upon in December 1941 by the US armed forces as the makings of a long-range transport. As such, it first flew in 1943, and was accepted for service as the C-69. In 1948 the USAF ordered, under the designation C-121, a military version of the L-749 Constellation, and in 1951 the C-121C derivative of the still larger L-1049. The type was also used by the US Navy as a passenger transport and radar aircraft, and the final versions for the USAF have been electronic versions with the prefix EC.

Lockheed-California Aircraft S-3A Viking

Type: anti-submarine aircraft

Crew: four

Wings: metal cantilever shoulder-wing monoplane

Fuselage: metal semi-monocoque

Tail unit: metal cantilever

Landing gear: hydraulically actuated retractable tricycle unit

Powerplant: two General Electric TF34-GE-2 turbofans, each rated at 9,275-lb (4,207-kg) static thrust

Fuel capacity: about 1,582 gallons (7,192 litres) in two integral inner wing tanks, plus provision for two 250-gallon (1,136-litre) underwing drop tanks

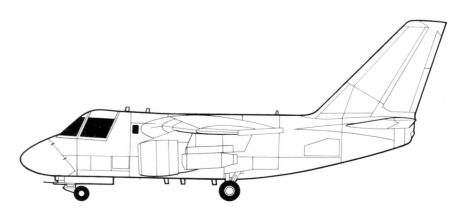

Avionics: comprehensive communication and navigation/attack equipment, including a Univac 1832A general-purpose digital computer, AN/APS-116 high-resolution radar, OR-89/AA forward-looking infra-red (FLIR) scanner, AN/ASQ-81 magnetic anomaly detector, and ALR-47 passive ECM receiving and measuring equipment

Armament: weapons bay can accommodate four MK-36 destructors, four MK-46 torpedoes, four MK-82 bombs, two MK-57 or four MK-54 depth bombs, or four MK-53 mines, with additional stores being carried on two underwing pylons. These latter can carry single or triple ejectors for mines, cluster bombs, flares, rocket pods, drop tanks and other stores

Dimensions: Span 68 ft 8 in (20.93 m)
Length 53 ft 4 in (16.26 m)
Height 22 ft 9 in (6.93 m)

Wing area: 598 ft² (55.56 m²)

Weights: Empty 26,650 lb (12,088 kg)
Loaded 42,500 lb (19,277 kg)
Maximum 47,000 lb (21,319 kg)

Performance: (at normal loaded weight) speed 518 mph (834 kph); cruising speed

426 mph (686 kph); patrol speed 184 mph (296 kph); climb more than 4,200 ft (1,280 m) per minute at sea level; service ceiling above 35,000 ft (10,670 m); combat radius more than 1,150 miles (1,851 km); ferry range more than 3,454 miles (5,558 km)

Used only by: USA

Notes: The S-3A provides the US Navy with a versatile and hard-hitting anti-submarine

aircraft for carrier operations. The prototype first flew in 1972, and the type entered service in 1974. The Viking is probably the most compact ASW aircraft in the world. There is also a carrier on-board delivery variant under development with the designations US-3A. This can carry 3,750 lb (1,700 kg) of freight or up to six passengers and 2,810 lb (1,275 kg) of freight.

Lockheed-California Aircraft SR-71 Blackbird

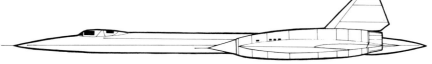

Type: strategic reconnaissance aircraft
Crew: two
Wings: titanium alloy cantilever delta mid-wing monoplane
Fuselage: titanium alloy semi-monocoque
Tail unit: titanium alloy cantilever
Landing gear: hydraulically actuated retractable tricycle unit
Powerplant: two Pratt & Whitney JT11D-P-20B turbojets, each rated at 32,500-lb (14,742-kg) static thrust with afterburning
Fuel capacity: more than 80,000 lb (36,288 kg)
Avionics: comprehensive communication and navigation equipment, and a mass of reconnaissance sensors of the optical, electronic and infra-red types
Armament: none
Dimensions: Span 55 ft 7 in (16.95 m)
Length 107 ft 5 in (32.74 m)
Height 18 ft 6 in (5.64 m)
Wing area:
Weights: Empty about 60,000 lb (27,215 kg)
Loaded
Maximum 170,000 lb (77,110 kg)

Performance: speed more than 2,000 mph (3,220 kph) or Mach 3 at high altitude; service ceiling more than 80,000 ft (24,400 m); range at Mach 3 at 78,740 ft (24,000 m) 2,982 miles (4,800 km)

Used only by: USA

Notes: Derived from the A-11 strategic reconnaissance aircraft, the Blackbird was first revealed as the YF-12A advanced interceptor, and only latterly as the SR-71 strategic reconnaissance aircraft. The most advanced conventional aircraft in the world, the SR-71 is built of specially developed alloys, and has performance limits of 2,200 mph (3,541 kph) and 84,000 ft (25,604 m) sustained altitude. The SR-71B and SR-71C are two-seat trainer versions of the basic SR-71.

Lockheed-California U-2

Type: strategic reconnaissance aircraft
Crew: one
Wings: metal cantilever mid-wing monoplane
Fuselage: metal semi-monocoque
Tail unit: metal cantilever
Landing gear: hydraulically actuated retractable bicycle unit, with stabilising outrigger wheels jettisoned at take-off
Powerplant: one Pratt & Whitney J75-P-13 turbojet, rated at 17,000-lb (7,711-kg) static thrust
Fuel capacity:
Avionics: comprehensive communication and navigation equipment, plus special reconnaissance sensors
Armament: none
Dimensions: Span 80 ft (24.38 m)
Length 49 ft 7 in (15.1 m)
Height 13 ft (3.96 m)
Wing area: about 565 ft² (52.5 m²)

Weights: Empty about 11,700 lb (5,305 kg)
Loaded about 15,850 lb (7,190 kg)
Maximum more than 21,000 lb (9,526 kg)

Performance: speed 528 mph (850 kph); service ceiling 85,000 ft (25,910 m); range 4,000 miles (6,440 km)
Used only by: USA

Notes: The U-2 entered service in 1956. The U-2A had the Pratt & Whitney J57-P-13A or 37A, and lower performance than its U-2B, C and D successors.

Lockheed-Georgia C-5A Galaxy

Type: strategic transport
Crew: five, plus up to 360 passengers
Wings: metal cantilever high-wing monoplane
Fuselage: metal semi-monocoque
Tail unit: metal cantilever
Landing gear: hydraulically actuated retractable tricycle unit
Powerplant: four General Electric TF39-GE-1 turbofans, each rated at 41,000-lb (18,539-kg) static thrust
Fuel capacity: 40,801 gallons (185,480 litres) in four main, four auxiliary and four extended range tanks, all located in the wings
Avionics: comprehensive communication and navigation equipment
Armament: none
Dimensions: Span 222 ft 8½ in (67.88 m)
Length 247 ft 10 in (75.54 m)
Height 65 ft 1½ in (19.85 m)
Wing area: 6,200 ft² (576.0 m²)
Weights: Empty 337,937 lb (153,285 kg)
Loaded
Maximum 769,000 lb (348,810 kg)
Performance: (at maximum take-off weight) speed 571 mph (919 kph) at 25,000 ft (7,620 m); cruising speed 553 mph (890 kph) at 25,000 ft (7,620 m); climb 1,800 ft (549 m) per minute at sea level; service ceiling at a weight of 615,000 lb (278,950 kg) 34,000 ft (10,360 m); range with a payload of 220,967 lb (100,228 kg) 3,749 miles (6,033 km); ferry range 7,991 miles (12,860 km)
Used only by: USA
Notes: In many respects the C-5A is the largest aircraft in the world, though the Boeing 747 is heavier and has more powerful engines. The Galaxy emerged from a 1963 requirement for a strategic transport able to operate from rough strips, and capable of carrying a payload of 125,000 lb (56,700 kg) over 8,000 miles (12,875 km). The first aircraft flew in 1968, and service introduction began in 1969. The maximum payload is 220,967 lb (100,228 kg), which can be made up of a vast variety of military stores. Typical loads consist of two M60 MBTs; or one M60 and two UH-1 helicopters, five M113 APCs and two lorries; or 16 ¾-ton lorries; or 10 Pershing surface-to-surface missiles with their launchers and tow vehicles; or 36 standard pallets.

Lockheed-Georgia C-140

Type: utility transport aircraft
Crew: two, plus up to 10 passengers
Wings: metal cantilever low-wing monoplane
Fuselage: metal semi-monocoque
Tail unit: metal cantilever
Landing gear: hydraulically actuated retractable tricycle unit
Powerplant: four Pratt & Whitney JT12-P-A6 turbojets, each rated at 3,000-lb (1,361-kg) static thrust
Fuel capacity: 2,237 gallons (10,168 litres) in four internal wing and two external glove tanks
Avionics: comprehensive communication and navigation equipment
Armament: none
Dimensions: Span 53 ft 8 in (16.36 m)
Length 60 ft 5½ in (18.43 m)
Height 20 ft 6 in (6.25 m)
Wing area: 543 ft² (50.45 m²)
Weights: Empty 18,450 lb (8,369 kg)
Loaded 30,680 lb (13,916 kg)
Maximum 38,940 lb (17,663 kg)
Performance: speed 573 mph (922 kph); cruising speed 540 mph (869 kph); climb 4,800 ft (1,463 m) per minute at sea level; service ceiling 45,000 ft (13,716 m); range 2,228 miles (3,586 km)
Used also by: Indonesia, West Germany
Notes: The C-140 is the military version of Lockheed's Model 1329 JetStar transport.

Lockheed-Georgia Aircraft C-141 Starlifter

Type: strategic transport
Crew: four, plus up to 154 passengers
Wings: metal cantilever high-wing monoplane
Fuselage: metal semi-monocoque
Tail unit: metal cantilever
Landing gear: hydraulically actuated retractable tricycle unit
Powerplant: four Pratt & Whitney TF33-P-7 turbofans, each rated at 21,000-lb (9,526-kg) static thrust
Fuel capacity: 19,652 gallons (89,335 litres)

216

Avionics: comprehensive communication and navigation equipment
Armament: none
Dimensions: Span 159 ft 11 in (48.74 m)
Length 145 ft (44.2 m)
Height 39 ft 3 in (11.96 m)
Wing area: 3,228 ft² (299.9 m²)
Weights: Empty 133,733 lb (60,678 kg)
Loaded
Maximum 316,600 lb (143,600 kg)
Performance: (at maximum take-off weight) speed 571 mph (919 kph) at 25,000 ft (7,620 m); cruising speed 495 mph (797 kph); climb 3,100 ft (945 m) per minute at sea level; service ceiling 41,600 ft (12,680 m); range with maximum payload 4,080 miles (6,565 km)
Used only by: USA
Notes: The C-141 has the distinction of being the USAF's first all-jet strategic transport, and began life in answer to a 1960 requirement. The first aircraft flew in 1963 and service introduction followed in 1964. The first machines were designated C-141A, and it was often found that the StarLifter's hold was packed to capacity long before the weight limit for the payload (70,847 lb/ 32,136 kg) had been reached. This has led to the development of the C-141B, which has the fuselage lengthened by 13 ft 4 in (4.06 m)

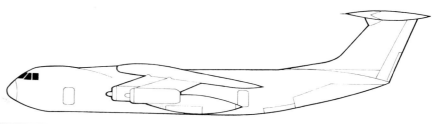

just in front of the wing, and 10 ft (3.05 m) just aft of it. The wing root fairings have also been altered to reduce drag, and so increase speed and range, and to increase airframe life. Production instructions for the modification of existing C-141As are expected. The maximum payload of the C-141B is 89,152 lb (40,439 kg), and maximum take-off weight in the order of 340,000 lb (154,229 kg).

McDonnell Douglas (Douglas Aircraft) C-9

Type: aeromedical transport, logistic support transport and VIP transport
Crew: five, and up to 90 passengers
Wings: metal cantilever low-wing monoplane
Fuselage: metal semi-monocoque
Tail unit: metal cantilever
Landing gear: hydraulically actuated retractable tricycle unit
Powerplant: two Pratt & Whitney JT8D-9 turbofans, each rated at 14,500-lb (6,577-kg) static thrust
Fuel capacity: 4,937 gallons (22,443 litres) internally
Avionics: comprehensive communication and navigation equipment

Armament: none
Dimensions: Span 93 ft 5 in (28.47 m)
Length 119 ft 3½ in (36.37 m)
Height 27 ft 6 in (8.38 m)
Wing area: 1,000.7 ft² (92.97 m²)
Weights: Empty (C-9B) 59,706 lb (27,082 kg)
Loaded
Maximum (C-9B) 110,000 lb (49,900 kg)
Performance: (C-9B at maximum take-off weight) maximum cruising speed 576 mph (927 kph); economical cruising speed 504 mph (811 kph); range with a payload of 10,000 lb (4,535 kg) 2,923 miles (4,704 km)
Used also by: Italy, Kuwait, Venezuela
Notes: Derived from the civil DC-9 airliner,

the C-9 serves the US armed forces in three versions:
1. C-9A Nightingale, for USAF aeromedical airlift transport, with a capacity for up to 40 litters, 40 walking patients, two nurses and three aeromedical personnel
2. C-9B Skytrain II fleet logistic support transport for the US Navy, with a total payload capacity of 32,444 lb (14,716 kg). The technical specification above applies to this type
3. VC-9C VIP transport for the USAF.

McDonnell Douglas (McDonnell Aircraft) F-15 Eagle

Type: air superiority and ground-attack fighter
Crew: one
Wings: metal cantilever shoulder-wing monoplane
Fuselage: metal semi-monocoque
Tail unit: metal cantilever
Landing gear: hydraulically actuated retractable tricycle unit
Powerplant: two Pratt & Whitney F100-PW-100 turbofans, each rated at 23,800-lb (10,796-kg) static thrust with afterburning
Fuel capacity: 11,600 lb (5,260 kg) in internal tanks, plus provision for two FAST Pack tanks, each holding 5,000 lb (2,268 kg) of fuel
Avionics: comprehensive communication and navigation/attack equipment, including Hughes APG-63 pulse-doppler detection and tracking radar, IBM central computer and McDonnell Douglas head up display
Armament: one M61A-1 20-mm multibarrel cannon with 940 rounds, plus provision for four AIM-7F Sparrow and four AIM-9L Sidewinder air-to-air missiles. There are also five weapon stations capable of carrying up to 16,000 lb (7,258 kg)

of bombs, ECM equipment, rockets and drop tanks: the fuselage point can take 4,500 lb (2,041 kg), the inner wing points 5,100 lb (2,313 kg) each, and the outer wing points 1,000 lb (454 kg) each
Dimensions: Span 42 ft 9¾ in (13.05 m)
Length 63 ft 9 in (19.43 m)
Height 18 ft 5½ in (5.63 m)
Wing area: 608 ft² (56.5 m²)
Weights: Empty about 28,000 lb (12,700 kg)
Loaded about 41,500 lb (18,824 kg)

Maximum 56,000 lb (25,401 kg)

Performance: speed more than 1,650 mph (2,660 kph) or Mach 2.5 at high altitude; speed over 921 mph (1,482 kph) or Mach 1.22 at low altitude; climb over 50,000 ft (15,240 m) per minute at sea level; service ceiling more than 70,000 ft (21,000 m); range on internal fuel about 1,200 miles (1,930 km); ferry range more than 3,450 miles (5,560 km)

Used also by: Israel, Japan, Saudi Arabia

Notes: The F-15 stems from a 1965 USAF requirement for an air superiority fighter capable of tackling the formidable MiG-23 and MiG-25. The first example flew in 1972, and the type entered US service in 1974. With a very high thrust: weight ratio (better than 1:1 in clean condition), the F-15 has spectacular performance, especially in climb: it holds the world time to height record in several forms, including 39,370 ft

(12,000 m) in only 59.38 seconds, compared with the previous record of 1 minute 17.1 seconds. Key to the type's long range at high speed is the specially developed FAST (fuel and sensor, tactical) pack, one of which can be attached on each side of the aircraft to the port and starboard engine

trunks. Each pack is highly streamlined and stressed, and contains both fuel and target designators or weapons. Attachment of a FAST pack takes only 15 minutes. There are currently two versions of the F-15:
 1. F-15A single-seat fighter
 2. TF-15A twin-seat trainer.

Northrop Corporation (Norair Division) T-38A Talon

Type: supersonic trainer
Crew: two, seated in tandem
Wings: metal cantilever low mid-wing monoplane
Fuselage: metal semi-monocoque
Tail unit: metal cantilever
Landing gear: hydraulically actuated retractable tricycle unit
Powerplant: two General Electric J85-GE-5 turbojets, each rated at 3,850-lb (1,746-kg) static thrust with afterburning
Fuel capacity:
Avionics: comprehensive communication and navigation equipment
Armament: none
Dimensions: Span 25 ft 3 in (7.7 m)
　　　　　　　Length 46 ft 4½ in (14.14 m)
　　　　　　　Height 12 ft 10 in (3.9 m)
Wing area: 170 ft² (15.79 m²)
Weights: Empty 7,164 lb (3,250 kg)
　　　　　　Loaded
　　　　　　Maximum 12,050 lb (5,466 m)
Performance: speed 820 mph (1,320 kph) or Mach 1.24 at 36,087 ft (11,000 m); climb 33,600 ft (10,241 m) per minute at sea level; service ceiling 53,600 ft (16,337 m); range 1,100 miles (1,770 km)
Used also by: Colombia, Portugal, Taiwan, West Germany
Notes: The T-38A was the USAF's first supersonic trainer, derived from the Northrop N-156 private venture lightweight fighter, eventually to emerge as the F-5 Freedom Fighter. The prototype T-38 was flown in 1959, and entered service in 1960.

Republic Fairchild (Republic Aviation) F-105 Thunderchief

Type: long-range fighter-bomber
Crew: one
Wings: metal cantilever mid-wing monoplane
Fuselage: metal semi-monocoque
Tail unit: metal cantilever
Landing gear: hydraulically actuated retractable tricycle unit
Powerplant: one Pratt & Whitney J75-P-19W turbojet, rated at 24,500-lb (11,113-kg) static thrust with afterburning
Fuel capacity:
Avionics: comprehensive communication and navigation/attack equipment, including a General Electric FC-5 integrated automatic flight and fire-control system, and Thunderstick or Thunderstick II all-weather blind attack bombing system
Armament: one 20-mm M-61 cannon with 1,029 rounds, plus 8,000 lb (3,629 lb) of weapons carried internally and another 6,000 lb (2,722 kg) carried on four underwing and one underfuselage pylon
Dimensions: Span 34 ft 11¼ in (10.65 m)
Length 64 ft 3 in (19.58 m)
Height 19 ft 8 in (5.99 m)
Wing area: 385 ft² (35.77 m²)
Weights: Empty 27,500 lb (12,474 kg)
Loaded
Maximum 52,546 lb (23,834 kg)
Performance: speed 1,480 mph (2,382 kph) or Mach 2.25; climb 34,500 ft (10,500 m) per minute at sea level; service ceiling 52,000 ft (15,850 m); combat radius 230 miles (370 km) with 16,750 lb (7,598 kg)

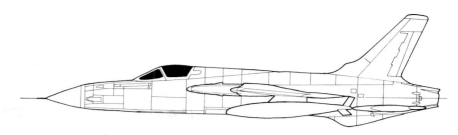

of weapons; ferry range 2,390 miles (3,846 km)
Used only by: USA
Notes: The F-105 prototype first flew in 1955, and entered service in 1956. It is the largest and heaviest single-engined single-seat military aircraft to date, with sophisticated electronics enabling the aircraft to deliver nuclear weapons with great accuracy in the worst conditions. There are several models:

1. F-105B, the initial production model with the 23,500-lb (10,660-kg) J75-P-5. Speed of 1,254 mph (2,018 kph)
2. F-105D all-weather fighter-bomber, to which the specification above applies
3. F-105F two-seat operational mission trainer, derived from the F-105D
4. F-105G ECM aircraft, with a crew of two and special electronics.

Rockwell International (North American Aircraft) A-5 Vigilante

Type: attack and reconnaissance aircraft
Crew: two, seated in tandem
Wings: metal cantilever shoulder-wing monoplane
Fuselage: metal semi-monocoque
Tail unit: metal cantilever
Landing gear: hydraulically actuated retractable tricycle unit
Powerplant: two General Electric J79-GE-10 turbojets, each rated at 17,860-lb (8,118-kg) static thrust with afterburning
Fuel capacity:
Avionics: comprehensive communication and navigation equipment, plus side-looking airborne radar (SLAR), and active and passive ECM equipment
Armament: none
Dimensions: Span 53 ft (16.15 m)
Length 75 ft 10 in (23.11 m)
Height 19 ft 5 in (5.92 m)
Wing area: 700 ft² (65.03 m²)
Weights: Empty about 38,000 lb (17,240 kg)
Loaded
Maximum 80,000 lb (36,285 kg)
Performance: speed 1,385 mph (2,230 kph) or Mach 2.1 at 40,000 ft (12,192 m); cruising speed 1,254 mph (2,018 kph); service ceiling 67,000 ft (20,400 m); range 3,200 miles (5,150 km) with external fuel
Used only by: USA
Notes: The A-5 was designed as an attack bomber designated the A3J. It first flew in 1958, entering service in 1960 as the A-5A. This was a remarkable aircraft, with a long bomb bay between the engines, from which the nuclear weapon was ejected to the rear over the target. The A-5B had leading-edge droop-blowing to allow a 15,000-lb (6,804-kg) increase in weight, and the RA-5C strategic re-

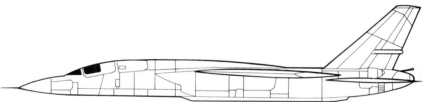

connaissance variant, to which the specification applies, has side-looking airborne radar (SLAR) and many other advanced sensors.

Rockwell International (North American Aircraft) T-39

Type: utility trainer and transport
Crew: two, and up to six passengers
Wings: metal cantilever low-wing monoplane
Fuselage: metal semi-monocoque
Tail unit: metal cantilever
Landing gear: hydraulically actuated retractable tricycle unit
Powerplant: two Pratt & Whitney J60-P-3 turbojets, each rated at 3,000-lb (1,361-kg) static thrust
Fuel capacity: 885 gallons (4,024 litres) in one fuselage and integral wing tanks
Avionics: comprehensive communication and navigation equipment
Armament: none
Dimensions: Span 44 ft 5 in (13.54 m)
Length 43 ft 9 in (13.34 m)
Height 16 ft (4.88 m)
Wing area: 342 ft² (31.77 m²)
Weights: Empty 9,300 lb (4,218 kg)
Loaded

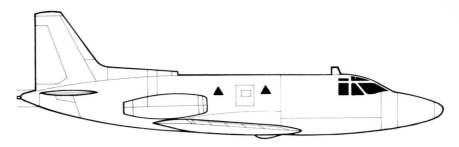

Maximum 17,760 lb (8,056 kg)
Performance: speed 595 mph (958 kph) at 36,000 ft (10,975 m); cruising speed 452 mph (727 kph) at 40,000 ft (12,190 m); climb 5,550 ft (1,692 m) per minute at sea level; service ceiling 45,000 ft (13,715 m); range 1,725 miles (2,776 km)
Used also by: Argentina, Bolivia
Notes: Derived from the Sabreliner business jet project, the prototype of the T-39 flew in 1958, and entered service in 1960. There are several versions:

1. T-39A pilot proficiency and administrative support aircraft for the USAF
2. T-39B radar trainer for the USAF
3. T-39D radar interception officer trainer for the US Navy
4. CT-39E rapid-response airlift aircraft for the US Navy
5. T-39F pilot and electronic warfare officer trainer for the USAF
6. CT-39G fleet tactical support aircraft for the US Navy.

Sikorsky Aircraft CH-53E

Type: heavy-lift multi-purpose helicopter
Crew: three, plus up to 55 passengers
Rotor: titanium and steel cantilever seven-blade main rotor; aluminium and titanium cantilever four-blade tail rotor
Fuselage: light alloy, steel and titanium semi-monocoque
Landing gear: hydraulically actuated retractable tricycle unit
Powerplant: three General Electric T64-GE-415 turboshafts, each rated at 4,380 shp for 10 minutes and 3,670 shp for continuous running

Fuel capacity:
Avionics: comprehensive communication and navigation equipment
Armament: none
Dimensions: Span 79 ft (24.08 m)
Length (fuselage) 73 ft 9 in (22.48 m)
Height 27 ft 9 in (8.46 m)
Rotor disc area: 4,902 ft² (455.4 m²)
Weights: Empty 32,048 lb (14,536 kg)
Loaded 56,000 lb (25,400 kg)
Maximum 69,750 lb (31,638 kg)
Performance: (at normal loaded weight) speed 196 mph (315 kph) at sea level; cruising speed 173 mph (278 kph) at sea

level; climb 2,380 ft (725 m) per minute at sea level; service ceiling 12,400 ft (3,780 m); hovering ceiling in ground effect 10,720 ft (3,265 m); range 306 miles (492 km)
Used only by: USA
Notes: The CH-53E is a three-turbine development of the CH-53, with an improved rotor system. Introduced into service in 1978, it can carry 93 per cent of a marine division's combat equipment, and lift 98 per cent of USMC aircraft without any disassembly. The CH-53E is the west's largest and most powerful helicopter.

Sikorsky Aircraft CH-54 Tarhe

Type: flying crane helicopter
Crew: three
Rotor: aluminium cantilever six-blade main rotor; aluminium and titanium cantilever four-blade tail rotor
Fuselage: aluminium and steel semi-monocoque
Landing gear: fixed tricycle unit
Powerplant: two Pratt & Whitney T73-P-1 turboshafts, each rated at 4,500 shp
Fuel capacity: 732 gallons (3,328 litres) in two fuselage tanks, plus provision for a 366-gallon (1,664-litre) auxiliary tank
Avionics: communication and navigation equipment
Armament: none
Dimensions: Span 72 ft (21.95 m)
Length (fuselage) 70 ft 3 in (21.41 m)
Height 18 ft 7 in (5.67 m)
Rotor disc area: 4,070 ft² (378.1 m²)
Weights: Empty 19,234 lb (8,724 kg)
Loaded 38,000 lb (17,237 kg)
Maximum 42,000 lb (19,050 kg)
Performance: (at normal loaded weight) speed 126 mph (203 kph) at sea level; cruising speed 105 mph (169 kph); climb 1,330 ft (405 m) per minute at sea level; service ceiling 9,000 ft (2,475 m); hovering ceiling in ground effect 10,600 ft (3,230 m); range 230 miles (370 km)
Used only by: USA
Notes: Designed under the company designation S-64, the CH-54 was produced to meet a US Army requirement for a military

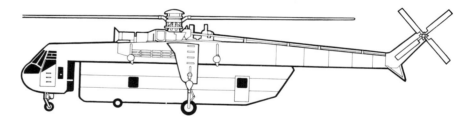

transport helicopter, its interchangeable pods suiting it to troop transport, cargo and missile transport, field hospital, minesweeping and other requirements. The first prototype flew in 1963, and the type entered service in 1964. There are two military versions:

1. CH-54A, the initial production version, to which the technical specification above applies. This model can carry 45 troops, or 24 litters, or loads of up

to 20,000 lb (9,072 kg), the maximum capacity of its removable hoist. This last capability was especially useful in Vietnam, where CH-54As rescued some 380 downed aircraft
2. CH-54B, an uprated version of the CH-54A, with two 4,800-shp Pratt & Whitney JFTD12-5A engines, a maximum weight of 47,000 lb (21,318 kg) and a maximum payload of 40,780 lb (18,497 kg).

Sikorsky Aircraft H-3 Jolly Green Giant

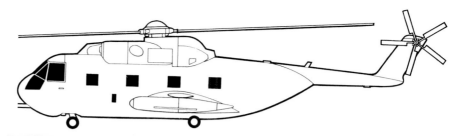

Type: amphibious transport helicopter
Crew: two or three, plus up to 30 passengers
Rotor: metal cantilever five-blade main rotor; aluminium cantilever five-blade tail rotor
Fuselage: metal semi-monocoque
Landing gear: hydraulically actuated retractable tricycle unit
Powerplant: two General Electric T58-GE-5 turboshafts, each rated at 1,500 shp
Fuel capacity: 535 gallons (2,430 litres) in two bladder-type tanks in the fuselage
Avionics: comprehensive communication and navigation equipment
Armament: provision for machine-gun armament in some models
Dimensions: Span 62 ft (18.9 m)
Length (fuselage) 57 ft 3 in (17.45 m)
Height 16 ft 1 in (4.9 m)
Rotor disc area: 3,019 ft² (280.5 m²)
Weights: Empty 13,255 lb (6,010 kg)
Loaded 21,247 lb (9,635 kg)
Maximum 22,050 lb (10,000 kg)
Performance: (at normal loaded weight) speed 162 mph (261 kph) at sea level; cruising speed 144 mph (232 kph); climb 1,310 ft (400 m) per minute at sea level; service ceiling 11,100 ft (3,385 m); hovering ceiling in ground effect 4,100 ft (1,250 m); range 465 miles (748 km)
Used also by: Argentina
Notes: The H-3 amphibious transport helicopter is basically the S-61R version of Sikorsky's S-61 for the US Navy, considerably modified for its new role with a hydraulically operated rear loading ramp, a 2,000-lb (907-kg) winch and other equip-

ment. The first example flew in 1963, and the type entered service with the USAF later in the same year. There are several models:
1. CH-3C for the USAF with 1,300-shp T58-GE-1 turboshafts
2. CH-3E version of the CH-3C for the USAF with 1,500-shp T56-GE-5 engines, to which the technical specification above applies

3. HH-3E Jolly Green Giant version of the CH-3E for the USAF Aerospace Rescue and Recovery Command, with armour, self-sealing tanks and in-flight refuelling capability
4. HH-3F version of the HH-3E for the US Coast Guard, with advanced electronics for the search and rescue role.

The maximum payload of the H-3 is 5,000 lb (2,270 kg).

Sikorsky Aircraft H-3 Sea King

Type: all-weather anti-submarine helicopter
Crew: four
Rotor: metal cantilever five-blade main rotor; metal cantilever five-blade tail rotor
Fuselage: metal semi-monocoque
Landing gear: boat hull, or hydraulically actuated retractable tailwheel unit with non-retracting tailwheel
Powerplant: two General Electric T58-GE-10 turboshafts, each rated at 1,400 shp
Fuel capacity: 700 gallons (3,180 litres) in three bladder-type fuselage tanks
Avionics: comprehensive communication and navigation/attack equipment, including Bendix AN/AQS-13 sonar, Teledyne AN/APN-130 doppler radar and a radar altimeter
Armament: up to 840 lb (381 kg) of homing torpedoes, depth bombs and other stores
Dimensions: Span 62 ft (18.9 m)
Length (fuselage) 54 ft 9 in (16.69 m)
Height 16 ft 10 in (5.13 m)
Rotor disc area: 3,019 ft² (280.5 m²)
Weights: Empty 9,763 lb (4,428 kg)
Loaded 18,626 lb (8,449 kg)
Maximum 21,000 lb (9,525 kg)
Performance: (at a take-off weight of 20,500 lb/9,300 kg) speed 166 mph (267 kph); cruising speed 136 mph (219 kph); climb 2,200 ft (670 m) per minute at sea level; service ceiling 14,700 ft (4,480 m); hovering ceiling in ground effect 10,500 ft (3,200 m); range 625 miles (1,005 km)
Used also by: Argentina, Canada, Denmark, Indonesia, Iran, Italy, Japan, Malaysia
Notes: The origin of the S-61 series of helicopters lies in a 1957 US Navy requirement for a submarine hunter/killer. The first

example flew in 1959, and the type entered service in 1961. There have been many versions of the S-61, including civil models:
1. SH-3A Sea King, the initial A/S variant for the USN, with two T58-GE-8B engines each developing 1,250 shp
2. CH-124 version of the SH-3A for the Canadian Armed Forces
3. S-61A amphibious transport based on the SH-3A, with the option of Rolls-Royce Gnome H.1200 engines. Used by the Royal Danish Air Force in the air-sea rescue role
4. S-61A-4 *Nuri* version of the S-61A for the Royal Malaysian Air Force

5. HH-3A armed search and rescue version of the SH-3A for the US Navy
6. SH-3D Sea King, standard A/S helicopter for the USN, to which the technical specification above applies. Also built by Westland in the UK, and by Agusta in Italy
7. S-61D-4 version of the SH-3D for the Argentinian Navy
8. VH-3D for VIP transport
9. SH-3G utility conversion of the SH-3A
10. SH-3H multi-role version of the SH-3G, with improved A/S equipment and missile detection equipment.

221

Sikorsky Aircraft H-53 Sea Stallion

Type: assault transport helicopter
Crew: three, plus up to 37 passengers
Rotor: aluminium, steel and titanium cantilever six-blade main rotor; aluminium and titanium cantilever four-blade tail rotor
Fuselage: aluminium, steel and titanium semi-monocoque
Landing gear: hydraulically actuated retractable tricycle unit
Powerplant: usually two General Electric T64-GE-6 turboshafts, each rated at 2,850 shp, but also 3,080-shp T64-GE-1 or 3,435-shp T64-GE-16(mod) turboshafts
Fuel capacity: 524 gallons (2,384 litres) in two bladder tanks in the fuselage
Avionics: comprehensive communication and navigation equipment
Armament: up to three 7.62-mm Miniguns can be carried on some models
Dimensions: Span 72 ft 3 in (22.02 m)
  Length (fuselage) 67 ft 2 in (20.47 m)
  Height 17 ft 1½ in (5.22 m)
Rotor disc area: 4,070 ft² (378.1 m²)
Weights: Empty 22,444 lb (10,180 kg)
  Loaded 35,000 lb (15,875 kg)
  Maximum 42,000 lb (19,050 kg)
Performance: speed 195 mph (314 kph) at sea level; cruising speed 172 mph (277 kph); climb 2,240 ft (683 m) per minute at sea level; service ceiling 18,550 ft (5,654 m); hovering ceiling in ground effect 8,200 ft (2,499 m); range 256 miles (412 km)
Used also by: Austria, Israel, West Germany
Notes: Designed as a heavy assault helicopter for the US Marine Corps under the company designation S-65A, the H-53 family was clearly derived from the S-61, with many components of the S-64. The first flight was made in 1964, and the type entered service in 1966. There are several

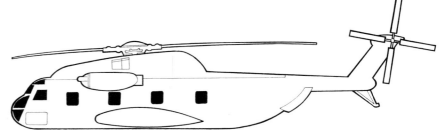

versions of the basic helicopter:

1. CH-53A Sea Stallion for the US Navy and Marine Corps, to which the technical specification above relates
2. HH-53B for the USAF Aerospace Rescue and Recovery Service, similar to the CH-53A but with 3,080-shp T64-GE-3 engines
3. HH-53C for the USAF, basically an improved version of the HH-53B with 3,925-shp T64-GE-7 engines and provision for 375-gallon (1,703-litre) drop tanks, increasing range to 540 miles (869 km), and an external cargo hook of 20,000-lb (9,070-kg) capacity
4. CH-53D for the US Marine Corps, with 3,925-shp T64-GE-413 engines and the ability to lift 55 troops. The type can also be used for minesweeping, with a towboom and hook system of 15,000-lb (6,803-kg) capacity
5. RH-53D minesweeping version for the US Navy, described separately
6. CH-53E heavy lift version for the US Navy and Marine Corps, described separately
7. CH-53G for Germany, with T64-GE-7 engines
8. S-65-Oe for Austria for alpine rescue.

Sikorsky Aircraft RH-53D

Type: mine countermeasures helicopter
Crew: basic crew of three
Rotor: aluminium, steel and titanium cantilever six-blade main rotor; aluminium and titanium cantilever four-blade tail rotor
Fuselage: aluminium, steel and titanium semi-monocoque
Landing gear: hydraulically actuated retractable tricycle unit
Powerplant: two General Electric T64-GE-415 turboshafts, each rated at 4,380 shp
Fuel capacity: 524 gallons (2,384 litres) in the forward part of the sponsons, plus provision for two 416-gallon (1,892-litre) external auxiliary tanks
Avionics: comprehensive communication and navigation equipment, with provision for the later retrofitting of an advanced navigation system
Armament: provision for two 12.7-mm (0.5-in) machine-guns for the detonation of surfaced mines
Dimensions: Span 72 ft 3 in (22.02 m)
  Length (fuselage) 67 ft 2 in (20.47 m)
  Height 17 ft 1½ in (5.22 m)
Rotor disc area: 4,070 ft² (378.1 m²)
Weights: Empty
  Loaded 42,000 lb (19,050 kg)
  Maximum 50,000 lb (22,680 kg)
Performance: speed 195 mph (314 kph) at sea level; cruising speed 172 mph (277 kph); climb 2,240 ft (683 m) per minute at sea level; service ceiling 18,550 ft (5,654

m); hovering ceiling in ground effect 8,200 ft (2,499 m); range 256 miles (412 km); endurance more than 4 hours
Used also by: Iran
Notes: The RH-53D was developed from the CH-53 as a specialist mine countermeasures helicopter, with a strengthened rear fuselage to take the extra equipment operated: Mark 103 mechanical, Mark 104 acoustic, Mark 105 magnetic and Mark 106 magnetic/acoustic mine counter-

measures gear. The RH-53D has a separate winch and hook, with a capacity of 7,000 lb (3,175 kg). The towboom has a capacity of 20,000 lb (9,072 kg), and the external cargo hook has a capacity of 25,000 lb (11,340 kg). A rescue hoist of 600-lb (272-kg) capacity is also fitted. Together with the cargo hook, this gives the RH-53D a transport and search and rescue capability.

Sikorsky Aircraft UH-60A Blackhawk

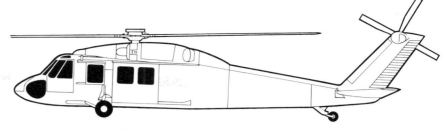

Type: combat assault transport
Crew: three, plus up to 11 passengers
Rotor: titanium and glassfibre cantilever four-blade main rotor; composite cantilever four-blade tail rotor
Fuselage: light alloy semi-monocoque
Landing gear: fixed tailwheel unit
Powerplant: two General Electric T700-GE-700 turboshafts, each rated at 1,543 shp
Fuel capacity:
Avionics: comprehensive communication and navigation equipment
Armament: provision for two 7.62-mm M60 machine-guns firing to the sides
Dimensions: Span 53 ft 8 in (16.36 m)
Length (fuselage) 50 ft 0¾ in (15.26 m)
Height 16 ft 10 in (5.13 m)
Rotor disc area: 2,261 ft² (210.05 m²)
Weights: Empty 10,900 lb (4,944 kg)
Loaded 16,450 lb (7,461 kg)
Maximum 20,250 lb (9,185 kg)

Performance: (at normal loaded weight) speed 184 mph (296 kph) at sea level; cruising speed 169 mph (272 kph) at 4,000 ft (1,220 m); climb 2,460 ft (750 m) per minute vertically at sea level; service ceiling 19,100 ft (5,820 m); hovering ceiling in ground effect 9,500 ft (2,895 m); range 345 miles (556 km)
Used only by: USA
Notes: Designed under the company designation S-70 for a 1972 US Army requirement for a utility tactical transport aircraft system (UTTAS), the UH-60A first flew in 1974. The type is intended to carry a squad of infantry into combat, and is designed to fit into US strategic transport aircraft. The cargo hook can carry a load of up to 8,000 lb (3,630 kg). The type entered service in the UTTAS role during 1978, and has also been selected for production as the US Navy's light airborne multi-purpose system (LAMPS) III aircraft, with provision for magnetic anomaly detector gear, torpedoes, surface search radar, sonobuoys and electronic support measures.

Boeing Aerospace AGM-69 SRAM

Type: air-to-surface strategic guided missile
Guidance: inertial, plus optional terrain-following radar
Dimensions: Span 35 in (89 cm)
Body diameter 17½ in (44.5 cm)
Length 14 ft (4.27 m)
Booster: Lockheed LPC-415 two-stage solid-propellant rocket
Sustainer: as above
Warhead: W-69 nuclear, 200-kiloton
Weights: Launch about 2,230 lb (1,010 kg)
Burnt out
Performance: speed more than Mach 3; range between 35 miles (55 km) in the 'low mode' and 100 miles (160 km) in the 'high mode'
Used only by: USA
Notes: The Short-Range Attack Missile (SRAM) was designed to destroy enemy last-ditch defences, especially surface-to-air missile sites, and to tackle primary strategic targets. Four flight trajectories can be used: semi-ballistic, terrain-following, inertial after a pull-up from behind radar screening terrain, and inertial with terrain-following. The SRAM can be carried by the Boeing B-52 (eight internally and twelve under the wings in four clusters of three), and the General Dynamics F-111 (two internally and four under the wings). The only current model is the AGM-69A, the proposed AGM-69B (with a W-80 nuclear warhead and a Thiokol motor) having been abandoned with the cancellation of the programme for the Rockwell B-1 bomber which was to have carried 24 AGM-69Bs. The radar signature of the SRAM is very small, no larger than that of a bullet.

Boeing Aerospace AGM-86A ALCM

Type: air-to-surface strategic cruise missile
Guidance: inertial and terrain comparison
Dimensions: Span 9 ft 6 in (2.9 m)
Body diameter 25 in (64.0 cm)
Length 14 ft (4.27 m)
Booster: none
Sustainer: Williams Research Corporation F107-WR-100 turbofan, rated at 600-lb (272-kg) static thrust
Warhead: W-80 nuclear, about 200-kiloton
Weights: Launch (with belly tank) 2,400 lb (1,088 kg); (without belly tank) 1,900 lb (860 kg)
Burnt out
Performance: speed Mach 0.7; range with-

out belly tank 745 miles (1,200 km)
Used by: under development for the USA
Notes: The Air-Launched Cruise Missile (ALCM) is a highly sophisticated winged missile of small size and radar signature, to be carried by the Boeing B-52 (eight internally and twelve externally) and perhaps by converted wide-body transport aircraft. The ALCM follows an inertially-controlled flight path, the missile checking its accuracy by comparing the terrain over which it is flying with its reconnaissance-derived computer memory of the terrain over which it should be flying. The missile has the ability to 'take out' hardened targets, and so each of the many missiles launched would have to be destroyed by the defending power. The object of launching waves of ALCMs, apart from actual target elimination, would be to saturate the defence and so allow other aircraft to penetrate. Missiles carried externally can be fitted with a belly tank, and the proposed ALCM-B has a fuselage some 18 ft 8 in (5.7 m) long for more fuel, increasing range to double that of the AGM-86A.

Boeing Aerospace LGM-30F Minuteman II

Type: intercontinental ballistic missile, silo-launched, three stages
Guidance: Rockwell International Autonetics inertial
Dimensions: Body diameter 5 ft 11 in (1.8 m) approximately at 1st-stage interstage
Length 59 ft 8½ in (18.2 m)
Booster (1st stage): Thiokol TU-122 solid-fuel rocket, delivering 200,620-lb (91,000-kg) thrust approximately
Sustainers (2nd stage): Aerojet SR19-AJ-1 solid-fuel rocket, delivering 60,625-lb (27,500-kg) thrust approximately; (3rd stage) Hercules solid-fuel rocket, delivering about 35,275-lb (16,000-kg) thrust
Warhead: thermonuclear, in the order of 2 megatons, in an Avco Type 11B or 11C re-entry vehicle with Mark 1 or Tracor Mark 1A penetration aids
Weights: Launch 31.25 tons (31.75 tonnes) Burnt out
Performance: range 6,990+ miles (11,250+ km); speed at burn-out 14,912+ mph (24,000+ kph); throw-weight 1,000 lb (454 kg); CEP 0.33 mile (0.54 km)
Used only by: USA
Notes: Introduced in 1966, as a replacement for the LGM-30A and LGM-30B Minuteman I ICBMs. The Minuteman II has improved performance and targeting capability, with a heavier payload and better penetration aids.

Boeing Aerospace LGM-30G Minuteman III

Type: intercontinental ballistic missile, silo-launched, three stages
Guidance: Rockwell International Autonetics inertial
Dimensions: Body diameter 6 ft 1 in (1.85 m) at 1st-stage interstage
Length 59 ft 8½ in (18.2 m)
Booster (1st stage): Thiokol TV-122 solid-fuel rocket, delivering 200,620-lb (91,000-kg) thrust approximately
Sustainers (2nd stage): Aerojet SR19-AJ-1 solid-fuel rocket, delivering 60,625-lb (27,500-kg) thrust approximately; (3rd stage) Aerojet & Thiokol SR73-AJ-1 solid-

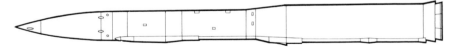

fuel rocket, delivering 34,170-lb (15,500-kg) thrust approximately; (post-boost propulsion) Bell Aerosystems package
Warhead: thermonuclear, 3 × W-78 350-kiloton General Electric Mark 12 re-entry vehicles in a MIRV package
Weights: Launch 33.95 tons (34.5 tonnes) Burnt out
Performance: range 8,078+ miles (13,000+ km); speed at burn-out 14,912+ mph (24,000+ kph); throw-weight 2,000 lb (907 kg); CEP less than 0.25 miles (0.4 km)
Used only by: USA
Notes: The Minuteman III is essentially a MIRVed version of the Minuteman II. The MIRV motor (300-lb/135-kg thrust) in effect makes a 4th stage, which contains the warheads, computer, chaff dispensers and decoys, the computer controlling the whole. The Minuteman III was introduced in 1970, and is the backbone of the US ICBM force.

General Dynamics (Pomona Division) AGM-78 Standard ARM

Type: air-to-surface tactical anti-radiation missile
Guidance: radar emission homing
Dimensions: Span 43 in (109.0 m)
Body diameter 13⅝ in (34.0 cm)
Length 14 ft 9 in (4.49 m)
Booster: Aerojet Mark 27 Model 4 dual-thrust solid-propellant rocket
Sustainer: as above
Warhead: high explosive
Weights: Launch 1,400 lb (635 kg) Burnt out

Performance: speed more than Mach 2; range probably more than 15½ miles (25 km)
Used only by: USA
Notes: Derived from the RIM-66A Standard 1 (MR), the AGM-78 is designed for the suppression of enemy radar sites. There are four versions, their main differences being in the frequency spectrum covered by their emission-homing heads. The versions are designated AGM-78B (the initial production model), AGM-78C, AGM-78D, and AGM-78D-2. The type is also used as a ship-launched missile, under the designation RGM-66D.

Hughes Aircraft AGM-65 Maverick

Type: air-to-surface tactical guided missile
Guidance: TV command
Dimensions: Span 28 in (71.0 cm)
              Body diameter 12 in (30.0 cm)
              Length 8 ft 1 in (2.46 m)
Booster: Thiokol TX-481 solid-propellant rocket
Sustainer: none
Warhead: high-penetration shaped-charge high explosive, weighing 130 lb (59 kg)
Weights: Launch 462 lb (210 kg)
         Burnt out
Performance: speed supersonic, range 8–14 miles (13–22.5 km)
Used also by: Iran, Israel, Saudi Arabia, South Korea, Sweden
Notes: The Maverick is designed for use against concentrated targets such as armoured formations. The missile is guided automatically once the TV camera in the nose has been locked onto the target image. There are currently four versions:

1. AGM-65A initial production model, to which the data above apply
2. AGM-65B Scene Magnification Maverick, to allow the pilot to lock the TV camera onto the target at longer range
3. AGM-65C Laser Maverick for close air-support missions with the target marked in day or night by an air or surface target designator
4. AGM-65D Infra-Red Maverick with an imaging infra-red (IIR) seeker for use in adverse weather conditions. This missile uses an infra-red image transmitted by a forward-looking infra-red (FLIR)-equipped aircraft for the homing image.

An infra-red Night-Attack Maverick is under development for the USN.

Hughes Aircraft AIM-4D Falcon

Type: air-to-air tactical guided missile
Guidance: infra-red homing
Dimensions: Span 20 in (50.8 cm)
              Body diameter $6\frac{2}{3}$ in (16.25 cm)
              Length 6 ft 6 in (1.98 m)
Booster: Thiokol TX-58 solid-propellant rocket
Sustainer: none
Warhead: high explosive
Weights: Launch about 132 lb (60 kg)
         Burnt out
Performance: speed about Mach 4
Used also by: Canada, Finland, Greece, Japan
Notes: Formerly known as the GAR-2D, the AIM-4D Falcon was developed after the AIM-4E, F and G. The object was to produce a lightweight high-performance missile capable of bettering enemy fighters, and this was achieved by the marriage of the AIM-4A airframe and motor with the homing head of the AIM-4G. AIM-4A and C Falcons are currently being brought up to AIM-4D standard. The type can engage targets from any direction. The AIM-4H is a development of the AIM-4D with a new warhead and an active optical (laser) fuse.

Hughes Aircraft AIM-4E and AIM-4F Super Falcon

Type: air-to-air tactical guided missile
Guidance: semi-active radar homing
Dimensions: Span (AIM-4E and F) 24 in (60.96 cm)
Body diameter (AIM-4E) 6½ in (16.5 cm); (AIM-4F) 6⅝ in (16.7 cm)
Length (AIM-4E and F) 7 ft 2 in (2.184 m)
Booster: Thiokol two-level solid-propellant rocket
Sustainer: as above
Warhead: high explosive
Weights: Launch (AIM-4E) about 140 lb (63.5 kg); (AIM-4F) 150 lb (68 kg)
Burnt out
Performance: (AIM-4F) speed Mach 3; range 7 miles (11.25 km)

Used only by: USA
Notes: These two Super Falcon models mark an increase in the performance of the basic Falcon missile by the use of a more powerful fuel. At the same time, improved electronics make the models less prone to ECM interference. Only relatively few AIM-4Es were produced before the AIM-4F superseded it in production.

Hughes Aircraft AIM-4G Super Falcon

Type: air-to-air tactical guided missile
Guidance: infra-red homing
Dimensions: Span 24 in (60.96 cm)
Body diameter 6⅝ in (16.7 cm)
Length 6 ft 9 in (2.057 m)
Booster: Thiokol two-level solid-propellant rocket
Sustainer: as above
Warhead: high explosive, weighing about 40 lb (18 kg)
Weights: Launch 145 lb (65.77 kg)
Burnt out
Performance: speed Mach 3; range 7 miles (11.25 km)

Used only by: USA
Notes: The AIM-4G is basically similar to the AIM-4F, but has an infra-red homing system in place of the earlier model's semi-active radar system. The IR seeker is a great improvement on that fitted to the AIM-4C.

Hughes Aircraft AIM-26 Super Falcon

Type: air-to-air tactical guided missile
Guidance: semi-active radar homing
Dimensions: Span 24 in (60.96 cm)
Body diameter 11 in (27.9 cm)
Length 7 ft (2.134 m)
Booster: Thiokol two-level solid-propellant rocket
Sustainer: as above
Warhead: (AIM-26A) nuclear; (AIM-26B) high explosive
Weights: Launch about 198 lb (90 kg)
Burnt out
Performance: speed Mach 2+; range 5 miles (8 km)
Used also by: Switzerland

Notes: The AIM-26 (formerly GAR-11) Super Falcon originated as a programme to improve on earlier models' capabilities, especially by adding head-on attack capability with the aid of semi-active radar homing. Only a few XAIM-26As were fitted with nuclear warheads, the production AIM-26B having a high explosive warhead.

Hughes Aircraft AIM-54 Phoenix

Type: air-to-air tactical guided missile
Guidance: AN/DSQ-26 semi-active radar, radar terminal homing
Dimensions: Span 36 in (91.44 cm)
Body diameter 15 in (38.1 cm)
Length 13 ft (3.96 m)
Booster: Rocketdyne Mark 47 Model 0, or Aerojet General Mark 60 Model 0 solid-propellant rocket
Sustainer: as above

Warhead: 132-lb (60-kg) continuous-rod high explosive
Weights: Launch 985 lb (447 kg)
Burnt out
Performance: speed more than Mach 4; estimated range between $68\frac{1}{3}$ and $102\frac{1}{2}$ miles (110 and 165 km)
Used also by: Iran
Notes: The Phoenix is a long-range air-to-air missile intended for use with the Hughes AWG-9 fire-control and armament system, developed for use with the cancelled Gen-

eral Dynamics F-111B and now used in the Grumman F-14A Tomcat. The Phoenix is an extremely powerful and versatile missile, and the AWG-9 system allows up to six targets to be engaged at the same time at very long range. There are several versions:
1. AIM-54A initial production model, to which the data above apply
2. AIM-54B developed model with digital guidance and other improvments
3. AIM-54C improved model with enhanced ECCM capability.

Hughes Aircraft BGM-71A TOW

Type: air-to-surface anti-tank tactical guided missile
Guidance: command by means of wire
Dimensions: Span 13½ in (34.0 cm)
  Body diameter 5 $\frac{9}{16}$ in (15.0 cm)
  Length 3 ft 9 $\frac{7}{16}$ in (1.18 m)

Booster: solid-propellant rocket
Sustainer: solid-propellant rocket
Warhead: armour-piercing shaped-charge high explosive, weighing 8 lb (3.6 kg)
Weights: Launch 48 lb (22 kg)
  Burnt out

Performance: speed over Mach 0.9; range from under 71 yards (65 m) to 4,100 yards (3,750 m)

Used by: USA and other nations
Notes: Originally designed for surface-to-surface use, the TOW (Tube-launched, Optically-tracked, Wire-guided) missile can also be fired from a helicopter, in US service the Bell Huey family, with the aid of an M65 sight. Up to eight TOWs can be carried on the AH-1 HueyCobra.

McDonnell Douglas Astronautics AGM-84A Harpoon

Type: air-to-surface tactical anti-shipping guided missile
Guidance: gyro and radio altimeter, plus active radar terminal homing
Dimensions: Span 36 in (91.44 cm)
  Body diameter 13½ in (34.0 cm)
  Length 12 ft 7 in (3.84 m)

Booster: none
Sustainer: Teledyne CAE J402-CA-400 turbojet, rated at 660-lb (299-kg) static thrust at sea level
Warhead: 500-lb (227-kg) NWC penetrating-blast high explosive
Weights: Launch 1,160 lb (526 kg)
  Burnt out

Performance: cruising speed about Mach 0.85; range about 70 miles (113 km)
Used only by: USA, but ordered by many other countries
Notes: The AGM-86A Harpoon is the air-launched variant of the RGM-86A Harpoon surface-to-surface anti-shipping missile, without the rocket booster.

McDonnell Douglas Astronautics AIR-2A Genie

Type: air-to-air tactical unguided missile
Guidance: none
Dimensions: Span 24 in (60.96 cm)
  Body diameter 17 in (43.18 cm)
  Length 9 ft (2.74 m)

Booster: Thiokol solid-propellant rocket
Sustainer: none
Warhead: nuclear
Weights: Launch about 816 lb (370 kg)
  Burnt out

Performance: speed Mach 3; ceiling over 49,210 ft (15,000 m); range 6 miles (9.6 km)

Used only by: USA
Notes: The Genie is designed for the air defence of the United States, its highly lethal nuclear warhead making virtually certain the destruction of any target engaged.

Martin Marietta (Orlando Division) AGM-12 Bullpup

Type: air-to-surface tactical guided missile
Guidance: optically tracked radio command
Dimensions: Span (AGM-12B) 37½ in (95.25 cm); (AGM-12C) 46⅓ in (1.18 m)
  Body diameter (AGM-12B) 12 in (30.5 cm); (AGM-12C) 17¼ in (43.9 cm)
  Length (AGM-12B) 10 ft 6 in (3.2 m); (AGM-12C) 13 ft 4 in (4.07 m)

Booster: Thiokol LR58 or LR62 liquid-propellant rocket
Sustainer: none
Warhead: 250 lb (113.4 kg) or 1,000 lb (453.6 kg) high explosive, or nuclear
Weights: Launch (AGM-12B) 570 lb (258 kg); (AGM-12C) 1,790 lb (812 kg)
  Burnt out

Performance: speed over Mach 2; range (small versions) about 7 miles (11.25 km); range (large versions) 10½ miles (17 km)
Used also by: Denmark, Israel, Norway, Taiwan
Notes: The Bullpup family is a large one, and is designed for air-to-surface attacks on land and sea targets. Designations run from AGM-12A to AGM-12E, and there is also an ATM-12 inert training series. Bullpups vary very considerably in size, performance and configuration from model to model as a result of their different tactical roles.

Martin Marietta (Orlando Division) AGM-62A Walleye

Type: air-to-surface tactical guided weapon
Guidance: automatic after TV camera lock-on onto target (electro-optical system)
Dimensions: Span (Walleye I) 3 ft 9 in (1.14 m)
Body diameter (Walleye I) 15 in (38.1 cm); (Walleye II) 18 in (45.7 cm)
Length (Walleye I) 11 ft 3 in (3.43 m); (Walleye II) 13 ft 3 in (4.04 m)

Booster: none
Sustainer: none
Warhead: (Walleye I) 850 lb (385 kg) high explosive; (Walleye II) 2,000 lb (907 kg) high explosive
Weights: Launch (Walleye I) 1,100 lb (499 kg); (Walleye II) 2,339 lb (1,061 kg) Burnt out
Performance: speed Mach 0.9; range up to 10 miles (16 km)
Used also by: Israel
Notes: The AGM-65 Walleye family is made up of three glide-bomb weapons, the flying surfaces giving the weapons the ability to home onto a target selected and locked into the guidance system's electro-optical circuits by the aircraft pilot or weapon operator. There are three versions:

1. Walleye I basic version
2. Walleye II larger version, designed for attacks on targets such as bridges, airfields, ships and port facilities
3. Extended Range, Data Link Walleye II, similar to the basic Walleye II but with larger wings and data link equipment to allow the weapon's TV guidance to be locked onto the target after launch.

Martin Marietta (Denver Division) LGM-25C Titan II

Type: intercontinental ballistic missile, silo-launched, two stages

Guidance: IBM/AC Spark Plug inertial

Dimensions: Body diameter 10 ft (3.05 m)
Length 102 ft 8¼ in (31.3 m)

Booster: Aerojet LR87 liquid-propellant rocket, delivering 429,000-lb (195,000-kg) thrust

Sustainer: Aerojet LR91 liquid-propellant rocket, delivering 99,210 lb (45,000-kg) thrust

Warhead: thermonuclear, General Electric Mark 6 re-entry vehicle with penetration aids, about 6/9-megaton

Weights: Launch 147.33 tons (149.7 tonnes)
Burnt out

Performance: range 9,320 miles (15,000 km) approximately; speed 14,912+ mph (24,000+ kph); ceiling 932 miles (1,500 km) approximately; throw-weight 8,157 lb (3,700 kg); CEP 0.6 mile (0.97 km)

Used only by: USA

Notes: Introduced to the Strategic Air Command in 1963, and carries the largest US ICBM payload. Its main use is against 'soft' targets.

Naval Weapons Center/Texas Instruments AGM-45A Shrike

Type: air-to-surface tactical anti-radiation guided missile

Guidance: radar emission homing

Dimensions: Span 3 ft (91.0 cm)
Body diameter 8 in (20.3 cm)
Length 10 ft (3.05 m)

Booster: Rocketdyne Mark 39 Model 7 or Aerojet General Mark 53 solid-propellant rocket

Sustainer: none

Warhead: 145 lb (66 kg) fragmentation high explosive

Weights: Launch 400 lb (182 kg)
Burnt out

Performance: speed more than Mach 1; range more than 8 miles (13 km)

Used also by: Israel

Notes: The Shrike was first known as the ARM (Anti-Radiation Missile), and is intended to suppress the enemy's radar systems by homing onto their emissions. There have been 12 versions of the Shrike (AGM-45-1, 1A, 2, 3, 3A, 3B, 4, 6, 7, 7A, 9 and 10) differing principally in the frequency coverage of their seeker heads. The Shrike is used by the USAF and USN.

230

Naval Weapons Center AIM-9 Sidewinder

Type: air-to-air tactical guided missile
Guidance: infra-red homing
Dimensions: Span 24¾ in (63.0 cm)
              Body diameter 5 in (12.7 cm)
              Length 9 ft 5 in (2.87 m)
Booster: Rocketdyne/Bermite Mark 36 Model 6 solid-propellant rocket
Sustainer: none
Warhead: WDU-17/B annular-blast high explosive with an active optical (laser) fuse
Weights: Launch 190 lb (86 kg)
          Burnt out
Performance: speed Mach 2.5; range about 6 miles (10 km)
Used also by: many other nations
Notes: The AIM-9 Sidewinder has been a front-line weapon since the mid-1950s, and there are many versions of this still effective air-to-air guided missile:

1. AIM-9A prototype model, fired successfully fired in 1953
2. AIM-9B initial production model by Philco and General Electric, with a fin span of 22 in (56.0 cm), a length of 9 ft 3½ in (2.83 m), a weight of 159 lb (72 kg), and a motor made by the Naval Powder Plant. Speed is Mach 2 and ceiling more than 49,210 ft (15,000 m), but range is only 1,202 yards (1,100 m)
3. AIM-9C semi-active radar homing version of the AIM-9B
4. AIM-9D with Rocketdyne Mark 36 Model 5 motor to provide greater speed and range. Span is 25 in (64.0 cm), length 9 ft 6½ in (2.91 m), weight 185 lb (84 kg), and notable visual differences to earlier models are broader chord foreplanes, more swept tailplanes, and a tapering nose
5. AIM-9E improved AIM-9B, produced by Philco for the USAF with Thiokol Mark 17 motors
6. AIM-9G improved version of the AIM-9D with enhanced target acquisition, made by Raytheon for the USAF and USN
7. AIM-9H, based on the AIM-9G, with solid-state guidance, updated electronics to improve flexibility, and improved close-range dogfighting abilities for the USN
8. AIM-9J advanced model of the AIM-9E, with improved dogfighting capabilities given by revised foreplanes, and being made for the USAF by Ford Aerospace (successor to Philco)
9. AIM-9J-3 (or AIM-9J+) updating of the AIM-9J with solid-state electronics
10. AIM-9L (Super Sidewinder), latest version for the USAF and USN, to which the technical specification above relates. This model is distinguishable from earlier Sidewinders by its double-delta foreplanes to improve manoeuvrability and hence dogfighting capabilities. The seeker head has also been improved, allowing aircraft fitted with the AIM-9L to attack from any angle.

Raytheon (Missile Systems Division) AIM-7 Sparrow III

Type: air-to-air tactical guided missile
Guidance: semi-active radar homing
Dimensions: Span 3 ft 4 in (1.02 m)
Body diameter 8 in (20.3 cm)
Length 12 ft (3.66 m)
Booster: Hercules Mark 58 Model O solid-propellant rocket
Sustainer: none
Warhead: 88 lb (40 kg) continuous-rod high explosive
Weights: Launch 500 lb (227 kg)
Burnt out
Performance: speed more than Mach 3.5; range 28 miles (44 km)
Used also by: Belgium, Greece, Japan, Iran, Israel, Italy, Spain, UK
Notes: The Sparrow is an all-weather all-altitude air-to-air missile of great power, and can also be used in the surface-to-surface, surface-to-air, and air-to-surface capacities. There are several versions of the Sparrow III:
1. AIM-7C initial production model, with an Aerojet General motor
2. AIM-7D improved model
3. AIM-7E, weighing 441 lb (200 kg). In its RIM-7H form, the AIM-7E is used in the NATO Sea Sparrow system
4. AIM-7F with a more powerful motor and warhead, plus greater manoeuvrability. The technical specification above relates to this model.

Rockwell International AGM-28B Hound Dog

Type: air-to-surface strategic guided missile
Guidance: inertial, upgraded by startracking
Dimensions: Span 12 ft (3.66 m)
Body diameter 28 in (71.12 cm)
Length 42 ft 8 in (13.0 m)
Booster: none

Sustainer: one Pratt & Whitney J52-P-3 turbojet, rated at 7,500-lb (3,402-kg) static thrust
Warhead: thermonuclear
Weights: Launch 9,920 lb (4,500 kg)
Burnt out
Performance: speed Mach 2+, ceiling more than 49,210 ft (15,000 m); range 600 miles (966 km)

Used only by: USA
Notes: The AGM-28 is now obsolescent. The method of carriage is below the wings of the Boeing B-52, which can carry two Hound Dog missiles, which entered service in 1961 under the designation GAM-77A. The AGM-28B is the improved version, formerly known as the GAM-77B. Targeting can be changed by the crew of the B-52.

Rockwell International (Missile Systems Division) GBU-15 HOBOS

Type: air-to-surface tactical guided weapon
Guidance: electro-optical, based on TV camera image lock-on
Dimensions: Span 4 ft 4 in (1.32 m)
Body diameter 2 ft (61.0 cm)
Length 12 ft 2 in (3.71 m)
Booster: none
Sustainer: none
Warhead: M118E1 3,000-lb (1,361-kg) bomb
Weights: Launch 3,404 lb (1,544 kg)
Burnt out
Performance: speed subsonic
Used also by: other nations
Notes: The HOBOS (HOming BOmb System) is a USAF programme for the fitting of guidance packages, small gliding wings and control surfaces to the Mark 84 2,000-lb (907-kg) or Mark 118E1 3,000-lb (1,361-kg) bombs. The aircraft crew lock the seeker in the missile onto the image of the target, drop the weapon, and then pull back as the bomb glides down onto the target. The latest version of the system is the GBU-15(V), a designation which covers a number of glide weapons.

Western Electric MIM-14B Nike Hercules

Type: long-range air defence missile
Guidance: radar command
Dimensions: Span 8 ft 9 in (2.67 m)
Body diameter $34\frac{3}{8}$ in (87.9 cm)
Length 41 ft 8 in (12.7 m)
Booster: solid-propellant rocket
Sustainer: solid-propellant rocket
Warhead: nuclear or high explosive
Weights: Launch 10,710 lb (4,858 kg)
Burnt out
Performance: range 87+ miles (140+ km); speed Mach 3.5; ceiling 28+ miles (45+ km)
Used also by: Belgium, Denmark, Greece, Italy, Japan, Netherlands, Norway, South Korea, Taiwan, Turkey, West Germany
Notes: 2nd-generation US air defence missile. It has limited ABM capability.

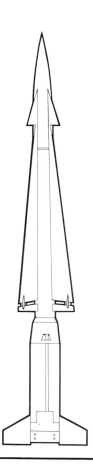

Upper Volta

2 C-47, 2 Nord 262, 1 HS748 transports.
5 light planes.

Uruguay

3,000 men and 30 combat aircraft.

1 fighter/trg sqn with 6 AT-33A.
1 COIN sqn with 8 A-37B.
1 recce/trg sqn with 10 T-6G, 6 U-17A.
Transports incl 10 C-47, 2 F-27, 3 FH-227, 2 Queen Air, 5 EMB-110C.
Helicopters incl 6 Bell UH-1H, 2 Hiller UH-2.
2 Cessna 182, 2 Piper Super Cub liaison ac.
Trainers incl 6 T-41, 2 C-45.
(1 EMB-110B1 transport on order.)

Naval Air Arm

3 S-2A MR ac, 3 SNB-5 (C-45) transports; 1 T-34B, 4 SNJ-4, 4 T-6 trainers, 2 Bell 47G, 2 SH-34J helicopters.

Empresa Brasileira de Aeronáutica EMB-110 *Bandeirante*

Type: utility transport
Crew: two, plus up to 18 passengers
Wings: aluminium and glassfibre cantilever low-wing monoplane
Fuselage: aluminium alloy semi-monocoque
Tail unit: metal cantilever
Landing gear: hydraulically actuated retractable tricycle unit
Powerplant: two Pratt & Whitney Aircraft of Canada PT6A-27 turboprops, each rated at 680 shp and driving a Hartzell metal three-blade propeller
Fuel capacity: 378 gallons (1,720 litres) in four integral wing tanks
Avionics: communication and navigation equipment
Armament: none
Dimensions: Span 50 ft 2½ in (15.3 m)
Length 46 ft 8¼ in (14.23 m)
Height 15 ft 6¼ in (4.73 m)
Wing area: 312.15 ft² (29.0 m²)
Weights: Empty 7,502 lb (3,403 kg)
Loaded
Maximum 12,345 lb (5,600 kg)
Performance: (at maximum take-off weight) speed 280 mph (452 kph) at 7,500 ft

(2,285 m); cruising speed 263 mph (424 kph) at 10,000 ft (3,050 m); climb 1,450 ft (442 m) per minute at sea level; service ceiling 25,300 ft (7,700 m) at a take-off weight of 11,684 lb (5,300 kg); range with maximum fuel 1,266 miles (2,037 km); range with maximum payload 287 miles (463 km)
Used also by: Brazil, Paraguay
Notes: The EMB-110 was developed as a light transport, and serves in several military guises:
1. EMB-110 (C-95) basic passenger transport, to which the technical specification above relates
2. EMB-110B (R-95) aerial photogrammetry version
3. EMB-110C 15-passenger version used by Uruguay
4. EMB-110K1 (C-95A) cargo version, with 750-shp PT6A-34 engines, an overall length of 49 ft 5¾ in (15.08 m), and a maximum payload of 3,421 lb (1,552 kg) compared with the EMB-110's 3,457 lb (1,568 kg).

The EMB-111 (P-95) is a maritime reconnaissance variant under development for Brazil.

Venezuela

8,000 men and 99 combat aircraft.

1 lt bomber sqn with 18 Canberra B2, 7 B(I).8, 2 PR.3, 2 T.4.
3 fighter sqns: 1 with 15 CF-5A, 4 CF-5B; 1 with 9 Mirage IIIEV, 4 VV, 2 VDV; 1 with 20 F-86K.
1 COIN sqn with 16 OV-10E.
2 transport sqns with 5 C-130H, 1 Boeing 737, 1 DC-9, 20 C-47, 12 C-123B Provider, 3 HS-748, 1 Cessna Citation.
Helicopters incl 13 *Alouette* III, 12 UH-1D/H, 10 UH-19.
Trg ac incl 12 Jet Provost T.52, 24 T-2D, 25 T-34, 2 Beech 95, 9 Queen Air, 12 Cessna 182.
R.530 AAM.
1 para bn.
(1 Mirage IIIEV fighter, 8 A 109 helicopters on order.)

Naval Air Arm

6 S-2E Tracker, 4 HU-16 SAR ac, 3 C-47 transports, 2 Bell 47J helicopters.
(6 AB-212 ASW helicopters on order.)

Army Air Arm

Some 20 *Alouette* III and Bell 47G helicopters.

Rockwell International (North American Aircraft) T-2 Buckeye

Type: trainer
Crew: two, seated in tandem

Wings: metal cantilever mid-wing monoplane
Fuselage: metal semi-monocoque
Tail unit: metal cantilever
Landing gear: hydraulically actuated retractable tricycle unit
Powerplant: two General Electric J85-GE-4

turbojets, each rated at 2,950-lb (1,338-kg) static thrust
Fuel capacity: 575 gallons (2,616 litres) in fuselage, inner wing and wingtip tanks
Avionics: comprehensive communication and navigation equipment
Armament: two underwing hardpoints, each with a capacity of 320 lb (145 kg), for the carriage of gun pods, practice bombs, and rocket pods. An alternative option adds to the above another four underwing hardpoints, to bring total capacity to 3,500 lb (1,588 kg)
Dimensions: Span 38 ft 1½ in (11.62 m)
Length 38 ft 3½ in (11.67 m)
Height 14 ft 9½ in (4.51 m)
Wing area: 255 ft² (23.69 m²)
Weights: Empty 8,115 lb (3,680 kg)
Loaded
Maximum 13,191 lb (5,983 kg)
Performance: (at maximum take-off weight) speed 530 mph (852 kph) at 25,000 ft (7,620 m); climb 5,900 ft (1,800 m) per minute at sea level; service ceiling 45,500 ft (13,870 m); range 1,070 miles (1,722 km)

Used also by: Greece, USA
Notes: The T-2 Buckeye was the North American contender for a naval jet trainer, and the first example flew in 1958. There have been five models:
1. T-2A initial production version, with a single 3,400-lb (1,542-kg) Westinghouse J34-WE-48
2. T-2B with two Pratt & Whitney J60-P-6 engines, each of 3,000-lb (1,361-kg) thrust
3. T-2C, similar to the T-2B but powered by a pair of 2,950-lb (1,338-kg) J85-GE-4 engines. The technical specification above relates to this model

4. T-2D for the Venezuelan Air Force, similar to the T-2C, but without carrier landing equipment and with different electronics
5. T-2E for the Hellenic Air Force, and similar to the T-2C except for new electronics and provision of a ground-attack capability kit to provide six wing stations with a capacity of 3,500 lb (1,587 kg).

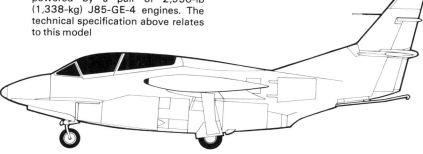

Vietnam

12,000 men and 300 combat aircraft.

1 lt bomber sqn with 10 Il-28.
8 FGA sqns with 120 MG-17, 30 Su-7.
6 interceptor sqns with 70 MiG-19/F-6, 70 MiG-21F/PF.

Transports incl 20 An-2, 4 An-24, 12 Il-14, 4 Il-18, 23 Li-2.
Helicopters incl 20 Mi-4, 10 Mi-6, 9 Mi-8.
AA-2 'Atoll' AAM.
About 30 trainers incl YAK-11/-18, MiG-15 UTI 21U.

Naval Air Arm
10 Mi-4 SAR helicopters.

West Germany

The West German Air Force

West Germany is basically the western two-thirds of the Germany which lost World War II, and was denied military services of any type until her access to the NATO alliance in 1955. Therefore the new *Luftwaffe* is of recent composition, looking back to World War I rather than World War II for its antecedents. West Germany is treaty-bound against any effort at national reunion with East Germany, and against attempts to increase her size territorially. The armed forces are therefore tailored exactly towards NATO requirements, the more so as any conflict between the armed forces of NATO and the Warsaw Treaty Organisation would almost certainly involve major conflict on the North German plain. Accordingly, the West Germans maintain an army designed to counter communist armour superiority with high-quality armoured and tank-destroyer land forces, with considerable air support to counter the WTO air forces and provide the allied land forces with protection and physical aid. The *Luftwaffe* has 106,200 personnel, some 21.68 per cent of the total strength of the armed forces, which receive an annual budget equalling 3.4 per cent of the gross national product.

For long-range operations, the *Luftwaffe* has eight squadrons operating the Pershing 1A surface-to-surface missile, with nine missiles to a squadron. Other missile units are intended for the defence of German installations and forces, and consist of 24 SAM batteries with 216 Nike Hercules, and 36 SAM batteries with 216 Improved HAWK missiles. The SAM forces will be further strengthened when 175 Roland missiles currently on order are delivered.

All-weather fighter operations are the responsibility of the four squadrons operating 60 F-4F Phantom II fighters. But the main offensive strength of the *Luftwaffe* lies in its 16 fighter/ground-attack squadrons, which muster 60 F-4F (four squadrons), 144 F-104G (eight squadrons), and 84 G91R (four squadrons) between them. The somewhat limited G91R is soon to be replaced by 175 of the FGA version of the Franco-German Alpha Jet, and the FGA forces will be modernised by the delivery of the last 10 F-4F on order, and 210 Tornado swing-wing multi-role fighters.

Tactical reconnaissance for these units is provided by the four reconnaissance squadrons, operating 81 RF-4E aircraft, and the trained personnel by two operational conversion units, which are equipped with 18 TF-104G and 37 G91T two-seat trainers.

Allied tactical doctrine stresses the need for great tactical flexibility and hence mobility, and here the Germans are well placed with five transport squadrons operating 88 Transall C-160 and four helicopter squadrons operating 114 Bell UH-1D general-purpose helicopters. Given the great superiority in AFVs enjoyed by the WTO forces, Germany is looking seriously at the attractive prospect of armed helicopters, with the PAH-1 and BO 105 on order, but these are to be operated by the army rather than by the air force.

The *Luftwaffe* operates a number of other transport, liaison, communication and general-purpose aircraft, as well as a number of trainers in Germany and in the United States, but perhaps the most important type of unit not yet covered is the aircraft control and warning regiment, of which Germany has four. These will be supplemented, at a far more advanced level, by the Boeing E-3A AWACS aircraft that it has been decided that NATO will buy as a collaborative defence move. These will be of great importance to West Germany, many of whose most important targets lie only minutes' flying from forward communist airfields.

Overall, though, the *Luftwaffe* is an effective support arm for the *Bundeswehr* or West German Army. Training is good, morale high, and aircraft suitable for their tasks. It is time that the Germans started thinking seriously about a new generation of FGA and fighter aircraft, for both the F-4 and the F-104 are approaching the ends of their useful lives in a European context. Germany, as well as other nations, is considering the prospect of a new generation of light fighters with extreme manoeuvrability when not carrying underwing stores, but the ability to carry and deliver accurately heavy loads when necessary. So far few of the projects are more than paper dreams, but it is time for all, but especially West Germany, to start serious development of this and other new types.

106,200 (38,000 conscripts) and 484 combat aircraft.

16 FGA sqns: 4 with 60 F-4F; 8 with 144 F-104G; 4 with 84 G91R-3 (to be replaced by AlphaJet).
4 AWX sqns with 60 F-4F.
4 recce sqns with 81 RF-4E.
2 OCU with 18 TF-104G, 37 G91T.
5 transport sqns with 88 Transall C-160.
4 helicopter sqns with 114 UH-1D.
Sidewinder AAM; AS.30 ASM.
8 SSM sqns with 72 Pershing 1A.
24 SAM btys with 216 Nike Hercules.
36 SAM btys with 216 Improved HAWK.
4 aircraft control and warning regts.
Other ac: 4 Boeing 707, 3 C-140, 9 HFB 320, 3 VFW 614, 3 Noratlas, 120 Do 28D, 16 OV-10Z.
(10 F-4F, 210 Tornado FGA, 175 Alpha Jet FGA, *Kormoran* ASM, Hot ASM, 175 Roland SAM on order.)

Naval Air Arm
6,000; 134 combat aircraft.
3 FB sqns with 85 F-104G.
1 recce sqn with 30 RF-104G.
2 MR sqns with 19 Atlantic.
1 SAR helicopter sqn with 21 Sea King Mk 41.
1 utility sqn with 20 Do 28 ac.
Kormoran ASM.
(110 Tornado FGA on order.)

Army Air Arm
3 army aviation comds (each with 1 lt, 1 med transport regt).
190 UH-1D, 225 *Alouette* II/III, 109 CH-53G helicopters; 5 CL-89 drones.
(212 PAH-1, 227 BO 105M helicopters on order.)

Avions Marcel Dassault/Breguet Aviation-Dornier AlphaJet

Type: trainer, close-support and battlefield reconnaissance aircraft
Crew: two, in tandem
Wings: metal cantilever shoulder-wing monoplane
Fuselage: metal semi-monocoque
Tail unit: metal cantilever
Landing gear: hydraulically actuated retractable tricycle unit
Powerplant: two SNECMA/Turboméca Larzac 04-C5 turbofans, each rated at 2,976-lb (1,350-kg) static thrust
Fuel capacity: 418 gallons (1,900 litres) in internal tanks, plus provision for two 68.2-gallon (310-litre) drop tanks
Avionics: comprehensive communications and navigation equipment, plus VDO/Kaiser head up display and other refinements in the close-support version
Armament: for armament training and close-support missions, the AlphaJet can carry under the fuselage a pod fitted with one 30-mm DEFA or 27-mm Mauser cannon with 150 rounds, or two machine-guns with 250 rounds per gun; there are also two hardpoints under each wing, the inner ones each capable of lifting 1,466 lb (665 kg) and the outer ones 738 lb (335 kg), the load consisting of bombs, rockets or reconnaissance pods. Maximum load for the five external stations is 4,960 lb (2,250 kg)
Dimensions: Span 29 ft 10¾ in (9.11 m)
Length 40 ft 3¾ in (12.29 m)
Height 13 ft 9 in (4.19 m)
Wing area: 188.4 ft² (17.5 m²)
Weights: Empty 7,374 lb (3,345 kg)
Loaded 11,023 lb (5,000 kg)
Maximum 15,983 lb (7,250 kg)
Performance: (at normal take-off weight) speed Mach 0.85 at high altitude; speed 622 mph (1,000 kph) at low altitude; climb less than 7 minutes to 30,000 ft (9,145 m); service ceiling 49,200 ft (15,000 m); endurance more than 3 hours 30 minutes at high altitude; trainer radius of action at low altitude 273 miles (440 km); combat radius with maximum external load on a lo-lo-lo ground-attack mission 254 miles (410 km); combat radius with maximum external load on a hi-lo-hi ground-attack mission 391 miles (630 km); ferry range 1,675 miles (2,700 km)
Used also by: Belgium, France, Ivory Coast, Morocco, Togo, Turkey
Notes: A joint Franco-West German project. The E1 is the French trainer version and the A1 the German attack version.

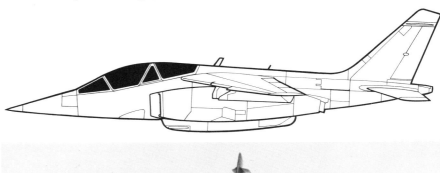

Fiat G91R

Type: reconnaissance fighter
Crew: one
Wings: metal cantilever low mid-wing monoplane
Fuselage: metal semi-monocoque
Tail unit: metal cantilever
Landing gear: hydraulically actuated retractable tricycle unit
Powerplant: one Rolls-Royce (Bristol Siddeley) Orpheus 803/02 turbojet, rated at 5,000-lb (2,268-kg) static thrust
Fuel capacity:
Avionics: comprehensive communication and navigation/attack equipment
Armament: four 0.5-in (12.7-mm) Colt Browning machine-guns with 300 rounds per gun, or two 30-mm DEFA 552 cannon with 125 rounds per gun, plus external stores up to a weight of 500 lb (227 kg) or 1,000 lb (454 kg)
Dimensions: Span 28 ft 1 in (8.57 m)
Length 33 ft 9¼ in (10.31 m)
Height 13 ft 1½ in (4.0 m)
Wing area: 176.7 ft² (16.42 m²)
Weights: Empty about 7,275 lb (3,300 kg)
Loaded
Maximum 12,500 lb (5,695 kg)
Performance: speed 675 mph (1,086 kph) at 5,000 ft (1,525 m); climb 6,000 ft (1,829 m) per minute at sea level; service ceiling 43,000 ft (13,106 m); combat radius 196 miles (315 km); ferry range 1,150 miles (1,850 km)
Used also by: Angola, Italy, Portugal
Notes: The Fiat G91 stemmed from a NATO attempt to standardise a new light fighter to replace the F-86 Sabre. There were

three French and one Italian contender for the 1953 specification, and it was the Fiat G91R which won the competition. The prototype first flew in 1956, and the type entered service in 1959. Despite NATO efforts at standardisation, only three NATO countries adopted the type.

Vereinigte Flugtechnische Werke-Fokker VFW 614

Type: short-haul transport
Crew: two, plus up to 44 passengers
Wings: metal cantilever low-wing monoplane
Fuselage: aluminium alloy semi-monocoque
Tail unit: metal cantilever
Landing gear: hydraulically actuated retractable tricycle unit
Powerplant: two Rolls-Royce M45H Mark 501 turbofans, each rated at 7,280-lb (3,302-kg) static thrust

Fuel capacity: 1,390 gallons (6,320 litres) in integral wing tanks
Avionics: comprehensive communication and navigation equipment
Armament: none
Dimensions: Span 70 ft 6½ in (21.5 m)
Length 67 ft 7 in (20.6 m)
Height 25 ft 8 in (7.84 m)
Wing area: 688.89 ft² (64.0 m²)
Weights: Empty 26,850 lb (12,180 kg)
Loaded
Maximum 44,000 lb (19,950 kg)
Performance: (at maximum take-off weight) speed 443 mph (713 kph) at a take-off

weight of 40,124 lb (18,200 kg) at 21,975 ft (6,700 m); cruising speed 438 mph (704 kph) at a take-off weight of 40,124 lb (18,200 kg) at 25,000 ft (7,620 m); climb 3,100 ft (945 m) per minute at sea level; maximum flying altitude 25,000 ft (7,620 m); range 748 miles (1,204 km) with a payload of 8,000 lb (3,630 kg)
Used only by: West Germany
Notes: Developed as a short-haul airliner, the VFW-Fokker VFW 614 has the unusual feature of its two engines being mounted on pylons above the wings.

Euromissile HOT

Type: anti-tank missile
Guidance: command to line-of-sight by means of wires
Dimensions: Span $12\frac{1}{4}$ in (31.0 cm)
        Body diameter $5\frac{1}{3}$ in (13.6 cm)
        (13.6 cm)
        Length 4 ft $2\frac{1}{8}$ in (1.275 m)
Booster: solid-propellant rocket
Sustainer: solid-propellant rocket
Warhead: hollow-charge HE
Weights: Launch $50\frac{3}{4}$ lb (23 kg)
        Burnt out
Performance: speed 590 mph (950 kph); range 82 to 4,374 yards (75 to 4,000 m)
Used only by: West Germany (as an aircraft weapon)
Notes: The HOT (*Haut subsonique Optiquement téléguidé tiré d'un Tube*, or High subsonic Optically guided Tube launched) is an advanced anti-tank missile that can be fired from the ground or the air. The warhead can penetrate more than $31\frac{1}{2}$ in (800 mm) of armour at 65°.

Messerschmitt-Bölkow-Blohm
Kormoran

Type: air-to-surface tactical anti-shipping guided missile
Guidance: inertial and radio altimeter, plus active or passive radar terminal homing
Dimensions: Span $39\frac{2}{5}$ in (1.0 m)
        Body diameter $13\frac{1}{2}$ in (34.4 cm)
        Length 14 ft 5 in (4.4 m)

Booster: two SNPE Prade solid-propellant rockets
Sustainer: SNPE Eole IV solid-propellant rocket
Warhead: 364 lb (165 kg) with 123 lb (56 kg) of high explosive
Weights: Launch 1,320 lb (600 kg)
        Burnt out
Performance: speed Mach 0.95; range 23 miles (37 km)
Used only by: West Germany
Notes: Produced by MBB of West Germany and Aérospatiale of France, the *Kormoran* is a powerful anti-ship weapon. With information of the target's location fed into its inertial system by the launch aircraft's sensors and computer, the *Kormoran* cruises towards the target at an altitude below 100 ft (30 m) after launch. After a given distance the terminal homing is turned on, locks onto the target, and brings the missile into the attack at sea level. The warhead is highly efficient, and can penetrate up to $3\frac{1}{2}$ in (90 mm) of armour.

Yugoslavia

40,000 men (7,000 conscripts) and 329 combat aircraft.

15 FGA sqns with 9 F-84G *Kraguj*, 110 *Galeb/Jastreb*.
6 interceptor sqns with 120 MiG-21F/PF/M.
3 recce sqns with 15 RT-33A, 25 *Galeb/Jastreb*.
OCU with 18 MiG-21U, 20 *Jastreb*.
Transports incl 15 C-47, 10 Il-14, 2 Il-18, 4 Yak-40, 1 Caravelle, 2 An-12, 9 An-26, 4 Li-2, 1 Boeing 727.
60 *Galeb/Jastreb*, 30 T-33 trainers.
Utility aircraft incl UTVA-75.
14 Mi-1, 20 Mi-4, 48 Mi-8, 12 Gazelle helicopters.
AA-2 'Atoll' AAM.
8 SA-2, 4 SA-3 SAM bns.
(102 Gazelle helicopters on order.)
Naval Air Arm
Mi-8, Ka-25 ASW, Gazelle helicopters.

Antonov An-26 'Curl'

Type: transport aircraft
Crew: five, and up to 40 passengers
Wings: metal cantilever high-wing monoplane
Fuselage: metal semi-monocoque
Tail unit: metal cantilever
Landing gear: hydraulically actuated retractable tricycle unit
Powerplant: two Ivchenko AI-24T turboprops, each rated at 2,820 ehp and driving a four-blade metal propeller
Fuel capacity: 12,125 lb (5,500 kg) in wing tanks
Avionics: comprehensive communication and navigation equipment
Armament: none
Dimensions: Span 95 ft 9½ in (29.2 m)
Length 78 ft 1 in (23.8 m)
Height 28 ft 1½ in (8.575 m)
Wing area: 807.1 ft² (74.98 m²)
Weights: Empty 33,113 lb (15,020 kg)
Loaded 50,706 lb (23,000 kg)
Maximum 52,911 lb (24,000 kg)

Performance: (at normal loaded weight) cruising speed 270 mph (435 kph) at 19,675 ft (6,000 m); climb 1,575 ft (480 m) per minute at sea level; service ceiling 26,575 ft (8,100 m); range with a payload of 9,920 lb (4,500 kg) 559 miles (900 km); range with a payload of 4,687 lb (2,126 kg) 1,398 miles (2,250 km)
Used also by: Angola, Bangladesh, Hungary, Iraq, Peru, Poland, Romania, Somali Republic, Syria, USSR
Notes: Derived from the An-24, the An-26 has more powerful engines and a new rear fuselage, with 'beaver tail' doors. Maximum payload is 12,125 lb (5,500 kg). There is also a derivative of the An-26, in the form of the An-32 'Cline', which is designed for operations in extremely high temperatures and from airfields at high altitude. Power is provided by a pair of 5,180-ehp Ivchenko AI-20M turboprops, allowing the type to take off from airfields some 14,750 ft (4,500 m) above sea level, and to operate in ambient air temperatures of 25°C.

Republic Aviation F-84 Thunderjet, Thunderstreak and Thunderflash

Type: fighter-bomber and reconnaissance aircraft
Crew: one
Wings: metal cantilever low mid-wing monoplane
Fuselage: metal semi-monocoque
Tail unit: metal cantilever
Landing gear: hydraulically actuated retractable tricycle unit
Powerplant: one Wright J65-W-7 turbojet, rated at 7,800-lb (3,538-kg) static thrust
Fuel capacity:
Avionics: comprehensive communication and navigation equipment
Armament: four 0.5-in (12.7-mm) Colt-Browning M-3 machine-guns
Dimensions: Span 33 ft 7¼ in (10.24 m)
Length 47 ft 7¾ in (14.51 m)
Height 15 ft (4.57 m)
Wing area:
Weights: Empty
Loaded 26,800 lb (12,156 kg)
Maximum 28,000 lb (12,700 kg)
Performance: 679 mph (1,093 mph) at sea level; climb 8,000 ft (2,438 m) per minute at sea level; service ceiling 46,000 ft (14,020 m); range 2,200 miles (3,540 km)
Used also by: Greece

Notes: The F-84 family, which was to undergo a number of drastic modifications during its career, began life as the P-84, which made its first flight in 1946. The first production model was the F-84B, which was delivered from May 1947. There were many variants:
1. F-84B Thunderjet with straight wings, a nose intake, and 4,000-lb (1,814-kg) J35-A-15C, plus an armament of four 0.5-in (12.7-mm) machine-guns and 32 5-in (127-mm) rockets
2. F-84C, with a new electrical system
3. F-84D, with the 5,000-lb (2,268-kg) J33-A-17D
4. F-84E, with a radar gunsight, a longer fuselage, and drop tanks
5. F-84G, with the 5,600-lb (2,540-kg) J33-A-29, and the ability to carry a nuclear bomb, delivered with the aid of the low-altitude bombing system (LABS)
6. F-84F Thunderstreak, with the 7,220-lb (3,275-kg) Wright J65-W-3, swept wings, an 'all-flying' tail, and up to 6,000 lb (2,722 kg) of bombs
7. RF-84F Thunderflash reconnaissance model, to which the technical specification applies. This has a solid nose, the intakes being relocated to the wing roots.

'Soko' Metalopreradivacka Industrija G2-A *Galeb*

Type: trainer
Crew: two, seated in tandem
Wings: light alloy cantilever low-wing monoplane
Fuselage: light alloy semi-monocoque
Tail unit: light alloy cantilever
Landing gear: hydraulically actuated retractable tricycle unit
Powerplant: one Rolls-Royce Bristol Viper 11 Mark 22-6 turbojet, rated at 2,500-lb (1,134-kg) static thrust

Fuel capacity: 1,720 lb (780 kg) in two fuselage tanks, plus 375 lb (170 kg) in each of two jettisonable wingtip tanks wingtip tanks
Avionics: comprehensive communication and navigation equipment
Armament: two 12.7-mm (0.5-in) machine-guns with 80 rounds per gun, plus underwing pylons for two 110- or 220-lb (50- or 100-kg) bombs, and four 57-mm or two 127-mm rockets. Total external weapon load is 660 lb (300 kg), which can also be made up of bomb clusters and bomblet containers

Dimensions: Span (over tanks) 38 ft 1½ in
(11.62 m)
Length 33 ft 11 in (10.34 m)
Height 10 ft 9 in (3.28 m)
Wing area: 209.14 ft² (19.43 m²)
Weights: Empty 5,775 lb (2,620 kg)
Loaded 7,690 lb (3,488 kg)
Maximum (strike) 9,480 lb (4,300 kg)

Performance: (at normal take-off weight) speed 505 mph (812 kph) at 20,350 ft (6,200 m); speed at sea level 470 mph (756 kph); cruising speed 453 mph (730 kph) at 19,680 ft (6,000 m); climb 4,500 ft (1,370 m) per minute at sea level; climb to 19,680 ft (6,000 m) in 5 minutes 30 seconds; service ceiling 39,375 ft (12,000 m); endurance at 23,000 ft (7,000 m) 2 hours 30 minutes; range with tip tanks at 29,520 ft (9,000 m) 770 miles (1,240 km)

Used also by: Libya, Zambia
Notes: Design work on the *Galeb* trainer and light strike aircraft began in 1957, the prototype flying in 1961. The Yugoslav Air Force took over its first aircraft in 1963 and 1964. There are two versions:
1. G2-A standard aircraft for Yugoslavia
2. G-2A-E export version with updated electronics.

'Soko' Metalopreradivicka Industrija J-1 and RJ-1 *Jastreb*

Type: light attack and reconnaissance aircraft
Crew: one
Wings: light alloy cantilever low-wing monoplane
Fuselage: light alloy semi-monocoque
Tail unit: light alloy cantilever
Landing gear: hydraulically actuated retractable tricycle unit
Powerplant: one Rolls-Royce Bristol Viper 531 turbojet, rated at 3,000-lb (1,361-kg) static thrust, plus provision for two 1,000-lb (454-kg) JATO units under the fuselage
Fuel capacity: 1,720 lb (780 kg) in two fuselage tanks, plus 485 lb (220 kg) in each of two jettisonable wingtip tanks
Avionics: comprehensive communication and navigation equipment, plus reconnaissance gear in the relevant models
Armament: three 12.7-mm (0.5-in) Colt Browning machine-guns with 135 rounds per gun, and a variety of external stores carried on eight underwing points. The two inner points can each carry two bombs (each weighing up to 551 lb/250 kg), two bomb clusters, two 44-gallon (200-litre)

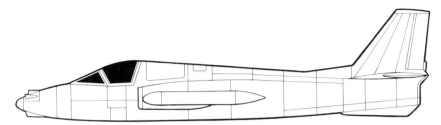

napalm tanks, two rocket pods (each holding twelve or sixteen 57-mm, or four 127-mm rockets), two multiple carriers each with three 112-lb (50-kg) bombs, two bomblet containers or two flares; the outer six points can each carry a 127-mm rocket
Dimensions: Span 34 ft 4½ in (10.47 m)
Length 35 ft 8½ in (10.88 m)
Height 11 ft 11½ in (3.64 m)
Wing area: 209.14 ft² (19.43 m²)
Weights: Empty 6,217 lb (2,820 kg)
Loaded
Maximum 11,243 lb (5,100 kg)
Performance: (at a weight of 8,748 lb/3,968 kg) speed 510 mph (820 kph) at 19,680 ft (6,000 m); cruising speed 460 mph (740 kph) at 16,400 ft (5,000 m); climb 4,135 ft

(1,260 m) per minute at sea level; service ceiling 39,375 ft (12,000 m); range at 29,520 ft (9,000 m) with tip tanks 945 miles (1,520 km)
Used also by: Zambia
Notes: Derived from the G2-A *Galeb*, the *Jastreb* has only a single cockpit, a more powerful engine, and updated electronics. There are four versions:
1. J-1 attack version for the Yugoslav Air Force
2. J-1-E export version of the J-1 with improved electronics
3. RJ-1 tactical reconnaissance version for the Yugoslav Air Force
4. RJ-1-E export version of the RJ-1 with updated equipment.

'Soko' Metalopreradivicka Industrija P-2 *Kraguj*

Type: close-support aircraft
Crew: one
Wings: metal cantilever low-wing monoplane
Fuselage: metal semi-monocoque
Tail unit: metal cantilever
Landing gear: fixed tailwheel unit
Powerplant: one Lycoming GSO-480-B1A6 inline engine, rated at 340 hp and driving a three-blade metal propeller
Fuel capacity: 53 gallons (240 litres) in two wing tanks
Avionics: communication and navigation equipment
Armament: two 7.7-mm machine-guns, plus external stores on underwing pylons
Dimensions: Span 33 ft 1½ in (10.1 m)
Length 25 ft 3 in (7.7 m)
Height 9 ft 10 in (3.0 m)
Wing area: 183 ft² (17.0 m²)
Weights: Empty 2,491 lb (1,130 kg)
Loaded
Maximum 3,580 lb (1,624 kg)
Performance: speed 183 mph (295 kph) at 5,000 ft (1,525 m); cruising speed 174 mph (280 kph) at 5,000 ft (1,525 m); climb 1,340 ft (408 m) per minute at sea level; range 497 miles (800 km) with maximum fuel
Used only by: Yugoslavia
Notes: The *Kraguj* was one of the first lightweight close-support aircraft, entering service in 1968.

UTVA Fabrika Aviona 75

Type: trainer and utility aircraft
Crew: two, seated side-by-side
Wings: metal cantilever low-wing monoplane
Fuselage: metal semi-monocoque
Tail unit: metal cantilever
Landing gear: fixed tricycle unit
Powerplant: one Lycoming IO-360-B1F piston engine, rated at 180 hp and driving a Hartzell two-blade metal propeller
Fuel capacity: 35 gallons (160 litres) in two integral wing tanks, plus provision for two 22-gallon (100-litre) drop tanks under the wings
Avionics: minimal communication and navigation equipment
Armament: optional light armament under the wings
Dimensions: Span 31 ft 11 in (9.73 m)
Length 23 ft 4 in (7.11 m)
Height 10 ft 4 in (3.15 m)
Wing area: 157.5 ft² (14.63 m²)
Weights: Empty 1,433 lb (650 kg)
Loaded
Maximum 2,116 lb (960 kg)
Performance: (at maximum take-off weight) speed 136 mph (220 kph); cruising speed 102 mph (165 kph); climb 885 ft (270 m) per minute at sea level; service ceiling 14,760 ft (4,500 m); range with drop tanks 1,242 miles (2,000 km)
Used only by: Yugoslavia
Notes: Designed as a light military and civilian utility aircraft, the UTVA 75 first flew in 1976 and entered service in 1977.

Zaire

3,000 men and 49 combat aircraft.

1 fighter sqn with 14 Mirage VM, 3 VDM.
2 COIN sqns with 12 M.B. 326GB, 8 AT-6G, 12 AT-28D.
1 observation sqn with 20 Reims Cessna FTB 337.
1 transport wing with 7 C-130H, 2 DC-6, 2 DHC-4A, 3 DHC-5, 4 C-54, 8 C-47, 2 Mu-2.
1 helicopter sqn with 14 *Alouette* III, 8 Puma, 1 Super *Frelon*, 7 Bell 47.
Trg ac incl 23 SF.260MC, 15 T-6, 15 Cessna A150, 15 Cessna 310.
(3 DHC-5 transports on order.)

Zambia

1,500 men and 30 combat aircraft.

1 FGA sqn with 6 *Galeb*, 6 *Jastreb*.
1 COIN/trg sqn with 18 M.B. 326G.
2 transport sqns: 1 with 2 Yak-40, 2 DC-6, 5 DHC-4, 7 DHC-5, 10 C-47, 1 HS 748; 1 with 7 DHC-2, 10 Do 28.
1 liaison sqn with 20 Saab Supporter.
Trainers incl 6 Chipmunk, 8 SF.260MZ.
1 helicopter sqn with 3 AB-205, 5 AB-206, 3 AB-212, 21 Bell 47G, 7 Mi-8.
1 SAM unit with 12 Rapier.
(An unrevealed number of additional Rapier and other AA weapons were delivered late in 1978.)

List of Abbreviations

AA	anti-aircraft		flt	flight
AAM	air-to-air missile		GW	guided weapon
AB	airborne		hy	heavy
ABM	anti-ballistic missile		ICBM	intercontinental ballistic missile
ac	aircraft		IRBM	intermediate-range ballistic missile
AD	air defence		MAD	magnetic anomaly detector
AEW	airborne early warning		MARV	manoeuvrable re-entry vehicle
ALBM	air-launched ballistic missile		MCM	mine countermeasures
ALCM	air-launched cruise missile		MIRV	multiple independently-targetable re-entry vehicles
ASM	air-to-surface missile		MR	maritime reconnaissance
A/S	anti-submarine		MRV	multiple re-entry vehicles
ASW	anti-submarine warfare		msl	missile
AWACS	airborne warning and control system		OCU	operational conversion unit
AWX	all-weather fighter		para	parachute
bbr	bomber		RATO	rocket-assisted take-off
bn	battalion		RV	re-entry vehicle
bty	battery		SAM	surface-to-air missile
CEP	circular error probable (*see* Introduction)		SAR	search and rescue
COIN	counter-insurgency		spt	support
ECCM	electronic counter-countermeasures		sqn	squadron
ECM	electronic countermeasures		SRAM	short-range attack missile
eqpt	equipment		SRBM	short-range ballistic missile
ESM	electronic support measures		STOL	short take-off and landing
EW	early warning		tpt	transport
FAC	forward air control		trg	training
FB	fighter-bomber		V/STOL	vertical/short take-off and landing
FGA	fighter ground-attack		VTOL	vertical take-off and landing

Index

Illustration Credits

Picture Editor: Jonathan Moore

Many organisations and archives kindly helped with photographic material during the preparation of this volume. We would wish particularly to thank the following for their invaluable assistance:

Aerospatiale, Paris; British Aerospace, London; Colonel Boulet of the Canadian National Defence Headquarters, Ottawa; Cessna Aircraft Company, Wichita; Avions Marcel Dassault-Breguet Aviation, Paris; Messerschmitt-Bölkow-Blohm GmbH, Munich; E. Speakman and S. Reed and the staff of the Press Photographs Department, Ministry of Defence, London; Margaret B. Livesey, US Department of the Air Force, Arlington; and Robert A. Carlisle, Head of the US Navy's Photojournalism Branch, Washington DC.

Unless otherwise indicated, all photographs were supplied through Military Archives & Research Services (MARS), London.

All artwork in this volume was produced by The County Studio, Coleorton, Leicestershire.

Key to picture positions: (T) = top, (C) = centre, (B) = bottom.

11	Mil Mi-1 helicopter in flight (Fotokhronika Tass, Moscow, USSR)
12	MiG-15UTI advanced trainer of the Finnish Air Force (Finnish Air Force, Helsinki)
13	Mil Mi-4 anti-submarine helicopter of the Soviet Navy; January 1974 (US Navy Official Photo)
14(T)	Fouga Super Magister of the Irish Army Air Corps (Irish Army Air Corps, Dublin)
(B)	C-47 transport of the Chilean Air Force (Chilean Air Force)
15	Turbo Skywagon (Cessna Aircraft Co, Kansas, USA)
16(T)	Detail of the nose of a Mirage IIIRD photo-recce aircraft of the French Air Force (Avions Marcel Dassault-Breguet Aviation, Paris)
(B)	Mirage IIIS interceptor of the Swiss Air Force making a rocket-assisted take-off (Swiss Air Force, Berne)
18	L.188 Electra transport being rolled out from the factory hangar (Lockheed Corp, USA)
19	Falcon 20 light transport of the Royal Norwegian Air Force (Royal Norwegian Air Force, Oslo)
20	CA Winjeel basic trainer of the Royal Australian Air Force (Defence PR, Canberra ACT)
21(T)	Three photographs showing the variable-geometry wing movements of a US Air Force F-111 two-seat tactical fighter-bomber (General Dynamics Corp, Texas, USA)
(B)	US Air Force FB-111 two-seat tactical fighter bomber (General Dynamics Corp, Texas, USA)
22	OH-58 Kiowa light observation helicopter of the US Army (Bell Helicopters/Textron, USA)
23	Saab 105 light fighter-bombers of the Austrian Air Force based at Linz (Saab/Scania/B Pettersson, Sweden)
25(T)	748 Andover (Crown Copyright, MOD RAF)
(B)	H-34G utility transport helicopter of the Federal German Navy (Federal German Navy, Wilhelmshaven)
27(T)	Hughes Model 500M helicopter (Hughes Helicopters, USA)
(B)	T-28B Trojan trainer of the US Navy parked at Ellyson Field NAS, Pensacola, Florida; 3 September 1970 (US Navy Official Photo)
28	AT-26 Xavante tandem two-seat basic trainer and light-attack aircraft of the Brazilian Air Force in flight. (Embraer SA, Brazil)
29	S2-E Tracker carrier-based anti-submarine warfare aircraft of the Brazilian Air Force (Brazilian Air Force, Brazilia)
30(T)	Westland Scout helicopter of British Army Aviation (Westland Helicopters Ltd, Yeovil, UK)
(B)	Westland Wasp of the Brazilian Navy (Westland Helicopters Ltd, Yeovil UK)
32	Chipmunk basic trainer of the RAF (Crown Copyright, MOD RAF, London)
33	T-33 electronic counter-measures aircraft of the Canadian Armed Forces (Canadian Armed Forces, Ottawa)
34(T)	CF-100 electronic counter-measures aircraft of the Canadian Armed Forces; 1975 (Canadian Armed Forces, Ottawa)
(B)	CP-107 Argus maritime patrol aircraft of the Canadian Armed Forces (Canadian Armed Forces, Ottawa)
35	CF-101 Voodoo fighter of the Canadian Armed Forces firing a missile; 1972 (Canadian Armed Forces, Ottawa)
36(T)	A-1H of the 6th Special Operations Squadron, US Air Force, while on a mission off the coast of Vietnam; 20 March 1969 (US Air Force, Virginia)
(B)	C-118 transport of the Chilean Air Force (Chilean Air Force)
37	Grumman HU-16B Albatross amphibian of the Chilean Air Force (Chilean Air Force)
39	CAAC Trident 2 airliner supplied to China, 12 November 1973 (British Aerospace HS, Surrey)
40	F-6/MiG 19 fighter/ground-attack aircraft of the Pakistan Air Force (Pakistan Air Force, Peshawar)
41(T)	Consolidated Catalina VI (PB2B-2)-JX637 in flight. This aircraft was delivered to the Australian Air Force (Boeing Airplane Co, Washington, USA)
(B)	HH-43 helicopter; April 1967 (US Air Force)
43	Soviet Ilyushin Il-18 transport aircraft; May 1973 (US Navy Official Photo)
44	Aero L-39 basic and advanced jet trainer of the Czech Air Force operating from a

250

212(T)	Grumman F-14A Tomcat tandem two-seat, carrier-based, variable-geometry, air-superiority and general-purpose fighter. (Grumman Corp, New York, USA)
(C)	A Grumman F-14A Tomcat tandem two-seat, carrier-based, variable-geometry, air-superiority and general-purpose fighter (Grumman Corp, New York, USA)
(B)	AH-64 attack helicopter of the US Army (Hughes Helicopters, USA)
213	An SH-2D Seasprite helicopter with the Light Airborne Multi-Purpose System (LAMPS) making its first flight; April 1971 (US Navy Official Photo)
214(T)	A US Air Force A-7D Corsair II single-seat, land-based, attack aircraft in flight in the early 1970s. The two outer pylons on each wing carry HE bombs with drop fuel tanks on the internal pylons (US Air Force, Virginia)
214(B)	Vought A-7E Corsair II from the US Navy carrier USS Constellation (Vought Corp, Texas, USA)
215(T)	S-3A Viking anti-submarine aircraft of the US Navy's Air Anti-Submarine Squadron 41 (VS-41) in flight over the coast of California with its MAD boom extended; 23 September 1974 (US Navy Official Photo)
C)	The Lockheed SR-71 'Blackbird' tandem two-seat long-range strategic reconnaissance aircraft (Lockheed Corp, California, USA)
(B)	U-2 long-range high-altitude photo-reconnaissance USAF aircraft (Lockheed Corp, USA)
216(T)	Loading a huge load of propulsion-reduction gear aboard a C-5 Galaxy; 24 March 1978 (Lockheed Corp, USA)
(B)	C-140 JetStar military/executive transport; 1957 (Lockheed Corp, California, USA)
217(T)	C-141 StarLifter heavy transport of the US Air Force (Lockheed Corp, USA)
217(B)	F-15 Eagle (McDonnell-Douglas Corp, USA)
218(T)	F-15A Eagle air-superiority fighter with four Sparrow air-to-air missiles; November 1975 (McDonnell-Douglas Corp, USA)
(C)	T-38 Talon of the US Air Force (Northrop Corp, California, USA)
(B)	T-38 Talons of the US Air Force (Northrop Corp, California, USA)
219(T)	US Air Force F-105 in flight over Nevada; 1 May 1970 (US Air Force Photo)
(B)	RA-5C Vigilante recce aircraft of the US Navy's Reconnaissance Attack Squadron 9 (RVAH-9) over Florida; 3 July 1975 (US Navy Official Photo, USA)
220	A Sikorsky Aircraft CH-54 Tarhe (Sikorsky Aircraft Corporation)
221(T)	HH-3E Jolly Green Giant helicopter refueling from an HC-130P Hercules tanker (Lockheed Corp, USA)
(B)	SH-3A Sea King helicopter lifting off from the flight deck of an amphibious assault ship; 24 July 1975 (US Navy Official Photo)
222(T)	A rescue HH-53 in flight over Utah; 1975 (US Air Force Photo)
(B)	An RH-53D Sea Stallion helicopter towing a magnetic orange pipe over Hon Gay Bay, North Vietnam; 18 March 1973 (US Navy Official Photo, Washington, USA)
223(T)	Short Range Attack Missile (SRAM) being fired from a B-52 bomber of Strategic Air Command (Boeing Aerospace Co, Washington, USA)
223(B)	AGM-86B Air Launch Cruise Missile being launched from a USAF B-52 strategic bomber (The Boeing Co, USA)
224	Lift-off of a Minuteman II intercontinental ballistic missile during a test-firing from Cape Kennedy; 14 March 1970 (US Air Force Photo)
225(T)	Maverick air-to-surface TV-guided powered missile, destined for the US Air Force, on its way to final testing at Hughes' Tuscon, Arizona facility (Hughes Aircraft Co, California, USA)
(B)	A Convair F-102 Delta Dagger of the South Dakota Air National Guard firing a Hughes Falcon air-to-air missile during feasibility tests in New Mexico; 5 February 1963 (US Air Force Official Photograph, Virginia, USA)
226	Hughes Missiles. In the foreground is the TOW wire-guided anti-tank missile. Behind, from the left, is a USAF long-range AIM-47A (developed for the F-12A); the AIM-4F Falcon (operational on the F-106); the USN TV-guided air-to-ground glide bomb; the AIM-26A Nuclear Falcon (operational on the F-102); the USAF TV-guided Maverick; the AIM-4D Falcon, a tactical air-to-air missile (operational on the F-4) and the USN long-range air-to-air Phoenix (developed for the F-14A fighter); November 1969 (Hughes Aircraft Co, California, USA)
227(T)	Phoenix (AIM-54A) anti-shipping missile being fired from a US Navy F-14 Tomcat fighter; May 1977 (US Navy Official Photo)
(B)	Phoenix long-range air-to-air missile on an F-111B; March 1967 (Hughes Aircraft Co, USA)
228(T)	Bullpup (AGM-12B) tactical air-to-surface missile being launched from a P-3B Orion patrol aircraft at Maine; 1 November 1971 (US Navy Official Photo)
(B)	Bullpup family of missiles. From top right, clockwise, AGM-12, ATM-12A, AGM-12B and AGM-12D (Martin Marietta Aerospace, Florida)
229(T)	An AGM-62 Walleye guided bomb being checked; July 1966 (US Navy Official Photo)
(B)	An AGM-62 Walleye guided bomb in position under the wing of a US Navy A-7 Corsair II attack aircraft at the Naval Air Test Facility, China Lake, California, USA; 9 May 1966 (US Navy Official Photo)
230(T)	Titan II intercontinental ballistic missile of the US Air Force being test-fired (Martin Marietta, Florida, USA)
(C)	Shrike (AGM-45A) anti-radiation air-to-surface missile being fired from a US Navy A-4F Skyhawk during test firings at China Lake, California, USA; 26 May 1968 (US Navy Official Photo)
(B)	An AGM-45A Shrike air-to-surface missile under the wing of an A-7E Corsair II Navy attack aircraft ready for test firing at the Naval Weapons Centre, China Lake, California, USA; 14 March 1972 (US Navy Official Photo, Washington)
231	RAF FGR.2 Phantom over Yorkshire armed with seven BL 755 cluster bombs and four Sparrow and four Sidewinder air-to-air missiles; September 1975 (Crown Copyright, MOD REP (S) PG, London)
232(T)	An AIM-7 Sparrow III missile (air-to-air) mounted on a modified UH-2C Seasprite helicopter; July 1972 (US Navy Official Photo)